ALGEBRA
IN EASY STEPS

EDWIN I. STEIN

AMERICAN BOOK COMPANY

AMERICAN BOOK COMPANY

Copyright © 1974 by D. C. Heath and Company

STEIN: ALGEBRA IN EASY STEPS

Published by American Book Company
450 West 3rd St., New York, N. Y. 10001

11   13   15   16   14   12   10

FOREWORD

Algebra In Easy Steps is a basal textbook in first-year algebra. The supplementary units found in this edition provide modern mathematics which may be integrated with the traditional content or used as supplementary topics in a regular course in algebra.

Algebra In Easy Steps has a carefully planned, flexible organization. The first 16 unit topics cover elementary algebra through quadratics. Unit Seventeen deals with numerical trigonometry, and Unit Eighteen with coordinate geometry. The motivating introductory material in each of these units explains the purpose and use of the material studied in the unit. The unit topics are subdivided into series of exercises. For each exercise the text gives (I) the aim, (II) the procedure to be followed, and (III) sample solutions completely worked out.

Following this developmental material come the diagnostic tests, keyed to the immediately succeeding practice examples. The examples in the diagnostic tests and related practice examples are carefully graded in difficulty. The final examples in each set of related practice examples may be used as an automatic end or mastery test of the exercise.

At the end of each unit the text provides an algebra review for the entire unit, a cumulative algebra review, and a keyed achievement test. Final comprehensive reviews of equations, formulas, fundamental processes, problems, facts, meanings, and concepts are also provided.

Algebra In Easy Steps is so organized that each student is directed to assignments that are specifically designed for him, thus enabling him to concentrate on learning those things he does not know, without wasting any time on meaningless practice.

Many programs in mathematics include for the first year some simple elements of coordinate geometry dealing with the slope of a straight line. This material is found in Unit Eighteen.

The supplement of contemporary mathematics consists of three units. Unit One includes Numbers and Number Systems, Properties of Number and Operations, Systems of Numeration, and Scientific Notation. In Unit Two the concept of set with its symbolisms is introduced, and operations with sets are presented and illustrated by Venn diagrams. There is considerable practice material for determining the solution set (or truth set) of equations and inequalities. The subject of inequalities may be taught without resorting to the language and notation of sets. The conjunction, disjunction, negation, and truth table are included in the lesson on logic.

Unit Three presents the graphing of sentences in one and two variables. Included are the graphing of equations and inequalities in one variable on the number line, and the graphing of equations and inequalities in two variables on a restricted number plane and on the real number plane.

EDWIN I. STEIN

CONTENTS

ALGEBRA IN EASY STEPS

CONTENTS

SUPPLEMENTARY UNITS

○○○

INVENTORY TEST

The numeral in the circle at the end of each problem indicates the exercise where help may be found.

1. Express as a formula: The base of a right triangle (b) is equal to the square root of the difference between the square of the hypotenuse (h) and the square of the altitude (a). ①

2. Find the value of $5x^2 + 3xy - 4y^2$ when $x = 6$ and $y = -2$. ㉒

3. What is the value of v when $V = 45$, $g = 32$, and $t = 10$, using the formula $v = V + gt$? ⑫

4. Find the sum of $6c^4 - 5c^2d^2 + 7d^4$, $8d^4 - 9c^4$, and $3c^4 - 4c^2d^2$. ㉔

5. Subtract $5xy - 2y^2$ from $3x^2 - 5xy - y^2$. ㉖

6. Multiply $6m^4 - m^3 - 4m^2 + 7m - 5$ by $3m - 9$. ㉛

7. Divide $15a^3 - 28a^2b + 7ab^2 + 6b^3$ by $5a - 6b$. ㉟

8. Remove parentheses and, if possible, add like terms:

$$6b - [-3b - (4b - 5)] + [-8b + (-b + 10)] \quad ㉗$$

9. Solve and check: (a) $4x - 15 = 41$ ⑪   (c) $46 - (-2d + 3) = 5(3d - 7)$ ㊱

    (b) $5y + 3 = 66 - 2y$ ㊱   (d) $(x + 5)(x - 1) = (x - 3)(x + 11)$ ㊱

10. The length of a rectangle is 15 meters more than the width. Its perimeter is 86 meters. What do the length and width each measure? ㊵

11. Find each of the following products at sight:

(a) $(4x - 3y)(4x + 3y)$ ㊼

(b) $(6c^2 - 5d)^2$ ㊾

(c) $(a + 7)(a - 9)$ (51)

(d) $(3m - 4n)(7m + 8n)$ (53)

12. Factor:

(a) $100b^2 - 49c^6d^8$ ㊽

(b) $16x^6y^2 + 48x^4y^4 - 64x^2y^6$ ㊹

(c) $20a^2 + 41a - 9$ (54)

(d) $36x^2 + 60xy + 25y^2$ ㊿

13. Express in simplest form:

$$\frac{a^2 - 4a - 5}{a^2 - 10a + 25}$$ (57)

14. Divide:

$$\frac{x^2 + 4x - 12}{3x + 12} \div \frac{x^2 + 9x + 18}{6x + 24}$$ (59)

15. Combine:

$$\frac{6}{b^2 - 8b + 16} - \frac{5}{b^2 - 16} + \frac{2}{b^2 - b - 12}$$ (63)

16. Solve and check: (a) $\dfrac{3x + 2}{4} - \dfrac{2x - 5}{5} = \dfrac{x}{2}$

(b) $\dfrac{y - 4}{y - 2} = \dfrac{y - 5}{y - 4}$ (66)

(c) $\dfrac{n}{n + 3} + \dfrac{n - 2}{n - 3} = \dfrac{2n^2 + 2}{n^2 - 9}$ (79)

17. Mrs. Smith invests \$10,000, part at 8% and the rest at 10% annual rate of interest. How much does she invest at each rate if her total annual interest from both investments is \$870? (75)

18. Solve for x and check: $\dfrac{x - n}{mx} + \dfrac{m}{nx} = \dfrac{1}{n}$ (77)

19. (a) Transform formula $I = \dfrac{nE}{R + nr}$, solving for r. (78)

(b) Find the value of r if $S = 186$, $a = 6$, and $l = 96$, using the formula $S = \dfrac{rl - a}{r - 1}$

20. In the formula $v = \dfrac{s}{t}$, $v = 32$ when $t = 2$. Find the value of v when $t = 8$ and s remains constant.

21. Use the slope-intercept method to draw the graph of $3x + y = 5$. (120)

22. Solve graphically and algebraically, then check: $2x - 3y = 11$
$5x + 2y = 18$ (82) (83)

23. Simplify and combine:
$2\sqrt{75} + 4\sqrt{50} - \sqrt{98} + 5\sqrt{27}$ (100)

24. Solve and check:
$2x^2 + x - 15 = 0$ (110)

25. The angle of depression of a boat at sea is 25°, as viewed from a cliff, 200 feet above the sea. How far is the boat from the foot of the cliff? (114)

Find the solution set of:

26. $5x - 9 = 11$ when the replacement set is the set of all odd numbers. (40s)

27. $2m + 7 = 4m + 3$ when the replacement set is the set of all prime numbers. (40s)

28. $-3y > 21$ when the replacement set is the set of all real numbers. (40s)

29. $9b - 2 < 14 + 2b$ when the replacement set is the set of all even natural numbers. (41s)

30. $12a - 5a \geqq a - 24$ when the replacement set is the set of all negative integers. (41s)

31. Using the system of real numbers, draw the graph of $x - 2 > 1$ on the number line. (62s)

32. If $U = \{-4, -3, -2, \cdots, 4\}$, $A = \{-4, -2, 0, 2\}$, and $B = \{-1, 0, 1, 3\}$, find each of the following:

(a) $A \cup B$ (b) $B \cap A$ (c) $\bar{B}$ (d) $\bar{A}$ (49s)

33. List all the ordered pairs of numbers which belong to the Cartesian product $A \times B$ when $A = \{-2, -1, 0, \cdots, 4\}$ and $B = \{-1, 0, 1, \cdots, 5\}$. (70s)

34. List all the ordered pairs of numbers belonging to the solution set which make the sentence $x + y < -2$ true when $U = \{-5, -4, -3, \cdots, 2\}$. Draw the graph. (70s)

35. Using tne system of all real numbers, solve graphically: $y > x + 1$
$x + y < 3$ (67s)

INTRODUCTION TO UNIT ONE

The language of algebra is symbolic. Both in arithmetic and informal geometry we have used mathematical symbols including the *addition* or plus symbol $+$, the *subtraction* or minus symbol $-$, the *multiplication* or times symbol $\times$ and the raised dot $\cdot$, the *division* symbols $\div$ or $\overline{)}$, the *equality* symbol $=$, the *inequality* symbols: the is greater than symbol $>$ and the is less than symbol $<$, *parentheses* ( ) or brackets [ ], the *square root* symbol $\sqrt{}$, and the raised numerals indicating *exponents*. In algebra we continue not only to use these symbols and arithmetic numbers but also variables that may represent a specific number or, under certain conditions, many numbers.

Arithmetic numbers are numbers represented by numerals like 6 or 43. Each arithmetic number is definite in value and is sometimes called a *constant*.

A *variable* holds a place open for a number, and is expressed by one of the following: a small letter; a capital letter; a letter with a subscript such as b_1 or b_2 which is read "b sub one or b sub two"; a letter with a prime mark, such as V' or V'', which is read "V prime or V double prime"; a frame, such as $\square$, $\triangle$, $\bigcirc$ and $\square$; a blank; a question mark. Sometimes the first letter of a key word is used to represent the variable.

A *numerical expression*, sometimes called a *numerical phrase*, consists of a single numeral with or without operational symbols like 41 or 57, or of two or more numerals with operational symbols like $6 + 4$, $82 - 19$, 7×53, $27 \div 3$, $9 \times (4 + 8)$, etc.

An *algebraic expression*, sometimes called an *algebraic phrase*, may be a numerical expression or an expression containing one or more variables joined by operational symbols. Sometimes numerals are also used. For example: r; $9y$; $3c - 7d$; $2x^2 - 4x + 5$; etc. are algebraic expressions.

Numerical expressions and algebraic expressions are called *mathematical expressions*.

When verbal phrases are translated into mathematical expressions or vice versa, the signs of operation may assume any one of several meanings:

Plus $(+)$ *symbol:* sum, add, more than, increased by, exceeded by

Minus $(-)$ *symbol:* difference, subtract, take away, less, less than, decreased by, diminished by

Times $(\times)$ *symbol or raised dot* $(\cdot)$: product, times, multiply

Division $(\div$ *or* $\overline{)}$ $)$ *symbols:* quotient, divide

The *equality* symbol $=$ and the *inequality* symbols (is greater than symbol $>$ and is less than symbol, $<$) are verb symbols used in mathematical sentences. A sentence that uses the equality symbol $=$ as its verb connecting two mathematical expressions is called an *equation*. $5b = 30$ and $8y - 7 = y + 14$ are equations. A mathematical rule expressing the relationship of two or more quantities by means of numerals, variables, and equality and operational symbols is a special kind of equation called a *formula*. Examples of formulas are: $A = lw$, $p = 4s$, $A = \pi r^2$, $p = 2l + 2w$, and $i = prt$.

A sentence that uses $<$ or $>$ or other symbols described on page 32S as its verb connecting two mathematical expressions is called an *inequality*.

UNIT ONE—SYMBOLS
EXERCISE 1

Using Algebraic Symbols

I. Aim: To express mathematical phrases and sentences by means of numerals, variables, and symbols of operation.

II. Procedure

To write algebraic expressions:

1. Write numerals, variables (usually letters), and operational symbols as required in proper order. See sample solutions 1 and 2.

2. If no letters are given, take key letters to represent the variables. See sample solutions 3 and 4.

3. No multiplication symbol is necessary between two letters or a numeral and letter. In the latter case the numeral precedes the letter. This number is usually called the *numerical coefficient* of the variable. Numbers that are multiplied together are called *factors*. See sample solutions 5 and 6.

4. In algebra the fraction form is generally used to indicate division. The word "over" is sometimes used to express the relationship of the numerator to the denominator. See sample solutions 7 and 8.

5. If the *square* of a number is required indicating the number is multiplied by itself, write the small figure "2" near the upper right of the numeral naming the number. This figure is called the *exponent* and indicates the *power* of the number. The power of a number is the product obtained when the number is multiplied by itself one or more times. Thus, the second power of a given number is the square of the number. See sample solutions 9 and 10.

6. If the *cube* of a number is required indicating the number is used three times as a factor in multiplication, write the exponent "3" near the upper right of the numeral naming the number. The third power of a given number is the cube of the number. See sample solutions 11 and 12.

7. If the *square root* of a number is required, write the square root symbol over the numeral naming the given number. The square root of a number is that number which when multiplied by itself produces the given number. See sample solutions 13 and 14.

8. If two or more numbers are to be grouped together so that they may be treated as a single quantity, write the numerals naming the numbers in parentheses ( ) or brackets [ ]. See sample solutions 15 and 16.

9. To express a mathematical sentence as an equation or formula, translate the verbal phrases and indicate *equals*, *is equal to*, or *is the same as* by writing the equality sign. See sample solutions 17 and 18.

III. Sample Solutions

1. The product of 5 and 6.
   Answer, 5×6 or $5 \cdot 6$

2. The sum of *m* and two.
   Answer, $m + 2$

3. The difference between the perimeter and the circumference. Answer, $p - c$

4. The distance divided by the rate of speed.
   Answer, $d \div r$

5. The product of the base (*b*) and the height (*h*).
   Answer, bh

6. Multiply *s* by nine. Answer, $9s$

7. Divide two by three. Answer, $\dfrac{2}{3}$

3

8. The quotient of the volume (V) divided by the width (w).

Answer, $\dfrac{V}{w}$

9. Multiply: $t \times t$.
Answer, t^2

10. The square of the radius.
Answer, r^2

11. Multiply: $a \cdot a \cdot a$.
Answer, a^3

12. The cube of the edge.
Answer, e^3

13. The square root of 30.
Answer, $\sqrt{30}$

14. The square root of the area (A).
Answer, $\sqrt{A}$

15. The quantity x plus six.
Answer, $(x+6)$

16. Seven times the quantity b minus three.
Answer, $7[b-3]$

17. s is equal to the sum of c and g.
Answer, $s = c + g$

18. Some number (n) increased by three equals eight.
Answer, $n + 3 = 8$

DIAGNOSTIC TEST

Express each of the following by means of numerals, variables, and symbols of operation:

1. Five increased by three.
2. The difference between eight and six.
3. The product of seven and nine.
4. The quotient of ten divided by two.
5. a divided by b.
6. The sum of d and twelve.
7. The loss (l) subtracted from the cost (c).
8. The diameter multiplied by Pi.
9. The difference between the product of the length and width and the product of the length and height.
10. One fourth of an amount (a). Express in three ways.
11. The sum of the squares of the altitude and the base.
12. The cube of the diameter decreased by four-thirds the product of Pi and the cube of the radius.
13. The square root of the difference between the square of the hypotenuse and the square of the altitude.
14. One half h times the quantity b_1 plus b_2.
15. Five times some number (n) equals forty.

Related Practice Examples

Express each of the following by means of numerals, variables, and symbols of operation:

SET 1(a)
1. Five plus four.
2. The sum of eight and six.
3. Add three and eight.
4. Six added to ten.
5. Eleven more than nine.

SET 1(b)
1. Seven more than three.
2. Twenty increased by two.
3. Nine exceeded by one.
4. The sum of twelve and seven.
5. Add six and fifteen.

SET 2(a)
1. Four minus one.
2. The difference between seven and three.
3. Twelve less nine.
4. From eight subtract two.
5. Subtract five from sixteen.

SET 2(b)
1. From twenty take six.
2. Take ten from fourteen.
3. Nine diminished by eight.
4. Four less than thirty.
5. Eighteen decreased by twelve.

SET 3
1. Eight times nine.
2. The product of six and two.
3. Multiply seven by five.
4. Six multiplied by ten.
5. Twice seven.

SET 4
1. Divide ten by five.
2. Twelve divided by three.
3. The quotient of sixty divided by fifteen.
4. Three over five.
5. The ratio of twenty to four.

SET 5

1. m divided by b.
2. x multiplied by n.
3. From v subtract g.
4. y added to a.
5. r times t.

SET 6

1. Add x and nine.
2. From five subtract a.
3. Multiply y by eight.
4. Divide n by 2.
5. Ten diminished by b.

SET 7

1. The sum of the principal (p) and the interest (i).
2. The difference between the selling price (s) and the gain (g).
3. The product of the force (F) and the distance (d).
4. The quotient of the distance (d) divided by the time (t).
5. 180° decreased by angle C.

SET 8

1. The profit divided by the cost.
2. 273° more than the Celsius temperature reading.
3. The amount less the interest.
4. Two times Pi times the radius.
5. The number of articles multiplied by the price of one article.

SET 9

1. The sum of fifteen and four decreased by seven.
2. Twice the length of the equal side (e) subtracted from the perimeter (p).
3. The product of the acceleration due to gravity (g) and time (t) added to the velocity (V).
4. The difference between the product of the altitude and base and the product of the length and width.
5. The sum of the product of twice Pi and the radius and the product of Pi, the radius, and the height.

SET 10

1. Write one fourth in two ways.
2. Write one third in two ways.
3. Write $\dfrac{a}{2}$ in two other ways.
4. Write one fifth of an amount (a) in three different ways.
5. Write one half of bh in three different ways.

SET 11

1. The square of the side (s).
2. V raised to the second power.
3. R times the square of I.
4. The difference between the square of the hypotenuse (h) and the square of the altitude (a).
5. The product of Pi, the square of the radius (r), and the height (h).

SET 12

1. The cube of the edge (e).
2. The third power of m.
3. The constant k times the cube of the velocity (v).
4. Seven times the cube of x increased by nine times the cube of y.
5. The cube of the diameter (d) decreased by four-thirds the product of Pi and the cube of the radius (r).

SET 13

1. The square root of 47.
2. The square root of the density (d).
3. The square root of the quotient of the power (P) divided by the resistance (R).
4. The square root of the product of b and c.
5. The square root of the sum of the squares of the altitude (a) and the base (b).

SET 14

1. Four times the sum of y and eight.
2. Twice the quantity l plus w.
3. d times the quantity n minus one.

4. The square of the sum of x and y.
5. The product of the sum of a and x and the difference of a and x.

Express each of the following as an equation:

SET 15(a)

1. The sum of seven and eight is equal to fifteen.
2. s times s times s is the same as the cube of s.
3. Five times the number n increased by four is equivalent to eight times the same number n decreased by twelve.
4. The cube of x divided by the square of x equals the square of x divided by x.
5. The square of the quantity c plus d equals the square of c plus twice the product of c and d plus the square of d.

SET 15(b)

1. Some number (n) decreased by fourteen is equal to thirty-five.
2. Seven added to twice what number (n) equals fifty-nine?
3. What number (n) divided by eight equals four?
4. Four times a certain number x is ten more than a second number y.
5. What number b increased by itself is equal to three times the number diminished by twenty-five?

Applications

I. Writing Formulas

Express the following mathematical, scientific, industrial, or commercial principles as formulas:

1. The volume of a rectangular solid (V) equals the product of the length (l), width (w), and height (h).
2. The average (A) of two numbers c and d equals the sum of the two numbers divided by two.
3. The distance (d) traveled at a uniform rate of speed equals the rate (r) times the time (t).
4. The cost of goods sold (c) is equal to the inventory at beginning (I_1) added to the purchases (p) less the inventory at the end (I_2).
5. The central angle of a regular polygon (a) equals 360° divided by the number of sides (n).
6. The entire surface area of a cylinder (A) is equal to twice Pi times the radius (r) times the sum of the radius (r) and the height (h).
7. The tip speed of a propeller ($T.S.$) is equal to Pi times the diameter (d) times the number of revolutions per second (N).
8. Centripetal force (F) equals the product of the weight of the body (w) and the square of the velocity (v) divided by the product of the acceleration of gravity (g) and the radius of the circle (r).
9. The valence number (N) is the quotient of the atomic weight ($A.W.$) divided by the equivalent weight ($E.W.$).
10. The horsepower of a steam engine (H.P.) equals the product of the steam pressure in lb (P), the length of stroke in ft. (L), the area of the piston in sq. in. (A), and the number of strokes per minute (N) divided by 33,000.

II. Translating Formulas

Express the following formulas as verbal sentences:

1. $A = bh$ where $A =$ area of parallelogram, $b =$ base, and $h =$ height.
2. $p = b + 2e$ where $p =$ perimeter of isosceles triangle, $b =$ base, and $e =$ length of each equal side.
3. $a = \sqrt{h^2 - b^2}$ where $a =$ altitude of right triangle, $h =$ hypotenuse, and $b =$ base.
4. $A = \pi r(r + l)$ where $A =$ entire area of a cone, $\pi = Pi$, $r =$ radius, and $l =$ slant height.

REVIEW OF UNIT ONE

I. Express the following by means of numerals, variables, and symbols of operation:

1. x increased by y decreased by z.
2. The annual depreciation (d) divided by the original cost (c).
3. Eight less than twice a certain number n.
4. The sum of angles R, S, and T.
5. The product of the length (span) of the airplane wing (s) and the width (chord) of the wing (c).
6. The difference between the selling price (s) and the margin (m).
7. The diameter of the driven pulley (D) multiplied by the number of revolutions the pulley makes per minute (R).
8. The quotient of the electromotive force (E) divided by the resistance (R).
9. The area of the piston (A) times the stroke (s).
10. The product of the drag of the airplane wing (D) and the velocity (V) divided by 550.

II. Write as algebraic expressions:

1. The square of the edge (e).
2. C raised to the second power.
3. The cube of the side (s).
4. The square of t multiplied by 16.
5. One sixth Pi times the cube of the diameter (d).
6. The square root of the weight (w).
7. The square root of the product of x and y.
8. Eight times the sum of n and three.
9. The product of the sum of c and d and the difference of a and b.
10. The difference between the squares of a and x.

III. Express the following mathematical, scientific, industrial, or commercial principles as formulas:

1. The number of gallons (g) in a given number of pints (p) is equal to the number of pints divided by 8.
2. The circumference of a circle (c) is equal to twice the product of Pi and the radius (r).
3. The capital (C) of a business is the difference between the assets (A) and the liabilities (L).
4. The rate of commission (r) is equal to the commission (c) divided by the sales (s).
5. The temperature reading on the Fahrenheit scale (F) is equal to nine fifths of the reading on the Centigrade scale (C) increased by 32°.
6. The surface speed (S) of a revolving pulley in feet per minute is equal to Pi times the diameter (d) in feet times the number of revolutions per minute (R).
7. In the study of levers, the product of one weight (W) by the length of its arm (L) equals the product of the other weight (w) by the length of its arm (l).
8. The distance (d) a freely falling body drops is one half the product of the acceleration due to gravity (g) and the square of the time of falling (t).
9. The hypotenuse (h) of a right triangle equals the square root of the sum of the squares of the altitude (a) and the base (b).
10. The radius of action of an airplane (R) is equal to the total flying time (T) multiplied by the quotient obtained by dividing the product of the ground speed out (GSO) and ground speed in (GSI) by their sum.

IV. Express the following formulas as verbal sentences:

1. $c = \pi d$ where c = circumference of circle, $\pi = Pi$ or 3.14, and d = diameter of circle.
2. $P = IE$ where P = power in watts, I = current in amperes, and E = electromotive force in volts.
3. $r = \dfrac{d}{t}$ where r = average rate of speed, d = distance traveled, and t = time of travel.
4. $n = l - d$ where n = net price, l = list price, and d = discount.
5. $A = p + prt$ where A = amount, p = principal, r = rate of interest per year, and t = time in years.

INTRODUCTION TO UNIT TWO

Many pupils in their seventh and eighth year mathematics have substituted numerical values for letters in a formula to determine a required value. This process is called *evaluating a formula*. In the formula $A = lw$, $A = 10$ when $l = 5$ and $w = 2$. However, when $l = 4$ and $w = 3$, A is equal to 12. The value of the expression lw depends upon the values of the variables l and w. In general, the value of any algebraic expression depends upon the values of the variables it contains. If these values change, the value of the expression usually changes.

Since this process of substituting given values in a given expression is used throughout the study of algebra, it is of utmost importance that algebra students acquire skill in its use. Evaluation will be used in conjunction with formulas, dependence, graphs of equations and formulas, checking equations, and checking answers of examples done by algebraic processes.

In this unit we study the evaluation of elementary expressions, expressions with parentheses, expressions with exponents, and formulas. It should be noted that parentheses are used to group two or more numbers so that they may be treated as a single quantity. Exponents are used to indicate the power of a given number. The power of a number is the product obtained when a number is multiplied by itself one or more times. The exponent "2" indicates the given number is used twice as a factor in multiplication, the exponent "3" indicates the number is used three times as a factor in multiplication, the exponent "4," 4 times, the exponent "5," 5 times, etc.

ARITHMETIC PRACTICE

Do the following examples:

1. Add:
a) $59 + 417 + 9 + 238$
b) $245 + 87 + 593 + 8,546$
c) $6\frac{3}{8} + 2\frac{7}{8}$
d) $1\frac{1}{16} + \frac{3}{4} + 3\frac{1}{2}$
e) $4.5 + .62$
f) $1 + .001 + 1.1$

2. Subtract:
a) $8,904 - 739$
b) $91,632 - 48,506$
c) $8 - 6\frac{3}{4}$
d) $4\frac{1}{3} - 1\frac{5}{6}$
e) $6 - .039$
f) $3.2 - .25$

3. Multiply:
a) 144×68
b) $5,280 \times 49$
c) $3\frac{1}{8} \times 12$
d) $2\frac{1}{2} \times 1\frac{1}{5}$
e) $1.5 \times .02$
f) $400 \times .001$

4. Divide:
a) $16,632 \div 24$
b) $120)\overline{111,240}$
c) $3\frac{1}{3} \div 15$
d) $9\frac{3}{4} \div 4\frac{1}{3}$
e) $6.85 \div .5$
f) $.04)\overline{8}$

5. Find (a) 6% of \$475; (b) 27% of \$81.35; (c) $83\frac{1}{3}$% of 732; (d) 125% of 5,000; (e) $4\frac{1}{2}$% of \$51; (f) 5.3% of 36.

6. (a) What part of 10 is 2? (b) What % of 25 is 7? (c) 18 is what part of 24? (d) 10 is what per cent of 16?

7. (a) $\frac{3}{8}$ of what number is 75? (b) .02 of what number is 9? (c) 20% of what number is 12? (d) 36% of what number is 180?

8. Round off to nearest (a) thousand: 520,601 (b) hundredth: 4.0341 (c) whole number: $6\frac{10}{21}$.

9. Use short methods: (a) $1,000 \times 82.5$ (b) $507 \div 100$ (c) $49.6 \div 1,000$ (d) $100 \times .7$ (e) $10 \times .004$.

10. Change to decimal fraction: (a) $\frac{3}{4}$ (b) $\frac{7}{8}$ (c) $\frac{3}{5}$; to common fraction: (d) .5 (e) .25 (f) .625.

UNIT TWO—EVALUATION

EXERCISE 2

Simple Expressions

I. Aim: To find the value of simple algebraic expressions.

II. Procedure

1. Copy given expression.
2. Substitute numbers for variables.
3. Find the value of each term (part of expression separated by the $+$ or $-$ sign). Note examples 6, 7 and 8.
4. Simplify to get answer.
5. If the expression is a fraction simplify, evaluate both numerator and denominator separately and then change to simplest form to get answer. See sample solution 8.

III. Sample Solutions

Find the value of the following expressions if $a=4$ and $b=2$:

1. $a+b$
$=4+2$
$=6$
Answer, 6

2. $a-b$
$=4-2$
$=2$
Answer, 2

3. ab
$=4\cdot2$
$=8$
Answer, 8

4. $\dfrac{a}{b}$
$=\dfrac{4}{2}=2$
Answer, 2

5. $5ab$
$=5\cdot4\cdot2$
$=40$
Answer, 40

6. $a+6b$
$=4+6\cdot2$
$=4+12$
$=16$
Answer, 16

7. $2ab-3b+2$
$=2\cdot4\cdot2-3\cdot2+2$
$=16-6+2$
$=12$
Answer, 12

8. $\dfrac{4a-3b}{3ab-4}$
$=\dfrac{4\cdot4-3\cdot2}{3\cdot4\cdot2-4}$
$=\dfrac{16-6}{24-4}$
$=\dfrac{10}{20}=\dfrac{1}{2}$
Answer, $\dfrac{1}{2}$

DIAGNOSTIC TEST

Find the value of the following algebraic expressions if $a=6$ and $x=2$:

1. $a+x$
2. $a-x$
3. ax
4. $\dfrac{a}{x}$

5. $4a$
6. $3ax$
7. $a+4x$
8. $a+4$

9. $2a+3x$
10. $3a-2x$
11. $5ax+6x$
12. $9a-4ax$

13. $3a+5x-3$
14. $4a+3ax-2x$
15. $\dfrac{a}{3}$
16. $\dfrac{12x}{a}$

17. $\dfrac{a+x}{a-x}$
18. $\dfrac{2a+7x}{13}$
19. $\dfrac{a+6x}{5a-3x}$
20. $\dfrac{2ax+7x-10}{4ax-3a-2}$

9

Related Practice Examples

Find the value of the following algebraic expressions:

A	B	C
if $a=8$ and $b=2$	if $x=6$ and $y=3$	if $c=7$ and $d=4$

#	A	#	B	#	C
1.	$a+b$	1.	$x+y$	1.	$c+d$
2.	$a-b$	2.	$x-y$	2.	$c-d$
3.	ab	3.	xy	3.	cd
4.	$\dfrac{a}{b}$	4.	$\dfrac{x}{y}$	4.	$\dfrac{c}{d}$
5.	$3a$	5.	$4y$	5.	$2c$
6.	$2ab$	6.	$5xy$	6.	$3cd$
7.	$a+3b$	7.	$x+4y$	7.	$5c+d$
8.	$a+3$	8.	$x+4$	8.	$5+d$
9.	$4a+5b$	9.	$3x+2y$	9.	$2c+3d$
10.	$5a-2b$	10.	$4x-5y$	10.	$3c-2d$
11.	$4ab+3b$	11.	$2xy+3x$	11.	$4cd+5c$
12.	$6a-2ab$	12.	$5xy-2y$	12.	$3cd-8c$
13.	$3a+5b+3$	13.	$4x-3y+7$	13.	$4c-3d-4$
14.	$3a+4ab+2b$	14.	$3x+5xy-y$	14.	$10c-2cd-3d$
15.	$\dfrac{a}{2}$	15.	$\dfrac{y}{3}$	15.	$\dfrac{c}{14}$
16.	$\dfrac{12b}{a}$	16.	$\dfrac{7x}{y}$	16.	$\dfrac{21d}{c}$
17.	$\dfrac{a+b}{a-b}$	17.	$\dfrac{x-y}{x+y}$	17.	$\dfrac{c-d}{c+d}$
18.	$\dfrac{4a+4b}{5}$	18.	$\dfrac{3x-2y}{6}$	18.	$\dfrac{5c-2d}{9}$
19.	$\dfrac{3a+8b}{a+b}$	19.	$\dfrac{2x-3y}{x+3y}$	19.	$\dfrac{c-d}{3c-5d}$
20.	$\dfrac{4ab-3b}{2a+13}$	20.	$\dfrac{5xy-2y}{4x-xy}$	20.	$\dfrac{cd+d-2}{2cd+c+7}$

EXERCISE 3

Expressions With Parentheses

I. **Aim**: To find the value of algebraic expressions with parentheses.

II. **Procedure**

1. Method is the same as that for simple algebraic expressions with the following additional step:

2. Evaluate each set of parentheses separately and use the result as a single term. Complete as directed. A numeral written immediately next to parentheses implies multiplication.

III. **Sample Solutions**

Find the value of the following expressions if $b=6$, $c=4$, and $x=2$:

1. $3(b+x)$
$=3(6+2)$
$=3(8)$
$=24$
Answer, 24

2. $(3b-2c)$
$=(3\cdot6-2\cdot4)$
$=(18-8)$
$=(10)$
$=10$
Answer, 10

3. $b(3c+x)$
$=6(3\cdot4+2)$
$=6(12+2)$
$=6(14)$
$=84$
Answer, 84

4. $4x+(2b-5)$
$=4\cdot2+(2\cdot6-5)$
$=8+(12-5)$
$=8+(7)$
$=8+7$
$=15$
Answer, 15

5. $b+c(c-x)$
$=6+4(4-2)$
$=6+4(2)$
$=6+8$
$=14$
Answer, 14

6. $(b+c)(c-x)$
$=(6+4)(4-2)$
$=(10)(2)$
$=20$
Answer, 20

7. $\dfrac{5(3x-c)}{x(5b-2c+6)}$
$=\dfrac{5(3\cdot2-4)}{2(5\cdot6-2\cdot4+6)}$
$=\dfrac{5(6-4)}{2(30-8+6)}$
$=\dfrac{5(2)}{2(28)}$
$=\dfrac{5}{28}$
Answer, $\dfrac{5}{28}$

DIAGNOSTIC TEST

Find the value of the following algebraic expressions if $a=6$, $c=4$, and $x=2$:

1. $3(a+c)$
2. $6(c-x)$
3. $(2a+3x)$
4. $2(4a+3c)$
5. $c(a+x)$
6. $x(4c-5x)$
7. $5c(2a+x)$
8. $a(ac+cx)$
9. $ax(6c-7)$
10. $3acx(2ac-6cx+5)$
11. $2a+(c+x)$
12. $2a-(c+x)$
13. $a+c+(a+x)$
14. $a+c(a+x)$
15. $(a+c)(a+x)$
16. $7a-c(a+x)$
17. $4(a+c)-x(2a-5x)$
18. $\dfrac{3(2a+3cx)}{4(7c-ac)}$

Related Practice Examples

Find the value of the following algebraic expressions:

A	B	C
if $a=6$, $b=3$, and $x=2$.	if $b=4$, $c=3$, and $d=1$.	if $a=8$, $x=4$ and $y=2$.
1. $2(a+b)$	1. $4(b+d)$	1. $3(x+y)$
2. $5(b-x)$	2. $6(c-d)$	2. $2(a-1)$
3. $(2a+b)$	3. $(3b+5d)$	3. $(3a-2y)$
4. $3(3a+2b)$	4. $2(3b-4c)$	4. $4(a-3y)$
5. $a(b+x)$	5. $c(b-d)$	5. $x(a+6)$
6. $b(4a+3b)$	6. $b(3c-2d)$	6. $a(3x-2y)$
7. $4x(a+5b)$	7. $3d(2c-b)$	7. $5x(2a-5y)$
8. $a(ax+bx)$	8. $c(bd-cd)$	8. $x(ax+ay+a)$
9. $ab(3a+2)$	9. $bd(2b-3)$	9. $xy(2a+3x-2)$
10. $5abx(4ax+3x)$	10. $4bcd(3cd-b)$	10. $6axy(2ay-x+ax)$
11. $3a+(b+x)$	11. $5b+(c-d)$	11. $3a+(ax-y)$
12. $3a-(b+x)$	12. $5b-(c-d)$	12. $4x-(xy+2)$
13. $a+b+(a+x)$	13. $b-d+(b-c)$	13. $2a-x+(2x-6)$
14. $a+b(a+x)$	14. $b+d(b-c)$	14. $2a+x(2x-6)$
15. $(a+b)(a+x)$	15. $(b-d)(b-c)$	15. $(2a-x)(2x-6)$
16. $5a-b(a+x)$	16. $b-d(b-c)$	16. $2a-x(2x-6)$
17. $2(a+b)-3(a-x)$	17. $3(5bd-4d)-c(cd+d)$	17. $2a(xy+2)-3x(a-2y)$
18. $\dfrac{5(ab+bx)}{4(ax-bx)}$	18. $\dfrac{4(bc-2d)}{9(2bc-4)}$	18. $\dfrac{5(x+3y)}{3x(a+3x-2xy)}$

EXERCISE 4

Expressions With Exponents

I. Aim : To find the value of algebraic expressions with exponents.

II. Procedure

1. Method is the same as that for simple algebraic expressions with the following additional step:

2. Raise each number as required to the proper power. Complete as directed.

III. Sample Solutions

Find the value of the following expressions if $b=2$, $x=4$, and $y=3$:

1. x^2
   $=(4)^2$
   $=16$
   Answer, 16

2. $3by^2$
   $=3\cdot2\cdot(3)^2$
   $=3\cdot2\cdot9$
   $=54$
   Answer, 54

3. $(bx)^2$
   $=(2\cdot4)^2$
   $=(8)^2$
   $=64$
   Answer, 64

4. b^3
   $=(2)^3$
   $=8$
   Answer, 8

5. y^4
   $=(3)^4$
   $=81$
   Answer, 81

6. x^2-3x+6
   $=(4)^2-3\cdot4+6$
   $=16-12+6$
   $=10$
   Answer, 10

DIAGNOSTIC TEST

Find the value of the following algebraic expressions if $a=4$, $b=3$, and $c=2$:

1. b^2
2. $2b^2$
3. bc^2
4. a^2b
5. a^2b^2

6. $5a^2bc^2$
7. a^3
8. $2a^2bc^3$
9. $(ab)^2$
10. c^4

11. b^5
12. a^2+b^2
13. $3a^2-2b^2$
14. b^2c+bc^2
15. a^2+6

16. a^2+2a-3
17. $b^2-2bc+c^2$
18. $\dfrac{b^3}{c^2}$
19. $\dfrac{b^2-4b+4}{b^2-4}$
20. $\dfrac{a^2}{4}+\dfrac{b^2}{9}$

Related Practice Examples

Find the value of the following algebraic expressions:

A	B	C
if $c=5$, $m=3$, and $x=2$	if $b=3$, $d=2$, and $y=1$	if $m=4$, $r=6$, and $x=3$
1. c^2	1. d^2	1. x^2
2. $2m^2$	2. $3y^2$	2. $4m^2$
3. cx^2	3. bd^2	3. mr^2
4. m^2x	4. b^2y	4. r^2x
5. c^2x^2	5. d^2y^2	5. m^2x^2
6. $4c^2mx$	6. $3bd^2y^2$	6. $5m^2r^2x$
7. c^3	7. d^3	7. m^3
8. $3c^3m^2x$	8. $4b^2dy^3$	8. $6m^3r^2x^2$
9. $(mx)^2$	9. $(by)^2$	9. $3(rx)^2$
10. x^4	10. b^4	10. x^4
11. m^5	11. y^5	11. r^5
12. c^2+m^2	12. b^2-d^2	12. m^2-x^2
13. $2m^2-3x^2$	13. $3d^2-2y^2$	13. $4r^2-2x^2$
14. c^2x+m^2x	14. b^2d-dy^2	14. mr^2-mx^2
15. m^2+7	15. b^3-5	15. x^2-3
16. c^2+6c-5	16. b^2-4b+4	16. x^2+6x+9
17. $m^2+2mx+x^2$	17. $d^2+5dy-6y^2$	17. $m^2-2mr+4r^2$
18. $\dfrac{c^2}{x^3}$	18. $\dfrac{d^3}{y^2}$	18. $\dfrac{m^2}{x^4}$
19. $\dfrac{c^2+6c+9}{c^2-9}$	19. $\dfrac{d^2-2d+1}{d-1}$	19. $\dfrac{r^2+8r+16}{r^2-2r+8}$
20. $\dfrac{c^2}{9}+\dfrac{x^2}{4}$	20. $\dfrac{2d^2}{3}-y^2$	20. $\dfrac{9r^2}{25}-\dfrac{4x^2}{9}$

EXERCISE 5
Evaluation of Formulas

I. Aim: To evaluate formulas.

II. Procedure

    1. Copy the formula.   2. Substitute given values for variables.

    3. Perform the necessary operations to obtain answer.

III. Sample Solutions

1. Find the value of A if $l=7$ and $w=4$.

    $A=lw$

    $A=7\cdot4$

    $A=28$

    Answer, 28

2. Find the value of A if $p=120$, $r=.04$, and $t=5$.

    $A=p+prt$

    $A=120+120\times.04\times5$

    $A=120+24$

    $A=144$ Answer, 144

3. Find the value of I if $W=100$ and $E=20$.

    $I=\dfrac{W}{E}$

    $I=\dfrac{100}{20}$

    $I=5$ Answer, 5

4. Find the value of V if $\pi=3.14$, $r=4$, and $h=6$.

    $V=\pi r^2 h$

    $V=3.14\times(4)^2\times6$

    $V=3.14\times16\times6$

    $V=301.44$

    Answer, 301.44

DIAGNOSTIC TEST

Find the value of:

1. d when $r=52$ and $t=4$, using the formula $d=rt$
2. p when $l=29$ and $w=16$, using the formula $p=2l+2w$
3. i when $A=125$ and $p=98$, using the formula $i=A-p$
4. I when $E=110$ and $R=5$, using the formula $I=\dfrac{E}{R}$
5. A when $\pi=3.14$ and $r=6$, using the formula $A=\pi r^2$
6. S when $n=6$, $a=3$, and $l=13$, using the formula $S=\dfrac{n}{2}(a+l)$

Related Practice Examples

Evaluate the following formulas:

SET 1(a)

Find the Value of	when	Formula
1. p	$s=6$	$p=4s$
2. A	$l=8$, $w=5$	$A=lw$
3. V	$B=50$; $h=7$	$V=Bh$
4. A	$a=16$; $b=9$	$A=ab$
5. c	$\pi=3.14$; $d=12$	$c=\pi d$

SET 1(b)

Find the Value of	when	Formula
1. E	$I=11$; $R=20$	$E=IR$
2. A	$a=18$; $b=26$	$A=\frac{1}{2}ab$
3. i	$p=200$; $r=.06$; $t=4$	$i=prt$
4. V	$l=12$; $w=8$; $h=7$	$V=lwh$
5. c	$\pi=\frac{22}{7}$; $r=21$	$c=2\pi r$

SET 1(c)

Find the Value of	when	Formula
1. d	$r=25$; $t=7$	$d=rt$
2. P	$H=100$; $D=64$	$P=HD$
3. $T.S.$	$\pi=3.14$; $d=7$; $N=30$	$T.S.=\pi dN$
4. W	$I=6$; $E=220$	$W=IE$
5. W	$F=125$; $d=8$	$W=Fd$

SET 2(a)

Find the Value of	when	Formula
1. A	$p=450; i=83$	$A=p+i$
2. s	$c=25; g=7$	$s=c+g$
3. p	$a=19; b=23; c=18$	$p=a+b+c$
4. p	$l=37; w=26$	$p=2l+2w$
5. A	$p=130; r=.03; t=8$	$A=p+prt$

SET 2(b)

Find the value of	when	Formula
1. A	$C=43$	$A=C+273$
2. D_t	$D_w=97.2; D_p=51.9$	$D_t=D_w+D_p$
3. v	$V=29; g=32; t=4$	$v=V+gt$
4. F	$C=82$	$F=1.8C+32$
5. A	$L=4,250; C=6,500$	$A=L+C$

SET 3(a)

Find the value of	when	Formula
1. B	$A=58$	$B=90-A$
2. C	$A=352$	$C=A-273$
3. l	$c=164; s=139$	$l=c-s$
4. C	$A=8,925; L=3,672$	$C=A-L$
5. p	$A=475; i=86$	$p=A-i$

SET 3(b)

Find the value of	when	Formula
1. C	$A=47; B=105$	$C=180-A-B$
2. g	$s=134; c=117$	$g=s-c$
3. i	$A=266; p=210$	$i=A-p$
4. b	$p=58; e=13$	$b=p-2e$
5. c	$s=81; g=29$	$c=s-g$

SET 4(a)

Find the value of	when	Formula
1. a	$n=5$	$a=\dfrac{360}{n}$
2. r	$d=42$	$r=\dfrac{d}{2}$
3. A	$a=18; b=6$	$A=\dfrac{ab}{2}$
4. r	$d=135; t=3$	$r=\dfrac{d}{t}$
5. V	$B=27; h=16$	$V=\dfrac{Bh}{3}$

SET 4(b)

Find the value of	when	Formula
1. I	$E=110; R=22$	$I=\dfrac{E}{R}$
2. d	$m=117; v=13$	$d=\dfrac{m}{v}$
3. W	$w=84; l=16; L=12$	$W=\dfrac{wl}{L}$
4. $H.P.$	$D_t=225; V=130$	$H.P.=\dfrac{D_tV}{375}$
5. I	$E=55; n=6; R=10; r=2$	$I=\dfrac{nE}{R+nr}$

SET 5(a)

Find the value of	when	Formula
1. A	$s=27$	$A=s^2$
2. A	$d=13$	$A=.7854d^2$
3. V	$e=8$	$V=e^3$
4. A	$\pi=3.14; r=16$	$A=\pi r^2$
5. V	$\pi=\frac{22}{7}; r=42; h=15$	$V=\pi r^2 h$

SET 5(b)

Find the value of	when	Formula
1. s	$t=6$	$s=16t^2$
2. W	$I=7; R=4$	$W=I^2R$
3. F	$W=48; v=60; g=32; r=12$	$F=\dfrac{Wv^2}{gr}$
4. K	$m=125; v=50$	$K=\frac{1}{2}mv^2$
5. L	$C_L=.64; d=.002; S=180; V=100$	$L=C_L\dfrac{d}{2}SV^2$

SET 6(a)

Find the value of	when	Formula
1. p	$l=38; w=45$	$p=2(l+w)$
2. A	$p=50; r=.06; t=5$	$A=p(1+rt)$
3. C	$A=62; B=97$	$C=180-(A+B)$
4. A	$\pi=3.14; r=6; h=14$	$A=2\pi r(r+h)$
5. S	$n=8; a=2; l=16$	$S=\dfrac{n}{2}(a+l)$

SET 6(b)

Find the value of	when	Formula
1. C	$F=68$	$C=\frac{5}{9}(F-32)$
2. A	$h=8; b=10; b'=4$	$A=\dfrac{h}{2}(b+b')$
3. l	$a=2; n=5; d=3$	$l=a+(n-1)d$
4. A	$\pi=\frac{22}{7}; r=35; l=72$	$A=\pi r(r+l)$
5. R	$T=3; GSO=236; GSI=214$	$R=T\left(\dfrac{GSO\times GSI}{GSO+GSI}\right)$

REVIEW OF UNIT TWO

Find the value of the following algebraic expressions if $a=8$, $b=5$, $c=3$, and $d=2$:

1. $2a-3b+6c$　　　　2. $a(bc-cd)$　　　　3. $a^2+2ab+b^2$　　　　4. $(b+c)(b-c)$

5. Find the value of V if $B=18$ and $h=3$, using the formula $V=Bh$.
6. Find the value of B if $A=29$, using the formula $B=90-A$.
7. What is the value of p when $l=24$ and $w=19$, using the formula $p=2l+2w$?
8. In the formula $s=16t^2$ what does s equal when $t=5$?
9. Find the value of A if $\pi=\frac{2\,2}{7}$, $r=7$, and $h=4$, using the formula $A=2\pi r(r+h)$.

10. Using the formula $I=\dfrac{E}{R}$, find the value of I when $E=115$ and $R=23$.

Find the value of the following algebraic expressions if $m=9$, $n=6$, $x=2$, and $y=1$:

11. $3m+2x-4y$　　　　12. $n+x(m-y)$　　　　13. $4x^2-3xy+7y^2$　　　　14. $\dfrac{2n^2-5n+6}{3n-2}$

15. Find the value of A if $L=5{,}200$ and $C=8{,}000$, using the formula $A=L+C$.
16. In the formula $W=Fd$, what does W equal when $F=175$ and $d=20$?
17. Using the formula $b=p-2e$, find the value of b when $p=34$ and $e=9$.
18. Find the value of W when $I=3$ and $R=40$, using the formula $W=I^2R$.

19. What is the value of d when $m=42$ and $v=14$, using the formula $d=\dfrac{m}{v}$?

20. Using the formula $R=T\left(\dfrac{GSO\times GSI}{GSO+GSI}\right)$, find the value of R when $T=3$, $GSO=170$, and $GSI=130$.

CUMULATIVE ALGEBRA REVIEW

Write each of the following as an algebraic expression:

1. The difference between 180 and B.　　　　2. The sum of twice the length (l) and twice the width (w).

Express the following principles as formulas:

3. The area of a circle (A) is equal to one fourth the product of Pi and the square of the diameter (d).
4. The wave length of sound waves (l) equals the velocity of the waves (v) divided by the frequency or number of waves per second (n).
5. What is the value of the expression $x-2y$ when $x=10$ and $y=4$?
6. Find the value of the expression $bc+(b+c)$ when $b=6$ and $c=3$.

7. What is the value of the expression $\dfrac{r^2s-rs^2}{3s-2}$ when $r=5$ and $s=4$?

8. Find the value of c when $\pi=\frac{2\,2}{7}$ and $r=35$, using the formula $c=2\pi r$.
9. Using the formula $A=p(1+rt)$, find the value of A when $p=620$, $r=.05$, and $t=8$.
10. What is the value of L when $C=.023$, $d=.002$, $S=160$, and $V=120$, using the formula $L=\dfrac{CdSV^2}{2}$?

KEYED ACHIEVEMENT TEST

If any answer is incorrect, turn to the exercise indicated by the numeral in the circle. Study the instructions and sample solutions in these exercises, then do as many practice examples as you need.

1. Write the following as an algebraic expression:
   One third the product of Pi, the square of the radius (r) and the height (h).　①
2. Find the value of the expression $x+3y$ when $x=10$ and $y=6$.　②
3. What is the value of the expression $a+d(n-1)$ when $a=5$, $d=3$, and $n=9$?　③

4. Find the value of the expression $\dfrac{b^2+2bx+x^2}{b+x}$ when $b=6$ and $x=4$.　④

5. Using the formula $A=2\pi r^2+2\pi rh$, find the value of A when $\pi=\frac{2\,2}{7}$, $r=14$, and $h=8$.　⑤

INTRODUCTION TO UNIT THREE

Algebra students are generally familiar with formulas that are studied in arithmetic and informal geometry. A mathematical formula is a rule that expresses the relationship between quantities by means of numerals, variables, and symbols of operation and equality. For example, the formula $p = 4s$ shows the relationship between the perimeter of a square and the length of its side.

Tables of related values are sometimes used to show the relationship between quantities. Very often data given in tabular form may be analyzed and their relationship determined. It is then possible to express this relationship by a formula.

Where the same mathematical situation occurs frequently, it is sometimes economical and practical to develop a formula covering the relationship involved.

In this unit formulas are derived from tables of related numbers and from groups of similar problems or mathematical situations.

ARITHMETIC MAINTENANCE DRILL

Do the following examples:

1. Add: 697
        4,529
          68
         196
       58,207

2. Subtract: 41,248
             27,109

3. Multiply: 507
             231

4. Divide: 144)85,968

5. Add: $4\frac{1}{2}$
        $3\frac{5}{8}$

6. Subtract: $7\frac{1}{8}$
             $5\frac{3}{4}$

7. Multiply: $1\frac{1}{2} \times 2\frac{1}{4}$

8. Divide: $6\frac{3}{4} \div 2$

9. Add: $.85 + 2.7 + 56$

10. Subtract: $453 - \$3.50$

11. Multiply: $24 \times \$5.26$

12. Divide: $.10)\$25.$

13. Round off to nearest million: 57,482,193

14. Change $\frac{3}{8}$ to a decimal fraction.

15. Multiply by short method: $1,000 \times 45.06$

16. Find 8% of $329.

17. What % of $9 is $6?

18. 25% of what number is 8?

19. Square 17.

20. What part of a yard is 16 inches?

UNIT THREE—MAKING FORMULAS

EXERCISE 6
Making Formulas

I. Aim: To make formulas from tables of numbers, groups of similar problems, geometric figures, and diagrams.

II. Procedure

1. From a table of numbers (see sample solution 1).
   a) Find the missing numbers.
   b) Write the word rule expressing the relationship between quantities.
   c) Express the word rule as a formula.

2. From groups of similar problems (see sample solution 2).
   a) Solve problems.
   b) Write the word rule expressing the relationship between quantities.
   c) Express the word rule as a formula.
   d) Solve given examples using the formula.

3. From geometric figures and diagrams (see sample solution 3).
   a) Study the geometric figure or diagram to find the relationship between quantities.
   b) If possible, write a word rule expressing this relationship.
   c) Write the formula.

III. Sample Solutions

1. Table of numbers
   Changing a given number of years into months

Number of Years (y)	1	2	3	4	6	9	11	15	23	30
Number of Months (m)	12	24	36							

   a) Missing numbers are 48, 72, 108, 132, 180, 276, 360.
   b) The number of months in a given number of years is equal to 12 times the number of years.
   c) Formula: $m = 12y$

2. Groups of similar problems
   a) Solve the following problem:
   1. A merchant bought a lamp for $6 and sold it for $8. How much did he gain?

      $8 selling price
      $6 cost
      ——————
      $2 gain   Answer, $2 gain

   b) The gain is equal to the selling price minus the cost.

   c) Formula: $g = s - c$.

   d) Solve the following example by formula: Find the gain if the cost is $30 and the selling price is $46.

      $g = s - c$
      $g = \$46 - \$30$
      $g = \$16$
      Answer, $16

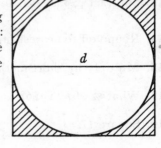

3. Geometric figures and diagrams
   A circle with diameter d is inscribed in a square whose side also measures d. Write a formula for the shaded area.
   a) Study shows that the shaded area can be found by subtracting the area of the circle from the area of the square. The formula for the area of the circle is $A = \frac{1}{4}\pi d^2$. The formula for the area of a square whose side measures d is $A = d^2$.
   b) The shaded area is equal to the area of the square minus the area of the circle.
   c) $A = d^2 - \frac{1}{4}\pi d^2$

DIAGNOSTIC TEST

1. Find the missing numbers.
2. Write the word rule expressing the relationship between quantities.
3. Write the formula.

1. The relationship between air pressure at the earth's surface and area is shown in the following table:

Area in square inches (A)	1	2	3	4	8	11	15	24
Air pressure in pounds (P)	15	30	45					

2. The following table compares the ages of two boys:

Tom's age in years (T)	2	3	6	7	9	12	16	25
John's age in years (J)	9	10	13					

3. Interest for 60 days at 6% on principals is given in the following table:

Principal (p)	$100	$250	$395	$418	$637	$700	$875	$940
Interest (i)	$1.00	$2.50	$3.95					

4. The following table shows the number of triangles in a polygon:

Number of sides (s)	3	4	7	8	12	14	17	20
Number of triangles (t)	1	2	5					

5. The cost of sending a package by parcel post in a certain zone is shown in the following table:

Weight in pounds (w)	1 or less	2	3	4	6	7	10	15
Total cost (c)	$1.00	$1.20	$1.40					

6. The following table shows annual statements of inventory:

Inventory at beginning ($I.B.$)	$5,000	$7,500	$8,200	$6,900	$9,350	$16,900	$1,400	$3,740
Purchases (P)	$8,000	$10,000	$9,600	$20,000	$18,490	$25,420	$17,300	$8,675
Sales (S)	$9,000	$15,500	$12,000	$17,400	$24,600	$23,780	$13,850	$10,429
Inventory at end ($I.E.$)	$4,000	$2,000						

7. a) Solve the following problems:

     1. A merchant buys a television set for $120 and sells it for $97. How much does he lose?
     2. A dealer buys a car for $1,450 and sells it for $1,285. How much does he lose?
     3. A merchant buys a desk for $90 and sells it for $65. How much does he lose?

b) Write a word rule expressing the amount lost (l) in terms of the cost (c) and the selling price (s).
c) Write the formula.
d) Solve the following problems by formula:

Find the loss if:	the cost is	selling price is		the cost is	selling price is
1.	$30	$20	4.	$300	$263
2.	$23	$16	5.	$725	$584
3.	$110	$75			

8. An inside horse on a merry-go-round makes path *A* and an outside horse makes path *B* in one turn.

Study the diagram, then write a word rule and formula showing the difference in the length of ride (*L*) if the diameter of the small circle is *d* and of the large circle is *D*.

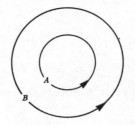

Related Practice Examples

1. Find the missing numbers.

2. Write the word rule expressing the relationship between quantities.

3. Write the formula.

(Copy the tables below and fill in missing numbers. *Do not write in this book.*)

SET 1

1. Changing days to hours:

Number of days (*d*)	1	2	3	4	7	13	21	40
Number of hours (*h*)	24	48	72					

2. Wages earned:

Number of hours (*h*)	5	6	7	8	14	25	32	70
Wages (*w*)	$30	$36	$42					

3. Changing meters to yards:

Number of meters (*m*)	2	5	8	9	11	15	22	45
Number of yards (*y*)	2.2	5.5	8.8					

4. Fire insurance rates:

Rate per $100 for 1 yr. (*r*)	$.08	$.12	$.14	$.18	$.20	$.26	$.34	$.38
Rate per $100 for 3 yr. (*R*)	$.20	$.30	$.35					

5. Cost of gasoline:

Number of gallons (*g*)	2	5	6	8	10	12	15	19
Cost (*c*)	$1.20	$3.00	$3.60					

SET 2

1. Total salary, fixed salary, and commission:

Commission (*c*)	$21	$39	$57	$63	$84	$96	$141	$165
Total Salary (*s*)	$99	$117	$135					

2. Interest and total amount paid back:

Interest (i)	$ 4	$ 5	$ 8	$9	$12	$14	$17	$20
Total amount (A)	$59	$60	$63					

3. Comparison of two rows of numbers:

Row a	12	13	15	16	18	21	25	36
Row b	18	19	21					

4. Total salary, fixed salary, and bonus:

Bonus (b)	$15	$36	$54	$69	$78	$93	$135	$150
Total salary (s)	$102	$123	$141					

5. Making coffee:

Number of cups of coffee required (C)	4	5	7	9	10	12	15	20
Number of tablespoonfuls of coffee (T)	5	6	8					

SET 3

1. Changing millimeters to centimeters:

Number of millimeters (mm.)	20	30	38	40	47	55	96	110
Number of centimeters (cm.)	2	3	3.8					

2. Changing nautical miles to degrees of latitude:

Number of nautical miles (m)	60	180	420	480	540	720	1080	1200
Latitude in degrees (L)	1	3	7					

3. Annual and monthly rent:

Rent per year (R)	$840	$912	$984	$1,056	$1,128	$1,200	$1,272	$1,344
Rent per month (r)	$70	$76	$82					

4. Weight and capacity of gasoline:

Weight in pounds (w)	30	42	48	54	78	90	108	162
Number of gallons (g)	5	7	8					

5. Perimeter and length of side of a regular hexagon:

Perimeter in feet (p)	24	42	48	54	72	96	120	168
Length of side in feet (s)	4	7	8					

SET 4

1. Number of diagonals in a polygon:

Number of sides (s)	4	5	6	7	9	12	13	16
Number of diagonals (d)	1	2	3					

2. Complementary angles:

Angle A in degrees	10	18	30	36	45	57	60	75
Angle B in degrees	80	72	60					

3. Comparison of two rows of numbers:

Row x	17	21	29	34	43	52	75	86
Row y	9	13	21					

4. Down payment and amount of mortgage on a house costing $24,000:

Down payment (p)	$6,000	$6,500	$7,000	$7,500	$8,000	$8,500	$9,000	$9,500
Amount of mortgage (m)	$18,000	$17,500	$17,000					

5. Ages of two girls:

Sally's age in years (S)	12	13	14	15	17	20	22	26
Dorothy's age in years (D)	5	6	7					

SET 5

1. Parcel Post — cost of sending a package in a certain zone:

Weight in pounds (w)	1 or less	2	4	6	9	10	15	25
Total cost (c)	$.61	$.65	$.73					

2. Cost of developing and printing a roll of film:

Number of prints (n)	1	4	5	6	8	10	11	12
Cost (c)	$1.11	$1.74	$1.95					

3. Long distance telephone charges for a certain zone:

Number of minutes (n)	3 or less	4	5	6	9	10	14	20
Cost (c)	$.50	$.65	$.80					

4. Cost of sending telegrams

Number of words (n)	15 or less	16	17	18	19	21	25	30
Cost (c)	$3.10	$3.18	$3.26					

5. Laundry charges:

Weight in pounds (w)	4 or less	5	6	10	12	15	16	20
Cost (c)	$1.00	$1.20	$1.40					

SET 6

1. Net profit:

Sales (s)	$79	$580	$450	$900	$360	$847	$1,200	$2,000
Cost of goods (c)	$60	$400	$275	$750	$287	$690	$ 925	$1,300
Expenses (e)	$ 8	$ 60	$ 75	$ 80	$ 43	$ 59	$ 150	$ 298
Net profit (p)	$11	$120	$100					

2. Navigation:

True Course (T.C.)	59°	125°	238°	93°	154°	26°	307°	290°
East Variation (E.V.)	4°	8°	5°	3°	2°	9°	12°	6°
West Deviation (W.D.)	7°	6°	1°	4°	2°	11°	5°	9°
Compass Course (C. C.)	62°	123°						

3. Bank discount:

Face of note (F)	$100	$250	$980	$160	$340	$850	$1,000	$520
Discount (D)	$ 6	$ 15	$ 49	$ 8	$ 17	$ 51	$ 40	$ 26
Proceeds of note (P)	$ 94	$235						

4. Real estate taxes:

Assessed value (v)	$6,000	$7,000	$8,000	$8,500	$9,400	$10,700	$15,000	$21,500
Tax rate per $100 (r)	$2.00	$3.00	$5.00	$4.00	$6.00	$6.50	$3.60	$5.20
Amount of tax (T)	$120	$210						

5. Area of trapezoid:

Lower base in feet (b_1)	8	13	15	12	21	20	25	29
Upper base in feet (b_2)	10	7	13	18	11	37	16	35
Height in feet (h)	5	8	10	7	12	6	13	47
Area in square feet (A)	45	80	140					

SET 7

1. a) Solve the following problems:

    1. A classroom has 5 rows with 9 seats in each row. Find the total number of seats.

    2. A school auditorium has 30 rows with 26 seats in each row. Find the total number of seats.

    3. A motion picture theater has 42 rows with 34 seats in each row. Find the total number of seats.

b) Write a word rule expressing the total number of seats (s) in terms of the number of rows (r) and the number of seats in each row (n).

c) Write the formula.

d) Solve the following problems by formula:
Find the total number of seats if there are:

    1. 20 rows and 10 seats in each row.

    2. 15 rows and 13 seats in each row.

    3. 30 rows and 28 seats in each row.

    4. 36 rows and 24 seats in each row.

    5. 50 rows and 40 seats in each row.

2. a) Solve the following problems:

    1. A furniture dealer buys a table for $28. Find the selling price if he wishes to make $13 profit.
    2. What is the selling price of a gas range if it cost $90 and the merchant wishes to make $35 profit?
    3. An electric appliance dealer buys a television set for $145. Find the selling price if he wishes to make $47 profit?

b) Write a word rule expressing the selling price (s) in terms of the cost (c) and the profit (p).

c) Write the formula.

d) Solve the following problems by formula:
Find the selling price if:

	the cost is	the profit is		the cost is	the profit is
1.	$30	$10	4.	$250	$150
2.	$55	$25	5.	$576	$225
3.	$180	$60			

3. a) Solve the following problems:

    1. Tom borrowed $50. At the end of one year he repaid his loan by paying $60. How much interest did he pay?
    2. How much interest did Harry's father pay if he borrowed $120 and after 2 years repaid $150?
    3. Marilyn's father borrowed $1,000. How much interest did he pay if he repaid $1,075 to clear his debt?

b) Write a word rule expressing the amount of interest paid (i) in terms of the total amount paid back (A) and the amount of money borrowed (p).

c) Write the formula.

d) Solve the following problems by formula:
Find the interest if:

	the amount borrowed is	the total amount repaid is
1.	$ 60	$ 80
2.	$ 18	$ 25
3.	$ 115	$ 150
4.	$ 320	$ 380
5.	$2,000	$2,120

4. a) Solve the following problems:

    1. A motorist traveled 80 miles in 2 hours. What was his average rate of speed per hour?
    2. An airplane flew 1,029 miles in 3 hours and 30 minutes. What was its average rate of speed per hour?
    3. A ship sailed 312 nautical miles in 12 hours. What was its average rate of speed per hour?

b) Write a word rule expressing the average rate of speed per hour (r) in terms of the distance traveled (d) and the number of hours (t).

c) Write the formula.

d) Solve the following problems by formula:
Find the average rate of speed per hour if:

	the distance traveled is	time		the distance traveled is	time
1.	1,200 miles	5 hours	4.	225 miles	9 hours
2.	180 miles	6 hours	5.	135 miles	3 hours
3.	2,350 miles	10 hours			

5. Measurements

   a) How many days are in 2 weeks? 5 weeks? Write a word rule and a formula expressing the number of days (d) in w weeks.

   b) How many gallons are in 8 quarts? 20 quarts? Write a word rule and a formula expressing the number of gallons (g) in q quarts.

   c) How many feet are in 72 inches? 120 inches? Write a word rule and a formula expressing the number of feet (f) in i inches.

   d) How many pecks are in 3 bushels? 15 bushels? Write a word rule and a formula expressing the number of pecks (p) in b bushels.

   e) One cubic foot of sea water weights 64 pounds. What is the weight of 5 cubic feet of sea water? 12 cubic feet of sea water? Write a word rule and a formula expressing the weight in pounds (w) of a given number of cubic feet ($c.f.$) of sea water.

SET 8

   1. Study the diagram.   2. Write the word rule expressing the required relationship.

          3. Write the formula.

Part 1 — Business

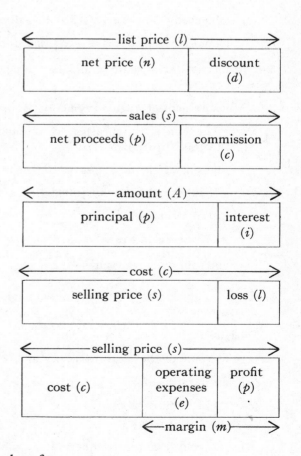

1. (a) List price in terms of net price and discount.
   (b) Net price in terms of list price and discount.
   (c) Discount in terms of list price and net price.

2. (a) Net proceeds in terms of sales and commission.
   (b) Commission in terms of net proceeds and sales.
   (c) Sales in terms of commission and net proceeds.

3. (a) Interest in terms of principal and amount.
   (b) Principal in terms of amount and interest.
   (c) Amount in terms of principal and interest.

4. (a) Loss in terms of cost and selling price.
   (b) Selling price in terms of cost and loss.
   (c) Cost in terms of loss and selling price.

5. (a) Selling price in terms of cost, operating expenses, and profit.
   (b) Margin in terms of operating expenses and profit.
   (c) Profit in terms of selling price, cost, and operating expenses.
   (d) Cost in terms of selling price and margin.
   (e) Operating expenses in terms of margin and profit.
   (f) Selling price in terms of cost and margin.
   (g) Profit in terms of operating expenses and margin.
   (h) Operating expenses in terms of cost, selling price, and profit.
   (i) Margin in terms of selling price and cost.
   (j) Cost in terms of selling price, operating expenses, and profit.

Part 2 — Measurement of Lines

1. (a) Dimension c in terms of a and b.

   (b) Dimension b in terms of a and c.

   (c) Dimension a in terms of b and c.

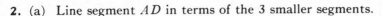

2. (a) Line segment AD in terms of the 3 smaller segments.

   (b) Line segment AB in terms of AD, BC, and CD.

   (c) Line segment BC in terms of AD, AB, and CD.

   (d) Line segment BD in terms of AD and one other segment.

   (e) Line segment BC in terms of AC and AB.

3. (a) Perimeter (p) of the isosceles triangle in terms of the three sides.

   (b) Side (b) in terms of the perimeter and the other two sides.

   (c) Side (e) in terms of the perimeter and side b.

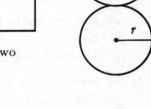

4. (a) Dimension y in terms of two other dimensions.

   (b) Dimension x in terms of two other dimensions.

   (c) Dimension c in terms of two other dimensions.

   (d) Dimension a in terms of two other dimensions.

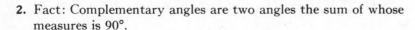

5. Distance one must skate in making the figure 8 in terms of the radius of the two equal circles.

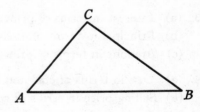

Part 3 — Measurement of Angles (Symbol $\angle$ represents the word angle)

1. Fact: The sum of the measures of the angles of a triangle is equal to 180°. In triangle ABC,

   (a) The sum of the measures of the angles is equal to 180°.

   (b) $\angle A$ in terms of the other angles.

   (c) $\angle B$ in terms of the other angles.

   (d) $\angle C$ in terms of the other angles.

   (e) The sum of the measures of $\angle A$ and $\angle C$ in terms of the third angle.

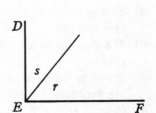

2. Fact: Complementary angles are two angles the sum of whose measures is 90°.

   In right angle DEF,

   (a) The sum of the measures of $\angle r$ and $\angle s$ is 90°.

   (b) $\angle r$ in terms of $\angle s$.

   (c) $\angle s$ in terms of $\angle r$.

   In right triangle ABC,

   (d) $\angle A$ and $\angle B$ are complementary and the sum of their measures is 90°.

   (e) $\angle B$ in terms of $\angle A$.

   (f) $\angle A$ in terms of $\angle B$.

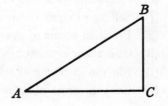

3. Fact: Supplementary angles are two angles the sum of whose measures is 180°.

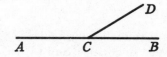

In straight angle ACB,

(a) The sum of the measures of angles BCD and DCA is 180°.

(b) $\angle BCD$ in terms of $\angle DCA$.

(c) $\angle DCA$ in terms of $\angle BCD$.

In the figure at the right $\angle a = \angle c$, $\angle b = \angle d$, and $\angle a$ and $\angle b$ are supplementary.

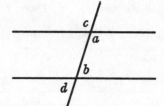

(d) The sum of the measures of $\angle c$ and $\angle d$.

(e) $\angle c$ in terms of $\angle b$.

(f) $\angle a$ in terms of $\angle d$.

(g) $\angle c$ in terms of $\angle d$.

(h) In the figure at the right, $\angle t$ and $\angle n$ are supplementary and the sum of the measures of $\angle r$, $\angle s$, and $\angle t$ is 180°. Express the relationship of $\angle n$ with $\angle r$ and $\angle s$.

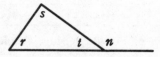

4. Fact: The sum of the measures of all the angles about a point on one side of a line passing through this point is 180°.

(a) The sum of the measures of angles a, b, c, d, and e is 180°.

(b) $\angle c$ in terms of angles a, b, d, and e.

(c) The sum of the measures of angles b, c, d, and e if $\angle a = 30°$.

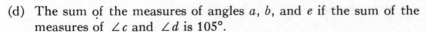

(d) The sum of the measures of angles a, b, and e if the sum of the measures of $\angle c$ and $\angle d$ is 105°.

(e) The sum of the measures of angles b, d, and e in terms of $\angle a$ and $\angle c$.

5. Fact: The opposite angles of a parallelogram are equal and the sum of the measures of the angles of any quadrilateral is 360°.

(a) The sum of the measures of the four angles is 360°

(b) $\angle A$ in terms of angles B, C, and D.

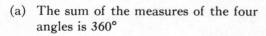

(c) The sum of the measures of angles B and D.

(d) $\angle C$ in terms of $\angle A$ and $\angle D$.

(e) $\angle D$ in terms of $\angle C$ and $\angle B$.

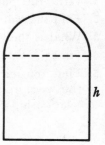

(Part 4–1.)

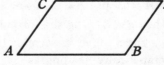

(Part 4–2.)

Part 4 — Measurement of Areas

1. A square whose side is s is cut out of a square whose side is S. Write a word rule and formula expressing the area that remains.

2. Write a word rule and formula expressing the area of a flat washer if its radius is R and the radius of the hole is r.

3. Write a formula for the entire area of the figure given at the right.

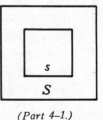

REVIEW OF UNIT THREE

In the following tables (1) find the missing numbers, (2) write the word rule expressing the relationship between quantities, and (3) write the formula.

1. Speed of Sound:

Time in seconds (*t*)	1	2	5	9	12
Distance in feet (*d*)	1,100	2,200	5,500		

5. Fire Insurance Rates per $100:

Rate for 1 yr. (*r*)	16¢	19¢	20¢	23¢	24¢
Rate for 5 yr. (*R*)	64¢	76¢	80¢		

2. Absolute-Celsius Temperature Readings:

Celsius (*C*)	6°	14°	25°	49°	100°
Absolute (*A*)	279°	287°	298°		

6. Developing and Printing a Roll of Film:

Number of prints (*n*)	1	2	5	8	12
Cost in cents (*c*)	$1.05	$1.25	$1.85		

3. Changing Watts to Kilowatts:

Watts (*w*)	2,000	3,100	5,670	8,000	9,300
Kilowatts (*Kw*)	2	3.1	5.67		

7. Bank Balance:

Previous balance (*P.B.*)	$ 80	$168	$287	$104	$ 85
Deposits (*D*)	250	349	430	793	922
Withdrawals (*W*)	125	491	526	259	868
Final balance (*F.B.*)	$205	$ 26			

4. Supplementary Angles:

Angle *A*	40°	70°	90°	120°	145°
Angle *B*	140°	110°	90°		

8. How many dozen are in 36 items? 84 items? Write a formula stating the number of dozen (*d*) in *n* items.

9. How many feet are in 4 miles? 7 miles? Write a formula stating the number of feet (*f*) in *m* miles.

10. If 15 degrees of longitude are equivalent to 1 hour of time, how many degrees of longitude are equivalent to 2 hours? 9 hours? Write a formula stating the number of degrees of longitude (*L*) in *T* hours.

CUMULATIVE ALGEBRA REVIEW

1. Write the following as an algebraic expression: Six more than a certain number *n*.

2. Express as a formula: The number of screw threads per inch (*n*) is equal to one divided by the pitch (*p*).

3. Find the value of the expression $c + 2d(c - 2d)$ when $c = 7$ and $d = 3$.

4. What is the value of the expression $a^2 - 2ab + b^2$ when $a = 9$ and $b = 4$?

5. Find the value of *C* when $A = 65$ and $B = 87$, using the formula $C = 180 - (A + B)$.

6. What is the value of *A* when $d = 5$, using the formula $A = .7854d^2$?

7. Write a formula expressing the number of seconds (*s*) in *m* minutes.

8. When the Fahrenheit temperature reading is 59°, what is the Celsius reading? Use the formula $C = \frac{5}{9}(F - 32)$.

KEYED ACHIEVEMENT TEST

1. Write the following as an algebraic expression: Seven less than the product of *x* and *y*.

2. Find the value of the expression $(c + x)(c - x)$ when $c = 8$ and $x = 1$.　③

3. What is the value of the expression $3s^2 - 5s + 8$ when $s = 4$?　④

4. Find the value of *K* when $m = 6$ and $V = 15$, using the formula $K = \frac{1}{2}mV^2$.　⑤

5. Find the missing numbers in the table. Write the word rule and the formula expressing the relationship between meters and centimeters.　⑥

Changing Meters to Centimeters

Meters (*m*)	3	4.2	6.85	7	9.48
Centimeters (*cm*)	300	420	685		

INTRODUCTION TO UNIT FOUR

Pupils are already acquainted with statements like:

$$?+4=7, \quad ?-2=6, \quad 5\times?=40, \quad \tfrac{?}{8}=2, \quad A=lw, \quad p=2l+2w, \quad i=prt$$

These are **equations** — statements that two expressions are equal. See also page 32S.

In this unit we shall study the four fundamental types of equations: $x+3=21$, $x-3=21$, $3x=21$, and $\frac{x}{3}=21$. In each case we are required to determine the number which the variable or *unknown* represents. Finding this number or **root** is called **solving the equation.**

An equation is called a **simple equation** if the variable is raised to the first power only or, if it contains fractions, the variable does not appear in the denominator. These equations are also known as **linear equations** or **equations of the first degree.**

The expression on the left side of the equality sign is the **left member** or **first member** of the equation and the expression on the right side is the **right member** or **second member.**

Testing whether the value found representing the variable will satisfy the conditions of the equation is called **checking the equation.** To check, the value is substituted for the variable in the given equation. If the resulting answers of the two members are the same, the value substituted is the root.

An equation is like balanced scales. To keep the equation in balance, any change on one side must be balanced by an equal change on the other. In the following exercises it will be shown that to find the value of the variable, the operation indicated by the relationship of the variable and its connected numeral is undone by using the opposite or inverse operation. The balance of the equation is maintained when the operation is performed on both sides of the equation. These basic equations can be solved also by using the additive inverse or the multiplicative inverse. See pages 10S, 112, and 37S.

The equation $x+3=21$ means some number increased by 3 equals 21. It may also appear as $3+x=21$, $21=x+3$, and $21=3+x$. The indicated operation is addition. To find the value of x we subtract, using the axiom "if equals are subtracted from equals, the remainders are equal."

The equation $x-3=21$ means some number decreased by 3 equals 21. It may also appear as $21=x-3$ but not as $3-x=21$. The indicated operation is subtraction. To find the value of x we add, using the axiom "if equals are added to equals, the sums are equal."

The equation $3x=21$ means 3 times some number equals 21. It may also appear as $21=3x$. The indicated operation is multiplication. To find the value of x we divide, using the axiom "if equals are divided by equals, the quotients are equal." Division by zero is excluded.

The equation $\frac{x}{3}=21$ means some number divided by 3 equals 21. It may also appear as $21=\frac{x}{3}$. The indicated operation is division. To find the value of x we multiply, using the axiom "if equals are multiplied by equals, the products are equal."

The equation is a powerful mathematical tool. Students will find it necessary to use the equation when solving problems and working with formulas in science and vocational subjects. The equation is the core of the study of algebra.

UNIT FOUR—EQUATIONS

EXERCISE 7

Equations—Solution by the Subtraction Axiom

I. Aim: To solve simple equations by the subtraction axiom.

II. Procedure

1. Subtract from both members of the equation the number which is on the same side of the equation as the variable. This will leave only the variable on that side.

2. If, in the answer, the variable is in the right member, rewrite terms on the proper sides. See sample solutions 3 and 4 below.

3. To check the equation, substitute the root (answer) in the given equation.

III. Sample Solutions

1.
$$x+8=14$$
$$8=8$$
$$\overline{x=6}$$
Answer, $x=6$

Check:
$$6+8=14$$
$$14=14$$

2.
$$6+x=9$$
$$6=6$$
$$\overline{x=3}$$
Answer, $x=3$

Check:
$$6+3=9$$
$$9=9$$

3.
$$7=x+4$$
$$4=4$$
$$\overline{3=x}$$
$$x=3$$
Answer, $x=3$

Check:
$$7=3+4$$
$$7=7$$

4.
$$10=2\tfrac{1}{2}+x$$
$$2\tfrac{1}{2}=2\tfrac{1}{2}$$
$$\overline{7\tfrac{1}{2}=x}$$
$$x=7\tfrac{1}{2}$$
Answer, $x=7\tfrac{1}{2}$

Check:
$$10=2\tfrac{1}{2}+7\tfrac{1}{2}$$
$$10=10$$

The solution of this type of equation can also be written as follows:

$$x+8=14$$
$$x+8-8=14-8$$
$$x=6$$
Answer, $x=6$

Note: The numerals naming the numbers which are subtracted are placed in the same line as the other terms of the equation.

DIAGNOSTIC TEST

Solve and check:

1. $x+5=12$
2. $3+a=8$
3. $9=b+2$
4. $15=6+y$
5. $c+5\tfrac{3}{4}=7$
6. $m+1.8=6.3$
7. $8+x=8$

Related Practice Examples

Solve and check:

SET 1

1. $x+2=6$
2. $b+5=9$
3. $x+8=10$
4. $x+12=15$
5. $a+6=28$
6. $b+9=17$
7. $c+4=19$
8. $x+15=32$
9. $y+20=50$
10. $x+18=45$

SET 2

1. $1+x=5$
2. $3+y=11$
3. $8+b=15$
4. $9+a=36$
5. $10+x=18$
6. $6+b=13$
7. $17+y=30$
8. $25+x=36$
9. $75+c=100$
10. $60+b=85$

SET 3	SET 4	SET 5	SET 6	SET 7
1. $7 = x + 4$	**1.** $9 = 6 + b$	**1.** $x + \frac{1}{8} = \frac{5}{8}$	**1.** $x + .2 = .6$	**1.** $x + 6 = 6$
2. $6 = y + 5$	**2.** $10 = 5 + x$	**2.** $x + \frac{1}{4} = \frac{1}{2}$	**2.** $a + .4 = 7.2$	**2.** $11 = b + 11$
3. $18 = a + 2$	**3.** $14 = 9 + a$	**3.** $b + \frac{1}{2} = 2\frac{1}{2}$	**3.** $b + .5 = 4$	**3.** $5 + y = 5$
4. $29 = b + 7$	**4.** $33 = 22 + b$	**4.** $a + 5\frac{1}{3} = 8\frac{2}{3}$	**4.** $1.9 + y = 6.3$	**4.** $x + \frac{1}{2} = \frac{1}{2}$
5. $38 = c + 13$	**5.** $69 = 38 + y$	**5.** $y + \frac{3}{4} = 5$	**5.** $20 = a + 4.9$	**5.** $b + .6 = .6$
6. $47 = m + 32$	**6.** $42 = 25 + y$	**6.** $x + 4\frac{1}{2} = 8$	**6.** $9.7 = .04 + y$	**6.** $2 = x + 2$
7. $40 = x + 18$	**7.** $56 = 41 + b$	**7.** $a + 6\frac{1}{4} = 9\frac{1}{2}$	**7.** $c + \$.06 = \$.85$	**7.** $a + 3 = 3$
8. $34 = b + 27$	**8.** $83 = 59 + x$	**8.** $\frac{3}{4} + x = 4\frac{1}{4}$	**8.** $\$10 = c + \$3.49$	**8.** $4\frac{1}{2} + b = 4\frac{1}{2}$
9. $80 = x + 15$	**9.** $110 = 37 + y$	**9.** $7 = b + \frac{3}{8}$	**9.** $s + \$1.37 = \$5.20$	**9.** $m + .02 = .02$
10. $95 = y + 29$	**10.** $150 = 100 + b$	**10.** $10\frac{1}{2} = 6\frac{7}{8} + x$	**10.** $\$7.98 = \$6.45 + m$	**10.** $9 = 9 + x$

EXERCISE 8

Equations—Solution by the Addition Axiom

I. **Aim:** To solve simple equations by the addition axiom.

II. **Procedure**

1. Add to both members of the equation the number which is on the same side of the equation as the variable. This will leave only the variable on that side.

2. If, in the answer, the variable is in the right member, rewrite terms on the proper sides (see sample solution 2 below).

3. To check the equation, substitute the root in the given equation.

III. **Sample Solutions**

1.
$$b - 3 = 8$$
$$3 = 3$$
$$\overline{b \quad = 11}$$
Answer, $b = 11$

Check:
$$11 - 3 = 8$$
$$8 = 8$$

2.
$$7 = m - 15$$
$$15 = 15$$
$$\overline{22 = m}$$
$$m = 22$$
Answer, $m = 22$

Check:
$$7 = 22 - 15$$
$$7 = 7$$

3.
$$x - 2\frac{1}{2} = 7$$
$$2\frac{1}{2} = 2\frac{1}{2}$$
$$\overline{x \quad = 9\frac{1}{2}}$$
Answer, $x = 9\frac{1}{2}$

Check:
$$9\frac{1}{2} - 2\frac{1}{2} = 7$$
$$7 = 7$$

4.
$$a - .4 = 2$$
$$.4 = .4$$
$$\overline{a \quad = 2.4}$$
Answer, $a = 2.4$

Check:
$$2.4 - .4 = 2$$
$$2 = 2$$

The solution of this type of equation can also be written as follows:

$$b - 3 \quad = 8$$
$$b - 3 + 3 = 8 + 3$$
$$b = 11$$
Answer, $b = 11$

Note: The numerals naming the numbers which are added are written in the same line as the other terms of the equation.

DIAGNOSTIC TEST

Solve and check:

1. $x - 8 = 12$

2. $7 = b - 2$

3. $a - 5 = 5$

4. $c - 3 = 0$

5. $x - \frac{1}{8} = 2\frac{3}{8}$

6. $x - 1.6 = 3.8$

Related Practice Examples

Solve and check:

SET 1	SET 2	SET 3	SET 4
1. $x-1=5$	1. $9=x-6$	1. $x-10=10$	1. $x-5=0$
2. $m-8=4$	2. $16=y-5$	2. $b-18=18$	2. $x-20=0$
3. $x-3=6$	3. $23=a-19$	3. $12=x-12$	3. $0=b-8$
4. $b-10=7$	4. $27=c-45$	4. $7=x-7$	4. $0=y-13$
5. $x-18=3$	5. $36=a-93$	5. $x-4=4$	5. $y-4=0$
6. $x-7=9$	6. $28=x-18$	6. $a-1=1$	6. $a-7=0$
7. $a-12=15$	7. $100=x-47$	7. $8=n-8$	7. $m-6=0$
8. $c-5=19$	8. $69=b-24$	8. $25=s-25$	8. $0=x-14$
9. $y-53=42$	9. $26=y-87$	9. $x-16=16$	9. $0=c-2$
10. $x-49=74$	10. $76=b-58$	10. $b-20=20$	10. $d-9=0$

SET 5

1. $x-\frac{1}{2}=\frac{1}{2}$	6. $c-3\frac{1}{4}=4\frac{1}{2}$
2. $b-\frac{2}{3}=1\frac{2}{3}$	7. $9\frac{1}{8}=x-7$
3. $y-\frac{7}{8}=2\frac{3}{8}$	8. $4\frac{1}{3}=x-1\frac{1}{3}$
4. $a-4=6\frac{1}{2}$	9. $10=b-7\frac{1}{4}$
5. $m-1\frac{1}{2}=5$	10. $20\frac{1}{2}=x-10\frac{7}{8}$

SET 6

1. $b-.2=.6$	6. $25=t-1.3$
2. $x-1.8=3.6$	7. $y-\$.08=\$.74$
3. $a-7=10.4$	8. $c-\$.59=\$2$
4. $m-.8=5$	9. $\$.67=l-\$.19$
5. $7.2=x-.04$	10. $a-\$1.25=\$4.98$

EXERCISE 9

Equations—Solution by the Division Axiom

I. Aim: To solve simple equations by the division axiom.

II. Procedure

1. Divide both members of the equation by the coefficient of the variable. This will leave the variable with the coefficient one (1) understood. This coefficient may be a larger number than the known (constant) term. See sample solutions 4 and 5.

2. If, in the answer, the variable is in the right member, rewrite terms on the proper sides.

3. To check the equation, substitute the root in the given equation.

III. Sample Solutions

1. $3x=15$ Check:

$$\frac{3x}{3}=\frac{15}{3}$$ $3\cdot5=15$

$x=5$ $15=15$

Answer, $x=5$

2. $12=4a$ Check:

$$\frac{12}{4}=\frac{4a}{4}$$ $12=4\cdot3$

$3=a$ $12=12$

$a=3$

Answer, $a=3$

3. $6x=8$ Check:

$$\frac{6x}{6}=\frac{8}{6}$$ $6\cdot1\frac{1}{3}=8$

$x=1\frac{1}{3}$ $8=8$

Answer, $x=1\frac{1}{3}$

4. $5m=3$ Check:

$$\frac{5m}{5}=\frac{3}{5}$$ $5\cdot\frac{3}{5}=3$

$m=\frac{3}{5}$ $3=3$

Answer, $m=\frac{3}{5}$

5. $12n = 4$

Check:

$$\frac{12n}{12} = \frac{4}{12}$$

$12 \cdot \frac{1}{3} = 4$
$4 = 4$

$$n = \tfrac{1}{3}$$

Answer, $n = \tfrac{1}{3}$

6. $.02r = 6.4$

Check:

$$\frac{.02r}{.02} = \frac{6.4}{.02}$$

$.02 \times 320 = 6.4$
$6.4 = 6.4$

$$r = 320$$

Answer, $r = 320$

7. $\tfrac{2}{3}c = 8$

Check:

$\tfrac{2}{3}c \div \tfrac{2}{3} = 8 \div \tfrac{2}{3}$

$\tfrac{2}{3} \cdot 12 = 8$
$8 = 8$

$c = 8 \times \tfrac{3}{2}$

$c = 12$

Answer, $c = 12$

DIAGNOSTIC TEST

Solve and check:

1. $3n = 6$
2. $32 = 8s$
3. $7b = 7$

4. $2y = 0$
5. $4x = 7$
6. $16c = 24$

7. $9r = 5$
8. $10m = 8$
9. $.06p = 18$

10. $\tfrac{3}{4}a = 27$
11. Find root correct to nearest hundredth: $12x = 14$

Related Practice Examples

Solve and check:

SET 1
1. $4x = 12$
2. $5x = 25$
3. $3y = 21$
4. $7c = 28$
5. $15a = 45$
6. $8b = 56$
7. $6x = 48$
8. $9y = 54$
9. $10a = 70$
10. $12r = 36$

SET 2
1. $8 = 2n$
2. $6 = 3y$
3. $18 = 6s$
4. $24 = 8w$
5. $32 = 4x$
6. $90 = 9m$
7. $22 = 11R$
8. $72 = 24y$
9. $95 = 5x$
10. $100 = 20h$

SET 3
1. $3x = 3$
2. $5b = 5$
3. $12y = 12$
4. $8a = 8$
5. $17b = 17$
6. $9 = 9y$
7. $2 = 2b$
8. $11a = 11$
9. $15 = 15t$
10. $21c = 21$

SET 4
1. $9b = 0$
2. $6x = 0$
3. $7c = 0$
4. $8r = 0$
5. $14y = 0$
6. $0 = 5x$
7. $0 = 4a$
8. $10z = 0$
9. $0 = 18r$
10. $25t = 0$

SET 5
1. $5n = 7$
2. $4y = 9$
3. $10a = 13$
4. $6c = 25$
5. $3m = 4$
6. $9 = 5b$
7. $23 = 7y$
8. $2x = 17$
9. $47 = 9d$
10. $25a = 49$

SET 6
1. $4y = 6$
2. $8n = 10$
3. $12x = 16$
4. $9d = 15$
5. $24c = 36$
6. $9 = 6y$
7. $14 = 10x$
8. $15t = 20$
9. $26 = 4s$
10. $42 = 12d$

SET 7
1. $3x = 1$
2. $5y = 2$
3. $9b = 4$
4. $10m = 7$
5. $21r = 4$
6. $1 = 2n$
7. $2 = 3w$
8. $7c = 5$
9. $9 = 10a$
10. $15a = 13$

SET 8
1. $6m = 2$
2. $8y = 4$
3. $12y = 10$
4. $20r = 5$
5. $18s = 12$
6. $15 = 45b$
7. $16 = 36a$
8. $88s = 33$
9. $26 = 39y$
10. $375n = 75$

SET 9
1. $8x = .16$
2. $.5a = 3.5$
3. $1.6y = 4.8$
4. $12 = .2a$
5. $.04p = 32$
6. $9c = \$.54$
7. $1.06x = \$33.92$
8. $\$.07n = \$1.12$
9. $\$213.75 = .95a$
10. $1.15c = \$345$

SET 10
1. $\tfrac{1}{3}a = 36$
2. $\tfrac{1}{4}n = 17$
3. $\tfrac{3}{8}x = 78$
4. $\tfrac{5}{6}c = 105$
5. $\tfrac{7}{12}y = 3\tfrac{1}{2}$
6. $52 = \tfrac{4}{5}a$
7. $\$4.77 = \tfrac{3}{10}s$
8. $1\tfrac{1}{2}c = 186$
9. $\tfrac{1}{5}s = \$.29$
10. $2\tfrac{3}{4}n = 3\tfrac{2}{3}$

SET 11
Find roots correct to nearest hundredth:

1. $6a = 8$
2. $11x = 25$
3. $7c = 31$
4. $50 = 13b$
5. $30m = 25$
6. $18y = 15$
7. $24x = 42$
8. $76 = 32c$
9. $\tfrac{5}{8}n = 56$
10. $1.7a = 81$

EXERCISE 10

Equations—Solution by the Multiplication Axiom

I. Aim: To solve simple equations by the multiplication axiom.

II. Procedure

1. Multiply both members of the equation by the denominator of the fractional coefficient of the variable. This will leave the variable with the coefficient one (1) understood.

2. If, in the answer, the variable is in the right member, rewrite terms on the proper sides.

3. To check the equation, substitute the root in the given equation.

III. Sample Solutions

1.
$$\frac{x}{7} = 4$$
$$7 \cdot \frac{x}{7} = 7 \cdot 4$$
$$x = 28$$
Answer, $x = 28$

Check:
$$\frac{28}{7} = 4$$
$$4 = 4$$

2.
$$\frac{b}{2} = 6$$
$$2 \cdot \frac{b}{2} = 2 \cdot 6$$
$$b = 12$$
Answer, $b = 12$

Check:
$$\frac{12}{2} = 6$$
$$6 = 6$$

3.
$$5 = \frac{a}{3}$$
$$3 \cdot 5 = 3 \cdot \frac{a}{3}$$
$$15 = a$$
$$a = 15$$
Answer, $a = 15$

Check:
$$5 = \frac{15}{3}$$
$$5 = 5$$

4.
$$\tfrac{1}{4}x = 2$$
$$\frac{x}{4} = 2$$
$$4 \cdot \frac{x}{4} = 4 \cdot 2$$
$$x = 8$$
Answer, $x = 8$

Check:
$$\tfrac{1}{4} \cdot 8 = 2$$
$$2 = 2$$

DIAGNOSTIC TEST

Solve and check:

1. $\dfrac{x}{3} = 5$

2. $\dfrac{b}{5} = 4$

3. $\dfrac{a}{3} = 6$

4. $\dfrac{x}{12} = 6$

5. $2 = \dfrac{b}{3}$

6. $\dfrac{c}{3} = 3$

7. $\dfrac{r}{7} = 1$

8. $\dfrac{m}{5} = 0$

9. $\tfrac{1}{3}x = 8$

Related Practice Examples

Solve and check:

SET 1

1. $\dfrac{x}{2} = 5$

2. $\dfrac{a}{7} = 10$

3. $\dfrac{b}{5} = 6$

4. $\dfrac{m}{4} = 9$

5. $\dfrac{b}{2} = 11$

SET 2

1. $\dfrac{c}{7} = 3$

2. $\dfrac{b}{5} = 2$

3. $\dfrac{c}{9} = 4$

4. $\dfrac{x}{4} = 3$

5. $\dfrac{y}{6} = 5$

SET 3	SET 4	SET 5	SET 6
1. $\dfrac{x}{4}=8$	1. $\dfrac{x}{4}=2$	1. $4=\dfrac{x}{3}$	1. $\dfrac{b}{2}=2$
2. $\dfrac{y}{2}=4$	2. $\dfrac{b}{9}=3$	2. $9=\dfrac{y}{5}$	2. $\dfrac{a}{5}=5$
3. $\dfrac{c}{7}=21$	3. $\dfrac{x}{12}=3$	3. $3=\dfrac{b}{5}$	3. $\dfrac{m}{8}=8$
4. $\dfrac{r}{3}=12$	4. $\dfrac{b}{16}=18$	4. $8=\dfrac{c}{2}$	4. $\dfrac{c}{6}=6$
5. $\dfrac{b}{5}=20$	5. $\dfrac{m}{15}=10$	5. $10=\dfrac{x}{20}$	5. $\dfrac{x}{15}=15$

SET 7

1. $\dfrac{a}{5}=1$ 2. $\dfrac{y}{3}=1$ 3. $\dfrac{b}{4}=1$ 4. $\dfrac{d}{8}=1$ 5. $\dfrac{x}{2}=1$

SET 8

1. $\dfrac{b}{4}=0$ 2. $\dfrac{m}{9}=0$ 3. $\dfrac{x}{10}=0$ 4. $\dfrac{y}{6}=0$ 5. $\dfrac{b}{18}=0$

SET 9

1. $\tfrac{1}{2}b=4$ 2. $\tfrac{1}{3}c=5$ 3. $\tfrac{1}{5}n=6$ 4. $\tfrac{1}{4}r=7$ 5. $3=\tfrac{1}{9}y$

EXERCISE 11

Mixed Equations

I. **Aim:** To solve more difficult equations involving the use of two or more axioms.

II. **Procedure**

1. Use any one of the four axioms which will bring about an equation having only one variable on one side and one known (constant) term on the other side of the equation. (Try to get an equation of the type $3x = 6$.)

2. In equations having two terms involving the variable on the same side, combine to get one term. See sample solution 3.

3. In equations having two known (constant) terms on the same side, combine to get one term. See sample solution 4.

4. If, in the answer, the variable is in the right member, rewrite terms on the proper sides.

5. To check the equation, substitute the root in the given equation.

III. **Sample Solutions**

1.
$$5x+6=41$$
$$6=6$$
$$\overline{5x=35}$$
$$x=7$$
Answer, $x=7$

Check:
$$5\cdot 7+6=41$$
$$35+6=41$$
$$41=41$$

2.
$$7=3x-5$$
$$5=5$$
$$\overline{12=3x}$$
$$4=x$$
$$x=4$$
Answer, $x=4$

Check:
$$7=3\cdot 4-5$$
$$7=12-5$$
$$7=7$$

3. $4a + 3a = 14$ Check:
$7a = 14$ $4 \cdot 2 + 3 \cdot 2 = 14$
$a = 2$ $8 + 6 = 14$
$14 = 14$

Answer, $a = 2$

4. $8x = 35 - 11$ Check:
$8x = 24$ $8 \cdot 3 = 35 - 11$
$x = 3$ $24 = 24$

Answer, $x = 3$

5. $n + .04n = 832$ Check:
$1.04n = 832$ $800 + .04 \times 800 = 832$
$n = 800$ $800 + 32 = 832$
$832 = 832$

Answer, $x = 800$

6. $\frac{2}{3}b = 10$ Check:
$\dfrac{2b}{3} = 10$ $\frac{2}{3} \cdot 15 = 10$
$10 = 10$
$2b = 30$
$b = 15$

Answer, $b = 15$

The following method may also be used: Multiply both sides of the equation by the reciprocal of the fractional coefficient of the variable to make the coefficient of the variable equal 1. This is another way of dividing both sides by the fractional coefficient.

$\frac{2}{3}b = 10$

$\frac{3}{2} \cdot \frac{2}{3}b = \frac{3}{2} \cdot 10$

$b = 15$

DIAGNOSTIC TEST

1. $4x + 7 = 15$
2. $5 + 3b = 26$
3. $13 = 2l + 3$
4. $69 = 5 + 32t$
5. $8n + 15 = 25$

6. $3a - 4 = 11$
7. $8 = 5m - 12$
8. $6r - 24 = 0$
9. $7x + 2x = 72$
10. $9y - 6y = 21$

11. $4m = 27 + 9$
12. $3x - x + 5x = 56$
13. $a + .02a = 510$
14. $\dfrac{3x}{4} = 12$

15. $\frac{2}{5}d = 16$
16. $\frac{7}{8}b - \frac{3}{8}b = 4$
17. $1.8c + 32 = 158$
18. $\frac{2}{3}a + 7 = 15$

Related Practice Examples

Solve and check:

SET 1
1. $2x + 5 = 13$
2. $6b + 3 = 15$
3. $9d + 1 = 28$
4. $12y + 8 = 56$
5. $5a + 4 = 29$
6. $8x + 7 = 15$
7. $7b + 8 = 71$
8. $3x + 5 = 17$
9. $5m + 24 = 84$
10. $4r + 20 = 100$

SET 2
1. $8 + 3r = 23$
2. $12 + 7x = 47$
3. $6 + 9y = 15$
4. $5 + 6x = 35$
5. $32 + 5b = 47$
6. $17 + 3x = 38$
7. $45 + 2d = 69$
8. $28 + 9x = 46$
9. $73 + 10b = 93$
10. $55 + 6m = 103$

SET 3
1. $9 = 2x + 1$
2. $14 = 5a + 4$
3. $26 = 6x + 2$
4. $38 = 11y + 5$
5. $56 = 7b + 21$
6. $19 = 4m + 15$
7. $35 = 8s + 11$
8. $77 = 9r + 23$
9. $80 = 3x + 56$
10. $91 = 10d + 1$

SET 4
1. $8 = 5 + 3x$
2. $15 = 3 + 6x$
3. $44 = 9 + 7y$
4. $60 = 32 + 4a$
5. $75 = 41 + 2m$
6. $82 = 27 + 11b$
7. $42 = 18 + 12d$
8. $52 = 25 + 3r$
9. $61 = 36 + 5y$
10. $147 = 75 + 8s$

SET 5
1. $2x + 7 = 10$
2. $3y + 9 = 16$
3. $5b + 12 = 15$
4. $8a + 11 = 17$
5. $4x + 15 = 25$
6. $8 + 6m = 12$
7. $3 + 7x = 11$
8. $45 = 12b + 24$
9. $64 = 4y + 59$
10. $48 = 18 + 9x$

SET 6
1. $4x - 3 = 9$
2. $5y - 4 = 6$
3. $3a - 5 = 16$
4. $2b - 3 = 17$
5. $8x - 16 = 24$
6. $7d - 32 = 31$
7. $9x - 57 = 15$
8. $10y - 21 = 9$
9. $6x - 48 = 6$
10. $12m - 71 = 25$

SET 7

1. $19 = 2x - 5$
2. $21 = 4b - 3$
3. $46 = 8y - 10$
4. $53 = 5m - 7$
5. $33 = 2y - 5$
6. $23 = 6x - 67$
7. $12 = 4a - 16$
8. $48 = 9r - 87$
9. $40 = 10x - 40$
10. $65 = 13b - 65$

SET 8

1. $2b - 4 = 0$
2. $8x - 32 = 0$
3. $5r - 60 = 0$
4. $7a - 12 = 0$
5. $9d - 6 = 0$
6. $4m - 3 = 0$
7. $18y - 12 = 0$
8. $0 = 3b - 9$
9. $0 = 4x - 5$
10. $0 = 8d - 2$

SET 9

1. $x + x = 10$
2. $2x + x = 12$
3. $4y + 7y = 66$
4. $8a + 2a = 50$
5. $b + 4b = 15$
6. $8 = 2x + 2x$
7. $18 = 3b + 2b$
8. $40 = 5y + 3y$
9. $28 = 6x + x$
10. $4x + 2x = 0$

SET 10

1. $4x - x = 6$
2. $8x - 3x = 10$
3. $5y - y = 24$
4. $9b - 2b = 56$
5. $3d - 2d = 4$
6. $6 = 10a - 4a$
7. $42 = 9x - 3x$
8. $30 = 11y - 6y$
9. $1 = 8b - 7b$
10. $5 = 3r - r$

SET 11

1. $2a = 9 + 3$
2. $3x = 15 + 6$
3. $8y = 19 + 13$
4. $5 + 3 = 4c$
5. $10 + 8 = 3b$
6. $6a = 18 - 6$
7. $8x = 17 - 9$
8. $15y = 31 - 1$
9. $51 - 9 = 6m$
10. $8 - 6 = 4s$

SET 12

1. $2x + 3x + 4x = 36$
2. $5b + b + 2b = 64$
3. $21 = x + x + x$
4. $8m - 2m - 4m = 12$
5. $10a - a - 2a = 35$
6. $48 = 21d - 3d - 2d$
7. $4x + x - 2x = 24$
8. $9x - 3x + 2x = 96$
9. $2y + 2y - 3y = 10$
10. $60 = 7b - 3b + 8b$

SET 13

1. $p + .15p = 69$
2. $c + .06c = \$74.20$
3. $a - .04a = 240$
4. $2.3y + 1.6y = 117$
5. $l - .25l = \$.78$

SET 14

1. $\dfrac{2d}{5} = 4$
2. $\dfrac{9a}{10} = 81$
3. $\dfrac{5x}{8} = 75$
4. $15 = \dfrac{5m}{6}$
5. $\dfrac{3x}{16} = 27$

SET 15(a)

1. $\frac{7}{8}b = 56$
2. $\frac{3}{8}a = 12$
3. $18 = \frac{3}{8}x$
4. $1\frac{3}{4}y = 28$
5. $72 = \frac{9}{16}x$

SET 15(b)

1. $\frac{5}{8}c = \$.25$
2. $\frac{3}{4}y = \$9.81$
3. $\frac{9}{10}s = \$.63$
4. $\$10.50 = 1\frac{5}{6}b$
5. $\frac{4}{5}a = \$.92$

SET 16

1. $\frac{1}{3}x + \frac{2}{3}x = 12$
2. $m + \frac{1}{4}m = 6\frac{1}{4}$
3. $\frac{7}{8}x - \frac{1}{8}x = 9$
4. $10 = \frac{5}{8}b - \frac{1}{8}b$
5. $s - \frac{2}{5}s = 30$

SET 17

1. $1.8c + 32 = 122$
2. $30 + .6t = 45$
3. $\$.05n + \$.13 = \$3.88$
4. $1.8c + 32 = 194$
5. $80 + 2.4t = 116$

SET 18

1. $\frac{1}{3}y + 6 = 15$
2. $\frac{3}{4}n + 4 = 10$
3. $\dfrac{5b}{8} - 3 = 7$
4. $22 = \dfrac{3x}{10} - 8$
5. $\frac{5}{6}a - 4 = 16$

EXERCISE 12
Evaluation of Formulas

I. Aim: To evaluate formulas, making use of the various types of equations.

II. Procedure

1. Copy formula.

2. Substitute numbers for variables.

3. Perform the necessary operations.

4. Solve the resulting equation.

III. Sample Solutions

1. Find the value of t if $d = 80$ and $r = 20$, using the formula $d = rt$.

$$d = rt$$
$$80 = 20t$$
$$4 = t$$
$$t = 4 \qquad \text{Answer, } t = 4$$

2. Find the value of w if $V = 96$, $l = 8$, and $h = 4$, using the formula $V = lwh$.

$$V = lwh$$
$$96 = 8 \cdot w \cdot 4$$
$$96 = 32w$$
$$3 = w$$
$$w = 3 \qquad \text{Answer, } w = 3$$

3. Find the value of r if $A = 54$, $p = 50$, and $t = 4$, using the formula $A = p + prt$.

$$A = p + prt$$
$$54 = 50 + 50 \cdot r \cdot 4$$
$$54 = 50 + 200r$$
$$50 = 50$$
$$\overline{}$$
$$4 = \qquad 200r$$
$$.02 = r$$
$$r = .02 \text{ or } 2\%$$

Answer, $r = .02$ or 2%

4. Find the value of E if $I = 11$ and $R = 20$, using the formula $I = \dfrac{E}{R}$

$$I = \frac{E}{R}$$
$$11 = \frac{E}{20}$$
$$220 = E$$
$$E = 220$$

Answer, $E = 220$

DIAGNOSTIC TEST

Find the value of:

1. w if $A = 40$, and $l = 8$, using the formula $A = lw$.
2. t if $i = 8$, $p = 50$, and $r = .04$, using the formula $i = prt$.
3. r if $d = 204$ and $t = 6$, using the formula $d = rt$.
4. l if $V = 672$, $w = 6$, and $h = 8$, using the formula $V = lwh$.
5. r if $i = 21$, $p = 60$, and $t = 7$, using the formula $i = prt$.
6. c if $s = 51$, and $g = 14$, using the formula $s = c + g$.
7. i if $A = 104$, and $p = 95$, using the formula $A = p + i$.
8. c if $l = 15$, and $s = 69$, using the formula $l = c - s$.
9. a if $l = 25$, $n = 8$, and $d = 3$, using the formula $l = a + (n-1)d$.
10. l if $p = 38$, and $w = 7$, using the formula $p = 2l + 2w$.
11. t if $A = 88$, $p = 80$, and $r = .02$, using the formula $A = p + prt$.
12. E if $I = 4$, and $R = 55$, using the formula $I = \dfrac{E}{R}$.
13. a if $A = 18$, and $b = 9$, using the formula $A = \dfrac{ab}{2}$.
14. p if $A = 230$, $r = .05$, and $t = 3$, using the formula $A = p + prt$.
15. r if $T = 36$, $R = 150$, and $t = 24$, using the formula $TR = tr$.

Related Practice Examples

Evaluate the following formulas:

SET 1(a)

	Find the value of	when	Formula
1.	s	$p = 54$	$p = 6s$
2.	s	$p = 60$	$p = 4s$
3.	r	$d = 38$	$d = 2r$
4.	s	$p = 21$	$p = 3s$
5.	s	$p = .80$	$p = 5s$

SET 1(b)

	Find the value of	when	Formula
1.	w	$A = 48, l = 8$	$A = lw$
2.	d	$c = 21.98; \pi = 3.14$	$c = \pi d$
3.	b	$A = 65; a = 13$	$A = ab$
4.	s	$p = 132; n = 12$	$p = ns$
5.	h	$V = 120; B = 15$	$V = Bh$

SET 1(c)

	Find the value of	when	Formula
1.	p	$c = 56; n = 14$	$c = np$
2.	r	$p = 9; b = 36$	$p = br$
3.	t	$d = 72; r = 18$	$d = rt$
4.	R	$E = 220; I = 5$	$E = IR$
5.	E	$W = 300; I = 4$	$W = IE$

SET 1(d)

	Find the value of	when	Formula
1.	t	$v = 65; a = 5$	$v = at$
2.	D	$P = 512; H = 8$	$P = HD$
3.	R	$W = 270; I = 3$	$W = I^2R$
4.	v	$P = 258; F = 86$	$P = Fv$
5.	d	$W = 960; F = 60$	$W = Fd$

SET 2(a)

	Find the value of	when	Formula
1.	h	$V = 90; l = 6; w = 3$	$V = lwh$
2.	t	$i = 12; p = 75; r = .02$	$i = prt$
3.	r	$c = 43.96; \pi = 3.14$	$c = 2\pi r$
4.	$r.p.s.$	$T.S. = 748; \pi = \frac{22}{7}; d = 7$	$T.S. = \pi d \times r.p.s.$
5.	D	$F = 84; A = 3; H = 4$	$F = AHD$

SET 2(b)

	Find the value of	when	Formula
1.	b	$A = 75.36; \pi = 3.14; a = 6$	$A = \pi ab$
2.	h	$V = 1{,}848; \pi = \frac{22}{7}; r = 14$	$V = \pi r^2 h$
3.	b	$A = 36; a = 8$	$A = \frac{1}{2}ab$
4.	t	$i = 8.1; p = 54; r = .03$	$i = prt$
5.	h	$V = 1{,}755; l = 15; w = 13$	$V = lwh$

SET 3(a)

	Find the value of	when	Formula
1.	l	$A = 85; w = 5$	$A = lw$
2.	b	$A = 72; h = 6$	$A = bh$
3.	n	$c = 112; p = 14$	$c = np$
4.	I	$W = 55; E = 220$	$W = IE$
5.	a	$A = 171; b = 19$	$A = ab$

SET 3(b)

	Find the value of	when	Formula
1.	I	$E = 110; R = 5$	$E = IR$
2.	r	$d = 424; t = 8$	$d = rt$
3.	B	$V = 108; h = 9$	$V = Bh$
4.	n	$p = 56; s = 7$	$p = ns$
5.	a	$v = 384; t = 12$	$v = at$

SET 4

	Find the value of	when	Formula
1.	p	$i = 4; r = .05; t = 2$	$i = prt$
2.	l	$V = 96; w = 2; h = 6$	$V = lwh$
3.	A	$F = 14{,}400; H = 9; D = 64$	$F = AHD$
4.	l	$V = 392; w = 8; h = 7$	$V = lwh$
5.	p	$i = 33.60; r = .06; t = 4$	$i = prt$

SET 5

	Find the value of	when	Formula
1.	w	$V = 270; l = 9; h = 5$	$V = lwh$
2.	a	$A = 251.2; \pi = 3.14; b = 8$	$A = \pi ab$
3.	r	$i = 60; p = 250; t = 6$	$i = prt$
4.	H	$F = 875; A = 2; D = 62\frac{1}{2}$	$F = AHD$
5.	d	$T.S. = 396; \pi = \frac{22}{7}; r.p.s. = 21$	$T.S. = \pi d \times r.p.s.$

SET 6(a)

Find the

	value of	when	Formula
1.	p	$A=46$; $i=9$	$A=p+i$
2.	c	$s=54$; $g=21$	$s=c+g$
3.	C	$A=312$	$A=C+273$
4.	A	$B=65$	$A+B=90$
5.	D_w	$D_t=98$; $D_p=36$	$D_t=D_w+D_p$

SET 6(b)

Find the

	value of	when	Formula
1.	L	$A=7,540$; $C=3,850$	$A=L+C$
2.	M	$N=93$	$M+N=180$
3.	p	$m=82$; $e=29$	$m=p+e$
4.	c	$s=67$; $m=25$	$s=c+m$
5.	n	$l=105$; $d=18$	$l=n+d$

SET 7(a)

Find the

	value of	when	Formula
1.	g	$s=64$; $c=49$	$s=c+g$
2.	d	$l=206$; $n=187$	$l=n+d$
3.	B	$A=16$	$A+B=90$
4.	i	$A=342$; $p=315$	$A=p+i$
5.	c	$s=570$; $p=491$	$s=p+c$

SET 7(b)

Find the

	value of	when	Formula
1.	e	$m=43$; $p=28$	$m=p+e$
2.	C	$A=9,138$; $L=1,252$	$A=L+C$
3.	D_p	$D_t=116$; $D_w=79$	$D_t=D_w+D_p$
4.	N	$M=135$	$M+N=180$
5.	m	$s=271$; $c=209$	$s=c+m$

SET 8(a)

Find the

	value of	when	Formula
1.	s	$g=17$; $c=56$	$g=s-c$
2.	A	$i=8$; $p=135$	$i=A-p$
3.	A	$C=59$	$C=A-273$
4.	l	$d=26$; $n=184$	$d=l-n$
5.	A	$C=3,575$; $L=962$	$C=A-L$

SET 8(b)

Find the

	value of	when	Formula
1.	A	$p=400$; $i=18$	$p=A-i$
2.	c	$l=33$; $s=114$	$l=c-s$
3.	m	$s=820$; $d=65$	$s=m-d$
4.	s	$c=46$; $g=13$	$c=s-g$
5.	s	$m=394$; $c=52$	$m=s-c$

SET 9

Find the

	value of	when	Formula
1.	b	$p=19$; $e=7$	$p=b+2e$
2.	V	$v=216$; $g=32$; $t=4$	$v=V+gt$
3.	a	$l=23$; $n=4$; $d=6$	$l=a+(n-1)d$
4.	b	$p=45$; $e=13$	$p=b+2e$
5.	a	$l=54$; $n=10$; $d=5$	$l=a+(n-1)d$

SET 10(a)

Find the

	value of	when	Formula
1.	l	$p=32$; $w=9$	$p=2l+2w$
2.	C	$F=77$	$F=1.8C+32$
3.	e	$p=63$; $b=17$	$p=b+2e$
4.	w	$p=58$; $l=16$	$p=2l+2w$
5.	t	$v=169$; $V=9$; $g=32$	$v=V+gt$

SET 10(b)

Find the

	value of	when	Formula
1.	C	$F=140$	$F=1.8C+32$
2.	d	$l=79$; $a=25$; $n=10$	$l=a+(n-1)d$
3.	n	$S=1,260$	$S=180n-360$
4.	t	$v=112$; $V=16$; $g=32$	$v=V+gt$
5.	l	$p=32$; $w=9$	$p=2l+2w$

SET 11

Find the

	value of	when	Formula
1.	r	$A=69$; $p=60$; $t=5$	$A=p+prt$
2.	h	$A=3,564$; $\pi=\frac{22}{7}$; $r=21$	$A=2\pi r^2+2\pi rh$
3.	l	$A=440$; $\pi=\frac{22}{7}$; $r=7$	$A=\pi r^2+\pi rl$
4.	t	$A=54$; $p=40$; $t=.05$	$A=p+prt$
5.	R	$E=75$; $I=3$; $r=9$	$E=Ir+IR$

SET 12(a)

	Find the value of	when	Formula
1.	d	$r = 8$	$r = \dfrac{d}{2}$
2.	s	$m = 6$	$m = \dfrac{s}{60}$
3.	w	$H.P. = 3$	$H.P. = \dfrac{w}{746}$
4.	c	$d = 13$	$d = \dfrac{c}{3.14}$
5.	i	$m = 4$	$m = \dfrac{i}{39.37}$

SET 12(b)

	Find the value of	when	Formula
1.	d	$r = 8; t = 5$	$r = \dfrac{d}{t}$
2.	p	$r = .24; b = 40$	$r = \dfrac{p}{b}$
3.	m	$d = 8; v = 12$	$d = \dfrac{m}{v}$
4.	E	$R = 11; I = 10$	$R = \dfrac{E}{I}$
5.	F	$P = 50; A = .3$	$P = \dfrac{F}{A}$

SET 12(c)

	Find the value of	when	Formula
1.	v	$a = 54; t = 9$	$a = \dfrac{v}{t}$
2.	W	$P = 4{,}000; t = 5$	$P = \dfrac{W}{t}$
3.	s	$R = 8; c = 6$	$R = \dfrac{s}{c}$
4.	W	$L = 7; A = 250$	$L = \dfrac{W}{A}$
5.	W	$E = 110; I = 1.5$	$E = \dfrac{W}{I}$

SET 13(a)

	Find the value of	when	Formula
1.	h	$V = 28; B = 7$	$V = \dfrac{Bh}{3}$
2.	b	$A = 16; a = 8$	$A = \dfrac{ab}{2}$
3.	V	$H.P. = 24; T = 88$	$H.P. = \dfrac{TV}{550}$
4.	N	$S = 4{,}400; \pi = \tfrac{22}{7}; d = 21$	$S = \dfrac{\pi d N}{12}$
5.	S	$L = 640; C_L = .64;$ $d = .001; V = 100$	$L = C_L \dfrac{d}{2} S V^2$

SET 13(b)

	Find the value of	when	Formula
1.	d	$P = 7{,}500; F = 250;$ $t = 10$	$P = \dfrac{Fd}{t}$
2.	h	$V = 628; \pi = 3.14; d = 8$	$V = \dfrac{\pi d^2 h}{4}$
3.	W	$K.E. = 40; v = 16;$ $g = 32$	$K.E. = \dfrac{Wv^2}{2g}$
4.	W	$F = 50; v = 20; g = 32;$ $r = 6$	$F = \dfrac{Wv^2}{gr}$
5.	S	$D = 300; C_D = .025;$ $d = .002; V = 200$	$D = C_D \dfrac{d}{2} S V^2$

SET 14

	Find the value of	when	Formula
1.	p	$A = 186; r = .04; t = 6$	$A = p + prt$
2.	I	$E = 52; r = 6; R = 7$	$E = Ir + IR$
3.	S	$a = 16; r = \tfrac{1}{2}$	$a = S - Sr$
4.	h	$A = 91; b = 18; b' = 8$	$2A = bh + b'h$
5.	p	$A = 57.50; r = .05; t = 3$	$A = p + prt$

SET 15

	Find the value of	when	Formula
1.	L	$W = 80; w = 60; l = 12$	$WL = wl$
2.	P_1	$P_2 = 42; T_1 = 15;$ $T_2 = 35$	$P_1 T_2 = T_1 P_2$
3.	r	$D = 24; R = 250; d = 20$	$DR = dr$
4.	V	$P = 42; P' = 36; V' = 14$	$PV = P'V'$
5.	T_1	$V_1 = 18; V_2 = 8; T_2 = 16$	$V_1 T_2 = T_1 V_2$

EXERCISE 13—PROBLEMS

PART I. NUMBER PROBLEMS

The process of finding a number when a fractional part or per cent of it is known is often employed in. the solution of commercial problems. Many pupils have difficulty in mastering the arithmetic solutions. However, when equations are used, the solutions are simplified.

When solving problems, read each problem carefully to determine the unknown and any facts which are related to the unknown. Represent the unknown by some letter. Form an equation by translating two equal facts, with at least one containing the unknown, into algebraic expressions and writing one expression equal to the other. Solve the equation. Then check the conditions of the problem. Where necessary, change the per cent to a common fraction or decimal equivalent.

Sample Solutions

1. Three times a certain number increased by 6 equals 78. Find the number.

Let n = the number
$$3n+6=78$$
$$6=6$$
$$\overline{3n=72}$$
$$n=24$$
Answer, 24.

2. $\frac{3}{5}$ of what number is 21?

Let a = the number
$$\tfrac{3}{5}a=21$$
$$\tfrac{5}{3}\cdot\tfrac{3}{5}a=\tfrac{5}{3}\cdot 21$$
$$a=35$$
Answer, 35.

3. 8% of what number is 30?

Let x = the number
$$.08x=30$$
$$\frac{.08x}{.08}=\frac{30}{.08}$$
$$x=375$$
Answer, 375.

PRACTICE PROBLEMS

A. General

1. A certain number increased by 39 equals 64. Find the number.
2. What number divided by 17 will give a quotient of 14?
3. Charlotte asked Marilyn to guess her age. She said, "If you add 15 to four times my age, you get 63." How old is Charlotte?
4. If 23 is subtracted from eight times a number, the result is 81. Find the number.
5. A number increased by six times the same number equals 126. What is the number?

B. Finding a number when a fractional part of it is known

Find the missing numbers:

SET 1

1. $\frac{1}{4}$ of what number is 16?
2. $\frac{2}{3}$ of what number is 52?
3. 75 is $\frac{5}{8}$ of what number?
4. 56 is $\frac{7}{12}$ of what number?
5. $\frac{9}{20}$ of what number is 63?

SET 2

1. $\frac{1}{3}$ of what number is 57?
2. 96 is $\frac{4}{5}$ of what number?
3. 81 is $\frac{3}{4}$ of what number?
4. $\frac{19}{100}$ of what number is 114?
5. $1\frac{1}{4}$ times what number is 375?

SET 3

1. .03 of what number is 6?
2. .8 of what number is 20?
3. 45 is .06 of what number?
4. 9 is .37$\frac{1}{2}$ of what number?
5. 1.04 of what number is 468?

SET 4

1. Tom received $\frac{3}{4}$ of all votes cast in the election for school president. If he received 876 votes, how many students voted?
2. Nancy bought a tennis racket at a sale paying $15.00 for it. If the price was reduced $\frac{1}{6}$, what was the regular price?
3. If the school baseball team won 15 games, or $\frac{5}{8}$ of the games played, how many games were lost?
4. The school athletic association sold 1,043 student membership tickets. If $\frac{7}{8}$ of the school became members, what was the school enrollment?
5. If 118 students, or $\frac{2}{5}$ of the graduating class, selected the college preparatory course, how many pupils were in the graduating class?

C. Finding a number when a per cent of it is known

Find the missing numbers:

SET 1	**SET 2**	**SET 3**

SET 1
1. 5% of what number is 21?
2. 9% of what number is 135?
3. 12% of what number is 60?
4. 80% of what number is 24?
5. 25% of what number is 13?

SET 2
1. 104% of what number is 26?
2. $37\frac{1}{2}$% of what number is 345?
3. 100% of what number is 53?
4. 9.3% of what number is 620?
5. $2\frac{1}{2}$% of what number is 50?

SET 3
1. 81 is 18% of what number?
2. 14 is 4% of what number?
3. 36 is 75% of what number?
4. 1,590 is 106% of what number?
5. 47 is 10% of what number?

SET 4

1. How much money must be invested at 4% to earn $2,500 per year?

2. Find the principal when the

Rate of interest is	5%	10%	6%	9%
Annual interest is	$31	$1,500	$348	$20.25

3. Find the face of a note when the

Rate of interest is	6%	3%	8%	5%
Annual interest is	$18	$45	$100	$400

4. The net price of a refrigerator is $204 when a 15% discount is allowed. What is its list price?

5. Find the list price when the

Rate of discount is	25%	10%	16%	$33\frac{1}{3}$%
Discount is	$19	$54	$72	$280

Rate of discount is	12%	5%	$37\frac{1}{2}$%	40%
Net price is	$352	$228	$45	$495

6. What is the weekly amount of sales Mr. Harrison must make to earn $60 commission each week if his rate of commission is 8%?

7. Find the amount of sales when the

Rate of comm. is	5%	7%	20%	$12\frac{1}{2}$%
Commission is	$57	$420	$137	$49

Rate of comm. is	15%	3%	9%	25%
Net proceeds are	$714	$5,723	$546	$69

8. What is the cost of a radio on which a dealer makes a profit of $6 at the rate of 30% profit on the cost?

9. Find the cost on which the

Rate of profit is	40%	25%	36%	$16\frac{2}{3}$%
Profit is	$90	$13	$54	$107

10. Find the selling price on which the

Rate of profit is	20%	35%	45%	$33\frac{1}{3}$%
Profit is	$11	$147	$423	$28

SET 5

1. The mark-up on a rug is $49. If the dealer uses a 35% mark-up on the cost, how much did he pay for it?
2. Marilyn received $31.50 commission last week. If she was paid at the rate of 9% on her sales, what was the amount of her sales?
3. The annual depreciation on a certain property is $478 based on a 2% rate of depreciation. What is the value of the property?
4. Find the regular price of a baseball glove that sold for $9.60 at a 25% reduction sale.
5. A note is discounted at 6% by a local bank. What is the face of the note if the bank discount for a year is $13.50?
6. A fur coat with a 6% tax included sells for $795. What is the selling price of the coat without the tax?
7. Henry paid $28 for a watch. If he was allowed a $12\frac{1}{2}$% reduction, what was the regular price of the watch?
8. A dealer sold a television set for $325, making a profit of 30% on the cost. How much did he pay for it?
9. What is the full amount to be repaid at the end of one year if, after 8% interest is deducted, the sum of $391 is obtained in a loan from a bank?
10. A salesman receives $60 per week as salary and an additional 4% commission on his sales. If he received $145 as his total salary, what was the amount of his sales for that week?

PART II. PROBLEMS SOLVED BY FORMULAS

Substitute values in the appropriate formula, then solve the resulting equation. In some cases it may be necessary to use more than one formula to find the required answer.

A. Geometry

1. Rectangle and Square

a) If the length of a rectangular wing of an airplane is 50 feet and its area is 325 square feet, what is its width?

$$p = 2l + 2w$$
$$A = lw$$

b) The width of a rectangular storage room is 48 feet and its floor area is 10,080 square feet. What is the perimeter of the room?

c) What is the area of a square garden if it takes 92 feet of fence to enclose the garden?

d) The perimeter of a rectangular airport site is 17,000 feet. If the length is 5,000 feet, find the area of the site in square feet.

$$p = 4s$$
$$A = s^2$$

2. Circle

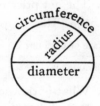

a) Find the area of the cross section of a tree trunk having a circumference of 3 feet 8 inches. $(\pi = \frac{22}{7})$

b) In making a complete turn about a pylon, an airplane travels $2\frac{3}{4}$ miles. How far away from the pylon did the plane fly? $(\pi = \frac{22}{7})$

c) What must the radius measure if a circular track is constructed so that the inside lane is 1 mile? How many square feet will be enclosed by this path of 1 mile? $(\pi = 3.14)$

$$d = 2r \qquad c = 2\pi r$$
$$r = \frac{d}{2} \qquad A = \pi r^2$$
$$\qquad \qquad A = \frac{1}{4}\pi d^2$$
$$c = \pi d$$

3. Rectangular Solid

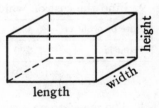

a) How long must a rectangular bin be to hold 1,800 cubic feet, if the width is 10 feet and height is 6 feet?

b) A rectangular flower box is 18 inches long, 4 inches high and has a volume of 432 cubic inches. What is its width?

c) How high must a packing crate be if it is required to hold 120 cubic feet and have a base of 24 square feet?

$$V = lwh$$
$$V = Bh$$

4. Cylinder

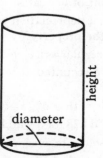

a) The lateral area of a cylindrical container is 132 square inches and the height is 7 inches. What is its volume? $(\pi = \frac{22}{7})$

b) A tin can is 6 inches high and its base has a diameter measuring 4 inches. If a second tin can has a base with a diameter of 6 inches, how high must it be to have the same volume as the first can?

c) 4,092 square feet of material is used to make a cylindrical tank including the two bases. How many cubic feet does the tank hold if the radius of the base is 21 feet? $(\pi = \frac{22}{7})$

$$V = \pi r^2 h$$
$$A = 2\pi rh$$
$$A = 2\pi r^2 + 2\pi rh$$
$$V = \frac{1}{4}\pi d^2 h$$

5. Other Problems

a) Find the base of a triangle if the area is 54 square feet and the altitude is 9 feet. $A = \frac{1}{2}ab$

b) The area of a triangle is 192 square meters and the base is 24 meters. What is the altitude? $A = \dfrac{ab}{2}$

c) Find the base of a parallelogram if the area is 371 square inches and height is 7 inches. $A = bh$

d) What is the height of a trapezoid if the area is 192 square feet, the upper base is 14 feet and lower base is 18 feet? $A = h\left(\dfrac{b+b'}{2}\right)$

e) The volume of a right circular cone is 12,474 cubic inches. Its base has a radius of 63 inches, Find its height. $(\pi = \frac{22}{7})$ $V = \frac{1}{3}\pi r^2 h$

B. Interest

1. How much money must be invested at 8% to earn an annual income of $6,000?

2. How many years will it take $1,000 invested at 5% to earn $450 interest?

3. Mrs. Jones borrowed $50 and at the end of 5 years paid $20 interest. Find the annual rate of interest.

4. Mr. Smith paid $72 interest at the end of 3 years. How much money did he borrow at 6% per year?

5. Joan's sister borrowed $400 at 8% interest per year. How long was she in debt if she paid $28 interest?

6. Carl repaid $192 of which $35 was interest. How much money did he borrow?

7. Mrs. Watson borrowed $200 at 7% per year. She repaid the loan with a check in the amount of $256 which included the interest. How long did she borrow the money?

8. Arnold borrowed $180. After 2 years he repaid $198 which included the interest. Find the annual rate of interest.

9. How much did Elaine borrow at 7% per year if at the end of 6 years she repaid $5,463 which included the interest?

10. At the end of 4 years Tom received $86.80 which included both the amount invested and the interest. How much money did he invest at 6% per year?

> Formulas
> $i = prt$
> $A = p + i$
> $A = p + prt$

C. Gears, Pulleys, and Sprockets

1. GEARS

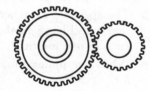

Suppose one gear with 36 teeth is meshed (teeth of one gear fit the grooves of the other) with another gear of 12 teeth. When the gear with 12 teeth makes one complete turn, the gear with 36 teeth has made one third of a turn. When the larger gear makes one complete revolution, the smaller gear has turned 3 times. Since one gear drives the other, one of the meshed gears is called the driving gear and the other the driven gear. The number of teeth (T) of the driving gear times its number of revolutions per minute (R) equals the number of teeth (t) of the driven gear times its number of revolutions per minute (r). This relationship is expressed by the formula: $TR = tr$.

2. PULLEYS

If two pulleys (wheels mounted so that they turn on axles) are belted together and one pulley drives the other, a relationship similar to the meshed gears exists.

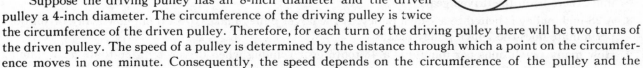

Suppose the driving pulley has an 8-inch diameter and the driven pulley a 4-inch diameter. The circumference of the driving pulley is twice the circumference of the driven pulley. Therefore, for each turn of the driving pulley there will be two turns of the driven pulley. The speed of a pulley is determined by the distance through which a point on the circumference moves in one minute. Consequently, the speed depends on the circumference of the pulley and the number of revolutions it makes per minute.

The circumference of the driving pulley times its number of revolutions per minute equals the circumference of the driven pulley times its number of revolutions per minute. Or, since the diameters of the two pulleys are related exactly as the circumferences, the diameter (D) of the driving pulley times its number of revolutions per minute (R) equals the diameter (d) of the driven pulley times its number of revolutions per minute (r). This relationship is expressed by the formula: $DR = dr$.

3. SPROCKETS

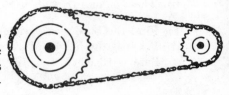

If two sprockets are connected by a chain, a relationship similar to meshed gears and belted pulleys exists. The number of teeth (T) of the driving sprocket times the number of revolutions per minute (R) equals the number of teeth (t) of the driven sprocket times its number of revolutions per minute (r). Formula: $TR = tr$.

Also, the diameter (D) of the driving sprocket times its number of revolutions per minute (R) equals the diameter (d) of the driven sprocket times its number of revolutions per minute (r). Formula: $DR = dr$.

Sample Problems

1. A gear with 48 teeth revolves at the rate of 150 r.p.m. (revolutions per minute) and drives a gear with 60 teeth. How many r.p.m. does the driven gear make?

Given $T = 48$ teeth $TR = tr$
         $R = 150$ r.p.m. $48 \times 150 = 60r$
         $t = 60$ teeth $7{,}200 = 60r$
Find r. $120 = r$
                   $r = 120$

Answer, 120 r.p.m.

2. Find the diameter of a driven pulley if a 24-inch pulley running at 125 r.p.m. is driving a pulley making 200 r.p.m.

Given $D = 24$ in. $DR = dr$
         $R = 125$ r.p.m. $24 \times 125 = d \times 200$
         $r = 200$ r.p.m. $3{,}000 = 200d$
Find d. $15 = d$
                  $d = 15$

Answer, 15 inches

PRACTICE PROBLEMS

1. How many teeth are required on a gear if it is to run at 210 r.p.m. when driven by a gear with 60 teeth running at 140 r.p.m.?

2. An 18-inch pulley turning 160 r.p.m. drives a 6-inch pulley. How many revolutions per minute is the 6-inch pulley turning?

3. The sprocket attached to the pedal of a bicycle has 32 teeth. The sprocket attached to the hub of the rear wheel has 8 teeth. If a boy turns the pedal 72 times per minute, how many times does the rear wheel turn in one minute?

4. What size pulley must be used on a motor running at 1,750 r.p.m. in order to drive a 16-inch pulley at 500 r.p.m.?

5. A tricycle with a chain drive has a sprocket with 15 teeth attached to the pedal and a sprocket with 5 teeth attached to the rear axle. If a youngster rotates the pedal 40 times per minute, how many times do the rear wheels turn in one minute?

6. Charlotte's bicycle has a sprocket with 30 teeth attached to the pedal and a sprocket with 10 teeth attached to the hub of the rear wheel. If she makes the pedal rotate at the average rate of 60 times per minute, how many times does the rear wheel turn in one minute? If the diameter of the rear wheel is 28 inches, how far can she go in one minute? At this rate how long will it take to ride a mile?

7. A 72-tooth gear running at 170 r.p.m. is required to drive a second gear at 255 r.p.m. How many teeth must there be in the driven gear?

8. A 28-inch pulley is belted to a 7-inch pulley. If the larger pulley makes 375 r.p.m., how many revolutions per minute does the 7-inch pulley make?

9. How many revolutions per minute is a 48-tooth gear running when driven by a 36-tooth gear running at 135 r.p.m.?

10. What size pulley is required on a machine if a 20-inch pulley on a shaft running at 240 r.p.m. is to drive the machine at 600 r.p.m.?

D. Electricity

The principles of electricity and related electrical formulas are employed in the fields of radio, television, and radar. Knowledge of some of the simpler elements is useful to the average person. Many technical terms such as watts, kilowatt-hours, volts, and amperes are commonly used.

Analysis and use of the following electrical formulas will enable pupils to understand some of the principles of electricity and the relationship between the technical terms.

(1) $E = IR$ (2) $W = IE$ (3) $H.P. = \dfrac{W}{746}$ (4) $K.W. = \dfrac{W}{1,000}$ (5) $K.W. Hr. = \dfrac{WT}{1,000}$

In these formulas E represents the *electromotive force*, sometimes called the difference in pressure or potential. This force pushes the electric current through the conductor and is measured by the unit called the *volt*. It may be compared to the force a pump exerts in pushing water through a pipe.

I represents the *intensity of current* or amount of electricity flowing and is measured by the unit called the *ampere*. This flow of electricity may be compared to the amount of water flowing through a pipe measured in gallons per minute.

R represents the *resistance* of the conductor and is measured by the unit called the *ohm*. This resistance may be compared to the resistance a clogged pipe or a pipe with a small diameter may offer to the flow of water.

W represents the *power* or *rate of work* done by the electric current and is measured by the unit called the *watt*. A *kilowatt* (K.W.) is 1,000 watts and is a unit measuring electric power. H.P. represents *horsepower* and is a unit measuring power. The *kilowatt-hour* is a unit measuring electrical energy. The amount of energy furnished may be found by multiplying the power in kilowatts by the time in hours.

The formula $E = IR$ shows the relationship between pressure, current, and resistance or between volts, amperes, and ohms. The number of *volts* equals the number of *amperes* times the number of *ohms*.

The formula $W = IE$ shows the relationship between power, current, and pressure or between watts, amperes, and volts. The number of *watts* equals the number of *amperes* times the number of *volts*.

Sample Problem

How much current does a 660-watt electric iron take when operated on a 110-volt circuit? What is the resistance of the iron?

Given $W = 660$ watts	$W = IE$	$E = IR$
$E = 110$ volts	$660 = I \cdot 110$	$110 = 6R$
Find R.	$660 = 110I$	$18\frac{1}{3} = R$
	$6 = I$	$R = 18\frac{1}{3}$ ohms
	$I = 6$ amperes	

Answers, 6 amperes; $18\frac{1}{3}$ ohms.

PRACTICE PROBLEMS

1. How many amperes of current are passing through a 110-volt circuit with a resistance of 30 ohms?
2. An electric iron has a resistance of 12 ohms. If it is used on a 110-volt circuit, how many amperes pass through it?
3. How many volts are required to ring a bell having a resistance of 40 ohms if a current of 0.2 amperes is used?
4. An electric broiler takes 3.5 amperes on a 110-volt circuit. What is the resistance of the broiler?
5. What is the resistance of an electric toaster if it takes 5 amperes at 110 volts?
6. How many amperes of current are flowing through a 40-watt lamp when operated on a 110-volt circuit?
7. A heating coil takes 20 amperes at 125 volts. How much power in watts is it consuming?
8. A 605-watt waffle iron is used on a 110-volt circuit. How much current does it take and what is the resistance of the waffle iron?

9. Find the voltage when a 100-watt lamp takes 0.4 amperes.

10. What is the resistance of a 25-watt, 110-volt lamp?

11. What power in kilowatts does a 110-volt lamp consume if it takes a current of 0.5 amperes?

12. If 75 amperes of current are used at 110 volts, what power in kilowatts is expended? In horsepower?

13. Find the horsepower consumed if a motor takes 12 amperes at 110 volts.

14. How much will it cost to burn five 40-watt lamps for 4 hours each evening for 30 days at the average price of 5 cents per kilowatt hour?

15. At 3 cents per kilowatt hour how much will it cost to operate for 8 hours a motor that uses 9 amperes of current at 125 volts?

E. Levers

The subject of the lever, a very common machine, is studied in physics. However, the simplest lever, the familiar seesaw or teeterboard, illustrates an important scientific principle which may be studied here.

In all likelihood you have seen two children at play with the seesaw. The heavier child sitting closer to the point of support balances a lighter child sitting further away from the point of support. The principle of balancing a teeterboard is the law of the lever.

The lever is a bar or board. Its point of support is called the *fulcrum*. The distance from the point where the weight is located to the fulcrum is called an *arm* of the lever.

The law of the lever states that one weight (W) times the length of its arm (L) is equal to the second weight (w) times the length of its arm (l). Expressed as a formula this relationship is: $WL = wl$.

Sample Problem

Where must Tom, who weighs 112 pounds, sit on a seesaw to balance Richard, who weighs 126 pounds, and sits 4 feet from the fulcrum?

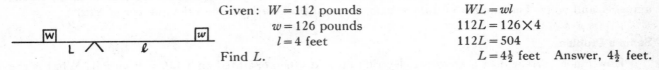

Given: $W = 112$ pounds $WL = wl$
          $w = 126$ pounds $112L = 126 \times 4$
          $l = 4$ feet $112L = 504$
Find L. $L = 4\frac{1}{2}$ feet   Answer, $4\frac{1}{2}$ feet.

PRACTICE PROBLEMS

1. When Marilyn sits 7 feet and Charlotte 6 feet from the fulcrum, they balance on the seesaw. How much does Charlotte weigh if Marilyn weighs 72 pounds?

2. Frank weighs 90 pounds and sits on a teeterboard 5 feet from the fulcrum. If Ed weighs 105 pounds, how far from the fulcrum must he sit to just balance Frank?

3. One arm of a lever is 8 inches long and the other is 10 inches long. If a weight of 4 pounds is placed on the 10-inch arm, how much weight is required on the 8-inch arm to balance the lever?

4. Where must a 120-pound weight be hung to balance an 80-pound weight hung 5 feet from the fulcrum of a lever?

5. Joe weighs 75 pounds and his cousin, Harold, weighs 50 pounds. If Joe sits 6 feet from the fulcrum of a teeterboard, where must Harold sit to balance the teeterboard?

6. How much downward pressure must Richard exert on a 9-foot lever arm to raise a weight of 135 pounds on a 6-foot lever arm?

7. Paul wants to lift a 60-pound rock with a 5-foot crowbar. If the fulcrum is 6 inches from the rock, how many pounds of pressure must he use to lift the rock?

8. How much downward pressure must be exerted to raise a 210-pound stone with a 6-foot crowbar if the fulcrum is 1 foot from the stone?

9. What downward force must be applied at a distance of 4 feet from the fulcrum to balance a downward force of 30 pounds applied 6 feet on the other side of the fulcrum?

10. What weight can Harry lift with a 5-foot crowbar when the fulcrum is 9 inches from the object and he exerts a downward pressure of 108 pounds?

F. Aviation

A great many technical problems in aeronautics involve the wing of the airplane. In this section a simple treatment of the airplane wing is undertaken, formulas are developed, and related problems are solved.

1. Area

The area of a rectangular wing is found by multiplying its length by its width. The length of an airplane wing is called the *span* and its width the *chord* so that, technically, the area equals the span times the chord. Expressed as a formula this relationship is: $A = sc$. If the wing is tapered, the average or mean chord is used.

2. Aspect Ratio

The ratio of the span to the chord of an airplane wing is called its *aspect ratio*. Expressed as a formula this relationship is: $R = \frac{s}{c}$. The aspect ratio is an important factor in the construction of an airplane. If the wing is built too narrow, it may not be strong enough to carry the weight of the airplane.

3. Wing Loading

The number of pounds of gross weight supported in flight by each square foot of the wing is called *wing loading*. The wing loading (L_w) of an airplane is found by dividing the gross weight (W) by the wing area (A). Expressed as a formula this relationship is: $L_w = \frac{W}{A}$.

4. Lift and Drag

The *lift* of an airplane is the force that supports the plane in flight. It is produced mostly by the effect the airflow has upon the wing of the plane. The *lift* (L) of the wing depends on a number of factors including the *wing area* (A) usually expressed in square feet, the *air speed* or *velocity* (V) expressed in feet per second, the *air density* (d), and the airfoil and angle of attack together called the *coefficient of lift* (C_L). The relationship between these quantities is expressed by the formula: $L = \frac{C_L d A V^2}{2}$.

The *drag* of an airplane is the resistance of the air to the motion of the plane. The *drag* (D) of the wing also depends on the *wing area* (A), the *air speed* or *velocity* of the plane (V), the *air density* (d), and a factor called *coefficient of drag* (C_D). Expressed as a formula this relationship is: $D = \frac{C_D d A V^2}{2}$.

Sample Problems

Find the (a) mean chord, (b) aspect ratio, and (c) the wing loading of a plane with a wing area of 392 sq. ft., a wing span of 56 ft., and a gross weight of 5,880 lb.

Given $A = 392$ square feet	$A = sc$	$R = \frac{s}{c}$	$L_w = \frac{W}{A}$
$s = 56$ feet	$392 = 56c$	$R = \frac{56}{7}$	$L_w = \frac{5880}{392}$
$W = 5{,}880$ pounds	$7 = c$	$R = 8$	$L_w = 15$ pounds per square foot
	$c = 7$ feet		

Find c, R, and L_w.   (a) Answer, 7 ft.   (b) Answer, 8.   (c) Answer, 15 lb. per sq. ft.

PRACTICE PROBLEMS

1. A plane with a wing span of 48 ft. and a mean chord of 6 ft. has a gross weight of 3,456 lb. Find the aspect ratio and the wing loading.

2. Find the mean chord, aspect ratio, and wing loading of a plane with a wing area of 486 sq. ft., a wing span of 54 ft., and a gross weight of 5,103 lb.

3. A plane has a wing span of 39 ft. and a wing area of 234 sq. ft. It has a gross weight of 2,574 lb. Find the mean chord, aspect ratio, and wing loading.

4. Determine the lift and drag on the wing of an airplane flying at 150 m.p.h. where the air density is 0.002. The wing has an area of 180 sq. ft. The coefficient of lift is 0.56 and the coefficient of drag is 0.028.

5. An airplane flying at 120 m.p.h. where the air density is 0.0018 has a wing area of 200 sq. ft. Find the lift and drag on the wing of the airplane if the coefficient of lift is 0.48 and the coefficient of drag is 0.024.

G. Temperature

In science, especially in the field of meteorology, we are often required to convert Fahrenheit, Celsius, and Absolute temperature readings from one scale to another.

Gabriel Fahrenheit, a German scientist, invented the Fahrenheit scale using the freezing point of water (32°) and the boiling point (212°) as the basis of his calibrations. Between these two limits are 180 equal divisions called *degrees*. In the United States the Fahrenheit scale is in general use.

Most Europeans use the Celsius scale. It is used universally for scientific purposes. On the Celsius scale the freezing point of water is 0° and the boiling point is 100°. Between these two points there are 100 equal division which compare to the 180 smaller divisions on the Fahrenheit scale.

A third scale called the Absolute scale is sometimes used. The readings are obtained by adding 273° to the Celsius readings. The zero on this scale, called *absolute zero*, marks the point where there is absolutely no heat.

The following formulas show the relationships of the three temperature scales:

$F = 1.8C + 32$ or $C = \frac{5}{9}(F - 32)$

$A = C + 273$

where F represents Fahrenheit reading

C represents Celsius reading

A represents Absolute reading

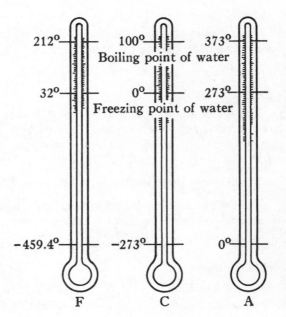

Sample Problem

Find the Celsius temperature reading corresponding to a Fahrenheit temperature reading of 86°.

Given $F = 86$ $F = 1.8C + 32$
Find C $86 = 1.8C + 32$
      $\underline{32 = \qquad 32}$
      $54 = 1.8C$
      $30 = C$
      $C = 30$
      Answer, 30° Celsius

Practice Problems

1. Change the following Fahrenheit readings to corresponding Celsius readings:
   a) 176° F   b) 41° F   c) 320° F   d) 185° F   e) 77° F

2. Change the following Celsius readings to corresponding Fahrenheit readings:
   a) 50° C   b) 75° C   c) 110° C   d) 18° C   e) 31° C

3. Change the following Celsius readings to corresponding Absolute readings:
   a) 28° C   b) 43° C   c) 87° C   d) 9° C   e) 112° C

4. If the temperature of standard air at sea level is 59° F, what is the corresponding reading on the Celsius scale?

5. If the temperature at an altitude of 1,000 feet is 29° C, what is the corresponding Fahrenheit reading?

6. The normal room temperature is 68° F. What would it be on the Celsius scale?

7. A French recipe calls for heating the oven at a temperature of 140° C. If the heat controls are calibrated in the Fahrenheit units, at what Fahrenheit temperature should the controls be set?

8. The normal body temperature is 98.6° F. What would it be on the Celsius scale?

9. Which is warmer, 108°F or 40° C?

10. The melting point of uranium is 1690° C. What is the corresponding reading on the Fahrenheit scale?

REVIEW OF UNIT FOUR

Solve and check:

1. $8c = 56$　　　　**3.** $n - 23 = 9$　　　　**5.** $3n + 5 = 32$　　　**7.** $26 = 5x$　　　**9.** $\frac{7}{8}b = 84$

2. $x + 17 = 42$　　**4.** $\frac{b}{6} = 24$　　　　**6.** $85 = 8s - 13$　　**8.** $11x + x = 132$　　**10.** $a + .06a = 265$

Find the value of:

11. w if $A = 192$ and $l = 12$, using the formula $A = lw$. **12.** l if $d = 27$ and $n = 108$, using the formula $d = l - n$.

13. C if $A = 8,950$ and $L = 5,300$, using the formula $A = L + C$.

14. d if $r = 36$ and $t = 9$, using the formula $r = \frac{d}{t}$. **15.** n if $S = 1,440$, using the formula $S = 180n - 360$.

16. p if $A = 984$, $r = .02$, and $t = 10$, using the formula $A = p + prt$.

17. How much money must be invested at 6% to get an annual income of $750?

18. The school baseball league's batting champion hit safely 42 times to earn a batting average of .375. How many official times at bat did he have? **19.** $\frac{4}{5}$ of what number is 48?

20. What is the area of a square garden if it requires 136 feet of fence to enclose the garden?

CUMULATIVE ALGEBRA REVIEW

1. Express as a formula: The distance at the equator in nautical miles (d) is 60 times the number representing degrees of longitude (L).

2. Find the value of the expression $2x^2 + 7x - 9$ when $x = 5$.

3. Find the value of R when $E = 66$, $I = 3$ and $r = 9$, using the formula $E = Ir + IR$.

4. One inch equals 25.4 millimeters. How many millimeters are in 3 inches? 8 inches? Write a formula expressing the number of millimeters ($mm.$) in i inches.

Solve and check:

5. $9b = 72$　　　　**6.** $x + 15 = 39$　　　**7.** $c - 8 = 26$　　　**8.** $4a + 8 = 60$　　　**9.** $86 = 7y - 19$

10. $\frac{m}{3} = 27$　　**11.** $\frac{5}{6}c = 80$　　　**12.** $3x + 4x = 63$　　**13.** $n + .05n = 882$　　**14.** $4 = 12x$

Find the value of:

15. B when $A = 57$, using the formula $A + B = 90$. **16.** e when $p = 51$ and $b = 19$, using the formula $p = b + 2e$.

17. V when H.P. $= 24$ and $D = 100$, using the formula H.P. $= \frac{DV}{550}$.

18. How much money must be invested at 8% to yield an annual income of $10,000?

19. Find the regular price of a baseball glove if the reduced prices is $8.80 when a reduction of 20% is allowed.

20. Ten equal angles plus 30 degrees equal a straight angle.(180°). How many degrees are in each equal angle?

∘○∘

KEYED ACHIEVEMENT TEST

1. Express as a formula:
The average or mean (M) of three numbers, a, b, and c, is the sum of the numbers divided by three. ①

2. Find the value of the expression $a(a^2 + b^2)$ when $a = 4$ and $b = 3$. ⑤

Solve the following equations:

3. $m + 27 = 42$ ⑦　**4.** $a - 14 = 9$ ⑧　**5.** $8c = 96$ ⑨　**6.** $\frac{b}{4} = 12$ ⑩　**7.** $5x - 4 = 31$ ⑪

8. Find the missing numbers, write the word rule and formula expressing the relationship between the sum of the interior angles and the number of sides of a polygon: ⑥

Number of sides (n)	3	4	5	6	8	11
Sum of the angles (s)	180	360	540			

9. Find the value of C if $F = 203$, using the formula $F = 1.8C + 32$. ⑫

10. If 108 students or 12% of the student body took part in the school play, what was the enrollment? ⑬

INTRODUCTION TO UNIT FIVE

The weather stations in the larger cities report daily both the high and low temperature readings. This information is published in many newspapers. In the winter some reported temperature readings have minus signs. Stock quotations generally found in the financial section of a newspaper also contain numbers preceded by plus and minus signs.

These signs preceding the numbers do not mean addition and subtraction. They are used to represent quantities which are opposites. The minus sign in the weather report indicates the temperature is below zero. The numbers without signs are temperature readings above zero. The plus sign in the stock report indicates a gain or rise in price while the minus sign indicates a loss or fall in price.

Plus and minus signs representing opposites are called *signs of quality*. A number preceded by a plus sign is called a *positive number*. A number preceded by a minus sign is called a *negative number*. Positive and negative numbers are sometimes called *signed numbers* or *directed numbers*. Plus and minus signs in arithmetic indicate the processes of addition and subtraction. They are therefore called *signs of operation*. You will notice, however, in algebra plus and minus signs are used to indicate both operation and quality.

In arithmetic all numbers are positive, although the plus sign is not written. Similarly in algebra any number without a sign is a positive number. The negative number always bears the minus sign.

The value of any signed number without its sign is called its *absolute value*. The absolute value of $+6$ is 6. The absolute value of -10 is 10.

Positive and negative numbers have many practical uses. In science and related fields they are employed in connection with temperature readings, upward and downward forces, clockwise and counterclockwise motion, positive and negative charges of electricity, proton and electron, and acceleration and deceleration.

In their directional sense they are useful in indicating north and south, east and west, north and south latitude, east and west longitude, above and below sea level, right and left, and up and down.

Stockbrokers employ them to show changes in price. They are used in everyday statistics to indicate changes such as the increase or decrease in cost of living or population, and to show the deviation from normal as found in weather reports. Statistics in sports and scoring of games often require the use of signed numbers.

In addition to these common uses, it is essential to learn to operate with signed numbers. Suppose it is required to find the Celsius temperature when the Fahrenheit temperature is 14°, using the formula $C = \frac{5}{9}(F - 32)$. The difficulty of subtracting 32 from 14 immediately arises. In this unit you will learn to add, subtract, multiply, and divide signed numbers and use them in evaluating formulas and other algebraic expressions.

Sometimes numerals with raised signs like $^{-}3$ and $^{+}7$ are used to name positive and negative numbers. However, numerals having the signs centered are more commonly used, as shown in the weather chart and stock report below.

TEMPERATURES IN CHICAGO

MAXIMUM, 1 P.M. 5
MINIMUM, 7 A.M. .... −7

3 A.M.	−5	Noon	2	Unofficial—	
4 A.M.	−5	1 P.M.	5	8 P.M.	2
5 A.M.	−5	2 P.M.	5	9 P.M.	2
6 A.M.	−6	3 P.M.	4	10 P.M.	0
7 A.M.	−7	4 P.M.	4	11 P.M.	−2
8 A.M.	−5	5 P.M.	3	Midnight	−2
9 A.M.	−4	6 P.M.	2	1 A.M.	−2
10 A.M.	−2	7 P.M.	2	2 A.M.	−4
11 A.M.	0				

For 24 hours ended 7 p.m., Jan. 27:

Mean temperature, −1; normal, 24; deficiency for January, 66 degrees.

Precipitation, none; deficiency for January, .12 of an inch; total since Jan. 1, 1:59 inches.

Highest wind velocity, 22 miles an hour, from the northwest at 12:47 A.M.

Barometer, 7 A.M., 30.44; 7 P.M., 30.49

1974 High	Low	Stocks and Div. In Dollars	P/E	Sales 100s	High	Low	Last	Net Chng
		A—B—C—D						
11⅜	9⅝	AAR Cp .07e	7	14	12¼	11¾	12¼	+ ⅞
6¼	4⅞	AAV Cos .25	3	8	5	4⅞	5	+ ⅛
7½	6¼	AbrdMf .40b	4	3	7	7	7	+ ⅛
2⅜	1¾	Aberden Pet	100	2	2	2	2	+ ⅛
4⅜	3⅛	Action Inc	4	25	3¾	3½	3½	− ¼
2⅜	2	Adam Russl	6	3	2¼	2¼	2¼	.....
13½	8⅝	AdobeOil Gs	16	25	9⅛	9	9	+ ¼
2⅝	1⅞	A&EPlast P	3	4	2½	2½	2½	− ⅛
4⅜	3¼	AeroFlo .15e	4	1	4	4	4	− ⅛
2¾	1	Aeronca inc		20	2⅜	2¼	2¼	− ¼
4¼	2⅜	AffilCap .11t	16	2	4¼	4¼	4¼	.....
6⅝	4	Affil Hsp .20	10	8	6⅛	6	6⅛	+ ⅛
8⅝	7	AffIPub .13e	5	30	8¼	8	8	− ¼
4¾	3¼	After Six .10	4	3	4¼	4¼	4¼	.....
3⅝	2¾	AIC Pht .56t	6	13	3⅛	3⅛	3⅛	.....
8⅛	6⅛	Airbbrn Frt	9	2	7⅞	7⅞	7⅞	− ⅛
7⅞	5¼	Airpax 45t	5	11	7	6⅞	6⅞	− ⅛
11	6½	Airwick .20	9	11	7½	7⅜	7⅜	− ¼

UNIT FIVE—POSITIVE AND NEGATIVE NUMBERS

EXERCISE 14

Meaning of Signed Numbers

I. Aim: To develop the meaning of signed numbers.

II. Procedure

1. Represent positive and negative numbers by words or statements opposite in meaning or direction.

2. Represent words or statements opposite in meaning or direction by positive and negative numbers.

III. Sample Solutions

1. If $+6$ miles means 6 miles north, what does -4 miles mean?
   Answer, 4 miles south

2. If 52 degrees above zero is represented by $+52°$, how can 8 degrees below zero be represented?
   Answer, $-8°$

DIAGNOSTIC TEST

1. If $+50$ pounds represents an upward force of 50 pounds, what does -70 pounds represent?
2. If $-3°$ means 3 degrees south latitude, what does $+7°$ mean?
3. If $5 deposited is represented by $+$5$, how can $3 withdrawn from the bank be represented?
4. If 4 yards lost in a football game is indicated by -4 yards, how can 6 yards gained be indicated?

Related Practice Examples

1. a) If $+4$ pounds means 4 pounds overweight, what does -3 pounds mean?
   b) If $+10$ floors indicates 10 floors up, what does -1 floor indicate?
   c) If $+8$ miles represents 8 miles east, what does -2 miles represent?
   d) If $+3$ points means a 3-point rise in the value of a stock, what does -5 points mean?
   e) If $+60$ represents a gain of $60 in a business transaction, what does $-$75$ represent?

2. a) If -100 feet represents 100 feet below sea level, what does $+200$ feet represent?
   b) If -5 years indicates 5 years ago, what does $+3$ years indicate?
   c) If -23 items means an inventory shortage of 23 items, what does $+49$ items mean?
   d) If -2 amperes represents a discharge of 2 amperes of electricity, what does $+8$ amperes represent?
   e) If $-12°$ means 12 degrees below zero, what does $+67°$ mean?

3. a) If 24 degrees north latitude is indicated by $+24°$, how can 43 degrees south latitude be indicated?
   b) If $17 earned is represented by $+$17$, how can $6 spent be represented?
   c) If $+2\%$ indicates an increase of 2% in the cost of living, how can a 3% decrease in the cost of living be indicated?
   d) If 9 degrees above normal temperature is represented by $+9°$, how can 7 degrees below normal be represented?
   e) If a tail wind of 25 miles per hour is indicated by $+25$ m.p.h., how can a head wind of 39 miles per hour be indicated?

4. a) If 29 degrees west longitude is indicated by $-29°$, how can 32 degrees east longitude be indicated?
   b) If 16 feet to the left is indicated by -16 feet, how can 18 feet to the right be indicated?
   c) If the business liabilities of $1,375 is represented by $-$1,375$, how can assets of $5,200 be represented?
   d) If 8 miles south is represented by -8 miles, how can 7 miles north be indicated?
   e) If the deficiency of 1.25 inches of rainfall is indicated by -1.25 inches, how can an excess of 0.75 inch of rainfall be indicated?

THE NUMBER SCALE

In algebra the number system is extended to include negative numbers. The number scale shows the relation of positive and negative numbers. This scale may be constructed by dividing a horizontal line in equal parts. Some point of division is taken as the starting point, or origin, and labeled zero. Each point of division to the right of zero is labeled with a positive number, $+1$ representing the first unit, $+2$ the second unit, etc. Each point of division to the left of zero is labeled with a negative number, beginning with -1.

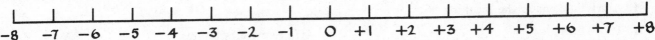

-8   -7   -6   -5   -4   -3   -2   -1   O   +1   +2   +3   +4   +5   +6   +7   +8

If you start from zero and go five units to the right, you reach $+5$. If you go seven units to the left of zero, you reach -7. However, any number on the scale may be used as the starting point and going to the right is considered the positive direction and to the left, the negative direction. Each signed number on the scale represents a distance and a direction.

The number scale may also be constructed vertically. The numbers above zero are considered positive and those below zero negative. The thermometer illustrates the vertical scale in use while the automobile battery gauge (ammeter) often employs the horizontal scale.

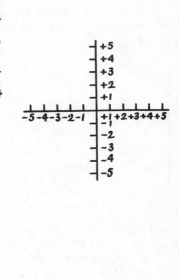

If the horizontal and vertical scales are combined, rectangular scales (cartesian co-ordinates) are formed. These scales are used in locating points and in graphing equations and formulas.

Although negative numbers may be regarded as less than zero, pupils should not misinterpret them as being less than nothing. In some applications it may be desirable to consider any number on the vertical scale greater than any other number below it, and on the horizontal scale greater than any number to the left of it. Zero is sometimes regarded as a quantity and other times as a point of reference.

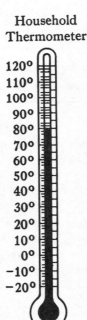

Household Thermometer

120°
110°
100°
90°
80°
70°
60°
50°
40°
30°
20°
10°
0°
-10°
-20°

Applications

In each of the following examples select a reasonable number scale, then mark off and label points indicating:

1. Temperature readings: 3 A.M., $-5°$; 7 A.M., $-9°$; 11 A.M., $-2°$; 3 P.M., $6°$; 7 P.M., $4°$; 11 P.M., $-1°$.
2. Reported positions of a plane: 100 miles west, 60 miles west, 30 miles west, 10 miles west, 20 miles east, 50 miles east, 90 miles east.
3. Historical dates: Battle of Thermopylae, 480 B.C.; Conquest of Carthage, 146 B.C.; Fall of Rome, 476 A.D.; Battle of Hastings, 1066 A.D.; World War II, 1939 A.D.
4. Longitude of some large cities: Washington, D. C., 77° W.; Milan, Italy, 9° E.; Rio de Janeiro, Brazil, 43° W.; Ankara, Turkey, 33° E.; Dublin, Ireland 6° W.
5. Latitude of some well known places: Panama Canal, 9° N.; Cape Horn, 56° S.; Chicago, Ill., 42° N.; Fairbanks, Alaska, 65° N.; Sydney, Australia, 34° S.

EXERCISE 15

Comparison of Signed Numbers

I. **Aim:** To compare signed numbers.

II. **Procedure**

1. When comparing two positive numbers, take the number whose absolute value is greater as the greater number.
2. When comparing two negative numbers, take the number whose absolute value is smaller as the greater number.
3. Any positive number is greater than zero or any negative number.
4. Zero is greater than any negative number.

III. **Sample Solutions**

1. Which is greater $+7$ or $+2$? Answer, $+7$.
2. Which is greater -5 or -1? Answer, -1.
3. Which is greater 0 or -1? Answer, 0.
4. Which is greater -6 or $+3$? Answer, $+3$.

DIAGNOSTIC TEST

Which is greater:

1. $+6$ or $+3$? **2.** -4 or -1? **3.** 0 or $+2$? **4.** -5 or 0? **5.** -7 or $+1$?

Which is smaller:

6. $+4$ or $+2$? **7.** -3 or -5? **8.** 0 or $+1$? **9.** 0 or -6? **10.** -3 or $+3$?

Arrange the following in order of size:

11. (largest first) -6, $+8$, -4, $+12$, 0, -1, $+15$, -100, $+23$, -16.
12. (smallest first) -4, $+6$, $+2$, -2, -8, 0, -25, $+30$, -50, $+18$.

Related Practice Examples

Select the greater of the two given signed numbers:

1. $+4$ or $+7$; $+5$ or $+3$; $+9$ or $+6$; $+8$ or $+10$; $+4$ or $+1$.
2. -2 or -1; -8 or -5; -3 or -4; -7 or -10; -6 or -5.
3. 0 or $+6$; $+8$ or 0; 0 or $+1$; $+3$ or 0; $+5$ or 0.
4. 0 or -3; -2 or 0; 0 or -7; 0 or -6; -9 or 0.
5. -2 or $+3$; $+4$ or -6; -5 or $+5$; -3 or $+2$; $+6$ or -8.

Select the smaller of the two given signed numbers:

6. $+3$ or $+5$; $+6$ or $+10$; $+12$ or $+1$; $+7$ or $+8$; $+2$ or $+4$.
7. -7 or -4; -3 or -1; -9 or -5; -2 or -8; -10 or -12.
8. 0 or $+5$; $+4$ or 0; $+10$ or 0; 0 or $+15$; 0 or $+7$.
9. 0 or -8; -3 or 0; 0 or -5; 0 or -7; -14 or 0.
10. -3 or $+4$; $+1$ or -7; -8 or $+5$; $+6$ or -3; $+10$ or -12.

11. Arrange the following in order of size (largest first):

    a) -2, $+6$, $+3$, -9, -1, 0, $+7$, $+1$, $+16$.
    b) $+38$, $+20$, -16, $+3$, -7, -5, $+23$, -35, $+8$, -2.
    c) $+15$, -12, -4, $+5$, $+2$, -8, $+10$, 0, -6, $+21$.
    d) -5, -3, $+7$, $+1$, $+15$, -9, -16, -11, $+20$, -14.

12. Arrange the following in order of size (smallest first):

    a) $+5$, 0, -3, -1, -10, $+9$, $+15$, -12, $+25$, -17.
    b) -14, $+9$, $+19$, -15, -22, $+7$, $+10$, -6, $+2$, -30.
    c) -2, $+5$, -7, $+18$, -26, -4, -13, $+10$, $+1$, -50.

EXERCISE 16

Addition of Signed Numbers

I. Aim: To add signed numbers.

II. Procedure

A. Graphic Addition

1. From zero count to the right or left on the horizontal scale or up or down on the vertical scale. The directions are indicated by the signed numbers. For positive numbers count to the right or up; for negative numbers count to the left or down.

2. The point that is finally reached is the sum.

For example, suppose a football team in two plays:

First gained 6 yds. then gained 2 yds.	First gained 6 yds. then lost 2 yds.	First lost 6 yds. then gained 2 yds.	First lost 6 yds. then lost 2 yds.	First lost 6 yds. then gained 6 yds.

Add:	Add:	Add:	Add:	Add:
$+6$	$+6$	-6	-6	-6
$+2$	-2	$+2$	-2	$+6$
$+8$	$+4$	-4	-8	0
Total gain, 8 yds.	Net gain, 4 yds.	Net loss, 4 yds.	Total loss, 8 yds.	No gain or loss

B. Algebraic Addition

1. To add two or more positive numbers, add their absolute values and prefix a plus sign to the answer.

2. To add two or more negative numbers, add their absolute values and prefix a minus sign to the answer.

3. To add a positive number and a negative number, subtract the smaller absolute value from the larger and prefix to the answer the sign of the number having the larger absolute value. Here one quantity offsets an equal number of units of the other quantity and the result is the remaining units.

4. To add three or more positive and negative numbers, add algebraically: first the positive numbers, then the negative numbers, and finally, the two answers.

5. The sum of two numbers of equal absolute value but opposite in sign is zero. Zero does not have any sign.

6. Horizontal addition is treated the same as vertical addition, using the signs as signs of quality and not of operation. See sample solution 8. Note: A number without any sign is a positive number.

III. Sample Solutions

1.	2.	3.	4.	5.	6.	7.
$+5$	-4	$+7$	-4	$+6$	$+3$	$+2$
$+2$	-1	-5	$+5$	-9	-3	-5
						-4
$+7$	-5	$+2$	$+1$	-3	0	$+6$
Answer, $+7$	Answer, -5	Answer, $+2$	Answer, $+1$	Answer, -3	Answer, 0	-1
						Answer, -1

8. Combine: $7-9+8-4$ Answer, $+2$

(Add $+7$ and $+8$ to get $+15$, Add -9 and -4 to get -13; Combine $+15$ and -13 to get $+2$.)

DIAGNOSTIC TEST

Add:

1. $+2$
   $+3$

2. -5
   -2

3. $+6$
   -4

4. $+3$
   -9

5. -7
   $+6$

6. -8
   $+15$

7. 0
   -5

8. -4
   $+4$

9. -5
   8

10. $2\frac{1}{2}$
    $-3\frac{1}{4}$

11. -0.6
    -1.9

12. $+2$
    $+13$
    $+4$

13. -8
    -9
    -12

14. $+3$
    -8
    $+7$

15. -7
    -9
    $+2$

16. -5
    $+3$
    -7
    $+8$

17. Add as indicated:
    $(+1)+(-8)$

18. Combine:
    $8-10+6-7+3$

Related Practice Examples

Add:

1.
| $+2$ | $+5$ | $+7$ | $+9$ | $+4$ | $+3$ | $+2$ | $+3$ | $+7$ | $+11$ |
| $+4$ | $+3$ | $+8$ | $+2$ | $+1$ | $+4$ | $+8$ | $+9$ | $+12$ | $+13$ |

2.
| -3 | -4 | -7 | -8 | -10 | -2 | -9 | -8 | -2 | -15 |
| -1 | -2 | -3 | -5 | -6 | -7 | -9 | -9 | -11 | -20 |

3.
| $+4$ | $+6$ | $+8$ | $+7$ | $+10$ | $+7$ | $+9$ | $+2$ | $+6$ | $+25$ |
| -2 | -1 | -3 | -4 | -5 | -6 | -3 | -1 | -3 | -18 |

4.
| $+1$ | $+6$ | $+3$ | $+7$ | $+2$ | $+5$ | $+4$ | $+15$ | $+9$ | $+23$ |
| -5 | -7 | -6 | -9 | -5 | -6 | -11 | -18 | -16 | -35 |

5.
| -5 | -7 | -8 | -6 | -5 | -12 | -15 | -18 | -25 | -60 |
| $+3$ | $+1$ | $+2$ | $+4$ | $+2$ | $+8$ | $+9$ | $+12$ | $+16$ | $+27$ |

6.
| -2 | -5 | -3 | -7 | -2 | -3 | -6 | -15 | -23 | -37 |
| $+8$ | $+10$ | $+12$ | $+14$ | $+9$ | $+4$ | $+8$ | $+21$ | $+32$ | $+49$ |

7.
| $+4$ | 0 | -2 | 0 | 0 | $+8$ | 0 | -5 | -9 | 0 |
| 0 | $+3$ | 0 | -8 | $+15$ | 0 | -6 | 0 | 0 | $+10$ |

8.
| $+1$ | $+7$ | -3 | -9 | $+12$ | -5 | $+2$ | $+4$ | -18 | $+25$ |
| -1 | -7 | $+3$ | $+9$ | -12 | $+5$ | -2 | -4 | $+18$ | -25 |

9.

6	12	6	5	0	9	−7	8	−15	2
2	− 4	−7	8	9	−4	5	0	4	−11

10.

$+\frac{1}{4}$	$-\frac{3}{8}$	$-\frac{11}{16}$	$+1\frac{1}{8}$	$-2\frac{2}{3}$	$-4\frac{1}{2}$	$+\frac{3}{4}$	$-1\frac{5}{8}$	$+3\frac{5}{6}$	$-2\frac{4}{5}$
$-\frac{3}{4}$	$+\frac{5}{8}$	$-\frac{9}{16}$	$+\frac{7}{8}$	$+3\frac{1}{3}$	$-2\frac{7}{8}$	$-3\frac{3}{8}$	$+4\frac{15}{16}$	$+7\frac{2}{3}$	$-1\frac{1}{2}$

11.

+1.3	+.7	−.5	−0.8	−.07	+1.90	−2.09	+4.25	−9.38	+1.625
+2.8	−.9	−.6	+1.5	−.96	−2.43	+3.04	+5.85	−1.79	−0.875

12.

+8	+4	+10	+14	+ 3	+14	+20	+26	+13	+15
+3	+1	+ 8	+ 9	+12	+ 8	+15	+14	+12	+22
+7	+9	+15	+ 6	+23	+29	+16	+11	+31	+83

13.

−2	−6	− 5	−15	−12	−16	−25	−14	−50	−28
−5	−8	−10	− 6	−19	−17	−30	−12	−30	−39
−4	−3	−23	−32	−24	−18	−40	−13	−20	−43

14.

+6	+ 8	+ 9	−8	−12	−15	+8	+ 9	+7	−25
+4	+15	+ 2	+4	+ 6	+ 9	−3	−25	−14	+17
−2	− 7	−11	+5	+ 5	+13	+5	+ 1	+ 7	+ 5

15.

−3	− 9	−15	+6	+18	+20	− 8	−25	−10	−18
−6	− 1	− 3	−9	−15	− 3	+15	+29	+30	−17
+8	+10	+25	−7	− 5	−19	− 7	− 8	−15	+35

16.

+8	−9	+6	− 8	+14	+7	−12	+ 5	− 2	−4
+5	−6	+8	− 9	−13	−2	+ 9	−19	−11	0
+6	−5	−3	+ 2	− 5	+6	− 2	+ 6	+64	7
+3	−9	−7	+15	+ 1	−9	+ 4	+25	−55	−3

17. Add as indicated:

1. $(+2)+(+6)$
2. $(-3)+(-3)$
3. $(-5)+(+7)$
4. $(0)+(-7)$
5. $(8)+(-5)$
6. $(-4)+(-3)$
7. $(+5)+(-4)$
8. $(2)+(0)$
9. $(-2)+(+2)+(-3)$
10. $(-6)+(+4)+(7)$

18. Combine:

a)
1. $8+7$
2. $5-3$
3. $2-6$
4. $5-7$
5. $6-5-7$
6. $4-9-2$
7. $3-5+2$
8. $11-4+3$
9. $1-5-3$
10. $-7-2-4$

b)
1. $3-5-1+6$
2. $7-8+4-5$
3. $1-7+2-4$
4. $2-5-7+3$
5. $8-2-5+3-7$
6. $2-4-3+9-1$
7. $-9+3-2-8+1+6$
8. $5-1+3-10+2-7$
9. $-3+7-2-4-8+6-4$
10. $2-3-5+6-12+3-7+2$

c)
1. $2-6-5+7$
2. $5+8-2+9$
3. $4-5-3-2$
4. $6+1-8-3-5$
5. $4-2-6+9+5$
6. $-5+7-3-6-5+1$
7. $3-8-4+7+6-2$
8. $-2-4+3-8-1+6-5$
9. $-5+6-1+4-5+7-10$
10. $4-6-3+15-2-8+7-6$

Miscellaneous Examples

Add:

a)

$+3$	$+3$	-3	-3	0	$+2$	$+2$	-2	-2	0
$+2$	-2	$+2$	-2	-2	$+3$	-3	$+3$	-3	$+3$

b) Combine the numbers in each set of parentheses, then add the answers:

1. $(8+3)+(2+7)$
2. $(4-2)+(6-3)$
3. $(10-4)+(1+5)$
4. $(9+7)+(8-14)$
5. $(2-6)+(4-1)$
6. $(5+8)+(3-4)+(7-3)$
7. $(4-5)+(2+1)+(6-9)$
8. $(12+9)+(6-6)+(4-13)$
9. $(1-2)+(7-10)+(8-4)$
10. $(8-5)+(6+3)+(1-7)$

Applications

Part 1 — Ground Speeds

Just as strong winds force a person to walk either more slowly or quickly depending upon the direction of the wind, so winds decrease or increase the speed developed by a plane in flight through the air. The speed of the plane in still air is called *air speed*. A "tail" wind increases the air speed of a plane because it blows in the direction the plane is flying. A "head" wind, blowing in the opposite direction, decreases the air speed. The actual speed of the plane measured by land markings is called *ground speed*.

Find the answers to the following by means of signed numbers and illustrate graphically:

1. What is the ground speed of a plane if the air speed is 160 miles per hour (m.p.h.) and the tail wind has a velocity (speed) of 20 miles per hour?

2. A plane develops an air speed of 340 m.p.h. Find the ground speed if it flies against a head wind of 35 m.p.h.

3. Find the actual speed of a plane headed due east at an air speed of 190 m.p.h. when a wind of 28 m.p.h. is blowing from the west.

4. What is the actual speed of a plane flying north at an air speed of 415 m.p.h. when a wind of 30 m.p.h. is coming from the north?

5. Find the ground speed of a plane meeting a head wind of 40 m.p.h. when the air speed of the plane is 225 m.p.h.

Part 2 — Miscellaneous

Find the answers to the following by means of signed numbers:

1. A football team gained 3 yards on the first play, lost 4 yards on the second play, gained 6 yards on the third play, and gained 5 yards on the fourth play. Did the team make a first down?

2. How far below the surface of the water is the top of a submarine mountain called San Juan Seamount off the Coast of California if the ocean floor depth is 12,000 feet and the mountain rises 10,188 feet?

3. At 8 A.M. the temperature was $-2°$. If the temperature rose 5 degrees in the next hour, what did the thermometer register at 9 A.M.

4. A certain stock closed on Monday at the selling price of $37\frac{3}{4}$. Find the closing price of the stock on Friday if it gained $\frac{7}{8}$ point on Tuesday, lost $1\frac{1}{4}$ points on Wednesday, lost $2\frac{1}{2}$ points on Thursday and gained $\frac{3}{8}$ point on Friday.

Part 3 — Equations

Solve the following equations by the addition axiom:

SET 1	SET 2	SET 3
1. $x-10=-4$	1. $-16=n-7$	1. $y-5=-5$
2. $a-3=-15$	2. $-6=d-11$	2. $-24=t-9$
3. $c-9=-8$	3. $-45=B-90$	3. $s-.08=-.26$
4. $m-2.4=-3.8$	4. $-6\frac{1}{2}=p-9\frac{1}{4}$	4. $-\frac{5}{8}=c-2\frac{3}{4}$
5. $s-5=-13$	5. $-48=l-76$	5. $-21=r-32$

EXERCISE 17
Subtraction of Signed Numbers

I. Aim: To subtract signed numbers.

II. Procedure

A. Graphic Subtraction

  1. Locate on the number scale the number representing the subtrahend.

  2. Count the number of units to the number representing the minuend.

      Counting to the right or up is the positive direction. Use the plus sign.

      Counting to the left or down is the negative direction. Use the minus sign.

Subtract +3 from +7.   Subtract −3 from +7.   Subtract +3 from −7.   Subtract −3 from −7.

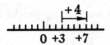 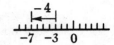

B. Algebraic Subtraction

  1. Change the sign of the subtrahend mentally.   2. Follow the rules for addition of signed numbers.

    This may be developed as follows:

To subtract +3 from +7 means to find the number which added to +3 will equal +7.	To subtract −3 from +7 means to find the number which added to −3 will equal +7.	To subtract +3 from −7 means to find the number which added to +3 will equal −7.	To subtract −3 from −7 means to find the number which added to −3 will equal −7.
Subtract: +7 +3 ――― +4 Answer, +4	Subtract: +7 −3 ――― +10 Answer, +10	Subtract: −7 +3 ――― −10 Answer, −10	Subtract: −7 −3 ――― −4 Answer, −4

    Compare each of the following addition examples to the above corresponding subtraction example. Note the identical answer in each case.

Add: +7 −3 ――― +4 Answer, +4	Add: +7 +3 ――― +10 Answer, +10	Add: −7 −3 ――― −10 Answer, −10	Add: −7 +3 ――― −4 Answer, −4

    Since these examples differ only in the sign of the lower terms, we can see that to subtract, we change the sign of the subtrahend and follow the rules for addition to get the required answer in each case.

III. Sample Solutions

  1. Subtract:

    −5   First change   −5   →   Then follow the   −5

    −7   →   mentally to   +7   rules for addition   +7

    ―――   ―――

                                                        +2   Answer, +2

  Subtract:

2.	+7 +4 ――― +3 Answer, +3	3.	−9 −8 ――― −1 Answer, −1	4.	−4 +2 ――― −6 Answer, −6	5.	+3 −5 ――― +8 Answer, +8
6.	+9 0 ――― +9 Answer, +9	7.	0 −2 ――― +2 Answer, +2	8.	−3 −3 ――― 0 Answer, 0	9.	−3 +3 ――― −6 Answer, −6

DIAGNOSTIC TEST

Subtract:

1. $+5$ $+2$	4. -4 -9	7. -12 $+\ 9$	10. 0 $+2$	13. 2 10	16. Subtract as indicated: $(-4)-(+3)$
2. $+3$ $+4$	5. $+8$ -6	8. -1 $+6$	11. -7 -7	14. $+\frac{3}{8}$ $-\frac{1}{4}$	17. Subtract 9 from 4.
3. -7 -1	6. $+\ 5$ -11	9. -3 $\ 0$	12. -4 $+4$	15. -3.6 -2.7	

Related Practice Examples

Subtract:

1.

| $+6$ $+4$ | $+8$ $+3$ | $+7$ $+1$ | $+10$ $+\ 3$ | $+9$ $+6$ | $+3$ $+2$ | $+5$ $+1$ | $+12$ $+\ 3$ | $+15$ $+\ 8$ | $+23$ $+17$ |

2.

| $+5$ $+7$ | $+2$ $+4$ | $+3$ $+7$ | $+1$ $+9$ | $+\ 8$ $+12$ | $+4$ $+5$ | $+\ 9$ $+14$ | $+\ 2$ $+11$ | $+16$ $+21$ | $+25$ $+34$ |

3.

| -6 -4 | -8 -1 | -9 -2 | -15 $-\ 8$ | -14 $-\ 6$ | -7 -3 | -5 -2 | -18 -17 | -23 -14 | -46 -39 |

4.

| -3 -5 | -1 -6 | $-\ 4$ -14 | $-\ 9$ -13 | $-\ 6$ -19 | -2 -3 | $-\ 8$ -10 | $-\ 7$ -15 | -13 -19 | -24 -31 |

5.

| $+4$ -1 | $+9$ -3 | $+7$ -2 | $+11$ -10 | $+15$ -12 | $+14$ -11 | $+22$ -15 | $+39$ -27 | $+27$ -19 | $+51$ -43 |

6.

| $+6$ -7 | $+4$ -8 | $+\ 9$ -14 | $+1$ -2 | $+7$ -18 | $+15$ -23 | $+21$ -36 | $+46$ -58 | $+53$ -56 | $+84$ -93 |

7.

| -7 $+2$ | -6 $+5$ | -8 $+6$ | -10 $+\ 9$ | -5 $+3$ | -12 $+\ 4$ | -17 $+12$ | -42 $+28$ | -59 $+41$ | -62 $+25$ |

8.

| -3 $+4$ | -2 $+8$ | -4 $+9$ | -1 $+7$ | -8 $+9$ | -10 $+15$ | -16 $+28$ | -36 $+42$ | -14 $+58$ | -47 $+61$ |

9.

| $+2$ 0 | $+8$ 0 | $+4$ 0 | $+5$ 0 | $+23$ 0 | -1 0 | -9 0 | -7 0 | -14 0 | -21 0 |

10.

| 0 $+3$ | 0 $+5$ | 0 $+2$ | 0 $+11$ | 0 $+15$ | 0 -1 | 0 -7 | 0 -9 | 0 -10 | 0 -35 |

11.

| $+3$ $+3$ | $+9$ $+9$ | $+8$ $+8$ | $+15$ $+15$ | $+43$ $+43$ | -4 -4 | -1 -1 | -10 -10 | -16 -16 | -13 -13 |

12.

$+5$	-4	$+7$	$+12$	-18	$+9$	-23	-1	-30	$+15$
-5	$+4$	-7	-12	$+18$	-9	$+23$	$+1$	$+30$	-15

13.

4	9	8	1	2	-3	-8	17	9	16
7	15	11	5	-4	6	2	13	-5	24

14.

$+\frac{3}{4}$	$-\frac{5}{6}$	$+\frac{1}{2}$	$+\frac{3}{4}$	$-1\frac{3}{16}$	$+2\frac{1}{8}$	$-3\frac{5}{8}$	$-8\frac{1}{2}$	$+5\frac{1}{4}$	$+1\frac{7}{8}$
$+\frac{1}{4}$	$+\frac{1}{6}$	$-\frac{1}{2}$	$+\frac{7}{8}$	$-\frac{7}{16}$	$-4\frac{1}{3}$	$-7\frac{3}{4}$	$+1\frac{5}{16}$	$-1\frac{1}{16}$	$+2\frac{1}{2}$

15.

$+.5$	-0.7	-1.5	$+4.1$	$-.72$	$+0.5$	-2.87	$+4.26$	-1.83	-3.01
$+.3$	-1.4	$+0.8$	-3.6	$+.94$	$+8.3$	$+5.09$	$+3.98$	-0.90	$+2.61$

16. Subtract as indicated:

1. $(+8)-(-4)$ 3. $(+4)-(+6)$ 5. $(-5)-(+2)$ 7. $(0)-(6)$ 9. $(5)-(9)$
2. $(-3)-(-3)$ 4. $(+3)-(+1)$ 6. $(-8)-(+12)$ 8. $(4)-(0)$ 10. $(-8)-(7)$

17.
1. From 5 subtract 7.
2. From 6 subtract 13.
3. From 15 take 20.
4. From 32 take 41.
5. From 26 subtract 55.
6. Subtract 8 from 2.
7. Subtract 11 from 9.
8. Take 37 from 23.
9. Subtract 83 from 46.
10. Take 24 from 18.

Miscellaneous Examples

Subtract:

a)

$+7$	-7	$+7$	-7	-7	$+4$	-4	$+4$	-4	0
$+4$	$+4$	-4	-4	0	$+7$	$+7$	-7	-7	-7

b)

$+8$	-6	$+6$	$+9$	-4	0	$+3$	$+1$	-6	$+8$
-3	$+5$	-7	$+8$	-6	$+9$	-5	0	-6	-8

c) Combine the numbers in each set of parentheses, then add or subtract answers as indicated:

1. $(3+2)-(4+6)$
2. $(6-7)-(3-1)$
3. $(4-4)-(8+5)$
4. $(2+10)-(1-6)$
5. $(15-21)-(3-12)$
6. $(5-7)-(1-4)-(8-2)$
7. $(6-1)-(3-5)+(4-7)$
8. $(9-5)+(4+1)-(2-8)$
9. $8+(4-9)-3-(7-2)$
10. $7-(5-1)-(2-6)-4$

Applications

Find the answers by means of signed numbers:

Part 1 — Interesting Facts

1. An ocean depth of 35,640 feet in the Marianas Trench near the island of Guam is the deepest place in the Pacific Ocean. The greatest depth in the Atlantic Ocean is 30,246 feet located near Puerto Rico. Find the difference in their depths.
2. In Asia Mount Everest is the highest point with an elevation of 29,002 feet and the Dead Sea is the lowest point at 1,286 feet below sea level. What is the difference in their altitudes?
3. Mount McKinley in Alaska with an elevation of 20,300 feet is the highest point in North America. Death Valley in California at 282 feet below sea level is the lowest point. Find the difference in their altitudes.
4. If 1 degree of latitude is equivalent to 60 nautical miles, how far does a ship sail due north from Perth, Australia 32° south latitude to Hongkong, China, 22° north latitude?
5. What is the difference between the longitude of Stockholm, Sweden, 18° east longitude and Denver, Colorado, 105° west longitude. Find the difference in sun time if 1 degree of longitude is equivalent to 4 minutes of time.

Part 2 — Changes and Deviations

1. Find the net changes in the prices of the following stocks and indicate them by means of signed numbers:

Stock	Close Tues.	Close Wed.	Net Change	Stock	Close Tues.	Close Wed.	Net Change
Allied Chemical	$43\frac{1}{2}$	$44\frac{5}{8}$		Gulf Oil	$22\frac{1}{4}$	$22\frac{7}{8}$	
Atlantic Richfield	$94\frac{3}{8}$	$96\frac{1}{2}$		RCA	$18\frac{3}{4}$	$18\frac{5}{8}$	
General Electric	$64\frac{3}{4}$	$64\frac{1}{4}$		Sears	89	$88\frac{3}{4}$	
General Motors	$48\frac{3}{4}$	51		Sperry Rand	$49\frac{7}{8}$	$49\frac{1}{4}$	
Grace	$25\frac{3}{8}$	$25\frac{1}{8}$		U.S. Steel	41	$40\frac{1}{4}$	

2. Find the net change in the average retail price of each food and indicate by means of signed numbers:

Item	Ham per lb.	Milk per qt.	Butter per lb.	Potatoes per lb.	Eggs per doz.	Flour per lb.
Cost during a certain week	$1.25	35.6¢	85.4¢	10.4¢	90.6¢	25.6¢
Cost the following week	$1.50	41.3¢	$1.10	9.3¢	$1.05	20.2¢
Net Change						

3. Using the average costs in 1970 to 1973 as the standard of 100%, food in the large United States cities during a certain year cost 112.6%, clothing, 106.9%, housing, 112.4%, transportation, 118.4%, and medical care, 111.1%. If these items during the following year were 114.5%, 105.8%, 114.6%, 126.2%, and 117.2% respectively, what were the net changes for each item. Indicate them by means of signed numbers.

4. Using the hourly temperature report, find:
   a) How many degrees the temperature dropped during the hour from 3 A.M. to 4 A.M.
   b) What temperature change occurred from 6 A.M. to 7 A.M.
   c) How many degrees the temperature rose during the hour from 9 A.M. to 10 A.M.
   d) What temperature change occurred from 2 A.M. to 3 A.M.

Time	Temp.	Time	Temp.
1 A.M.	8	7 A.M.	−6
2 A.M.	6	8 A.M.	−5
3 A.M.	2	9 A.M.	−2
4 A.M.	−1	10 A.M.	2
5 A.M.	−3	11 A.M.	5
6 A.M.	−7	Noon	9

5. a) The record high temperature in Cleveland is 103° and the record low is −17. Find the difference in temperatures.
   b) The lowest temperature recorded in Omaha is −32°. The record low in Boston is −18°. What is the difference in the temperature lows?
   c) The normal temperature in an eastern city for the month of February is 31.2°. The temperature for the same month this year is 29.6°. Represent this deviation from normal by means of a signed number.
   d) The normal precipitation for the month of April in a western city is 1.6 inches. Represent the deviation from normal by a signed number if the precipitation for April last year was 2.3 inches.

Part 3 — Equations

Solve the following equations by the subtraction axiom:

SET 1	SET 2	SET 3	SET 4
1. $n+6=4$	1. $8+r=3$	1. $x+2=-6$	1. $-4=a+8$
2. $x+21=8$	2. $26=m+36$	2. $b+12=-15$	2. $27+c=-27$
3. $d+53=46$	3. $75=90+t$	3. $x+78=-29$	3. $-.95=s+.15$
4. $y+.21=.18$	4. $2\frac{1}{3}+s=1\frac{5}{8}$	4. $t+3.4=-5.2$	4. $-\frac{5}{8}=1\frac{1}{2}+n$
5. $c+6=1$	5. $57=l+98$	5. $y+20=-10$	5. $12+n=-19$

EXERCISE 18
Multiplication of Signed Numbers

I. Aim: To multiply signed numbers.

II. Procedure

1. To multiply two numbers having like signs (both plus or both minus), find their product and prefix it with a plus sign.

This may be illustrated by the following:

If Tom deposits 5 cents each week in the school bank, 3 weeks from now he will have 15 cents more than he has now.

$$\begin{array}{r} +5 \text{ cents} \\ +3 \\ \hline +15 \text{ cents} \end{array}$$

If Tom withdraws 5 cents each week from the school bank, 3 weeks ago he had 15 cents more than he has now.

$$\begin{array}{r} -5 \text{ cents} \\ -3 \\ \hline +15 \text{ cents} \end{array}$$

2. To multiply two numbers having unlike signs (one plus and the other minus), find their product and prefix it with a minus sign.

This may be illustrated by the following:

If Tom withdraws 5 cents each week from the school bank, 3 weeks from now he will have 15 cents less than he has now.

$$\begin{array}{r} -5 \text{ cents} \\ +3 \\ \hline -15 \text{ cents} \end{array}$$

If Tom deposits 5 cents each week in the school bank, 3 weeks ago he had 15 cents less than he has now.

$$\begin{array}{r} +5 \text{ cents} \\ -3 \\ \hline -15 \text{ cents} \end{array}$$

3. The product of a signed number and zero is zero. See sample solutions 5 and 6.

4. Numbers in parentheses written immediately next to each other without any sign of operation infer multiplication. See sample solutions 7, 8, and 9.

5. To multiply three or more signed numbers, find their product. If the number of negative signs is odd, the product is negative. However, if the number of negative signs is even, the product is positive. Thus, an odd power of a negative number is minus and an even power of a negative number is plus. See sample solutions 8, 9, 10, and 11.

III. Sample Solutions

Multiply:

1. $\begin{array}{r} +4 \\ +3 \\ \hline +12 \end{array}$ Ans., $+12$

2. $\begin{array}{r} -8 \\ -2 \\ \hline +16 \end{array}$ Ans., $+16$

3. $\begin{array}{r} +6 \\ -2 \\ \hline -12 \end{array}$ Ans., -12

4. $\begin{array}{r} -2 \\ +5 \\ \hline -10 \end{array}$ Ans., -10

5. $\begin{array}{r} 0 \\ -2 \\ \hline 0 \end{array}$ Ans., 0

6. $\begin{array}{r} +7 \\ 0 \\ \hline 0 \end{array}$ Ans., 0

7. $(-9)(+2) = -18$ Answer, -18

8. $(-3)(5)(-2) = +30$ Answer, $+30$

9. $(-2)(+1)(-3)(-2) = -12$ Answer, -12

10. $(-5)^3 = (-5)(-5)(-5) = -125$ Answer, -125

11. $(-1)^4 = (-1)(-1)(-1)(-1) = +1$ Answer, $+1$

DIAGNOSTIC TEST

Multiply:

1. $\begin{array}{r} +2 \\ +5 \\ \hline \end{array}$

2. $\begin{array}{r} -6 \\ -7 \\ \hline \end{array}$

3. $\begin{array}{r} +3 \\ -4 \\ \hline \end{array}$

4. $\begin{array}{r} -8 \\ +3 \\ \hline \end{array}$

5. $\begin{array}{r} 10 \\ -5 \\ \hline \end{array}$

6. $\begin{array}{r} 0 \\ +2 \\ \hline \end{array}$

7. $6(-5)$

8. $(-9)(+1)$

9. $(-\frac{3}{8})(-\frac{1}{4})$

10. $(+.2)(-.3)$

11. $(-4)(+5)(-2)$

12. $(-2)^3$

Related Practice Examples

Multiply:

1.

+6	+9	+7	+4	+5	+2	+3	+8	+10	+12
+5	+4	+3	+8	+9	+4	+6	+1	+ 9	+ 4

2.

−3	−5	−9	−7	−6	−2	−8	−12	−13	−20
−1	−4	−5	−7	−8	−6	−9	− 3	− 5	− 8

3.

+8	+3	+7	+9	+10	+4	+ 3	+5	+ 2	+15
−2	−9	−5	−4	− 9	−5	−10	−5	−14	− 3

4.

−6	−4	−9	−8	−12	− 7	− 3	−24	−17	−19
5	+7	+6	+7	+ 5	+11	+12	+ 5	+ 4	+10

5.

8	6	4	−12	6	−5	−8	15	−9	− 8
4	−2	−9	− 3	−6	14	−8	−10	6	−15

6.

+4	0	0	−5	−8	4	0	−10	0	0
0	+8	−1	0	0	0	−6	0	+9	+20

7.
1. $9 \times (-3)$
2. $4(-6)$
3. $0 \times (+1)$
4. $(-5) \times 0$
5. $8(-9)$
6. $7(-3)$
7. $-2(-8)$
8. $-9(-6)$
9. $-2(+3)$
10. $8(-1)$

8.
1. $(2)(-1)$
2. $(-8)(+3)$
3. $(-4)(-5)$
4. $(7)(2)$
5. $(0)(-7)$
6. $(+3)(0)$
7. $(-2)(+4)$
8. $(-1)(-1)$
9. $(+8)(-9)$
10. $(-3)(-3)$

9.
1. $\frac{1}{2}(-18)$
2. $\frac{5}{6}(-30)$
3. $\frac{3}{4}(-\frac{2}{3})$
4. $(-\frac{1}{3})(-12)$
5. $(-\frac{5}{8})(+\frac{1}{2})$
6. $(+\frac{1}{4})(-\frac{1}{3})$
7. $(-\frac{3}{5})(-\frac{5}{8})$
8. $(+48)(-\frac{5}{8})$
9. $(-\frac{1}{4})(+\frac{4}{5})$
10. $(-\frac{1}{2})(-\frac{1}{2})$

10.
1. $(-.3)(-.3)$
2. $(-.2)(+7)$
3. $(10)(-.4)$
4. $(-.5)(-.6)$
5. $(+1.4)(-.7)$
6. $(-.25)(100)$
7. $(-.8)(-.01)$
8. $(+9)(-.3)$
9. $(-.8)(-.9)$
10. $(-.03)(+1.5)$

11.
1. $6 \times 2 \times 4$
2. $(8)(5)(-3)$
3. $(-1)(-1)(-1)$
4. $(3)(-2)(-3)$
5. $(-2)(1)(-8)$
6. $(5)(-4)(0)$
7. $(-6)(-5)(3)$
8. $(-2)(-3)(-4)$
9. $(5)(-1)(-2)(-4)$
10. $(-6)(-4)(-4)(-2)$

12.
1. $(+3)^2$
2. $(-5)^2$
3. $(-1)^2$
4. $(-1)^3$
5. $(+1)^4$
6. $(-3)^3$
7. $(-4)^3$
8. $(+5)^4$
9. $(-2)^4$
10. $(-3)^5$

Miscellaneous Examples

Multiply:

a)

−8	+6	9	+2	−4	+5	−3	+4	0	+8
+7	0	5	−2	−4	+8	−6	−5	−10	−2

b)

+6	−6	+6	−6	0	+9	−3	−8	+9	−4
+4	+4	−4	−4	+4	−3	−1	+5	−2	+5

Simplify:

c)
1. $6(4+1)$
2. $7(4-4)$
3. $-5(8+2)$
4. $4(6-9)$
5. $-2(5-6)$
6. $1(6-7)$
7. $6(1+2)-2(4+3)$
8. $4+(8-1)\times 3$
9. $-2(4-7)-(1-2)$
10. $5-3(7-5)+2(3-1)$

Part 1 — Miscellaneous

Applications

Find the answers by means of signed numbers:

1. During the past two months Margaret's baby sister gained on an average 7 ounces per week. Compare her weight 6 weeks ago with her present weight.

2. The normal reduction in the temperature of a parcel of air is 3.6° Fahrenheit for each 1,000 feet it rises. How much less is the temperature at the altitude of 5,000 feet than the surface temperature?

3. If a battery is being discharged at the rate of 15 amperes per hour, how many more amperes of electricity did the battery have 4 hours ago?

4. If the temperature is falling at the rate of 3 degrees per hour, how does the temperature five hours ago compare with the present temperature?

5. The temperature of a parcel of air decreases at the rate of $5\frac{1}{2}$° Fahrenheit for each 1,000 feet it rises following the dry adiabat. How many degrees less is the temperature at an altitude of 8,000 feet than at the surface if the dry adiabatic lapse rate is used?

Part 2 — Equations.

Solve the following equations by the multiplication axiom:

SET 1	SET 2	SET 3
1. $\dfrac{n}{5} = -4$	1. $\dfrac{x}{-6} = 18$	1. $\dfrac{b}{-4} = -20$
2. $\dfrac{a'}{10} = -12$	2. $\dfrac{t}{-2} = 35$	2. $\dfrac{b}{-3} = -3$
3. $\dfrac{r}{2} = -6$	3. $5 = \dfrac{c}{-9}$	3. $\dfrac{d}{-4} = -28$
4. $-24 = \dfrac{d}{8}$	4. $\dfrac{n}{-7} = 7$	4. $-5 = \dfrac{x}{-10}$

EXERCISE 19

Division of Signed Numbers

I. Aim: To divide signed numbers.

II. Procedure

1. To divide two numbers having like signs (both plus or both minus), find their quotient and prefix it with a plus sign.

To divide $+6$ by $+2$ means to find the number which multiplied by $+2$ will equal $+6$.
The answer is $+3$.
$$\frac{+6}{+2} = +3$$

To divide -6 by -2 means to find the number which multiplied by -2 will equal -6.
The answer is $+3$.
$$\frac{-6}{-2} = +3$$

2. To divide two numbers having unlike signs (one plus and the other minus), find their quotient and prefix it with a minus sign.

To divide $+6$ by -2 means to find the number which multiplied by -2 will equal $+6$.
The answer is -3.
$$\frac{+6}{-2} = -3$$

To divide -6 by $+2$ means to find the number which multiplied by $+2$ will equal -6.
The answer is -3.
$$\frac{-6}{+2} = -3$$

3. Zero divided by any signed number is zero. See sample solution 5.

III. Sample Solutions

Divide:

1. $\dfrac{+10}{+5} = +2$ 2. $\dfrac{-21}{-3} = +7$ 3. $\dfrac{-20}{+4} = -5$ 4. $\dfrac{+24}{-12} = -2$ 5. $\dfrac{0}{-7} = 0$ 6. $(-15) \div (-3)$

Answer, +2   Answer, +7   Answer, −5   Answer, −2   Answer, 0   Answer, +5

DIAGNOSTIC TEST

Divide:

1. $\dfrac{+12}{+3}$ 3. $\dfrac{-18}{+6}$ 5. $\dfrac{-9}{+9}$ 7. $\dfrac{0}{+6}$ 9. $(-\tfrac{1}{2}) \div (+\tfrac{3}{4})$

2. $\dfrac{-8}{-4}$ 4. $\dfrac{+24}{-8}$ 6. $\dfrac{-35}{7}$ 8. $(+4) \div (-2)$ 10. $(+3.2) \div (-4)$

11. $-5\overline{)-20}$

Related Practice Examples

Divide:

1. $\dfrac{+8}{+4}$ $\dfrac{+6}{+1}$ $\dfrac{+25}{+5}$ $\dfrac{+24}{+6}$ $\dfrac{+36}{+4}$ $\dfrac{+42}{+14}$ $\dfrac{+50}{+5}$ $\dfrac{+44}{+11}$ $\dfrac{+100}{+20}$ $\dfrac{+80}{+16}$

2. $\dfrac{-8}{-2}$ $\dfrac{-12}{-4}$ $\dfrac{-21}{-7}$ $\dfrac{-27}{-3}$ $\dfrac{-56}{-8}$ $\dfrac{-60}{-10}$ $\dfrac{-48}{-8}$ $\dfrac{-54}{-9}$ $\dfrac{-85}{-5}$ $\dfrac{-90}{-18}$

3. $\dfrac{-6}{+3}$ $\dfrac{-14}{+7}$ $\dfrac{-8}{+1}$ $\dfrac{-30}{+6}$ $\dfrac{-45}{+9}$ $\dfrac{-84}{+12}$ $\dfrac{-72}{+24}$ $\dfrac{-90}{+30}$ $\dfrac{-98}{+49}$ $\dfrac{-54}{+18}$

4. $\dfrac{+9}{-3}$ $\dfrac{+35}{-5}$ $\dfrac{+63}{-7}$ $\dfrac{+72}{-9}$ $\dfrac{+28}{-4}$ $\dfrac{+46}{-2}$ $\dfrac{+45}{-15}$ $\dfrac{+64}{-8}$ $\dfrac{+81}{-27}$ $\dfrac{+100}{-25}$

5. $\dfrac{+4}{+4}$ $\dfrac{-4}{-4}$ $\dfrac{-4}{+4}$ $\dfrac{+4}{-4}$ $\dfrac{-1}{-1}$ $\dfrac{+6}{-6}$ $\dfrac{+10}{-10}$ $\dfrac{-8}{+8}$ $\dfrac{-12}{-12}$ $\dfrac{+17}{-17}$

6. $\dfrac{-10}{2}$ $\dfrac{-32}{8}$ $\dfrac{56}{-7}$ $\dfrac{84}{-6}$ $\dfrac{-100}{4}$ $\dfrac{-5}{5}$ $\dfrac{-78}{3}$ $\dfrac{81}{-9}$ $\dfrac{23}{-1}$ $\dfrac{-40}{10}$

7. $\dfrac{0}{+5}$ $\dfrac{0}{+2}$ $\dfrac{0}{-9}$ $\dfrac{0}{-8}$ $\dfrac{0}{+10}$ $\dfrac{0}{-3}$ $\dfrac{0}{-1}$ $\dfrac{0}{+4}$ $\dfrac{0}{-15}$ $\dfrac{0}{+25}$

8. 1. $(+8) \div (-4)$ 3. $(-27) \div (+3)$ 5. $(66) \div (-11)$ 7. $(-48) \div (-6)$ 9. $(-15) \div (15)$
   2. $(0) \div (-9)$ 4. $(-54) \div (-6)$ 6. $(-100) \div (10)$ 8. $(0) \div (+8)$ 10. $(90) \div (-10)$

9. 1. $(-\tfrac{3}{4}) \div (+\tfrac{1}{8})$ 3. $(-\tfrac{2}{3}) \div (4)$ 5. $(+\tfrac{4}{5}) \div (+6)$ 7. $(-1\tfrac{1}{2}) \div (-\tfrac{1}{6})$ 9. $(-\tfrac{7}{16}) \div (+\tfrac{1}{2})$
   2. $(-\tfrac{5}{8}) \div (-\tfrac{5}{8})$ 4. $(0) \div (-\tfrac{1}{4})$ 6. $(-18) \div (+\tfrac{2}{3})$ 8. $(+6\tfrac{1}{4}) \div (-2\tfrac{1}{2})$ 10. $(-20) \div (-3\tfrac{1}{3})$

10. 1. $(-7.5) \div (+5)$ 3. $(+.48) \div (-4)$ 5. $(-1.9) \div (100)$ 7. $(+3) \div (-.3)$ 9. $(-36) \div (+.04)$
    2. $(-8.1) \div (-.3)$ 4. $(-8) \div (-1.6)$ 6. $(+.06) \div (+2)$ 8. $(-9.5) \div (-.05)$ 10. $(+.45) \div (-.15)$

11. 1. $2\overline{)-8}$ 3. $-6\overline{)-54}$ 5. $-12\overline{)-96}$ 7. $-8\overline{)+1.6}$ 9. $-.2\overline{)+2}$
    2. $-9\overline{)+72}$ 4. $+7\overline{)+42}$ 6. $5\overline{)-65}$ 8. $+.4\overline{)-2.8}$ 10. $-3\overline{)-51}$

Miscellaneous Examples

Divide:

a) $\dfrac{+12}{+4}$ $\dfrac{+12}{-4}$ $\dfrac{-12}{-4}$ $\dfrac{-12}{+4}$ $\dfrac{0}{-4}$ $\dfrac{-5}{+5}$ $\dfrac{4}{-2}$ $\dfrac{7}{-1}$ $\dfrac{-15}{3}$ $\dfrac{48}{-4}$

b) $\dfrac{+6}{+3}$ $\dfrac{-45}{+5}$ $\dfrac{+16}{-4}$ $\dfrac{-36}{-12}$ $\dfrac{-81}{-9}$ $\dfrac{0}{+7}$ $\dfrac{-9}{-1}$ $\dfrac{-3}{-3}$ $\dfrac{20}{-5}$ $\dfrac{-40}{10}$

c) $\dfrac{-1.8}{+6}$ $\dfrac{+.22}{11}$ $\dfrac{+1.4}{+.7}$ $\dfrac{-.56}{+.8}$ $\dfrac{-7.2}{-1.2}$ $\dfrac{+.08}{+.04}$ $\dfrac{+69}{-.23}$ $\dfrac{0}{-.15}$ $\dfrac{-96}{-2.4}$ $\dfrac{+100}{-.5}$

Combine and simplify:

d)

1. $\dfrac{8+6}{7}$
2. $\dfrac{3-7}{2}$
3. $\dfrac{5-1}{-4}$
4. $\dfrac{-8-2}{-2}$
5. $\dfrac{6-3(4)}{3}$
6. $\dfrac{4(-5)+2(10)}{6}$
7. $\dfrac{8(-3)+3(-4)}{2(-3)}$
8. $\dfrac{5(6-3)+4(4-6)}{2(9-2)}$
9. $\dfrac{4(6-5)-6(5-1)}{-8(7+4)}$
10. $\dfrac{(2)^2-(-1)^2}{(3)^2}$

Applications

Part 1 — Averages

Find the answers by means of signed numbers:

1. The fullback of the school football team in five attempts gained 6 yards, gained 3 yards, lost 2 yards, gained 7 yards, and lost 4 yards.

What was his average gain per try?

2. The temperatures reported at 3-hour intervals on a winter day were: 7°, 6°, 2°, −1°, −5°, −4°, 0°, and 3°. Find the average temperature.

3. The net changes of a certain stock during a week were: $-1\frac{5}{8}$, $+2\frac{3}{8}$, $+1$, $-\frac{1}{8}$, and $+\frac{7}{8}$. What was the average net change?

4. A merchant lost $9.75 on one transaction, $4.50 on another, and $8.25 on a third. Find the average loss per transaction.

5. The hourly temperatures for a 12-hour period were: 12°, 7°, 5°, 2°, 0°, −1°, −3°, −4°, −2°, 0°, 3° and 5°. What was the average temperature?

Part 2 — Equations

Solve the following equations by the division axiom:

SET 1	SET 2	SET 3	SET 4
1. $5n=-30$	1. $-4r=28$	1. $-3a=-42$	1. $-n=8$
2. $8b=-56$	2. $45=-5c$	2. $-14d=-35$	2. $20=-y$
3. $-16=24x$	3. $-9n=9$	3. $-72=-8x$	3. $-x=-2$
4. $.04y=-32$	4. $\frac{1}{4}x=-11$	4. $-90=-10n$	4. $-40=-g$
5. $15t=-600$	5. $80m=-48$	5. $-15s=-75$	5. $-c=31$

EXERCISE 20
Evaluation—Simple Expressions

I. **Aim:** To evaluate simple algebraic expressions using signed numbers.

II. **Procedure**

1. Same as Exercise 2.

2. If necessary, use operation rules for signed numbers.

III. **Sample Solutions**

Find the value of the following expressions if $a=4$, $b=-2$, and $c=-5$:

1. $b+c$
$=(-2)+(-5)$
$=-7$
Answer, -7

2. $b-c$
$=(-2)-(-5)$
$=+3$
Answer, $+3$

3. ac
$=(4)(-5)$
$=-20$
Answer, -20

4. $\dfrac{a}{b}$
$=\dfrac{4}{-2}$
$=-2$
Answer, -2

5. $-4ab$
$=-4(4)(-2)$
$=32$
Answer, 32

6. $2a-3bc+5ac$
$=2(4)-3(-2)(-5)+5(4)(-5)$
$=8-30-100$
$=-122$
Answer, -122

DIAGNOSTIC TEST

Find the value of the following algebraic expressions if $a=8$, $b=-2$, and $c=-1$:

1. $a+b$
2. $a-b$
3. ab
4. $\dfrac{a}{b}$
5. $b+c$
6. $b-c$
7. bc
8. $\dfrac{b}{c}$
9. $3b$
10. $-5c$
11. $3ac$
12. $2a-5b+3c$
13. $5ac-2ab-3bc$
14. $4bc-ac+5$
15. $\dfrac{2ab-3bc}{2c}$
16. $\dfrac{3ac-4bc+8}{3a-ab}$

Related Practice Examples

Find the value of the following algebraic expressions if

A
$m=6$, $n=-4$, and $x=-2$

1. $m+n$
2. $m-n$
3. mn
4. $\dfrac{m}{n}$
5. $n+x$
6. $n-x$

B
$b=6$, $c=-3$, and $d=-2$

1. $b+c$
2. $b-c$
3. bc
4. $\dfrac{b}{c}$
5. $c+d$
6. $c-d$

C
$a=-2$, $x=-10$, and $y=5$

1. $x+y$
2. $y-x$
3. xy
4. $\dfrac{x}{y}$
5. $a+x$
6. $a-x$

A	B	C
$m=6$, $n=-4$, and $x=-2$	$b=6$, $c=-3$, and $d=-2$	$a=-2$, $x=-10$, and $y=5$

A $m=6$, $n=-4$, and $x=-2$

7. nx

8. $\dfrac{n}{x}$

9. $5n$
10. $-4x$
11. $2mx$
12. $4m-6n$
13. $2mn-nx+3mx$
14. $5mx-4x-2$

15. $\dfrac{2m-3x}{3}$

16. $\dfrac{4n-5x+16}{m-n}$

B $b=6$, $c=-3$, and $d=-2$

7. cd

8. $\dfrac{c}{d}$

9. $2c$
10. $-3d$
11. $5bd$
12. $3b+5c-3d$
13. $4bc-2cd-5bd$
14. $3bd-5cd+4$

15. $\dfrac{5c-2cd}{c}$

16. $\dfrac{2cd-5bd+3bc}{4b-2c}$

C $a=-2$, $x=-10$, and $y=5$

7. ax

8. $\dfrac{a}{x}$

9. $4x$
10. $-5a$
11. $-6ay$
12. $5a-4x-3y$
13. $3ax-2xy-6ay$
14. $4ay-ax-1$

15. $\dfrac{3ax-2xy}{2ax}$

16. $\dfrac{2xy+ax-5ay}{4ax-3xy}$

Applications

I. Find the value of:

1. A if $C=-8$, using the formula $A=C+273$.
2. F if $C=-40$, using the formula $F=1.8C+32$.
3. C if $A=725$ and $L=950$, using the formula $C=A-L$.
4. v if $a=-30$ and $t=2$, using the formula $v=at$.

5. M if $a=-8$, $b=3$, and $c=-10$, using the formula $M=\dfrac{a+b+c}{3}$.

6. Find the Centigrade temperature reading that is equal to 100° Absolute temperature. Use formula $C=A-273$.

7. The assets of a certain business are \$3,980 and the liabilities amount to \$5,245. Find the capital or net worth of the business. Use formula $C=A-L$

8. Find the Centigrade temperature when the Fahrenheit temperature is 5°. Use formula $C=\dfrac{5F-160}{9}$.

9. What is the average or median of the scores 8, -4, 10, and -2?

10. Find the Fahrenheit temperature when the Centigrade temperature is $-35°$. Use formula $F=\frac{9}{5}C+32$.

II. Solve and check:

SET 1	SET 2	SET 3	SET 4
1. $x-8=-6$	1. $a+7=5$	1. $r+6=-4$	1. $4x=-8$
2. $c-10=-7$	2. $x+16=9$	2. $x+89=-38$	2. $9b=-72$
3. $-12=d-4$	3. $7+g=2$	3. $-3=a+9$	3. $-10=15m$
4. $-225=A-150$	4. $26=90+t$	4. $y+11=-17$	4. $.08c=-6$
5. $y-9=-9$	5. $49=p+63$	5. $4+x=-13$	5. $12m=-168$

SET 5	SET 6	SET 7	SET 8
1. $-3a=12$	1. $-7c=-21$	1. $-x=4$	1. $\dfrac{x}{6}=-7$
2. $-5d=5$	2. $-18g=-45$	2. $13=-n$	2. $-8=\dfrac{s}{16}$
3. $56=-8x$	3. $-4r=-3$	3. $-s=-1$	3. $\dfrac{a}{-4}=20$
4. $-\frac{1}{2}y=25$	4. $-63=-9x$	4. $-25=-l$	4. $\dfrac{n}{-3}=-12$
5. $-48t=32$	5. $-20a=-100$	5. $-y=40$	5. $\dfrac{d}{-8}=-8$

EXERCISE 21

Evaluation—Expressions Involving Parentheses

I. Aim: To evaluate algebraic expressions involving parentheses and using signed numbers.

II. Procedure

1. Same as Exercise 3.

2. If necessary, use operation rules for signed numbers.

III. Sample Solutions

Find the value of the following expressions if $m=-6$, $n=-2$, and $x=3$:

1. $2m(3n-5x)$
   $=-12(-6-15)$
   $=-12(-21)$
   $=+252$
   Answer, $+252$

2. $m+x+(m-n)$
   $=-6+3+(-6+2)$
   $=-6+3+(-4)$
   $=-7$
   Answer, -7

3. $m-n(m-x)$
   $=-6+2(-6-3)$
   $=-6+2(-9)$
   $=-6-18$
   $=-24$
   Answer, -24

DIAGNOSTIC TEST

Find the value of the following algebraic expressions if $a=4$, $m=-5$, and $x=-2$:

1. $2(a+m)$
2. $-5(a-m)$
3. $-4(m+x)$
4. $(2a+5x)$
5. $a(m-2x)$
6. $x(am+5m)$
7. $2mx(3m-4ax)$
8. $5x+(4m-6mx)$
9. $a+m+(m-x)$
10. $a+m(m-x)$
11. $(a+m)(m-x)$
12. $\dfrac{2(3a-6x)}{a(m-x)}$

Related Practice Examples

Find the value of the following algebraic expressions if

A	B	C
$a=2$, $b=-4$, and $c=-1$	$x=8$, $y=-4$, and $z=-2$	$r=2$, $s=-10$, and $t=-5$
1. $3(a+b)$	1. $4(y+z)$	1. $2(r+s)$
2. $-4(a-c)$	2. $-5(x-z)$	2. $-3(r-s)$
3. $-2(b+c)$	3. $-6(y+z)$	3. $-5(s-t)$
4. $(2a-5b)$	4. $(3x+7y)$	4. $(2s-4t)$
5. $a(b-6c)$	5. $x(y-2z)$	5. $r(s+2t)$
6. $b(3a+b)$	6. $z(xz-2y)$	6. $-t(rs-st)$
7. $3ac(2a-5bc)$	7. $-4yz(xy+2xz)$	7. $2rt(3s-5rs)$
8. $2b+(a-c)$	8. $3x+(y+5z)$	8. $-4t-(2r+3s)$
9. $a+b+(a-c)$	9. $x-z+(2y+z)$	9. $r+s-(s-t)$
10. $a+b(a-c)$	10. $x-z(2y+z)$	10. $r+s(s-t)$
11. $(a+b)(a-c)$	11. $(x-z)(2y+z)$	11. $(r+s)(s-t)$
12. $\dfrac{4(a+b)}{a(b-2c)}$	12. $\dfrac{x(y+2z)}{4(x+xz)}$	12. $\dfrac{2r(s-3t)}{5(2s-3t)}$

EXERCISE 22

Evaluation—Expressions Involving Exponents

I. Aim: To evaluate algebraic expressions involving exponents and using signed numbers.

II. Procedure

1. Same as Exercise 4.   2. If necessary, use operation rules for signed numbers.

III. Sample Solutions

Find the value of the following expressions if $a = -4$, and $x = -3$:

1. a^2	2. x^3	3. x^4	4. $6ax^2$	5. $a^2 - 2ax + x^2$
$= (-4)^2$	$= (-3)^3$	$= (-3)^4$	$= 6(-4)(-3)^2$	$= (-4)^2 - 2(-4)(-3) + (-3)^2$
$= 16$	$= -27$	$= 81$	$= 6(-4)(9)$	$= 16 - 24 + 9$
Answer, 16	Answer, -27	Answer, 81	Answer, -216	Answer, 1

DIAGNOSTIC TEST

Find the value of the following algebraic expressions if $c = 4$, $d = -6$, and $x = -3$:

1. d^2

2. $-2x^2$

3. $c^2 d$

4. x^3

5. $d^3 x^2$

6. $2c^2 - 3d^2$

7. $d^2 x + dx^2$

8. $d^2 - 3d - 4$

9. $d^2 - 2dx + x^2$

10. $\dfrac{3d^2}{2x^3}$

11. $\dfrac{x^2 - 4x - 5}{x^2 - 1}$

12. $\dfrac{c^2}{4} - \dfrac{d^2}{9}$

Related Practice Examples

Find the value of the following algebraic expressions if

A	B	C
$a = 3$, $c = -4$, and $y = -3$	$b = 4$, $x = -2$, and $y = -1$	$d = 8$, $m = -6$, and $n = -2$
1. c^2	1. x^2	1. m^2
2. $-5y^2$	2. $-3y^2$	2. $-2n^2$
3. $a^2 c$	3. $b^2 x$	3. mn^2
4. y^3	4. y^3	4. $-n^3$
5. $c^3 y^2$	5. $x^3 y^2$	5. $m^3 n^2$
6. $3a^2 - 2c^2$	6. $2b^2 - 5y^2$	6. $2d^2 - 3mn$
7. $c^2 y + cy^2$	7. $x^2 y - xy^2$	7. $m^2 n - mn^2$
8. $c^2 + 5c - 6$	8. $x^2 - 8x - 2$	8. $m^2 - 5m + 6$
9. $c^2 - 2cy + y^2$	9. $x^2 - 5xy - 2y^2$	9. $m^2 - 3mn - 4n^2$
10. $\dfrac{c^2}{y^3}$	10. $\dfrac{2b^2}{x^3}$	10. $\dfrac{d^2}{2mn}$
11. $\dfrac{y^2 - 3y - 3}{y^2 - 4}$	11. $\dfrac{x^2 - 4xy - 3y^2}{x - y}$	11. $\dfrac{m^2 + mn - 6n^2}{m^2 - 2n^2}$
12. $\dfrac{a^2}{3} + \dfrac{c^2}{8}$	12. $\dfrac{x^2}{2} - \dfrac{b^2}{4}$	12. $\dfrac{m^2}{3} - \dfrac{5n^2}{2}$

REVIEW OF UNIT FIVE

1. (a) If $+3\%$ means an increase of 3% in the cost of living, what does -5% mean?
   (b) If a head wind of 36 m.p.h. is indicated by -36 m.p.h., how can a tail wind of 25 m.p.h. be indicated?

2. Select a reasonable scale, mark off and label points indicating the following temperature readings: 2 A.M., $-6°$; 6 A.M., $-8°$; 10 A.M., $-3°$; 2 P.M., $7°$; 6 P.M., $5°$; 10 P.M., $-1°$.

3. Add the following: $+8 \quad -2 \quad +7 \quad -10 \quad -8$
   $\quad\quad\quad\quad\quad\quad\quad -9 \quad -6 \quad +5 \quad +7 \quad +8$

5. Multiply the following: $-4 \quad +7 \quad -2 \quad +8 \quad 0$
   $\quad\quad\quad\quad\quad\quad\quad\quad\quad -3 \quad -5 \quad +2 \quad +1 \quad -9$

4. Subtract the following: $+5 \quad -3 \quad 0 \quad -9 \quad +6$
   $\quad\quad\quad\quad\quad\quad\quad\quad +6 \quad -8 \quad +3 \quad +5 \quad -6$

6. Divide the following: $\dfrac{+16}{-2} \quad \dfrac{-20}{+4} \quad \dfrac{-56}{-8} \quad \dfrac{0}{-1} \quad \dfrac{+12}{+12}$

7. (a) Combine: $7-9+3-6+8$ (b) Subtract 11 from 5.

8. Find the value of F if $C = -40$, using the formula $F = \frac{9}{5}C + 32$.

9. The record high temperature in Nashville is $106°$ and the record low is $-6°$. Find the difference in the temperatures.

10. Use signed numbers to show how the temperature three hours ago compares to the present temperature if the temperature is falling at the rate of 2 degrees per hour.

CUMULATIVE ALGEBRA REVIEW

1. Express as a formula: The area of a triangle (A) is equal to one half the product of the altitude (a) and the base (b).

2. How many ounces are in 3 lb.? 7 lb.? Write a formula stating the number of ounces (z) in P pounds.

Solve and check: 3. $3x = 84$,   4. $25 + g = 61$,   5. $m - 7 = 19$,   6. $\frac{c}{12} = 6$,   7. $3a + 11 = 50$.

8. Find the value of d when $l = 39$, $a = 7$, and $n = 9$, using the formula $l = a + (n-1)d$.

9. If the area of a rectangular building lot is advertised to be 1,850 square feet with a frontage (width) of 25 feet, what is its depth (length)?   10. 40% of what number is 18?

11. If 1.5 inches of rainfall above normal is represented by $+1.5$ in., how can 2.3 inches of rainfall below normal be represented?

12. (a) Add, (b) subtract; (c) multiply: 13. Divide the following:

$\begin{array}{ccccc} +8 & +5 & -9 & -3 & +4 \\ -13 & +7 & +1 & -8 & -4 \end{array}$ $\dfrac{-12}{-3} \quad \dfrac{+5}{-1} \quad \dfrac{-6}{+6} \quad \dfrac{+48}{+8} \quad \dfrac{0}{-4}$

14. (a) Combine: $6-8+3-7-2+4-1$.   (b) Find value of expression $2a^2 - 3ab + b^2$ when $a = 4$ and $b = -3$.

15. The assets of a certain business are $6,150. The liabilities are $8,225. Find the capital or net worth of the business, using signed numbers.

KEYED ACHIEVEMENT TEST

1. Express as a formula: The sum of angles A, B, C, and D of quadrilateral $ABCD$ is equal to $360°$. ①

2. Solve and check: $9b - 5 = 49$. ⑪

3. Find the value of t if $v = 314$, $V = 26$, and $g = 32$, using the formula $v = V + gt$. ⑫

4. How long will it take $5,000 invested at the annual rate of 2% to bring $1,500 simple interest? ⑬

5. If a charge of 6 amperes of electricity is represented by $+6$ amperes, how can a discharge of 4 amperes of electricity be represented? ⑭

6. Add: -5 7. Subtract: -4 8. Multiply: ⑱   9. Divide: $\dfrac{-63}{+9}$
   ⑯ $\underline{-9}$ ⑰ $\underline{-7}$ $(-3)(+2)(-5)$ ⑲

10. Find the value of the expression $x^2 - 3x - 4$ when $x = -2$. ㉒

INTRODUCTION TO UNIT SIX

Before a student may proceed further in his study of algebra, he must learn how to add, subtract, multiply, and divide algebraic expressions. This knowledge is essential in the solution of the many different types of equations studied in algebra which include the simple equation, fractional equation, literal equation, quadratic equation, and systems of equations. The solution of practical problems also requires the use of these algebraic operational techniques and skills since the solution of verbal problems and the evaluation of formulas depend upon the equation.

In this unit many technical algebraic words are used. Although some of them have been used in the preceding units, their meanings are reviewed together with the meanings of new words.

1. An *algebraic expression* is an expression composed of arithmetic numbers, letters, and signs of operation. $6a^2 - 3ab + b^2$ is an algebraic expression.

2. A *term* is an arithmetic number, letter, group of letters, or group composed of an arithmetic number and letters which are joined by multiplication or division. 9, s, cd, $8x^2y$ are terms.

3. A *term of an expression* is that part of it which is connected to the other parts of the expression by either a plus or minus sign. In the expression $2x + 3$, $2x$ is one term, 3 is another term.

4. A *monomial* is an algebraic expression of one term. The terms $6y^2$ or $-mx$ are monomials.

5. A *binomial* is an algebraic expression of two terms. The expressions $7b + 5$ or $3c - 2d$ are binomials.

6. A *trinomial* is an algebraic expression of three terms. The expression $3c^2 - 5cd + 6d^2$ is a trinomial.

7. A *polynomial* is an algebraic expression of one or more terms. Binomials and trinomials are special types of polynomials. Although a monomial is considered a polynomial, it is treated separately in this book.

8. A *factor* is any one of two or more numbers that are multiplied together. Since $3 \times 7 = 21$, 3 and 7 are factors of 21.

9. If two factors form a product, either factor is the *coefficient* of the other. In the product $8m$, 8 is the coefficient of m and m is the coefficient of 8.

10. The number factor of a product is the *numerical coefficient* of the remaining factors. The numerical coefficient of t^2 in the term $16t^2$ is 16. When the numerical coefficient is not given, one (1) is understood. The numerical coefficient of xy in the term xy is 1.

11. The letter factor of a product is the *literal factor*. The literal factor in the product $6x$ is x.

12. *Like terms* or *similar terms* are terms which have the same literal factors. They may differ in their numerical coefficients. $5mn$ and $2mn$ are like terms.

13. *Unlike terms* are terms which have different literal factors. $4x$ and $9y$ are unlike terms.

14. An *exponent* is the small number written to the right and a little above a quantity to show how many times the quantity is used as a factor in multiplication.

15. The *power* of a number is the product obtained when a number is multiplied by itself one or more times. x^2 is read x squared or x to the second power, x^3 is read x cubed or x to the third power, x^4 is read x fourth or x to the fourth power, x^5 is read x fifth or x to the fifth power, etc.

16. The *base* is the literal or arithmetic number that is multiplied by itself one or more times. c is the base in the term c^7, 10 is the base in the term 10^4.

17. A polynomial is expressed in *descending powers* of one of the literal numbers if the terms are arranged so that the exponents of this literal number decrease from term to term, starting from the left. The terms of the polynomial $x^3 - 5x^2 + 3x - 4$ are arranged in descending powers of x. When the exponents of the literal number increase from term to term, the polynomial is said to be expressed in *ascending powers* of that literal number. The terms of the polynomial $6 + 4y - 7y^2 + 2y^3$ are arranged in ascending powers of y.

18. The processes of addition and multiplication are *commutative*. That is: One number added to a second number will give the same answer as the second number added to the first. $6 + 2 = 2 + 6$ or $a + b = b + a$. Also, one number multiplied by a second number will give the same answer as the second number multiplied by the first. $6 \times 2 = 2 \times 6$ or $ab = ba$. See page 7S for other number properties.

UNIT SIX—FUNDAMENTAL OPERATIONS
ADDITION
EXERCISE 23
Addition of Monomials

I. Aim: To add monomials.

II. Procedure

1. To add similar terms, find the algebraic sum of the numerical coefficients and prefix it to their common literal factors.

2. The addition of terms which are not similar can only be indicated. Their sum cannot be written as a single sum. See sample solutions 8 and 9.
   Note: a) $1x$ is written as x (the coefficient 1 is understood).
   b) $0x$ is equal to 0.

3. Check by adding again or by numerical substitution.

III. Sample Solutions

1. $$\begin{array}{r} +6b \\ +2b \\ \hline +8b \end{array}$$
   Answer, $+8b$

2. $$\begin{array}{r} -4x^3 \\ -3x^3 \\ \hline -7x^3 \end{array}$$
   Answer, $-7x^3$

3. $$\begin{array}{r} +6ab \\ -\ ab \\ \hline +5ab \end{array}$$
   Answer, $+5ab$

4. $$\begin{array}{r} -5x^2y \\ +4x^2y \\ \hline -\ x^2y \end{array}$$
   Answer, $-x^2y$

5. $$\begin{array}{r} -3ax \\ +3ax \\ \hline 0 \end{array}$$
   Answer, 0

6. $$\begin{array}{r} -2cd^2 \\ +5cd^2 \\ -\ cd^2 \\ \hline +2cd^2 \end{array}$$
   Answer, $+2cd^2$

7. $$\begin{array}{r} 2(x+y) \\ -3(x+y) \\ -4(x+y) \\ \hline -5(x+y) \end{array}$$
   Answer, $-5(x+y)$

8. $$\begin{array}{r} x^2 \\ +3x \\ \hline x^2+3x \end{array}$$
   Answer, x^2+3x

9. Find the sum of:
   $2a$, $-4b$, and $3c$.
   Answer, $2a-4b+3c$

10. Combine: $4x-9x+2x$
   Think $+4x$ added to $-9x$ added to $+2x$
   Answer, $-3x$

11. Check of example 6 by numerical substitution:
   If $c=2$ and $d=3$, then
   $$\begin{array}{r} -2cd^2 = -2\cdot2\cdot9 = -36 \\ +5cd^2 = +5\cdot2\cdot9 = +90 \\ -\ cd^2 = -\ \ 2\cdot9 = -18 \\ \hline +2cd^2 = +2\cdot2\cdot9 = +36 \end{array}$$

Note: If the answer is correct, the sum of the numerical values of the addends should equal the numerical value of the answer.

DIAGNOSTIC TEST

Add:

1. $+6m$ $+4m$	5. $-3b^2$ $5b^2$	9. $-5s^2$ $+4s^2$	13. $-4a^2b$ $+6a^2b$ $-5a^2b$	17. $-.4b$ $+.2b$
2. $-5x$ $-3x$	6. $-6ax$ $-3ax$	10. $+2dx$ $-2dx$	14. $-7x$ $2x$ $4x$ $-x$	18. x^2 $+x$
3. $+3b$ $-7b$	7. $-x$ $-x$	11. 0 $+y$	15. $6(a+b)$ $-3(a+b)$ $4(a+b)$	19. Find the sum of b^3, b^2, and $-2b$
4. $-8a$ $+2a$	8. $3c$ $-c$	12. $-4a^3b^2x$ $+7a^3b^2x$	16. $+\frac{1}{2}ax$ $+\frac{1}{2}ax$	20. Combine: $2y-5y+6y-4y$

Related Practice Examples

Add:

1. $+8a$ / $+2a$ $+5x$ / $+7x$ $+9y$ / $+6y$ $+15c$ / $+8c$ $+6b$ / $+6b$ $5m$ / $4m$ $2b$ / $7b$ $9x$ / $15x$ $21y$ / $14y$ $27a$ / $34a$

2. $-2d$ / $-5d$ $-3b$ / $-2b$ $-7x$ / $-4x$ $-9z$ / $-5z$ $-8m$ / $-8m$ $-2s$ / $-10s$ $-12r$ / $-7r$ $-6t$ / $-14t$ $-18x$ / $-12x$ $-50y$ / $-20y$

3. $+6x$ / $-4x$ $+8c$ / $-5c$ $+7m$ / $-9m$ $+3h$ / $-8h$ $+5n$ / $-9n$ $+8b$ / $-11b$ $+15y$ / $-5y$ $+23z$ / $-10z$ $+13t$ / $-25t$ $+18s$ / $-21s$

4. $-8y$ / $+3y$ $-9a$ / $+6a$ $-4c$ / $+6c$ $-2x$ / $+8x$ $-3k$ / $+7k$ $-9m$ / $+4m$ $-5d$ / $+10d$ $-16t$ / $+24t$ $-17r$ / $+12r$ $-33x$ / $+41x$

5. $+3a^2$ / $+2a^2$ $-6x^2$ / $-4x^2$ $+8c^2$ / $-6c^2$ $-7x^3$ / $+9x^3$ $5y^4$ / $5y^4$ $-4b^3$ / $7b^3$ $5c^5$ / $-2c^5$ $-8x^2$ / $-4x^2$ $-15y^3$ / $7y^3$ $12m^4$ / $-16m^4$

6. $+4xy$ / $+5xy$ $-6ab$ / $+8ab$ $-4cd$ / $-4cd$ $+5bc$ / $-8bc$ $6mn$ / $7mn$ $9x^2y$ / $-13x^2y$ $-5ab^2$ / $11ab^2$ $-2a^2x$ / $-7a^2x$ $4bx^2$ / $-9bx^2$ $-15x^2y^2$ / $6x^2y^2$

7. $+a$ / $+a$ $-d$ / $-d$ $+x$ / $+x$ $-m$ / $-m$ c / c $+a^2$ / $+a^2$ $-x^2$ / $-x^2$ $-bx$ / $-bx$ $+abc$ / $+abc$ $-x^2y^2$ / $-x^2y^2$

8. $+4b$ / $-b$ $-8x$ / $+x$ $+3ab$ / $+ab$ $-7x^2$ / $-x^2$ $+x$ / $-5x$ $-a$ / $+9a$ x^2 / $6x^2$ $-9xy$ / $-xy$ $-a^2x$ / $5a^2x$ $6a^2b^2$ / $-a^2b^2$

9.

$+3x$	$-5b$	$-4y$	$+6m$	$-2d$	$+9x^2$	$-4am$	$3nx$	$11a^2b$	$-15m^2n^2$
$-2x$	$+6b$	$+3y$	$-7m$	$+d$	$-8x^2$	$5am$	$-4nx$	$-10a^2b$	$14m^2n^2$

10.

$+b$	x^2	$-a^2b^2$	$+5x$	$-2a$	$9bx$	$-6m^2$	$4x^2$	$7a^2y$	$-3x^2y^2$
$-b$	$-x^2$	a^2b^2	$-5x$	$+2a$	$-9bx$	$6m^2$	$-4x^2$	$-7a^2y$	$3x^2y^2$

11.

$+x$	$-b$	$-2b$	$3a^2$	$-5a^2x^2$	0	0	0	0	0
0	0	0	0	0	$+c$	$-m$	$-4x$	$2y^2$	$-7b^2y^2$

12.

$+6a^2bx$	$-9ax^4y^2$	$+8a^2b^3m$	$-5b^2c^5d^6$	$9x^5y^2z^4$
$+4a^2bx$	$-2ax^4y^2$	$-3a^2b^3m$	$+3b^2c^5d^6$	$7x^5y^2z^4$

$-a^4c^3y^2$	$-5m^2x^4y$	$-6a^4b^2x^2$	$+3m^3x^2y$	$-5bm^3x^2$
$-a^4c^3y^2$	$-m^2x^4y$	$+6a^4b^2x^2$	$-4m^3x^2y$	$-5bm^3x^2$

13.

$+5x$	$-3a$	$+5xy$	$-7a^2$	$-x$
$+2x$	$-4a$	$+2xy$	$-5a^2$	$5x$
$+4x$	$-a$	$-3xy$	$+3a^2$	$-x$

$-2ab^2$	$-3x^2y^2$	$-8a^2b^2c^2$	$+ab^3c$	a^4m^3x
$-3ab^2$	$+5x^2y^2$	$+4a^2b^2c^2$	$-2ab^3c$	a^4m^3x
$-4ab^2$	$-8x^2y^2$	$+5a^2b^2c^2$	$-2ab^3c$	$-3a^4m^3x$

14.

$-2x$	$-xy$	$+4b^2$	$-5a^2x$	$-5c^2d^4x^3$
$+8x$	$-2xy$	$+2b^2$	$+2a^2x$	$-2c^2d^4x^3$
$-5x$	$+3xy$	$-5b^2$	$-4a^2x$	$+3c^2d^4x^3$
$+4x$	$-xy$	$-b^2$	$+9a^2x$	$+c^2d^4x^3$

15.

$5(c+d)$	$-9(x-y)$	$8(s-a)$	$-4(s-a+b)$	$-12(a+b-c)$
$3(c+d)$	$6(x-y)$	$-5(s-a)$	$-2(s-a+b)$	$-4(a+b-c)$
		$3(s-a)$	$+7(s-a+b)$	$9(a+b-c)$

16.

$+\frac{1}{3}x$	$-\frac{3}{4}x$	$-\frac{3}{4}b^2$	$-4\frac{1}{2}ab$	$-2\frac{1}{2}x^3y^2$
$+\frac{1}{2}x$	$-\frac{1}{2}x$	$-1\frac{1}{4}b^2$	$+3\frac{5}{8}ab$	$-1\frac{3}{4}x^3y^2$

17.

$+.3a$	$-1.6x$	$+7.3bc$	$-3.2m^2n$	$.4bx^2$
$+.9a$	$-.4x$	$-3.9bc$	$+.8m^2n$	$-6.2bx^2$

18.

$+x$	$-5x$	x^2	$2a^3$	b
$+3$	y	$+2x$	$3a^2$	-5

$-c$	d^2+d	x^3	b^2-5b	$3a^2$ $+7$
$-x$	-7	$-x^2+x$	-4	$+2a$

19. Find the sum of:

1. $+5c$ and $+3d$.
2. $-8r$ and $+5$.
3. $-a$ and $+b$.
4. $3x$ and $2y$.
5. $6x^2$ and $4x$.
6. $+4a$ and $-2b$.
7. $3x$ and -4.
8. x^3, $2x^2$, and $-3x$.
9. $-7b^3$, $-2b^2$, and $-5b$.
10. $8w$, $-2x$, $-5y$, and $6z$.

20.

Combine: (a)

1. $8b+3b$
2. $9xy+15xy$
3. $\frac{1}{2}c+\frac{3}{4}t$
4. $1.5a+2.3a$
5. $6y^2-4y^2$
6. $3d-9d$
7. $x-7x$
8. $4.1n-2.6n$
9. $a+.05a$
10. $p-.06p$

(b)

1. $5x+6x+2x$
2. $8m-7m+m$
3. $2a^2-5a^2-3a^2$
4. $cd+6cd-9cd$
5. $x+3x+7x$
6. $-xy^2+2xy^2-4xy^2$
7. $6b^2+2b^2-8b^2$
8. $-l-3l-2l$
9. $4m^2n^2-m^2n^2+3m^2n^2$
10. $8r^3-10r^3+6r^3$

(c)

1. $2x-3x-x+4x$
2. $4y-8y+6y-4y$
3. $5a+6a-3a-a$
4. $-x^2+2x^2-x^2-3x^2+6x^2$
5. $ab+7ab-2ab+ab-4ab$
6. $2x^2y-3x^2y-x^2y+x^2y-3x^2y$
7. $4t-2t-6t+3t+t-5t$
8. $6R+8R-4R-7R+3R-9R$
9. $7m^4x^2-m^4x^2-2m^4x^2+3m^4x^2-m^4x^2$
10. $2cr-5cr+7cr+cr-6cr+2cr$

Applications

1. Find the perimeters of the following figures in terms of the literal dimensions:

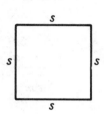
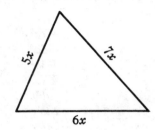
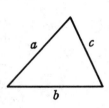
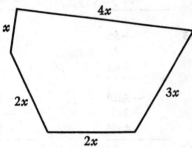

2. Find the sum of the angles in each of the following figures expressed in terms of the literal angular measure:

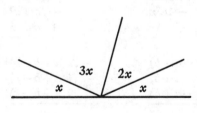
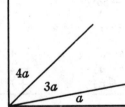
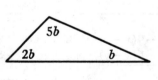
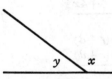

3. To solve the following equations, combine similar terms then use the division axiom. Check each root.

SET 1

1. $x+x=18$
2. $2m+3m=75$
3. $42=8b+6b$
4. $81=2y+y$
5. $7r+5r=132$

SET 2

1. $6a-a=85$
2. $3s-s=94$
3. $54=5w-2w$
4. $10e-2e=72$
5. $9n-3n=78$

SET 3

1. $3c+c+2c=96$
2. $4l-5l+3l=38$
3. $84=x+8x-2x$
4. $a+9a-6a=56$
5. $-y-7y+16y=112$

4. Magic Squares

A square subdivided into an odd number of squares on a side, each containing a number, is called a magic square provided the sum of each column, row, and diagonal of numbers is the same.

Find the sum of each column, row, and diagonal in the following squares to determine which are magic squares:

$7x$	$2x$	$9x$
$8x$	$6x$	$4x$
$3x$	$10x$	$5x$

$3d$	$-4d$	$5d$
$2d$	d	d
$-d$	$7d$	$-2d$

$-7a$	$-12a$	$-5a$
$-6a$	$-8a$	$-10a$
$-11a$	$-4a$	$-9a$

EXERCISE 24
Addition of Polynomials

I. **Aim**: To add polynomials.

II. **Procedure**

1. If the polynomials are so arranged that similar terms are in vertical columns, then add each column.

2. Otherwise, place one polynomial under the other so that similar terms are in vertical columns, then add each column.

3. In some cases it will be necessary to rewrite the polynomials in descending powers or ascending powers of one letter.
   Note: a) If the sum of a vertical column is zero, it will be unnecessary to write the zero if the sum of one or more of the other columns is not zero.
   b) If the sums of all vertical columns are zero, only one zero is written in the result.

4. Check by adding again or by numerical substitution.

III. **Sample Solutions**

1.
$$2x^2 - 3xy + 5y^2$$
$$x^2 + 2xy - 3y^2$$
$$-5x^2 + 5xy - y^2$$
$$\overline{-2x^2 + 4xy + y^2}$$

Answer, $-2x^2 + 4xy + y^2$

2.
$$3a + 5b - 4c$$
$$2a - 5b - 4c$$
$$\overline{5a \qquad - 8c}$$

Answer, $5a - 8c$

3.
$$3x - 2y + 7$$
$$x - 3y - 4$$
$$-4x + 5y - 3$$
$$\overline{0}$$

Answer, 0

4. Find the sum of $a^2 - b^2$, $2a^2 - 3ab + b^2$, and $5ab - a^2 + b^2$

$$a^2 \qquad - b^2$$
$$2a^2 - 3ab + b^2$$
$$- a^2 + 5ab + b^2$$
$$\overline{2a^2 + 2ab + b^2}$$

Answer, $2a^2 + 2ab + b^2$

5. **Add similar terms mentally, then write the result:**
Simplify: $2c^2 - 3c + 6 - 2c + 7c^2 - 3 + c - 3c^2 - 4 + c^2$
$$= 7c^2 - 4c - 1$$
Answer, $7c^2 - 4c - 1$

DIAGNOSTIC TEST

Add:

1.
$$2a + 3$$
$$3a - 5$$

2.
$$4x - 2y$$
$$2x - 5y$$

3.
$$5b - 1$$
$$-4b + 2$$

4.
$$2a + b$$
$$a - b$$

5.
$$8m^2 - 7n^2$$
$$-8m^2 + 7n^2$$

6.
$$5a^2 - 4ab - 3b^2$$
$$2a^2 + 2ab - 5b^2$$

7.
$$7r - 3s - 4t$$
$$9r + 3s - 2t$$

8.
$$2b - 2c - d$$
$$-6b - 3c$$

9.
$$9m + 8r^2$$
$$3m - 5r^2$$
$$-15m + 2r^2$$

10.
$$6a^2b^2 + 3ab - 5$$
$$a^2b^2 - 5ab - 2$$
$$-5a^2b^2 - 4ab$$

11. Find the sum of $4x^2 + 6x - 3$ and $2x^2 - 2x + 5$.
12. Find the sum of $x^2 - y^2$, $2x^2 - 4xy + y^2$, and $2y^2 - 3xy - x^2$.
13. Add $(c^2 - 2cd) + (2cd + d^2) + (d^2 - c^2)$.
14. Simplify $2x^2 - 5 - 2x + x^2 - 3x + 6 - x^2 - 4x - x^2 + 2$.

Related Practice Examples

Add:

1.

$5x+2$	$2b+7$	$3b-2$	$6m-3$	$y+3$
$3x+4$	$4b+1$	$4b-5$	$7m+9$	$y-7$

$2x^2-5$	$8ab+5$	$-3a+9$	x^2+2	$-6x-2$
$2x^2+3$	$6ab-2$	$5a-2$	$-6x^2+3$	$-\ x-5$

2.

$3a+2b$	$x+3y$	$5c-2d$	$3m-4n$	$2x^2-5x$
$2a+4b$	$2x+\ y$	$c-3d$	$4m+8n$	$9x^2+2x$

$3ab-9xy$	$9a^2-4b^2$	$-\ c^2+5c$	$4xy+\ y^2$	$-2a^2b+7ab^2$
$7ab+4xy$	$-2a^2+7b^2$	$-4c^2+8c$	$2xy-6y^2$	$4a^2b-3ab^2$

3.

$4a+6b$	$-2x-9$	$-\ b^2+5$	$9-3cd$	$9x^2-3$
$3a-5b$	$x-2$	$2b^2-4$	$6+2cd$	$-8x^2+2$

4.

$5x+3$	$2a-7b$	$x+y$	a^2-3b^2	$-2x^2-5xy$
$2x-3$	$9a+7b$	$x-y$	$-a^2-3b^2$	x^2+5xy

5.

$x-4$	$9-b^2$	$4x^2+9y^2$	$-2xy-y^2$	$3ab-4bc$
$-x+4$	$-9+b^2$	$-4x^2-9y^2$	$+2xy+y^2$	$-3ab+4bc$

6.

$2a+3b+1$	$5x+4y-3$	$3b-4m+2x$	x^2+2x-7	$x^2+2xy+\ y^2$
$4a+2b+7$	$2x+8y-5$	$5b-6m-4x$	x^2-5x+3	$2x^2-\ xy-2y^2$

$4a^2-2ab-9b^2$	$2c^2-5cd+\ d^2$	$9m^2-3m-5$	$3m^3+2m^2-4m$	$7a^3b-3a^2b^2+4ab^3$
$-\ a^2+4ab-\ b^2$	$4c^2-8cd-4d^2$	$2m^2-9m+6$	$2m^3+8m^2-5m$	$2a^3b-2a^2b^2-9ab^3$

7.

$3a-4b+5c$	$9x^2-4x+6$	$-4x^2+2xy-9$	$8m^2-2mn+n^2$	$2y^2-y+6$
$7a-5b-5c$	$5x^2+4x-3$	$4x^2-3xy+8$	$6m^2+2mn-n^2$	$-2y^2+y-6$

8.

$4x^2-8$	$5b^2-3b+2$	$2a$	$4x^2-5x$	$5x^2\qquad -\ y^2$
$2x^2$	$4b^2-7b$	$4a+6$	$2x^2+3x-4$	$2x^2+2xy+5y^2$

$-3a\qquad-2c$	x^2+xy	$4c^2-6cd$	$2x^2-7xy$	b^3+3b^2-4b
$5a+4b$	$+xy+y^2$	$+6cd-9d^2$	$6xy-2y^2$	$-3b^2+4b-27$

9.

$4a-3b$	$2a^2-6$	$8x^2-3xy$	$-\ 3a^2-4ab$	$10b^2-\ c^2$
$5a-4b$	$-3a^2+1$	$6x^2-4xy$	$-\ 5a^2$	$-\ 4b^2-\ c^2$
$-2a-\ b$	$-4a^2+4$	$-9x^2+7xy$	$+10a^2-4ab$	$-\ 6b^2+2c^2$

10.

$2c^2+4c+5$	$5x^2-2x+3$	$4a^2-3ab+\ b^2$	$x^2-2xy+y^2$	$2d^2+3d-9$
$4c^2+5c+2$	$2x^2-4x-5$	$2a^2-5ab-2b^2$	$2x^2-2xy-y^2$	$-\ d^2+\ d+5$
$8c^2+3c+1$	$-\ x^2+3x-7$	$3a^2-\ ab+\ b^2$	$-\ x^2+5xy-y^2$	$-\ d^2-5d+3$

$$
\begin{array}{l}
2x^2 \quad\ - y^2 \\
x^2 + 2xy + 3y^2 \\
\underline{\ - xy - 6y^2}
\end{array}
\qquad
\begin{array}{l}
2a^3 - 2a^2 + 6a \\
4a^3 \qquad - 5a \\
\underline{5a^3}
\end{array}
\qquad
\begin{array}{l}
5c^2 - 5cd - 2d^2 \\
3c^2 - \ cd \\
\underline{\quad\quad + 9cd - \ d^2}
\end{array}
\qquad
\begin{array}{l}
a^3 \qquad\qquad +4 \\
a^2 + 5a - 1 \\
\underline{3a^3 + a^2 - 3a + 6}
\end{array}
\qquad
\begin{array}{l}
4x^4 + 3x^2y^2 - 2y^4 \\
-5x^4 - \ x^2y^2 + \ y^4 \\
\underline{\ - x^4 - 2x^2y^2 + \ y^4}
\end{array}
$$

$$
\begin{array}{l}
x^3 + 6x^2 \\
5x^2 + 3x \\
\underline{\qquad\quad 5x - 7}
\end{array}
\qquad\qquad
\begin{array}{l}
2b^3 - 4b^2c \\
4b^2c - 3bc^2 \\
\underline{\qquad\quad 3bc^2 - 6c^3}
\end{array}
\qquad\qquad
\begin{array}{l}
a^4 + 5a^3b \\
-3a^3b - 2a^2b^2 \\
\quad - \ a^2b^2 + 2ab^3 \\
\underline{\qquad\qquad - 2ab^3 - 6b^4}
\end{array}
$$

SET 11

Find the sum of:

1. $6x - 2y$ and $3x + 5y$
2. $2a - 3b + 4c$ and $7a - 5b - 3c$
3. $3a - 4x$, $5a - 3x$, and $a - 2x$
4. $2x^2 - 3x + 6$, $x^2 - 5x - 1$, and $2x^2 - 2x - 4$
5. $8a^2 - 2ab - b^2$, $4a^2 - ab - b^2$, and $a^2 - ab - b^2$

SET 12a

Find the sum of:

1. $x^2 + x$ and $x + 3$
2. $a^2 + 2ab$ and $-3ab - b^2$
3. $5x + y$ and $8y + 7$
4. $x^2 + 3x$ and $-2x + 9$
5. $a^2 - 6ax$ and $6ax - x^2$

SET 12b

1. $6a^2 - 2a + 7$, $2a^2 - 3$, and $5a + 1$
2. $8c^2 - 4d^2$, $3c^2 - 5cd + d^2$, and $4c^2 - 2cd + d^2$
3. $2x^4 + 3x^3 + x^2$, $2x^3 - 3x^2 + 6$, and $x^2 - 5x + 7$
4. $5ab - 3ab^2 + 5ab^3$, $6ab^2 - 2ab - 3ab^3$, and $6ab^3 - 2ab^2$
5. $8x^3y - 2x^2y^2$, $5x^2y^2 - 2xy^3$, and $6x^3y - 5xy^3$

SET 13

Add the following:

1. $(5x) + (3x)$
2. $(-4x^2) + (-2x^2)$
3. $(7y) + (-2y) + (-5y)$
4. $(8c) + (-3d) + (2d) + (-5c)$
5. $(3ax^2) + (4a^2x^2) + (-5ax^2) + (-ax^2)$

6. $(x - 5) + (2x - 3) + (x - 4)$
7. $(c + d) + (2c - 3d) + (c - d)$
8. $(a - b) + (b - a) + (2b - a)$
9. $(x^2 - 3xy) + (3xy + y^2) + (y^2 - x^2)$
10. $(x^2 - 3x + 7) + (2x + x^2 - 3) + (8 - x - 2x^2)$

SET 14

Combine:

1. $3b + 5 + 4b$
2. $a + 3 + 2a + 6$
3. $9 - 4x - 3$
4. $c^2 - 7c + 6 + 2c^2 - 12$
5. $m^2 - 2mn + n^2 - m^2 + n^2$
6. $2x^2y - 3xy^2 + x^2y - 4x^2y - 2xy^2$

7. $5s - 3 + 7s + 8 - s - 9s - 5$
8. $4n^2 - 8n + 7 - 6 + 2n - n^2 - 3n^2 + n - 8 - n^2$
9. $9x^2 - 3xy - y^2 - 3x^2 - 5xy - x^2 - 4xy + y^2 - 7y^2$
10. $7b^3 + b^2 - b + 5 - 3b^2 - 3b - 6 - 4b^3 - b + 5b^2$

Applications

1. Find the perimeter of the following figures:

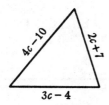

2. Find the sum of the angles in the following figures expressed in literal angular measure:

3. Solve the following equations by combining similar terms. Check each root.

1. $5x + 3x + 4 = 180$
2. $7b + 6 - 2b = 51$
3. $9 - a + 3a + 8 = 39$
4. $x + x + 15 + 4x = 87$
5. $w + w + 6 + w + w + 6 = 108$
6. $9n - 5 - 6n + 4 = 11$
7. $2x - 8 + 4x + 8x = 90$
8. $32 = l + l - 2 + l - 5$
9. $b + b - 7 + b + b - 7 = 42$
10. $a + 4 + 6a - 18 + 13 - 4a = 360$

SUBTRACTION

EXERCISE 25

Subtraction of Monomials

I. Aim: To subtract monomials.

II. Procedure

1. To subtract similar terms, change the sign of the subtrahend mentally and proceed as in addition.

2. The subtraction of terms which are not similar can only be indicated. However, the sign of the subtrahend must be changed. See sample solution 7.

3. Check by addition or by numerical substitution.

III. Sample Solutions

1. $+2xyz$
   $-5xyz$
   _____
   $+7xyz$

   Answer, $+7xyz$

2. $-5ab^2$
   0
   _____
   $-5ab^2$

   Answer, $-5ab^2$

3. 0
   $-2b$
   _____
   $+2b$

   Answer, $+2b$

4. $-3b^2c$
   $-3b^2c$
   _____
   0

   Answer, 0

5. From $-3a$ take $4a$
   $-3a$
   $4a$
   _____
   $-7a$

   Answer, $-7a$

6. Subtract $5x^2$ from $4x^2$.
   $4x^2$
   $5x^2$
   _____
   $-x^2$

   Answer, $-x^2$

7. Subtract $3y$ from $4x$.
   $4x$
   $+3y$
   _____
   $4x-3y$

   Answer, $4x-3y$

8. $(-6xy^2)-(-2xy^2)$
   $-6xy^2$
   $-2xy^2$
   _____
   $-4xy^2$

   Answer, $-4xy^2$

DIAGNOSTIC TEST

Subtract the lower term from the upper term:

1. $+6x$
   $+4x$

2. $-3y$
   $-8y$

3. $+5abc$
   $-7abc$

4. $-6b^2$
   $+8b^2$

5. $-2d$
   $-d$

6. $6xy$
   0

7. 0
   $-5a$

8. $9xy^2$
   $9xy^2$

9. $-4a^2$
   $+4a^2$

10. $\frac{1}{4}a^3$
    $-\frac{3}{4}a^3$

11. $-3.6x^2$
    $1.5x^2$

12. $-7(x-y-z)$
    $4(x-y-z)$

Subtract as indicated:

13. $(c^2y^3)-(-2c^2y^3)$

14. From $4r$ take $-6r$.

15. Subtract $-2x$ from $-8x$.

16. From 0 subtract $2y$.

17. $+x^2$
    $+x$

18. Subtract $2b$ from $6a$.

Related Practice Examples

Subtract the lower term from the upper term:

1.
$$+8x \quad +6a \quad +9c \quad +4b^2 \quad +2xy \quad 7m \quad 9x^2 \quad 3y \quad 5d^3 \quad 6ab^2$$
$$+3x \quad +2a \quad +3c \quad +8b^2 \quad +9xy \quad 4m \quad 6x^2 \quad 10y \quad 7d^3 \quad 8ab^2$$

2.
$$-5b \quad -6x \quad -9a^2 \quad -7xy \quad -8m^2 \quad -2a \quad -4x^2 \quad -3b^3 \quad -7cd \quad -8x^2y^2$$
$$-2b \quad -3x \quad -4a^2 \quad -2xy \quad -6m^2 \quad -8a \quad -9x^2 \quad -6b^3 \quad -12cd \quad -10x^2y^2$$

3.
$$+6a \quad +7m \quad +2c^2 \quad +4bx \quad +3d^3y \quad 8s \quad 6d^2 \quad 5cy \quad 2a^2b \quad 6xyz$$
$$-2a \quad -3m \quad -8c^2 \quad -6bx \quad -4d^3y \quad -5s \quad -4d^2 \quad -3cy \quad -5a^2b \quad -9xyz$$

4.
$$-5x \quad -8y \quad -9d^3 \quad -3mx \quad -5r^2t \quad -6b \quad -7ac \quad -2ry^2 \quad -4abc \quad -3b^2c^2$$
$$+3x \quad +2y \quad +5d^3 \quad +7mx \quad +8r^2t \quad 3b \quad 2ac \quad 5ry^2 \quad 6abc \quad 10b^2c^2$$

5.
$$+6m \quad +9cd \quad +3x^2 \quad 2a^2c \quad 2ay^2 \quad -9x \quad -4y \quad -6c^3 \quad -7bc \quad -axy$$
$$+5m \quad +8cd \quad +4x^2 \quad a^2c \quad 3ay^2 \quad -8x \quad -3y \quad -7c^3 \quad -8bc \quad -2axy$$

6.
$$3x \quad 5y \quad 2b^4 \quad a \quad 5m^2x \quad -2b \quad -3m \quad -x \quad -5c^2x^2 \quad -2bxy$$
$$0 \quad 0 \quad 0 \quad 0 \quad 0 \quad 0 \quad 0 \quad 0 \quad 0 \quad 0$$

7.
$$0 \quad 0 \quad 0 \quad 0 \quad 0 \quad 0 \quad 0 \quad 0 \quad 0 \quad 0$$
$$+4b \quad +6x \quad +3a^2 \quad 9ab \quad 5b^2c \quad -6x \quad -2y \quad -7m^2 \quad -8rt \quad -2x^2y^2$$

8.
$$+a \quad +5x \quad +8n^2 \quad 2xy^3 \quad b^2c^2 \quad -x \quad -4b^3 \quad -9abc \quad -6a^3x \quad -10abc$$
$$+a \quad +5x \quad +8n^2 \quad 2xy^3 \quad b^2c^2 \quad -x \quad -4b^3 \quad -9abc \quad -6a^3x \quad -10abc$$

9.
$$+x \quad +3a \quad +5x^2 \quad 2abc \quad 7x^4y \quad -b^2 \quad -2y \quad -8c^2 \quad -4bc \quad -5x^2y$$
$$-x \quad -3a \quad -5x^2 \quad -2abc \quad -7x^4y \quad +b^2 \quad +2y \quad 8c^2 \quad 4bc \quad 5x^2y$$

10.
$$+\tfrac{3}{4}x \qquad -\tfrac{3}{2}m^4 \qquad \tfrac{1}{3}cd^2 \qquad \tfrac{7}{8}xyz \qquad -\tfrac{3}{8}a^2xy$$
$$+\tfrac{1}{4}x \qquad +\tfrac{1}{2}m^4 \qquad -\tfrac{2}{3}cd^2 \qquad \tfrac{5}{8}xyz \qquad -\tfrac{1}{10}a^2xy$$

11.
$$+.8y \qquad +4.5b^2 \qquad -7.3\ ac \qquad 2.6b^2m^3 \qquad -7.05b^2c$$
$$+.3y \qquad -3.7b^2 \qquad -\ .49ac \qquad 3.8b^2m^3 \qquad 1.6\ b^2c$$

12.
$$3(a+b) \qquad -2(x-y) \qquad 8(a+b-c) \qquad -7(a-x-y) \qquad 4(s^2-c^2)$$
$$5(a+b) \qquad -7(x-y) \qquad -2(a+b-c) \qquad 9(a-x-y) \qquad 3(s^2-c^2)$$

Subtract as indicated:

13.
1. $(4d)-(3d)$
2. $(+5x)-(+2x)$
3. $(+6y)-(-3y)$
4. $(-8a)-(5a)$
5. $(-5c)-(4c)$
6. $(x^2)-(-x^2)$
7. $(-4abx)-(-6abx)$
8. $(a^2b^3)-(a^2b^3)$
9. $(-9x^2y)-(-9x^2y)$
10. $(-5mnx)-(-6mnx)$

SET 14

1. From $4b$ subtract $3b$.
2. From $-5m$ take $7m$.
3. Find the difference between $2x$ and $-4x$.
4. From $-8abc$ take $-9abc$.
5. Find the difference between $-2x^3y$ and x^3y.
6. From $9b^2c$ take $-5b^2c$.
7. Find the difference between $-8x^2$ and $3x^2$.
8. From $-7x^2y^3$ subtract $-8x^2y^3$.
9. Find the difference between $-6m$ and $+6m$.
10. From $-mx^2y$ subtract $4mx^2y$.

SET 15

1. Take $2x$ from $7x$.
2. Subtract $-x^2$ from $3x^2$.
3. Take $-4ab$ from $-5ab$.
4. Take $3c^2d$ from $-2c^2d$.
5. Subtract $-8xy$ from $-8xy$.

SET 16

1. From 0 take $-3xy$.
2. From $2a^2c$ subtract 0.
3. Subtract $-3ab^2$ from 0.
4. Take xy from 0.
5. Find the difference between 0 and $-2x$.

SET 17

Subtract the lower term from the upper term:

$$\begin{array}{cccccc} a & x & b & 5 & -b^2 & 2x^2 \\ \underline{+b} & \underline{-y} & \underline{+4} & \underline{-c} & \underline{-c^2} & \underline{+3y^2} \end{array}$$

$$\begin{array}{cccc} 5a^2b & -8mx & 6a^2y & a^4 \\ \underline{-2ab^2} & \underline{-2nx} & \underline{3ay} & \underline{+a^3} \end{array}$$

SET 18

1. From x take y.
2. From $-2b$ subtract $3c$.
3. Find the difference between $3y^2$ and $-y$.
4. From $-a$ subtract -6.
5. From $3b^2$ take $-9c^2$.
6. Subtract $5y$ from $7x$.
7. Subtract -2 from $6m$.
8. Take $4ab$ from $-3xy$.
9. Take $-bc$ from $-2ab$.
10. Subtract -9 from b^2.

Applications

1. Find the literal dimensions of the required lengths in the following figures:

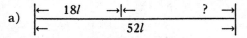
a)

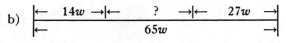
b)

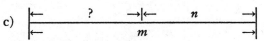
c)

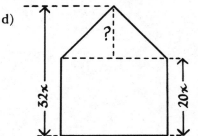
d)

2. Find the literal angular measures of the required angles in the following figures:

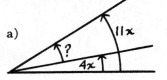
a)

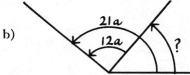
b)

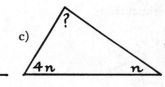
c)

The sum of the angles in a triangle equals 180°.

EXERCISE 26
Subtraction of Polynomials

I. Aim: To subtract polynomials

II. Procedure

1. If the polynomials are so arranged that similar terms are in vertical columns, change the sign of each term of the subtrahend mentally and proceed as in addition.

2. Otherwise, place the subtrahend under the minuend so that similar terms are in vertical columns, and proceed as in rule 1.

3. In some cases it will be necessary to rewrite the polynomials in descending powers or ascending powers of one letter.

4. Check by addition or by numerical substitution.

III. Sample Solutions

1. $2x^2 - 5xy + y^2$
   $x^2 + 2xy - 3y^2$
   _____
   $x^2 - 7xy + 4y^2$

   Answer, $x^2 - 7xy + 4y^2$

3. $c^2 + 2cd$
   $4cd - d^2$
   _____
   $c^2 - 2cd + d^2$

   Answer, $c^2 - 2cd + d^2$

5. $(b^2 - 3b) - (2b - 5)$.
   $b^2 - 3b$
   $2b - 5$
   _____
   $b^2 - 5b + 5$

   Answer, $b^2 - 5b + 5$

2. $4a^2 - 3a + 6$
   $-2a^2 - 3a + 7$
   _____
   $6a^2 \quad\quad - 1$

   Answer, $6a^2 - 1$

4. Subtract $8 - 4b^2$ from $3b^2 - 4b + 3$.
   $3b^2 - 4b + 3$
   $-4b^2 \quad\quad + 8$
   _____
   $7b^2 - 4b - 5$

   Answer, $7b^2 - 4b - 5$

DIAGNOSTIC TEST

Subtract the lower expression from the upper expression:

1. $7a - 5$
   $2a + 8$

2. $a + 2b$
   $2a - 3b$

3. $6x^2 - 5x + 2$
   $3x^2 - 4x - 6$

4. $2a^2 - 3ab - b^2$
   $a^2 - 3ab + b^2$

5. $6a^2 - 5a + 7$
   $6a^2 - 5a + 7$

6. $4m^2 - 5mn + n^2$
   $3m^2 + 3mn$

7. x^3
   $2x^3 - x^2 + 4x$

8. 0
   $2x - 3y + z$

Subtract as indicated:

9. $(x^2 - x) - (x - 1)$.
10. Find the difference between $2a - 3b + 6c$ and $3a - 4b - 2c$.
11. From $x^2 - y^2$ subtract $2x^2 - 3xy - y^2$.
12. Take $3x - y$ from $x - 2xy$.

Related Practice Examples

Subtract the lower expression from the upper expression:

1.
$$\begin{array}{c} 4a+5 \\ 3a+2 \\ \hline \end{array} \qquad \begin{array}{c} 6x+3 \\ 4x+7 \\ \hline \end{array} \qquad \begin{array}{c} 5y^2+1 \\ 9y^2+8 \\ \hline \end{array} \qquad \begin{array}{c} 4r+6 \\ r-3 \\ \hline \end{array} \qquad \begin{array}{c} 2m+4 \\ 6m-5 \\ \hline \end{array}$$

$$\begin{array}{c} x^2-6 \\ 3x^2+5 \\ \hline \end{array} \qquad \begin{array}{c} 2y^2-8 \\ y^2+1 \\ \hline \end{array} \qquad \begin{array}{c} 6ab-9 \\ 8ab-2 \\ \hline \end{array} \qquad \begin{array}{c} 6x^2y-3 \\ 5x^2y-7 \\ \hline \end{array} \qquad \begin{array}{c} -2b-7 \\ 5b+2 \\ \hline \end{array}$$

2.
$$\begin{array}{c} 4x+7y \\ 2x+5y \\ \hline \end{array} \qquad \begin{array}{c} 5a+2b \\ 3a+6b \\ \hline \end{array} \qquad \begin{array}{c} a-3c \\ 4a-5c \\ \hline \end{array} \qquad \begin{array}{c} 2x^2-\ y^2 \\ x^2+3y^2 \\ \hline \end{array} \qquad \begin{array}{c} 4ab-3c \\ 5ab-2c \\ \hline \end{array}$$

$$\begin{array}{c} 8m+3n \\ 6m-5n \\ \hline \end{array} \qquad \begin{array}{c} 2c^2-3d^2 \\ 5c^2-4d^2 \\ \hline \end{array} \qquad \begin{array}{c} x^2+\ y^2 \\ 2x^2-3y^2 \\ \hline \end{array} \qquad \begin{array}{c} 4cd-\ d^2 \\ cd+2d^2 \\ \hline \end{array} \qquad \begin{array}{c} 5m^3-\ n^2 \\ -2m^3+4n^2 \\ \hline \end{array}$$

3.
$$\begin{array}{c} 4a+3b+6c \\ 2a+\ b+2c \\ \hline \end{array} \qquad \begin{array}{c} 2x^2-3x+7 \\ 3x^2+\ x-9 \\ \hline \end{array} \qquad \begin{array}{c} 7a^2-5ab-6b^2 \\ 3a^2-4ab-2b^2 \\ \hline \end{array} \qquad \begin{array}{c} 3b^2-4b-7 \\ b^2-\ b-6 \\ \hline \end{array} \qquad \begin{array}{c} 8m^2+mn-3n^2 \\ 2m^2-3mn+2n^2 \\ \hline \end{array}$$

$$\begin{array}{c} 2x^3-4x^2+5x \\ 4x^3-2x^2+7x \\ \hline \end{array} \qquad \begin{array}{c} -5cd-2cd^2+3cd^3 \\ cd+\ cd^2-5cd^3 \\ \hline \end{array} \qquad \begin{array}{c} 8r^4-2r^2+6 \\ 6r^4-8r^2-3 \\ \hline \end{array} \qquad \begin{array}{c} 5x^3-4x^2+3x-1 \\ 3x^3-5x^2-\ x+6 \\ \hline \end{array} \qquad \begin{array}{c} 4a^3-5a^2b-6ab^2+\ b^3 \\ 6a^3-4a^2b+8ab^2-2b^3 \\ \hline \end{array}$$

4.
$$\begin{array}{c} a+6 \\ a-3 \\ \hline \end{array} \qquad \begin{array}{c} 2a-b \\ a-b \\ \hline \end{array} \qquad \begin{array}{c} 5x^2-2x+6 \\ 2x^2-2x+8 \\ \hline \end{array} \qquad \begin{array}{c} 2x^2-3xy+2y^2 \\ x^2+2xy+2y^2 \\ \hline \end{array} \qquad \begin{array}{c} 4a^4-5a^2b^2-9b^4 \\ 4a^4-6a^2b^2-9b^4 \\ \hline \end{array}$$

5.
$$\begin{array}{c} x-2 \\ x-2 \\ \hline \end{array} \qquad \begin{array}{c} -4x^2+9y^2 \\ -4x^2+9y^2 \\ \hline \end{array} \qquad \begin{array}{c} x-a+2b \\ x-a+2b \\ \hline \end{array} \qquad \begin{array}{c} 2x^2-3xy-5y^2 \\ 2x^2-3xy-5y^2 \\ \hline \end{array} \qquad \begin{array}{c} 3r^2-9r+6 \\ 3r^2-9r+6 \\ \hline \end{array}$$

6.
$$\begin{array}{c} 7a+6b \\ 4a \\ \hline \end{array} \qquad \begin{array}{c} 6m-2n \\ 8m \\ \hline \end{array} \qquad \begin{array}{c} 2x^2-2x+8 \\ x^2+5x \\ \hline \end{array} \qquad \begin{array}{c} 5b^2-2bc+3c^2 \\ -8c^2 \\ \hline \end{array} \qquad \begin{array}{c} 4m^2-mx-3x^2 \\ -mx \\ \hline \end{array}$$

7.
$$\begin{array}{c} a \\ a-3 \\ \hline \end{array} \qquad \begin{array}{c} 4y \\ 2x-3y \\ \hline \end{array} \qquad \begin{array}{c} a^2\quad-b^2 \\ a^2-2ab+b^2 \\ \hline \end{array} \qquad \begin{array}{c} 6c^2-3cd \\ 4c^2+7cd-d^2 \\ \hline \end{array} \qquad \begin{array}{c} 3r^3\qquad-1 \\ 2r^3-4r^2-5r \\ \hline \end{array}$$

8.
$$\begin{array}{c} 0 \\ 4x^2-2y^2 \\ \hline \end{array} \qquad \begin{array}{c} 0 \\ 3ab-2ab^2-5ab^3 \\ \hline \end{array} \qquad \begin{array}{c} 0 \\ 4c^2-3c+6 \\ \hline \end{array} \qquad \begin{array}{c} 0 \\ -x^2-xy+2y^2 \\ \hline \end{array} \qquad \begin{array}{c} 0 \\ 3m^3-m^2+2m-6 \\ \hline \end{array}$$

9. Subtract as indicated:

1. $(3x+5)-(x-2)$
2. $(a-b)-(a+b)$
3. $(a+b)-(a+c)$
4. $(2s-a)-(s+b)$
5. $(x^2-x+2)-(2x^2+x-2)$

6. $(2c^2-cd+3d^2)-(c^2-2d^2)$
7. $(x^2-y^2)-(2x^2-2xy)$
8. $(m^3-3m^2-2m)-(m^3-2m^2-2)$
9. $(5-a+a^2)-(a^2+7-2a)$
10. $(3b-c)-(x-y)$

SET 10

1. From $8x-3$ subtract $2x+7$.
2. From $2a-7c+4x$ take $-5a+6c-8x$.
3. Find the difference between $4x^2-2x+6$ and x^2-5x-9.
4. Subtract $6b^3-5b^2-b$ from $3b^3+5b^2-b$.
5. Take $4c^2-3cd+5d^2$ from $7c^2-3cd+6d^2$.

SET 11

1. From $a^2 - 2ab + 2b^2$ take $a^2 - 3b^2$.
2. From zero subtract $5x - 3y + 7z$.
3. From $c^2 - 5d^2$ take $3c^2 - 7cd - d^2$.
4. From 8 take $4x - 2$.
5. Find the difference between $a^2 + b^2$ and $a^2 - c^2$.
6. From $2m^2 - 3mn + n^2$ subtract zero.
7. Find the difference between $8x - 7$ and $2y - 9$.
8. From m^2 take $2mn - n^2$.
9. From $b^3 - 2b$ subtract $4b^2 - 5b + 2$.
10. Find the difference between $3a^3 - 4a^2b + 3ab^2$ and $5ab^2 - 2a^2b + b^3$.

SET 12

1. Subtract $2c - 4$ from $3c$.
2. Subtract $8y - 3$ from $2x + 7$.
3. Take $4x^3 - 3x + 8$ from zero.
4. Take $x^2 - 5x + 27$ from $x^3 - 81$.
5. Subtract $2a^2 + a - 1$ from $a^3 + 2a^2 - a$.
6. Take $5x^2$ from $2x^2 - 3x$.
7. Subtract $3m - 5$ from $-m$.
8. Subtract $2c^2 - d^2$ from $c^2 - 2cd - d^2$.
9. Take $2a - 7c$ from $4a + 3b$.
10. Take $-3mn + n^2$ from $m^2 - 2mn$.

Miscellaneous Examples

1. How much must be added to $7x^2 - 3x + 8$ to get $3x^2 + 5x - 9$?
2. How much more than $b^2 - 4d^2$ is $b^2 + 4bd + 4d^2$?
3. From the sum of $m^2 - 2mn + n^2$ and $m^2 + 2mn + n^2$ subtract $m^2 - 4mn + 4n^2$.
4. Subtract the sum of $9b^2 - 3c^2$ and $2b^2 + bc - 2c^2$ from the sum of $2b^2 - 2bc - c^2$ and $c^2 + bc - b^2$.
5. From $5x^2 - 3x + 7$ subtract the sum of $2x^2 - 2x + 4$ and $x^2 - x - 2$.

Applications

1. Find the literal dimensions of the required lengths in the following figures:

   a) Lines

   b) Trapezoid

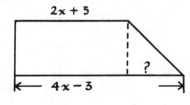

2. Find the literal angular measures of the required angles in the following figures:

   a. Find the complement of an angle measuring $x + 30$ degrees.
   b. Find the supplement of an angle measuring $a - 18$ degrees.
   c. Find the third angle of a triangle in which one angle measures $5x + 10$ degrees, the second angle measures $4x - 5$ degrees, and the sum of the angles of the triangle is 180 degrees.

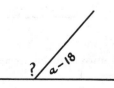

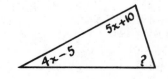

PARENTHESES

EXERCISE 27

Removal by Addition or Subtraction

I. Aim: To remove parentheses.

II. Procedure

1. If the parentheses are preceded by a plus (+) sign, remove the parentheses and rewrite all the terms which are within the parentheses without changing their signs.

2. If the parentheses are preceded by a minus (−) sign, remove the parentheses and rewrite all the terms which are within the parentheses but with their signs changed.

3. In case of parentheses within parentheses, remove one set at a time, starting with the innermost parentheses.

4. Combine similar terms.

III. Sample Solutions

1. $4x+(3x-5)$
    $=4x+3x-5$
    $=7x-5$
    Answer, $7x-5$

2. $3a^2-2a-(2a^2-5a+4)$
    $=3a^2-2a-2a^2+5a-4$
    $=a^2+3a-4$
    Answer, a^2+3a-4

3. $3a-[4b+5-(-2a+9b-1)+a]$
    $=3a-[4b+5+2a-9b+1+a]$
    $=3a-[3a-5b+6]$
    $=3a-3a+5b-6$
    $=5b-6$
    Answer, $5b-6$

DIAGNOSTIC TEST

Remove parentheses and, if possible, add like terms:

1. $6b+(5b+7)$
2. $8x+(4x-3y)$
3. $10+(-6a+3)$
4. $5m+(-8m-4n)$
5. $9-(7a+5)$
6. $4a-(3a-2x)$
7. $-2x^2-(-x^2+4x)$
8. $3x-(-4y-6x)$
9. $4-(2a^2-5a-3)$
10. $9c-5d+(3d-4c)$
11. $2b^2-4-(-5+6b^2)$

12. $(x-3y)+(4x-2y)$
13. $(c^2-3cx+x^2)-(2c^2-2cx+3x^2)$
14. $(2a^3-5a^2-3a)-2a^2$
15. $5a-(4a-2x)+3a$
16. $2x-(3x+2)-5+(2x-7)$
17. $[2c-(3c+2d)-d]$
18. $-[4x^2+(2x+3)-7]$
19. $4b+[3-(2b-4)]$
20. $3m-[m-(4m+3n)+5n]$
21. $2x^2-[x^2+2x+(2x^2-5)-4]-4x$
22. $3a-4b+[2a-(3b-4a)]-(5a-7b)$

Related Practice Examples

Remove parentheses and, if possible, add like terms:

SET 1

1. $2x+(3x+5)$
2. $3y+(7c+4y)$
3. $6+(3a+9)$
4. $-10+(5b+9)$
5. $7a+(4c+5d)$

SET 2

1. $5m+(4m-2)$
2. $8x^2+(3b^2-2x^2)$
3. $15+(9-3c)$
4. $-2x+(5x^2-4x)$
5. $4a^2+(ab-2b^2)$

SET 3

1. $8+(-4y+6)$
2. $5b+(-3b+7c)$
3. $2x+(-5y+4x)$
4. $-10m+(-3m+5n)$
5. $2x^2+(-xy+3y^2)$

SET 4

1. $7r+(-3r-4s)$
2. $3m^2+(-4n^2-3m^2)$
3. $14+(-6b-8)$
4. $-5d+(-8a-4d)$
5. $8c^2+(-2c-5)$

SET 5

1. $3a-(2a+6)$
2. $5m-(4y+3m)$
3. $9-(4x+7)$
4. $-4c-(5c+4d)$
5. $8x-(3y+9)$

SET 6

1. $8c-(3c-8)$
2. $5d-(2a-3d)$
3. $4-(7x-9)$
4. $-3s^2-(2r^2-8s^2)$
5. $4m-(5x-3y)$

SET 7

1. $10a-(-4a+1)$
2. $5xy-(-xy+2y^2)$
3. $6r^3-(-2r^4+4r^3)$
4. $-8b-(-3a+4b)$
5. $5m^2-(-2m+9)$

SET 8

1. $8t-(-4t-7)$
2. $3ab-(-5ab-2b^2)$
3. $2a^2x-(-a^2x^2-2a^2x)$
4. $-4c^3-(-2c^2-5c^3)$
5. $3x^2-(-4xy-3y^2)$

SET 9

1. $5a+(3a-4b+2c)$
2. $3x+(-5x^2-4x+7)$
3. $3ab-(6a^2-4ab+b^2)$
4. $25-(c^2-8c+16)$
5. $m^3+(2m^2-5m+1)$

SET 10

1. $4b+6+(3b+7)$
2. $5x^2-3x+(2x-3x^2)$
3. $2b^2-4bc+(5c^2-2bc)$
4. $a^3+a^2b+(-2a^2b-b^4)$
5. $x-3y+(-4x+8y-2z)$

SET 11

1. $3c+2-(c+6)$
2. $5d-3s-(2d-4s)$
3. $4y^2-5y-(-2y+9)$
4. $8b^2-3x^2-(-4xy-6b^2)$
5. $a^3-a^2+a-(2a^2-a^3+5)$

SET 12

1. $(3x-4)+(2x+3)$
2. $(a-3b)+(4a-2b)$
3. $(x^2-2x+5)+(2x^2-3x-9)$
4. $(a^2-3ab+b^2)+(4b^2-2bc+c^2)$
5. $(9-2c+3c^2)+(-3c-c^2+4)$

SET 13

1. $(x-5)-(2x-9)$
2. $(3c-9d)-(-4c+2d)$
3. $(x^2+2y^2)-(4y^2-3x^2)$
4. $(b^2-5b+3)-(3b-7-2b^2)$
5. $(m^2-n^2)-(5mn-3n^2)$

SET 14

1. $(9x+3)+4x$
2. $-(2ab-3ab^2)+4ab^2$
3. $(10b^2-4b)-3b$
4. $-(49-a^2)-5a^2$
5. $(r^2-2r+6)+3r-7$

SET 15

1. $8m+(6m+4)+6$
2. $2x^2+(3x^2-5x)+2x$
3. $3d-(4a-7d)+8d$
4. $4n^2-(n^2-8x)-8x$
5. $2a+b+(3a-4b+1)-3b+2$

SET 16

1. $2c+(4b-3c)-(4c-5b)$
2. $(3x-5y)-2x+6y-(4x-y)$
3. $5a^2-(2a+6)-3a+(a^2-1)$
4. $-(x^3-4x^2-3x)+2x^2+(2x^3-4x)$
5. $8m^4-(2m^4-m^2n^2)+(2m^2n^2-n^4)-2n^4$

SET 17

1. $[5+(3x+2)]$
2. $[2a+(3b-a)-b]$
3. $(6x^2-[2x^2-y^2]-2y^2)$
4. $(m^2+1-[2m+m^2]+3)$
5. $[2a-5c+(3b+6c)-b]$

SET 18

1. $-[2s+(3s-5)]$
2. $-[-2b-(3b+8c)]$
3. $-(18-[3x-4x^2])$
4. $-(bx+[2bx-9cx+3]-4)$
5. $-[2x^3-x^2-(5x^3-3x)-4x^3+2x]$

SET 19

1. $8x + [2 + (4x + 3)]$
2. $5d - [3m - (2d - m)]$
3. $x^2 + (2x^2 - [x^2 + 2x - 3])$
4. $a^2b - 5ab^2 + [2a^3 - (-3a^2b - ab^2)]$
5. $m^3 - 2m^2 - [m^2 + (m^3 - 3m^2 - 4m)]$

SET 20

1. $3t + [4t + (2t - 5) + 7]$
2. $4r^2 - [2r^2 - r + (3r + 6) - 2]$
3. $m^3 - [4m^2 - (2m^3 - m^2) + m^2]$
4. $2ab + 5 + (3ab - 4 - [6 - 4ab] - 9)$
5. $8c^2d - 2cd^2 + [2c^2d - (cd^2 - 4c^2d) - 5cd^2]$

SET 21

1. $3x + [6 + (4x - 1)] - 7$
2. $y^4 + [y^2 - (3y^4 - 2y^2)] - 5y^2$
3. $c^3 - d^3 - [2c^3 + (d^3 - 4c^3)] + 7d^3$
4. $5b^4 - 2b^2c^2 - (b^4 - [c^4 - 2b^2c^2] - c^4) + 2c^4$
5. $2x^2 - xy + [2y^2 + (3xy + x^2) - 4xy] - y^2$

SET 22

1. $5x - 6 + (2x - 3) - [4x + (7 - 2x)]$
2. $3a - 9b - (4b - 3a) - [2a - (3a - 5b)]$
3. $(5c - 4d) - (4c - 5d) + [3d + (c - d)]$
4. $[2x - (4x - y)] - [-5x + (2x - 7y)]$
5. $x^2 - [x + (2x^2 - 1)] + 3x + [2x - (x^2 - 1)] - 2$

EXERCISE 28

Inclosing Terms within Parentheses

I. **Aim**: To inclose terms within parentheses.

II. **Procedure**

1. If the parentheses are to be preceded by a plus (+) sign, place in parentheses the terms which are to be inclosed without changing their signs.
2. If the parentheses are to be preceded by a minus (−) sign, place in parentheses the terms which are to be inclosed but with their signs changed.

III. **Sample Solutions**

Inclose the last two terms within parentheses and precede it by a plus (+) sign.
1. $4a - 3b + 6c - 2d$ Answer, $4a - 3b + (6c - 2d)$
2. $5b^3 - 2b^2 - 3b + 5$ Answer, $5b^3 - 2b^2 + (-3b + 5)$

Inclose the last two terms within parentheses and precede it by a minus (−) sign.
3. $2b - 5c - 3x + 7y$ Answer, $2b - 5c - (3x - 7y)$
4. $3x^3 - 4x^2 + x - 5$ Answer, $3x^3 - 4x^2 - (-x + 5)$

DIAGNOSTIC TEST

Inclose the last two terms of each expression within parentheses and precede it by a plus (+) sign:
1. $2a + 3b + 4c + 5d$ 3. $4b^3 + 5b^2 - 5b - 8$
2. $4x^4 - 5x^3 + 6x^2 - 3x$ 4. $a^4 - a^3b + a^2b^2 - ab^3 + b^4$

Inclose the last three terms within parentheses and precede it by a plus (+) sign:
5. $c^5 - 5c^4 - 10c^3 - 10c^2 + 5c - 1$

Inclose the last two terms of each expression within parentheses and precede it by a minus (−) sign:
6. $2ab + 5ac - 3bc - 4cd$ 8. $2y^3 - 3y^2 + 6y + 8$
7. $9a^2 + 4b^2 - 3c^2 + 5d^2$ 9. $m^4 - 8m^3 + 12m^2 + 16m - 18$

Inclose the last three terms within parentheses and precede it by a minus (−) sign:
10. $4x^4 - 2x^3y + 3x^2y^2 - 2xy^3 + y^4$

Related Practice Examples

Inclose the last two terms of each expression within parentheses and precede it by a plus (+) sign:

SET 1

1. $a + x + b + y$
2. $3c - 2d + 4m + 5x$
3. $x^3 + 3x^2 + 2x + 7$
4. $-b^4 - b^3 + b^2 + 3b$
5. $d^3y + d^2y^2 + dy^3 + y^4$

SET 2

1. $c + d + m - n$
2. $x^3 - 2x^2 + 4x - 8$
3. $b^4 + 3b^3 + 5b^2 - 7b$
4. $a^3b - a^2b^2 + ab^3 - b^4$
5. $-m^4 - 2m^3 + 4m^2 - 3m$

SET 3

1. $b + d - x - y$
2. $4ab - 3ac - 2ad - 5xy$
3. $y^3 + 4y^2 - 3y - 9$
4. $x^4 - x^3y + x^2y^2 - xy^3 - y^4$
5. $-a^4 - 2a^3 - 5a^2 - 7a - 2$

SET 4

1. $m + r - s + x$
2. $3a - 4b - 5c + 8d$
3. $x^3 - 5x^2 - 8x + 2$
4. $c^4 - 2c^3d + 2c^2d^2 - 5cd^3 + d^4$
5. $-s^4 + 2s^3 - 4s^2 - 3s + 7$

Inclose the last three terms of each expression within parentheses and precede it by a plus (+) sign:

SET 5

1. $3a + 7b + 5c + 9d + 4e$
2. $4x^4 - 3x^3 + 2x^2 - 3x + 4$
3. $a^4 - 2a^3 - 5a^2 - 4a - 9$
4. $c^4 + 5c^3 - 6c^2 + 7c - 3$
5. $x^4 - 2x^3y - 7x^2y^2 - 3xy^3 + 5y^4$

Inclose the last two terms of each expression within parentheses and precede it by a minus (−) sign:

SET 6

1. $c + d - m - x$
2. $5a - 3b - 4c - 6d$
3. $x^3 + x^2 - 2x - 5$
4. $c^4 + c^3d + c^2d^2 - cd^3 - d^4$
5. $b^4 - 2b^3 + 3b^2 - 5b - 7$

SET 7

1. $b + c - x + y$
2. $4m - 3n - 2s + 3t$
3. $c^3 - 5c^2 - 3c + 4$
4. $-t^4 + 3t^3 - 2t^2 - 8t + 3$
5. $a^4 - 5a^3b + 7a^2b^2 - 4ab^3 + b^4$

SET 8

1. $a + c + m + n$
2. $3b - 5c + 9x + 3y$
3. $d^3 + 2d^2 + 3d + 4$
4. $-a^5 - a^4 + a^3 + a^2$
5. $m^4 + 2m^3n - 8m^2n^2 + 3mn^3 + m^4$

SET 9

1. $r + s + t - x$
2. $s^3 - 7s^2 + 3s - 6$
3. $2a^3 + a^2 + 5a - 1$
4. $x^4 - 4x^3y + 8x^2y^2 + 3xy^3 - 5y^4$
5. $-x^4 + 5x^3 - 2x^2 + x - 2$

Inclose the last three terms of each expression within parentheses and precede it by a minus (−) sign:

SET 10

1. $5b + 2d + 9m + 3x + y$
2. $n^4 - 5n^3 - n^2 - 6n - 5$
3. $3c^4 - 2c^3 + 5c^2 - 8c + 2$
4. $x^4 + 9x^3 - 7x^2 + 3x - 8$
5. $c^4 - 3c^3d - 2c^2d^2 - 6cd^3 + 5d^4$

MULTIPLICATION

EXERCISE 29

Monomial by a Monomial

I. Aim: To multiply a monomial by a monomial.

II. Procedure

1. Multiply their numerical coefficients, using the law of signs for multiplication.

2. Add the exponents of the same letters.
   To multiply a^4 by a^3 means to multiply $a \cdot a \cdot a \cdot a$ by $a \cdot a \cdot a$ or $a \cdot a \cdot a \cdot a \cdot a \cdot a \cdot a$. Here the literal number a is used 7 times as a factor in multiplication. Thus, $a^4 \cdot a^3 = a^{4+3} = a^7$.

3. If the letters are unlike, rewrite the letters in alphabetical order without changing exponents.

4. Multiply the product of the numerical coefficients (answer found in step 1) by the product of the literal factors (answer found in step 2 or 3).
   Note: a) This is done by writing the numerical product in front of the literal product.
        b) Numerical coefficients should always precede the literal factors.

5. Check by numerical substitution or division.

III. Sample Solutions

1. $\begin{array}{r} -5a^3b^4 \\ +2ab^2 \\ \hline -10a^4b^6 \end{array}$	2. $\begin{array}{r} -bx \\ -3 \\ \hline +3bx \end{array}$	3. $\begin{array}{r} 4a^2 \\ -c \\ \hline -4a^2c \end{array}$	4. $\begin{array}{r} -5bx^2 \\ 3xy^2 \\ \hline -15bx^3y^2 \end{array}$
Answer, $-10a^4b^6$	Answer, $+3bx$	Answer, $-4a^2c$	Answer, $-15bx^3y^2$

5. $(-2dx)(dx^2) = -2d^2x^3$
Answer, $-2d^2x^3$

6. $6c(5b^2c) = 30b^2c^2$
Answer, $30b^2c^2$

7. $(4a^2x)(-2ax)(-3ax^2) = +24a^4x^4$
Answer, $+24a^4x^4$

8. $(-3x^3)^3 = -27x^9$
Answer, $-27x^9$

DIAGNOSTIC TEST

Multiply:

1. $\begin{array}{c} b^6 \\ b^3 \end{array}$	6. $\begin{array}{c} -2r^4 \\ 8r^3 \end{array}$	11. $\begin{array}{c} 3c^2 \\ -a \end{array}$	16. $(-7ac)(8a^2c)$
2. $\begin{array}{c} x \\ x^4 \end{array}$	7. $\begin{array}{c} -2ab^2c^2 \\ 3a^2bc^3 \end{array}$	12. $\begin{array}{c} 2ab^2 \\ 3b^4 \end{array}$	17. $-3a(-5b)$
3. $\begin{array}{c} 4c^2 \\ 2c^4 \end{array}$	8. $\begin{array}{c} -3x^5y \\ x^6y \end{array}$	13. $\begin{array}{c} -4a^3x \\ 7x^2y \end{array}$	18. $(2ab)(-bc^2)(-3a^2c)$
4. $\begin{array}{c} -3a^3 \\ -4a^2 \end{array}$	9. $\begin{array}{c} -ax \\ 5 \end{array}$	14. $\begin{array}{c} -.8rt^2 \\ -1.2rt \end{array}$	19. $(-2b^2)^3$
5. $\begin{array}{c} +5m^3 \\ -4m^7 \end{array}$	10. $\begin{array}{c} -x^2 \\ -1 \end{array}$	15. $\begin{array}{c} \frac{1}{4}c^4d^2 \\ 2c^3d^3 \end{array}$	20. $-5xy^2$ by $3x^2$

Related Practice Examples

Multiply:

1.

x^3	c^8	b^2	m^5	r^3	y^{10}	t^8	a^7	2^4	5^8
x^2	c^4	b^4	m^2	r^3	y^5	t^{13}	a^{21}	2^3	5^6

2.

c	b^2	a	b^5	m	x	d^6	h^7	n	3^4
c	b	a^2	b	m^9	x	d	h	n^4	3

3.

$3b^2$	$5a^3$	$2x^5$	$8y$	$9w^4$	$6m^6$	$7s^6$	$10t^{10}$	$8d^4$	$6x$
$2b^2$	$7a$	$6x^3$	$4y$	$5w^6$	$8m^8$	$2s^5$	$5t^2$	$9d^8$	$12x^9$

4.

$-5a^2$	$-6x$	$-4b^3$	$-9m^4$	$-7c^4$	$-3d^8$	$-6x^6$	$-4y$	$-5w^5$	$-3w^4$
$-4a^3$	$-7x$	$-2b$	$-6m^6$	$-8c^2$	$-9d^3$	$-6x^6$	$-7y^4$	$-9w^5$	$-10w^5$

5.

$+6s$	$+7r^2$	$+4x$	$+5b^2$	$+7d^3$	$2x^9$	$4t^4$	$9v^2$	$10y^6$	$12z^{12}$
$-2s$	$-3r^3$	$-8x^4$	$-5b^3$	$-9d^7$	$-8x^2$	$-3t^5$	$-8v^2$	$-4y$	$-5z^5$

6.

$-9x^5$	$-7c^2$	$-8a^2$	$-6w^4$	$-4r^5$	$-7d^6$	$-3y^7$	$-2b$	$-8m^3$	$-4t^{10}$
$+4x^3$	$+5c^4$	$+7a^2$	$+3w^3$	$+4r^5$	$4d^3$	$9y$	$10b$	$12m^8$	$20t^{10}$

7.

$2ab$	$-4x^2y$	$6c^3d^2$	$-9a^2b^4$	$-8x^4y^3z$	$4c^5d^6x^2$	$3x^3y^2z$	$-2ab^2c$	$-8m^2n^2y$	$-9b^3d^2x^3$
$5ab$	$-8xy^2$	$-4c^4d^5$	$6a^3b^2$	$-8xyz^2$	$9c^8d^4x^7$	$-7x^4y^3z$	$2a^3bc$	$6mn^2y^3$	$-7b^5d^4x^6$

8.

$4x^3$	$-5x$	$3c^2$	$-8b^4d^2$	$-6axy$	x^8	$-a^2b^4$	$-x$	mn^2	$-bcx$
x^2	$-x$	$-c^5$	b^2d	$-a^2xy$	$5x^2$	$-7a^3b$	$3x^6$	$-9m^2n$	$-4bcx$

9.

a	8	x^2	$-y$	$-m^2n$	$5a$	7	$-3x^2y$	$-7abc$	$2d^2y$
3	b^3c^2	-2	-3	5	2	$3abc$	4	-5	-4

10.

ax	$-5ab$	1	1	$7x^4$	$-c^2d^3$	$-9x^2z$	-1	-1	-1
1	1	$4x^2y$	$-b^2cd^3$	-1	-1	-1	$3by$	$-mn^2$	$-2dx^4$

11.

b	$-x$	$-m^2$	d^5	$2b$	$5a$	$-m$	$-2b$	by	$-4a^2y$
a	y	$-n^3$	$-c^4$	d	$-c$	$-6y$	ax	$3cx$	$-bx^2$

12.

$4x^2y$	$5a$	$-2x^2$	$-9c^2d$	$-cm^2$	$5abc$	$-4xyz^2$	$-9n^2x^3$	$-4acxy$	$6ab^2d^3$
$2x^3$	$-ab$	$-3x^4y$	$6d^2$	$-8m^3$	$2ab^2$	$-7xz^2$	$3mnx$	$-ac^2y$	$-8b^3d^2$

13.

$5bx$	$-6a^2m$	$-9cy^3$	$6abc$	$8acy$	$-3bxz$	$4a^2bc^2$	$-5am^2y$	m^3xy	$4a^2bcx^2$
$3cx$	$2an$	$-3by^2$	$3cdx$	$-9abx$	$8bx^2y$	$-b^3x$	$-6bx^2y^4$	$-7m^2n$	$2adxy^2$

14.

$.6x^8y$	$-1.4\ a^2b$	$.07m^2x$	$-3.7ab^2c$	$-1.04d^2m^3x$
$.3x^2y^3$	$-.05abc^2$	$-.01n^2y$	$.15a^2bc^2$	$-7\ d^3x^2y$

15.

$\frac{1}{2}ac^2$	$-\frac{1}{4}\pi d^2$	$-9m^2x^4$	$20a^4c^2d^8$	$-\frac{3}{8}m^5xy$
$6a^3c$	$8\pi d$	$-\frac{1}{3}m^2x^5$	$-\frac{1}{10}a^3d^2x^5$	$-16n^2x^4z^2$

SET 16
1. $6x \cdot x$
2. $7cm^2 \times 6c^2m$
3. $(3a)(4a^2)$
4. $(-2b)(-5b)$
5. $(5a^2x)(9x^5y^2)$
6. $(-6bn^2)(3b^5n^2)$
7. $(-x)(-5x^3)$
8. $(4b^2c^3d)(-3b^3c^4d^5)$
9. $(-8x^2yz^3)(-2xy^2z^4)$
10. $(-4m^4)(4m^4)$

SET 17
1. $4(3b)$
2. $2a(4a^2)$
3. $-5b^2(b^3)$
4. $-x(-y)$
5. $-a(-a)$
6. $3x^2(-3x^2)$
7. $-4a^2b(5ab^2)$
8. $3x(5xy)$
9. $-1(-4x^2y)$
10. $6m^3n^2(-am^2y)$

SET 18
1. $3a^2 \cdot 2a^2 \cdot a^4$
2. $4by^3 \cdot 5xy \cdot 2bx^2$
3. $8c \cdot 3b \cdot 5c$
4. $3a^2 \cdot 3a^2 \cdot 3a^2$
5. $(-x)(-x)(-x)$
6. $(2bx^2)(3b^2x^3)(-4bx)$
7. $(-5ac)(-6bc)(-cd)$
8. $(-7ab^2)(a^5b)(-3ab^3)$
9. $(-2x)(-2x)(-2x)(-2x)$
10. $(ab^2)(-2a)(+3ab)(-4a^2b)$

SET 19
1. $(b^2x)^2$
2. $(4a^6)^2$
3. $(-3a^2b)^2$
4. $(2mn^3x)^2$
5. $(-5b^5xy^2)^2$
6. $(a^5x^2z)^3$
7. $(-4b^2x^3)^3$
8. $(2b)^4$
9. $(-4c^2d^3)^4$
10. $(3x^2y^3)^5$

SET 20
1. Multiply $4mn$ by 3
2. Multiply $-6x^2y^2$ by $-2xy$
3. Multiply $-a^2b^3$ by $7ax^2$
4. Multiply $9rt^4$ by -1
5. Multiply $12a^2b$ by a^3b^4
6. Multiply $-8m^5x^4y$ by $3m^4x^5y^8$
7. Multiply $3a^3$ by $3a^3$
8. Multiply $-9b^8x$ by $-4a^4y^2$
9. Multiply $-mn$ by $2m^2x$
10. Multiply $-5ab$ by $-6a^4bc^3$.

Applications

I. Literal Representations

1. The length of a rectangle is $6x$ inches and its width is $4x$ inches. Find its area.

2. What is the area of a square if its side measures $9a$ inches?

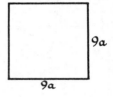

3. Find the volume of a rectangular solid having a length of $8n$ feet, a width of $2n$ feet, and a height of $6n$ feet.

4. How far can an airplane fly in 7 hours at an average speed of $80r$ miles per hour?

5. Find the cost of $5m$ dozen at $2n$ dollars per dozen.

II. Powers of Ten

Multiples of ten may be expressed as powers of ten. $10 = 10^1$; $100 = 10 \times 10 = 10^2$; $1,000 = 10 \times 10 \times 10 = 10^3$; $10,000 = 10 \times 10 \times 10 \times 10 = 10^4$; etc. Thus, exponents may be used to compare, multiply, and divide large numbers. For example, to multiply 400,000 by 20,000 by means of exponents, 400,000 is expressed as 4×10^5 since it equals $4 \times 100,000$ and 20,000 is expressed as 2×10^4 since it equals $2 \times 10,000$. Thus, $400,000 \times 20,000 = 4 \times 10^5 \times 2 \times 10^4 = 8 \times 10^9$.

1. Multiply the following vertically:

a) 3×10^7
   4×10^9

b) 9×10^6
   2×10^{11}

c) 1×10^8
   5×10^3

d) 7×10^5
   8×10

e) 6×10^{13}
   9×10^8

2. Express each of the following numbers in powers of 10:

a) 9,000,000   b) 300,000   c) 40,000,000   d) 5,000,000,000   e) 610,000,000

f) The area of the earth is about 200,000,000 square miles.

g) The population of the United States is estimated to be 140,000,000 persons.

h) The distance from the earth to the sun is approximately 93,000,000 miles.

i) A light-year is a distance of approximately 6,000,000,000,000 miles.

j) The distance from the planet Pluto to the sun is about 3,700,000,000 miles.

3. Multiply the following by means of exponents:

a) $30,000 \times 2,000$ b) $700,000 \times 50,000$ c) $4,000,000 \times 800,000$ d) $9,000,000,000 \times 500,000$

EXERCISE 30

Polynomial by a Monomial

I. Aim: To multiply a polynomial by a monomial.

II. Procedure

1. Multiply each term of the polynomial by the monomial and combine the results.

2. Check by numerical substitution or by division.

III. Sample Solutions

1. $-5(2a^2-3a+1) = -10a^2+15a-5$ Answer, $-10a^2+15a-5$

2. $b(5a-b+4) = 5ab-b^2+4b$ Answer, $5ab-b^2+4b$

3. $3x^2y(x^2-2xy-3y^2) = 3x^4y-6x^3y^2-9x^2y^3$ Answer, $3x^4y-6x^3y^2-9x^2y^3$

4. Multiply:
$$4c^2-5cd+d^2$$
$$-\ 3cd^2$$
$$\overline{}$$
$$-12c^3d^2+15c^2d^3-3cd^4$$

     Answer, $-12c^3d^2+15c^2d^3-3cd^4$

DIAGNOSTIC TEST

Multiply:

1. $3(a+4)$
2. $5(3x-7)$
3. $-2(4m+3)$
4. $-9(-d-5)$
5. $6(3x-4y)$
6. $-4(2c^2+8cd-3d^2)$

7. $x(x+1)$
8. $-x^4(2x^2-3)$
9. $b^2(3b^4-b^3-b^2+2b)$
10. $-m(m^3-5m)$
11. $ab(2a-4b)$
12. $-c^3(-b^2+3x)$

13. $x^2y(4x^2y^2-3xy+5)$
14. $2ab(3a^2b+5ab^2)$
15. $-3cd^2(2c^2-4cd-3d^2)$
16. $\frac{1}{4}r^2x(8r^2+12rx-4x^2)$
17. $.5a^4b^2(2a^2b^2+.6ab-.1)$
18. $4b^2-3b+6$
$$-2b^2$$
$$\overline{}$$

19. $a^3-3a^2b+3ab^2-b^4$ by $2a^2b^2$

Related Practice Examples

Multiply:

SET 1
1. $2(x+5)$
2. $9(a+3)$
3. $5(4b+1)$
4. $8(3m+9)$
5. $4(5x^2+10)$

SET 2
1. $3(c-5)$
2. $8(m-6)$
3. $7(3x-4)$
4. $2(3ab-1)$
5. $5(-x^2-9)$

SET 3
1. $-4(w+8)$
2. $-5(3x+2)$
3. $-2(5y+6)$
4. $-8(4y^2+1)$
5. $-6(2xy+4)$

SET 4
1. $-3(a-5)$
2. $-9(2x-9)$
3. $-4(b^2-3)$
4. $-7(-5c-1)$
5. $-2(-3ab-6)$

SET 5
1. $4(a+b)$
2. $7(2a+5x)$
3. $10(3x-7y)$
4. $9(-2x^2-4x)$
5. $12(2b^2-3b+1)$

SET 6
1. $-5(c+d)$
2. $-3(2b-5x)$
3. $-9(m^2-2m)$
4. $-12(x^3-2x^2-5)$
5. $-20(2b^2-bc+3c^2)$

SET 7

1. $b(b+3)$
2. $m(2m-4)$
3. $x^2(3x^3+5)$
4. $y^3(-2y^2-9)$
5. $abc(3a^2bc+3)$

SET 8

1. $-x(x-5)$
2. $-a(a^2+3)$
3. $-d^2(4d^4-1)$
4. $-m^2n(-m^2n-6)$
5. $-bx^3(-4bx+2)$

SET 9

1. $c(c^2+c)$
2. $x(x^3+3x^2-x)$
3. $m^2(2m^6-5m^4-m^2)$
4. $cd(c^3d-c^2d^2+2cd^3)$
5. $x^2y^3(-x^2y+2xy-3xy^2)$

SET 10

1. $-s(s-10s^3)$
2. $-n(-n^2-n)$
3. $-h^2(2h+5h^2)$
4. $-xy(3x^2y-4xy^2)$
5. $-b^3c^2(2b^3c-b^2c^2-4bc^3)$

SET 11

1. $x(x+y)$
2. $-b(3a-5b)$
3. $ay(2a^2y-3ax)$
4. $b^2x(-2bx^2+4cx)$
5. $-c^2d^3(-5c^2+3cd-d^2)$

SET 12

1. $a(x+3z)$
2. $x(c^2-d^2)$
3. $-b(5m-2x)$
4. $m^2(-a-4d)$
5. $a^2c(3x-5y)$

SET 13

1. $abc(a^2b^2c^2-2abc+1)$
2. $c^2d(c^3d-4c^2d^2-5cd^3)$
3. $-xy^2(2x^3-3xy-4y^3)$
4. $-b^3(4b^4-3b^3-2b^2+b-5)$
5. $m^2n^3(m^3-m^2n+2mn^2-7n^3)$

SET 14(a)

1. $6a(4a^2+3a)$
2. $5x^2(3x^5-2x^2)$
3. $4b(b^2-5b+6)$
4. $3x^3(x^2-3x+7)$
5. $9mn(m^2-5mn+1)$

SET 14(b)

1. $3x(4x^3-5x^2+6x)$
2. $5my(2m^2-4my+y^2)$
3. $4a^2x(-5a^2+ax-5x^2)$
4. $7b^2x^2(2b^2x^2-3bx+7)$
5. $6bc^3y(2b^2-5c^2-y^2+3)$

SET 15(a)

1. $-3b(b^2-5b)$
2. $-9a(2a^2-a+6)$
3. $-4x^2(x^2-5x-1)$
4. $-2s^3(-3r+7s-5t)$
5. $-7xy^2(4x^2-3xy+8)$

SET 15(b)

1. $-4y(2y^3-5y^2+y)$
2. $-2ab(3a^2+4ab-5b^2)$
3. $-6mn^2(m^3-m^2n^2-3n^4)$
4. $-9a^2d^2(-2a^2d-5a^2d^2+7a^2d^3)$
5. $-3x^4yz^3(x^3y-6y^2z+xz^4-4)$

SET 16

1. $\frac{1}{2}(4b^2-8b+6)$
2. $\frac{1}{4}b(12b^2-4ab+16)$
3. $-\frac{1}{3}ax(6a^2-9ab-21b^2)$
4. $\frac{2}{5}c^3(5c^3-10c^2-20c+5)$
5. $\frac{3}{4}x^2y^2(8x^3+4x^2y-16xy^2-20y^3)$

SET 17

1. $3(.4x+.9y)$
2. $.4(.5b-2c)$
3. $.2a(a^2-.3a-7)$
4. $-1.5b^2x(.2b^3-4bx+.1x^2)$
5. $.6xy^3(.12x^2+.7xy-1.1y^2)$

SET 18

Multiply:

1.
$$\begin{array}{r} 4b+5 \\ 3 \\ \hline \end{array}$$

2.
$$\begin{array}{r} a^2-4ab \\ -b \\ \hline \end{array}$$

3.
$$\begin{array}{r} 5x-3y \\ 7xy \\ \hline \end{array}$$

4.
$$\begin{array}{r} 9c^2-4d^2 \\ 6cd \\ \hline \end{array}$$

5.
$$\begin{array}{r} 2a^3b-5ab^4 \\ -4a^2b^2 \\ \hline \end{array}$$

6.
$$\begin{array}{r} a^2+2ab+b^2 \\ a \\ \hline \end{array}$$

7.
$$\begin{array}{r} 7cd+d^2+6c^2 \\ -3cd \\ \hline \end{array}$$

8.
$$\begin{array}{r} x^4-2x^3-x^2+3 \\ 4x \\ \hline \end{array}$$

9.
$$\begin{array}{r} a^3-3a^2+3ax^2-x^3 \\ -2ax \\ \hline \end{array}$$

10.
$$\begin{array}{r} a^5+2a^4-3a^3+a^2-a+1 \\ 3a^2 \\ \hline \end{array}$$

SET 19

1. Multiply $a+4$ by 3.
2. Multiply $2a^3-1$ by -1.
3. Multiply $6b+5m$ by $-4m$.
4. Multiply $5ab-3c$ by $3ac$.
5. Multiply $12b^2x-4y$ by $-2z$.
6. Multiply x^2+2x+1 by x.
7. Multiply $5b^2+3b-2$ by -3.
8. Multiply $x^4-2x^3-x^2+3$ by $4x^2$.
9. Multiply $ab-bc+cd$ by $-b^2c$
10. Multiply $r^3-6r^2x+2rx^2-8x^3$ by $-6r^2x^3$.

EXERCISE 31

Polynomial by a Polynomial

I. **Aim:** To multiply a polynomial by a polynomial.

II. **Procedure**

1. Arrange the terms of both multiplicand and multiplier in ascending or descending powers of one of the letters.

2. Starting at the left, multiply all the terms in the multiplicand by each term of the multiplier.

3. Add the partial products.

4. Check by numerical substitution or by division.

III. **Sample Solutions**

1.
$$\begin{array}{r} x+6 \\ x-2 \\ \hline x^2+6x \\ -2x-12 \\ \hline x^2+4x-12 \end{array}$$

Answer, $x^2+4x-12$

2.
$$\begin{array}{r} 3x-4y \\ 5x-2y \\ \hline 15x^2-20xy \\ -6xy+8y^2 \\ \hline 15x^2-26xy+8y^2 \end{array}$$

Answer, $15x^2-26xy+8y^2$

3.
$$\begin{array}{r} 4a-d \\ 4a+d \\ \hline 16a^2-4ad \\ +4ad-d^2 \\ \hline 16a^2 \quad\ -d^2 \end{array}$$

Answer, $16a^2-d^2$

4.
$$\begin{array}{r} 2x^2+5 \\ x+1 \\ \hline 2x^3 \quad\ +5x \\ 2x^2 \quad\ +5 \\ \hline 2x^3+2x^2+5x+5 \end{array}$$

Answer, $2x^3+2x^2+5x+5$

5.
$$\begin{array}{r} 3x^2-5x+4 \\ 2x-3 \\ \hline 6x^3-10x^2+8x \\ -9x^2+15x-12 \\ \hline 6x^3-19x^2+23x-12 \end{array}$$

Answer, $6x^3-19x^2+23x-12$

6.
$$\begin{array}{r} 2b^2-b-3 \\ 4b^2+2b-5 \\ \hline 8b^4-4b^3-12b^2 \\ 4b^3-2b^2-6b \\ -10b^2+5b+15 \\ \hline 8b^4 \quad\ -24b^2-b+15 \end{array}$$

Answer, $8b^4-24b^2-b+15$

DIAGNOSTIC TEST

Multiply:

1. $\begin{array}{r}x+4\\x+3\end{array}$	**6.** $\begin{array}{r}x+y\\x+y\end{array}$	**11.** $\begin{array}{r}6+b\\5-2b\end{array}$	**16.** $\begin{array}{r}8bc+x\\3bc-2x\end{array}$	**21.** $\begin{array}{r}x^2-6xy+9y^2\\x+3y\end{array}$
2. $\begin{array}{r}d+8\\d-5\end{array}$	**7.** $\begin{array}{r}c-d\\c-d\end{array}$	**12.** $\begin{array}{r}5ax-3\\3ax-8\end{array}$	**17.** $\begin{array}{r}x^2+x\\x+1\end{array}$	**22.** $\begin{array}{r}s^2-2s+6\\2s^2+3s-4\end{array}$
3. $\begin{array}{r}y-7\\y+3\end{array}$	**8.** $\begin{array}{r}a+x\\a-x\end{array}$	**13.** $\begin{array}{r}2s-3\\4+5s\end{array}$	**18.** $\begin{array}{r}5x^2+2\\x+7\end{array}$	**23.** $\begin{array}{r}b^3-3b^2+9b-27\\b+3\end{array}$
4. $\begin{array}{r}a-5\\a-4\end{array}$	**9.** $\begin{array}{r}m^2+3\\m^2-9\end{array}$	**14.** $\begin{array}{r}2c-3d\\3c+4d\end{array}$	**19.** $\begin{array}{r}a+b\\a+c\end{array}$	**24.** $(5b+2c)(3b-7c)$
5. $\begin{array}{r}c-2\\c+2\end{array}$	**10.** $\begin{array}{r}2x-7\\4x+3\end{array}$	**15.** $\begin{array}{r}3a^2-4b^2\\2a^2-3b^2\end{array}$	**20.** $\begin{array}{r}y^2-2y+1\\y-1\end{array}$	**25.** $3a^2+2a-7$ by $a-8$

Related Practice Examples

Multiply:

1.	$a+7$ $a+5$	$x+1$ $x+1$	$b+6$ $b+3$	$c+2$ $c+8$	$m+5$ $m+5$
2.	$s+4$ $s-2$	$n+7$ $n-6$	$d+5$ $d-9$	$y+\ 3$ $y-10$	$w+1$ $w-2$
3.	$x-8$ $x+2$	$b-5$ $b+4$	$h-9$ $h+7$	$t-2$ $t+6$	$y-\ 6$ $y+15$
4.	$a-3$ $a-2$	$d-6$ $d-6$	$x-1$ $x-9$	$s-3$ $s-8$	$n-\ 9$ $n-10$
5.	$x+8$ $x-8$	$b+4$ $b-4$	$r-3$ $r+3$	$d-1$ $d+1$	$y-9$ $y+9$
6.	$a+b$ $a+b$	$c+d$ $c+d$	$m+n$ $m+n$	$b+c$ $b+c$	$r+s$ $r+s$
7.	$x-y$ $x-y$	$b-c$ $b-c$	$a-x$ $a-x$	$m-n$ $m-n$	$s-t$ $s-t$
8.	$c+d$ $c-d$	$x+y$ $x-y$	$w-x$ $w+x$	$a-b$ $a+b$	$y-z$ $y+z$
9.	b^2+4 b^2+2	a^2-3 a^2+5	x^2-4 x^2-7	x^3+6 x^3+6	c^4-3 c^4+3
10.	$4c+5$ $3c+2$	$6b+3$ $6b+3$	$2a+5$ $3a+4$	$5y+7$ $2y-3$	$4x-6$ $4x-2$
	$5d+4$ $6d+7$	$3m-4$ $m+5$	$6x-9$ $-2x-5$	$-\ a-1$ $8a-1$	$2d+7$ $2d-7$
11.	$2+x$ $3-x$	$8+2x$ $5+7x$	$7-b$ $7+b$	$1-4y$ $6+7y$	$5-3b^2$ $5-\ b^2$
12.	$3ab+6$ $2ab+5$	$6xy-3$ $8xy-4$	$2m^2n-8$ $-\ m^2n+7$	$9abc+3$ $5abc-8$	$1-2c^2y$ $4-3c^2y$
13.	$x+4$ $3+x$	$b-5$ $8-b$	$2c-4$ $9\ +5c$	$3b^2+8$ $10\ \ +2b^2$	$4xy+9$ $5\ \ +3xy$

14.

$$2x+3y$$
$$3x+2y$$

$$5m+9n$$
$$3m+6n$$

$$6a+2c$$
$$4a-3c$$

$$2a-\ b$$
$$a+3b$$

$$8n-3r$$
$$9n+6r$$

$$6b-5m$$
$$2b-4m$$

$$7x-2y$$
$$3x-4y$$

$$5b+3d$$
$$4b-3d$$

$$8c-4x$$
$$-\ c-5x$$

$$4a-\ y$$
$$2a-5y$$

15.

$$x^2+y^2$$
$$x^2+y^2$$

$$a^4-b^4$$
$$a^4+b^4$$

$$6m^3-4s^3$$
$$2m^3-9s^3$$

$$7x^2-2y$$
$$3x^2-4y$$

$$6a+3d^2$$
$$-4a-3d^2$$

16.

$$8ab+c$$
$$3ab+c$$

$$2x+3xy$$
$$3x+4xy$$

$$5mn-\ s$$
$$2mn+3s$$

$$7cd^2-2d$$
$$6cd^2-5d$$

$$4x^2y+2xy^2$$
$$3x^2y-5xy^2$$

17.

$$a^2+a$$
$$a+4$$

$$2x^2-3x$$
$$x-2$$

$$b^3-b^2$$
$$2b-5$$

$$c^3-2c^2$$
$$3c+7$$

$$d^4-\ d^3$$
$$d^2-2d$$

18.

$$4m^2+1$$
$$m+3$$

$$3y^2-9$$
$$5y+2$$

$$2a^3-1$$
$$a-1$$

$$4x+7$$
$$3x^2-9$$

$$7-3a^2$$
$$8-\ a$$

19.

$$a+b$$
$$c+d$$

$$r-2s$$
$$c+3d$$

$$6x^2+3y$$
$$4x-3y$$

$$5ab-2c$$
$$4ac-7b$$

$$12b^2x-4y$$
$$3a^2x-2z$$

20.

$$x^2+2x+1$$
$$x+1$$

$$a^2+4a+4$$
$$a-2$$

$$5b^2+3b-2$$
$$b+3$$

$$1+8y-y^2$$
$$2+y$$

$$3a-5+a^2$$
$$4-a$$

21.

$$a^2+2ab+b^2$$
$$a+b$$

$$3c^2+2cd-4d^2$$
$$c-d$$

$$2b^2+4bc-\ c^2$$
$$7b-3c$$

$$7xy-\ y^2+6x^2$$
$$5y+2x$$

$$9m^2-4mn-5n^2$$
$$-3m-\ n$$

22.

$$a+b+c$$
$$a-b+c$$

$$x^2+x+3$$
$$x^2-x-2$$

$$4m^2-3m-2$$
$$m^2+5m+4$$

$$x^2-2xy+y^2$$
$$x^2+2xy+y^2$$

$$a^3-\ a^2-\ a$$
$$a^2+2a-3$$

23.

$$x^3-2x^2-x+3$$
$$4x-5$$

$$c^3-2c^2d+5cd^2-\ d^3$$
$$c-3d$$

$$a^5+2a^4-3a^3+a^2-a+1$$
$$a-1$$

$$x^3-x^2+x-1$$
$$x^2-x+1$$

$$a^3-3a^2x+3ax^2-x^3$$
$$a^2-2ax+x^2$$

SET 24

1. $(c+3d)(2c-4d)$
2. $(1-x)(1-x)$
3. $(2x-4)(-3x+9)$
4. $(5b^2-4x)(2b^2+9x)$
5. $(3a^2b+5ab^2)(2a^2b-7ab^2)$
6. $(3a^2+2a-7)(-a-8)$
7. $(2c^2-5c+3)(3c-4)$
8. $(b+c-4x)(b+c-3y)$
9. $(2b^2-4bc-c^2)(7b-3c)$
10. $(x^4+2x^3-3x^2+7x+5)(3x-4)$

SET 25

1. Multiply $x+8$ by $x+6$
2. Multiply $c-d$ by $c-d$
3. Multiply $2x-y$ by $2x+y$
4. Multiply $5b+2$ by $4-3b$
5. Multiply $4m-3n$ by $7m+n$
6. Multiply $3b-5b^2+9$ by $2b-5$
7. Multiply $2r^2-3rs-6s^2$ by $r-s$
8. Multiply $b-c-d$ by $b+c-d$
9. Multiply $6-5x+4x^2-3x^3+x^4$ by $3-x$
10. Multiply $a^4-4a^3x+7a^2x^2-ax^3+5x^4$ by $a-2x$

PARENTHESES
EXERCISE 32
Removal by Multiplication

I. **Aim**: To remove parentheses by means of multiplication.

II. **Procedure**

1. If the parentheses are immediately preceded by a term, remove parentheses by multiplying each term in the parentheses by the term which precedes it.
   Note: In the example $6a + 5(a-3)$ the quantity $a-3$ is thought of being immediately preceded by the term 5 and not by the term $6a$.

2. If the parentheses are preceded by either a plus $(+)$ or a minus $(-)$ sign with no term between the sign and the parentheses, the monomial 1 is understood to precede the parentheses. Here remove parentheses by multiplying each term in parentheses by either $+1$ or -1, using the value whose sign corresponds to the sign preceding the parentheses.
   Note: In the example $4b + (2a-5)$ the quantity $2a-5$ is thought of as being preceded by the plus $(+)$ sign and not by the term $4b$.

3. Combine similar terms.

III. **Sample Solutions**

1. $3a + 5(a-2)$
   $= 3a + 5a - 10$
   $= 8a - 10$
   Answer, $8a - 10$

2. $2b - 5b(3b-2) + 18b^2$
   $= 2b - 15b^2 + 10b + 18b^2$
   $= 3b^2 + 12b$
   Answer, $3b^2 + 12b$

3. $5x - (2x-3) + 4$
   $= 5x - 2x + 3 + 4$
   $= 3x + 7$
   Answer, $3x + 7$

4. $(x+2)(x-3) - (x-5)(x-1)$
   $= (x^2 - x - 6) - (x^2 - 6x + 5)$
   $= x^2 - x - 6 - x^2 + 6x - 5$
   $= 5x - 11$
   Answer, $5x - 11$

DIAGNOSTIC TEST

Remove parentheses and, if possible, add like terms:

1. $3(x+4) + 2x$
2. $-5(4b-3) + 6b - 4$
3. $-a(a+6) - 4a^2$
4. $4 + 6(y-3)$
5. $9 - 3(2c+7)$
6. $8b - b(3b-1)$
7. $bc + 2c(b-3c)$
8. $4x - 3x(5x-4) + 20x^2$
9. $9xy - (2xy + 8y^2)$
10. $a^2 + 3a + 2a(a-4) - 3a(a-3) - 4a$
11. $b^2 - b - 4[2b + 3(b-4)]$
12. $(x+2)(x+3) + (x-1)(x-2)$
13. $(m-5)(m+4) - (m-6)(m-2)$
14. $4x(x+1) - 2x(x-3) - (x+2)(x-8)$

Related Practice Examples

Remove parentheses and, if possible, add like terms:

SET 1

1. $2(a+3) + 5$
2. $3(5b+7) + 4b$
3. $9(x-2) - 3x + 10$
4. $4(2a-3y) - 7y - 3a$
5. $6(-5m+n) + 9m + 4n$

SET 2

1. $-3(c+6) + 10$
2. $-6(8-4c) - 5c$
3. $-5(-2b^2-b) + 15b^2 - 3b$
4. $-7(4a-5x) - 4x + 30a$
5. $-2(9m^2-3m+2) + m^2 - 5m$

SET 3

1. $x(x+4)-2x$
2. $b^2(b-3)-5b^2$
3. $-d(3a+4c)+7ad-2cd$
4. $-a^3(2a^2-a+6)+3a^4-4a^3$
5. $-ax(-6a-5x)+7ax^2-4a^2x$

SET 4

1. $3+4(y+3)$
2. $7+5(2x-4)$
3. $9+3(-m+6)$
4. $b+7(-7a-2b)$
5. $5c+2(3x-9c)$

SET 5

1. $8-2(x+6)$
2. $6-4(3x-1)$
3. $5-5(-b^2-2)$
4. $7a-2(3a-b)$
5. $4x-6(2x-3y)$

SET 6

1. $6b+b(1+b)$
2. $5x-x(3x-5)$
3. $2y^2-y(x-y)$
4. $6x^2+x(4x-5)$
5. $9b^3-b^2(a-2b)$

SET 7

1. $ax+2x(a+x)$
2. $4by-3b(y-2b)$
3. $3mn-2m(-3m-n)$
4. $9x^2y+5x(2xy-y)$
5. $4a^4b^2-4ab(2a^2b+3ab^2)$

SET 8

1. $2c+c(5c+3)+4c^2$
2. $9bx-x(2b-5x)-2x^2$
3. $6x+3(7-4x)+28$
4. $4m^2-2m(m-3n)-5mn$
5. $2c^2y-5c(4cy-y)+9cy$

SET 9

1. $2a+(4a-3b)$
2. $9x+3-(2x-5)$
3. $4a^2-3a-(4a-9a^2)$
4. $2cd-d^2+(c^2-2cd)$
5. $x^3-5x^2-(3x+3-x^3)$

SET 10

1. $x^2+4x-2(x+3)+x(2x-4)$
2. $2b^2-b(b-2)+3b(2b-5)$
3. $a^2-2a-(2a^2-5a)+3a(a-4)$
4. $3x^2+(x^2-3x+1)+2x-x(x+3)-8$
5. $4a^2b-a(2ab+b^2)-2ab^2-3b(4ab-3a^2)-2a^2b$

SET 11

1. $4a+2[4a+2(3a-5)]$
2. $x^2-5x-3[2x+x(x-3)]$
3. $3a^2b-ab^2-b[3a+b(a+1)]$
4. $5m^3-2m^2[5m-2(m-3)]+3m^2$
5. $4x^2y+3x[xy-3(y^2-2xy)]-4xy^2$

SET 12

1. $(x+4)(x+2)+(x+2)(x+2)$
2. $(a-3)(a+1)+(a+6)(a+3)$
3. $(3y-5)(4y-2)+(y+4)(y-3)$
4. $(x+y)(x+y)+(x-y)(x+y)$
5. $(c-3d)(c+3d)+(5c-4d)(2c+5d)$

SET 13

1. $(c-2)(c+7)-(c+1)(c+1)$
2. $(a-b)(a-b)-(a+b)(a-b)$
3. $(2x-3)(3x-2)-(4x-1)(3x+5)$
4. $(3c-5d)(3c+2d)-(2c-7d)(5c-3d)$
5. $(x^2-y^2)(x^2+y^2)-(x^2-y^2)(x^2-y^2)$

SET 14

1. $2a(a+2)+(a-3)(a-5)$
2. $(x-5)(x+5)-3x(x-3)+6x$
3. $8y-(2y-3)(2y+5)-3y(y+2)$
4. $-5b(b+c)+3bc-(b-c)(b-2c)$
5. $(a-b)(a+b)-b(a-b)+a(a+b)-b^2$

DIVISION

EXERCISE 33

A Monomial by a Monomial

I. Aim: To divide a monomial by a monomial.

II. Procedure

1. Divide their numerical coefficients, using the law of signs for division.

2. Subtract the exponents of letters in the divisor from the exponents of the same letters in the dividend.

   To divide n^8 by n^2 means to divide $n \cdot n \cdot n \cdot n \cdot n \cdot n \cdot n \cdot n$ by $n \cdot n$

   or $\dfrac{\cancel{n} \cdot \cancel{n} \cdot n \cdot n \cdot n \cdot n \cdot n \cdot n}{\cancel{n} \cdot \cancel{n}} = n \cdot n \cdot n \cdot n \cdot n \cdot n = n^6$. Thus, $n^8 \div n^2$ or $\dfrac{n^8}{n^2} = n^{8-2} = n^6$.

3. If letters in dividend have no like letters in the divisor, rewrite letters in alphabetical order without changing exponents.

4. Multiply the quotient of the numerical coefficients (answer found in step 1) by the quotient of literal factors (answer found in step 2 or 3).

5. Check by numerical substitution or multiplication.

III. Sample Solutions

1. $\dfrac{-12a^5}{+4a^3} = -3a^2$

   Answer, $-3a^2$

2. $\dfrac{-6b^4}{-2b^4} = +3$

   Answer, $+3$

3. $\dfrac{+5c^2mx^3}{-5cx^2} = -cmx$

   Answer, $-cmx$

4. $\dfrac{8x^2y}{-x} = -8xy$

   Answer, $-8xy$

5. $\dfrac{35a^3b^2c^4}{5a^3bc} = 7bc^3$

   Answer, $7bc^3$

6. $\dfrac{2a^2c}{-2a^2c} = -1$

   Answer, -1

DIAGNOSTIC TEST

Divide:

1. $\dfrac{x^6}{x^2}$

2. $\dfrac{c^4}{c^4}$

3. $\dfrac{a^4b^5c^2}{a^2b^3c}$

4. $\dfrac{x^4y^3z^7}{x^3z^4}$

5. $\dfrac{m^2r^3s^4}{mrs^4}$

6. $\dfrac{8b}{2}$

7. $\dfrac{-6m^4}{-3}$

8. $\dfrac{21m^3n^2}{-7}$

9. $\dfrac{-36h^6x^3y}{9}$

10. $\dfrac{7s^3t^2}{-1}$

11. $\dfrac{-12xy}{-12}$

12. $\dfrac{16c^8}{4c^2}$

13. $\dfrac{-56a^9y^4}{-7a^3y^2}$

14. $\dfrac{-63b^8x^2}{9b^6x}$

15. $\dfrac{6x^4y^5z^2}{-2xyz}$

16. $\dfrac{-21b^2}{3b^2}$

17. $\dfrac{6x^2y}{-6x^2y}$

18. $\dfrac{4a^6b^2}{-b}$

19. $\dfrac{-1.2h^2k^5}{.4hk^2}$

20. $(5x^2y^3) \div (-xy^2)$

21. $-14m^5x^2y$ by $-2m^2xy$

Related Practice Examples

Divide:

1. $\dfrac{a^5}{a^2}$ $\quad$ $\dfrac{b^7}{b^3}$ $\quad$ $\dfrac{x^4}{x^2}$ $\quad$ $\dfrac{y^9}{y^3}$ $\quad$ $\dfrac{m^{10}}{m^5}$ $\quad$ $\dfrac{s^3}{s^2}$ $\quad$ $\dfrac{x^8}{x}$ $\quad$ $\dfrac{v^2}{v}$ $\quad$ $\dfrac{2^{10}}{2^4}$ $\quad$ $\dfrac{5^8}{5^6}$

2. $\dfrac{b^2}{b^2}$ $\quad$ $\dfrac{x^5}{x^5}$ $\quad$ $\dfrac{a^3}{a^3}$ $\quad$ $\dfrac{u^4}{u^4}$ $\quad$ $\dfrac{d}{d}$ $\quad$ $\dfrac{m^2}{m^2}$ $\quad$ $\dfrac{w^{10}}{w^{10}}$ $\quad$ $\dfrac{r^8}{r^8}$ $\quad$ $\dfrac{3^7}{3^7}$ $\quad$ $\dfrac{8^{10}}{8^{10}}$

3. $\dfrac{m^4n^3}{m^2n^2}$ $\quad$ $\dfrac{a^8x^5}{a^4x^2}$ $\quad$ $\dfrac{b^9c^4}{b^6c^2}$ $\quad$ $\dfrac{a^2b^3c^4}{ab^2c^3}$ $\quad$ $\dfrac{x^4y^2z^7}{xyz^6}$ $\quad$ $\dfrac{m^4x^5y^6}{m^2xy^3}$ $\quad$ $\dfrac{b^5y^8z^7}{b^4y^4z^4}$ $\quad$ $\dfrac{a^4m^5x^9}{am^2x^5}$ $\quad$ $\dfrac{c^6x^4z^8}{c^4x^3z^5}$ $\quad$ $\dfrac{b^4n^6x^8}{bn^3x^7}$

4. $\dfrac{a^5x}{a^3}$ $\quad$ $\dfrac{c^3d^3}{c^2}$ $\quad$ $\dfrac{m^2n^5}{n^4}$ $\quad$ $\dfrac{x^9y^6}{y^2}$ $\quad$ $\dfrac{a^2c^5d^3}{ac^3}$ $\quad$ $\dfrac{m^2n^3y^5}{ny}$ $\quad$ $\dfrac{c^4x^3y^6}{c^3y^2}$ $\quad$ $\dfrac{bn^3t^7}{n^2t^4}$ $\quad$ $\dfrac{r^9s^5x^6}{x^4}$ $\quad$ $\dfrac{a^3x^3y}{x^2}$

5. $\dfrac{bc^2}{bc}$ $\quad$ $\dfrac{c^3x^2}{c^3}$ $\quad$ $\dfrac{m^5y}{m^2y}$ $\quad$ $\dfrac{c^4d^2}{c^2d^2}$ $\quad$ $\dfrac{a^5b^4c^3}{ab^2c^3}$ $\quad$ $\dfrac{c^7d^2x^5}{c^2d^2x^3}$ $\quad$ $\dfrac{r^8s^8t^4}{r^3st^3}$ $\quad$ $\dfrac{m^7n^2x^6}{m^5x^6}$ $\quad$ $\dfrac{a^4c^2m}{a^3c^2m}$ $\quad$ $\dfrac{b^5d^4y^2}{b^5d^4y}$

6. $\dfrac{6b}{3}$ $\quad$ $\dfrac{12ab}{4}$ $\quad$ $\dfrac{20c^8}{5}$ $\quad$ $\dfrac{16a^4b}{2}$ $\quad$ $\dfrac{18xyz}{3}$ $\quad$ $\dfrac{24a^2c}{6}$ $\quad$ $\dfrac{50mn^2}{10}$ $\quad$ $\dfrac{32x^2y^3}{8}$ $\quad$ $\dfrac{27a^2xy}{9}$ $\quad$ $\dfrac{45b^4xy^3}{5}$

7. $\dfrac{-4a}{-2}$ $\quad$ $\dfrac{-9x^2}{-3}$ $\quad$ $\dfrac{-21bc}{-7}$ $\quad$ $\dfrac{-15a^2x}{-5}$ $\quad$ $\dfrac{-12dy^2}{-6}$ $\quad$ $\dfrac{-18m^2x^2}{-9}$ $\quad$ $\dfrac{-28x^4y}{-4}$ $\quad$ $\dfrac{-63abc}{-9}$ $\quad$ $\dfrac{-48a^2my}{-12}$ $\quad$ $\dfrac{-60b^4cx^2}{-5}$

8. $\dfrac{8x}{-4}$ $\quad$ $\dfrac{6c^2}{-2}$ $\quad$ $\dfrac{10b^8}{-5}$ $\quad$ $\dfrac{27ay}{-9}$ $\quad$ $\dfrac{24b^2c}{-6}$ $\quad$ $\dfrac{36m^4x^4}{-4}$ $\quad$ $\dfrac{42cy^3}{-7}$ $\quad$ $\dfrac{54bcd}{-6}$ $\quad$ $\dfrac{72x^3yz}{-8}$ $\quad$ $\dfrac{80m^3n^2y^2}{-16}$

9. $\dfrac{-8x}{2}$ $\quad$ $\dfrac{-10m}{5}$ $\quad$ $\dfrac{-14x^3}{7}$ $\quad$ $\dfrac{-15bd}{3}$ $\quad$ $\dfrac{-25x^2y}{5}$ $\quad$ $\dfrac{-40b^3c^2}{8}$ $\quad$ $\dfrac{-32c^4d^4}{16}$ $\quad$ $\dfrac{-50bcx}{25}$ $\quad$ $\dfrac{-28b^2cd}{7}$ $\quad$ $\dfrac{-56dm^2x^5}{8}$

10. $\dfrac{3n}{1}$ $\quad$ $\dfrac{5s}{1}$ $\quad$ $\dfrac{-9ab}{1}$ $\quad$ $\dfrac{-x}{1}$ $\quad$ $\dfrac{-5c^3x}{1}$ $\quad$ $\dfrac{2x}{-1}$ $\quad$ $\dfrac{7s^3}{-1}$ $\quad$ $\dfrac{-6a^2x}{-1}$ $\quad$ $\dfrac{-9b^2y^2}{-1}$ $\quad$ $\dfrac{-a^5}{-1}$

11. $\dfrac{3d}{3}$ $\quad$ $\dfrac{4a^2}{4}$ $\quad$ $\dfrac{-6bd}{6}$ $\quad$ $\dfrac{-2c^2x}{2}$ $\quad$ $\dfrac{-10y^2z^3}{10}$ $\quad$ $\dfrac{4x^4}{-4}$ $\quad$ $\dfrac{12bd}{-12}$ $\quad$ $\dfrac{-9n^3r^4}{-9}$ $\quad$ $\dfrac{-25x^5y^4}{-25}$ $\quad$ $\dfrac{-32a^3b^2c}{-32}$

12. $\dfrac{12x^8}{2x^2}$ $\quad$ $\dfrac{15m^6}{3m}$ $\quad$ $\dfrac{27a^3b^2}{9a}$ $\quad$ $\dfrac{36c^5d^4}{18cd}$ $\quad$ $\dfrac{24b^2x^7}{6bx^4}$ $\quad$ $\dfrac{49m^6x^3}{7m^3x}$ $\quad$ $\dfrac{50a^3b^2c}{5a^2b}$ $\quad$ $\dfrac{64m^4x^2}{8m^2x^2}$ $\quad$ $\dfrac{72a^2b^5}{9a^2b^2}$ $\quad$ $\dfrac{75m^2n^2y}{25mn^2y}$

13. $\dfrac{-4d^7}{-2d^3}$ $\qquad$ $\dfrac{-6b^8}{-3b^5}$ $\qquad$ $\dfrac{-15b^5c^3}{-5c^2}$ $\qquad$ $\dfrac{-18r^4t^2}{-3rt}$ $\qquad$ $\dfrac{-30s^3x}{-6s^2}$

$\dfrac{-42at^2}{-7at}$ $\qquad$ $\dfrac{-21m^5n^2}{-3m^2n^2}$ $\qquad$ $\dfrac{-54x^2yz}{-9xyz}$ $\qquad$ $\dfrac{-48a^4c^3d}{-8a^2cd}$ $\qquad$ $\dfrac{-64d^2r^2t^3}{-16dt^2}$

14. $\dfrac{-6a^9}{2a^3}$ $\qquad$ $\dfrac{-12b^5}{3b^2}$ $\qquad$ $\dfrac{-16m^4n}{4mn}$ $\qquad$ $\dfrac{-32d^4r}{8d^3}$ $\qquad$ $\dfrac{-35r^4t^2}{7rt^2}$

$\dfrac{-52gt^3}{4gt}$ $\qquad$ $\dfrac{-72m^4n^2}{12mn^2}$ $\qquad$ $\dfrac{-80a^3b^2x^4}{5abx}$ $\qquad$ $\dfrac{-44c^5d^4x}{11c^2d}$ $\qquad$ $\dfrac{-96m^5nx}{16m^2x}$

15. $\dfrac{10b^2}{-5b}$ $\dfrac{16c^5}{-8c^3}$ $\dfrac{21a^2c^4}{-7ac}$ $\dfrac{34b^2c}{-17b}$ $\dfrac{45x^4y}{-15x}$

     $\dfrac{96a^5x^9}{-12a^2x^7}$ $\dfrac{63d^4y^7}{-7dy^8}$ $\dfrac{81c^4d^3x}{-9c^3d^3x}$ $\dfrac{54d^5x^2y^3}{-6dxy}$ $\dfrac{98a^4b^2c^5}{-49a^4b^2}$

16. $\dfrac{16a^4}{8a^4}$ $\dfrac{-25c^3d}{5c^3d}$ $\dfrac{-30xy^2}{-3xy^2}$ $\dfrac{28abc}{-7abc}$ $\dfrac{48b^2x^3y}{16b^2x^3y}$

     $\dfrac{6a^4}{6a^2}$ $\dfrac{-15bc^2}{-15bc}$ $\dfrac{-28c^3d}{28c}$ $\dfrac{9m^4x^3}{-9mx^2}$ $\dfrac{-20r^2s^3t}{-20rst}$

17. $\dfrac{2x}{2x}$ $\dfrac{-9b^2}{9b^2}$ $\dfrac{-4m^2n}{-4m^2n}$ $\dfrac{16bx^2}{-16bx^2}$ $\dfrac{5bcd}{5bcd}$

     $\dfrac{-3amy}{-3amy}$ $\dfrac{-14c^8y}{14c^8y}$ $\dfrac{8a^2b^2y}{-8a^2b^2y}$ $\dfrac{-23rst^2}{-23rst^2}$ $\dfrac{19x^3yz^4}{-19x^3yz^4}$

18. $\dfrac{3mn}{m}$ $\dfrac{4x^2}{-x}$ $\dfrac{-2b^2c}{bc}$ $\dfrac{-9x^3y}{-y}$ $\dfrac{6x^8}{x^4}$

     $\dfrac{-5ab}{a}$ $\dfrac{-2xy^2}{-x}$ $\dfrac{7a^3b^2c}{-abc}$ $\dfrac{15d^2rt^3}{-dt^3}$ $\dfrac{-8x^4y^2z^5}{-x^2yz^4}$

19. $\dfrac{.6a^5x^2}{.2a^2x}$ $\dfrac{-1.8r^2t}{.3rt}$ $\dfrac{-.08m^3x^2y^4}{-.2mxy^2}$ $\dfrac{3.9a^4b^4c}{-1.3a^3b^4}$ $\dfrac{-8c^3xy^5}{-.5xy^2}$

SET 20

1. $x^9 \div x^3$
2. $(-3b^3x) \div (-3bx)$
3. $(15m^5) \div (3m^2)$
4. $(-32c^4y) \div (8c^2)$
5. $(-42m^6n^6) \div (7m^3n^2)$
6. $(14a^5b) \div (-ab)$
7. $(-12b^7cx^2) \div (-4b^2c)$
8. $(-9d^4x^3y^5) \div (9d^2xy^3)$
9. $(60b^5m^4t^2) \div (15b^5m^4t^2)$
10. $(-2.1c^6r) \div (-.3c^4)$

SET 21

1. Divide $-20ab$ by $-a$.
2. Divide $49m^2n$ by $-7mn$.
3. Divide $-36a^4b$ by $4b$.
4. Divide $22cd$ by 11.
5. Divide $-5m^8y^2$ by $-5y^2$.
6. Divide $10b^3c^2x$ by $2bcx$.
7. Divide $-16x^2yz^4$ by $8xyz^4$.
8. Divide $9a^2bcx^4$ by $-acx^2$.
9. Divide $-64d^2r^3t^8$ by $-32d^2r^3t^7$.
10. Divide $-100a^4t^2y$ by $25at^2y$.

EXERCISE 34

A Polynomial by a Monomial

I. **Aim**: To divide a polynomial by a monomial.

II. **Procedure**

1. Divide each term of the polynomial by the monomial and combine the results.

2. Check by numerical substitution or by multiplication.

III. **Sample Solutions**

1. $\dfrac{3x-12}{3} = x-4$

Answer, $x-4$

2. $\dfrac{5m^2-m}{-m} = -5m+1$

Answer, $-5m+1$

3. $\dfrac{4a^2b-8ab+12ab^2}{4ab} = a-2+3b$

Answer, $a+3b-2$

4. $\dfrac{15m^4n^2+10m^3n^3-5m^2n^4}{-5m^2n} = -3m^2n-2mn^2+n^3$

Answer, $-3m^2n-2mn^2+n^3$

DIAGNOSTIC TEST

Divide:

1. $\dfrac{6x+4}{2}$

2. $\dfrac{5a-10}{-5}$

3. $\dfrac{8b-4}{4}$

4. $\dfrac{3a+6b}{3}$

5. $\dfrac{-16xy+24yz}{-8}$

6. $\dfrac{12b^2-18bc+24c^2}{6}$

7. $\dfrac{4b^2+3c^2-d^2}{-1}$

8. $\dfrac{m^3-m^2}{m}$

9. $\dfrac{2x-5x^2}{-x}$

10. $\dfrac{5d^4+3d^2}{d^2}$

11. $\dfrac{4c^2-c}{-c}$

12. $\dfrac{x^5y-2x^4y^2+x^3y^3}{x^2y}$

13. $\dfrac{8a^3-6ab}{2a}$

14. $\dfrac{9c^5d^3-27c^2d^2+6c^3d^5}{-3cd^2}$

15. $\dfrac{7m^6n^3x^2-14m^5n^2x^4+21m^4n^2x^4-28m^3n^2x}{7m^3n^2x}$

16. $(6r^2t-4rt+8rt^2) \div (-2rt)$

17. Divide $9x^2y^2+3x^2y-6xy^2$ by $3xy$

Related Practice Examples

Divide:

1. $\dfrac{9a+6}{3}$ $\qquad$ $\dfrac{16x^2+24}{8}$ $\qquad$ $\dfrac{5ay-15}{5}$ $\qquad$ $\dfrac{12r-8}{4}$ $\qquad$ $\dfrac{-50b-30}{10}$

2. $\dfrac{8x+10}{-2}$ $\qquad$ $\dfrac{7m+21}{-7}$ $\qquad$ $\dfrac{18a-81}{-9}$ $\qquad$ $\dfrac{15c^2-24}{-3}$ $\qquad$ $\dfrac{-24d+36}{-12}$

3. $\dfrac{5y+5}{5}$ $\qquad$ $\dfrac{24cd+8}{8}$ $\qquad$ $\dfrac{30m-6}{-6}$ $\qquad$ $\dfrac{3s-3}{-3}$ $\qquad$ $\dfrac{-6a^2-2}{2}$

4. $\dfrac{4c+8d}{4}$ $\dfrac{21b^2-28c^2}{7}$ $\dfrac{36ab+18cd}{9}$ $\dfrac{42m-18m^2}{6}$ $\dfrac{-3b^2+9bc}{3}$

5. $\dfrac{10b+6x}{-2}$ $\dfrac{15x+25y}{-5}$ $\dfrac{64r^2-8d}{-8}$ $\dfrac{-20rs+12st}{-4}$ $\dfrac{-56m^3-35m^2}{-7}$

6. $\dfrac{8a+12b-16}{4}$ $\dfrac{9a^2-18x^2+27y^2}{9}$ $\dfrac{6x^2-9xy+36y^2}{-3}$ $\dfrac{5x^3-10x^2-25x+15}{-5}$ $\dfrac{16b^4-8b^3+40b^2-24b}{8}$

7. $\dfrac{2a+5d}{1}$ $\dfrac{3x^2-7y^2}{1}$ $\dfrac{4c-6}{-1}$ $\dfrac{x^2-4xy+2y^2}{-1}$ $\dfrac{a^3+4a^2-6a-1}{-1}$

8. $\dfrac{b^4+b^3}{b}$ $\dfrac{cx-cv}{c}$ $\dfrac{x^8-x^7y}{x}$ $\dfrac{5m^6-m^4}{m}$ $\dfrac{3a^2-a^3+2a^4}{a}$

9. $\dfrac{ad+bd}{-d}$ $\dfrac{2h^2-h^4}{-h}$ $\dfrac{3y^6-4xy}{-y}$ $\dfrac{5c^8+c^6-3c^2}{-c}$ $\dfrac{-xy+x^2y-x^2y^3}{-x}$

10. $\dfrac{a^4-a^6}{a^2}$ $\dfrac{4x^9-3x^5}{x^3}$ $\dfrac{5xz^4-y^2z^3}{-z^2}$ $\dfrac{n^8x-2n^4y}{-n^4}$ $\dfrac{-4c^8+3c^7-c^6}{-c^5}$

11. $\dfrac{m^2+m}{m}$ $\dfrac{4r^2-r}{r}$ $\dfrac{2x^4-x}{-x}$ $\dfrac{s^8+s^2}{s^2}$ $\dfrac{-3y^6+y^3}{-y^3}$

12. $\dfrac{a^3b+a^2b^2-5ab^3}{ab}$ $\dfrac{5c^4d^2-c^3d^3+2c^2d^4}{-c^2d}$ $\dfrac{-3xy^4+4xy^3-xy^2}{xy^2}$ $\dfrac{6m^6n^4-2m^3n^2-m^4n^6}{m^3n^2}$ $\dfrac{b^4c^2d^3+2b^2c^3d^4-b^3c^4d^4}{-b^2cd^3}$

13. $\dfrac{6b^2-12b^6}{3b}$ $\dfrac{15m^4-25m^3}{-5m}$ $\dfrac{-4a^2b+12ab^2}{4a}$ $\dfrac{8x^5y-2xy}{-2x}$ $\dfrac{16y^3-24xy}{-8y}$

       $\dfrac{4a^2b-6ab^2}{2ab}$ $\dfrac{12m^4n^3-6mn}{-6mn}$ $\dfrac{54x^6+81x^4}{9x^2}$ $\dfrac{7c^5-21c^3d^2}{-7c^3}$ $\dfrac{-8b^3d^4-12b^2d^3}{4bd^2}$

14. $\dfrac{16b^4-8b^3+24b^2}{4b}$ $\dfrac{3a^5+6a^4-9a^2}{3a^2}$ $\dfrac{15b^2c^2+30b^2c-15b^2}{-15b^2}$ $\dfrac{14ax^2-21a^2x+28a^3x}{7ax}$

   $\dfrac{-18x^2y^3z+9x^3yz^2-27xy^2z^3}{9xyz}$ $\dfrac{12g^2t^4-36g^2t^3-18g^2t^2}{6gt^2}$ $\dfrac{36x^3y^3+72x^2y^2-54x^2y}{-18x^2y}$ $\dfrac{13c^2d^2x-26cd^3x+39cd^2x}{13cd^2}$

       $\dfrac{10r^8s^4-15r^6s^5-20r^3s^3}{-5r^2s^3}$ $\dfrac{64d^6r^3t^5-24d^3r^5t^4+72d^2r^4t^6}{8d^2r^3t^4}$

15. $\dfrac{2x^4-4x^3+6x^2-4x}{-2x}$ $\dfrac{3a^4y-9a^3y^2-6a^2y^3+12ay^4}{3ay}$ $\dfrac{5ab^3-10a^2b^2+5ab^2-15ab^4}{-5ab^2}$

      $\dfrac{6mn+12m^2n^2-18m^3n^3+24m^4n^4}{6mn}$ $\dfrac{4a^4b^3c^2+8a^3b^4c-8a^2b^4c^3-4a^2b^3c}{-4a^2b^3c}$

SET 16

1. $(-c^2+c)\div(-c)$
2. $(6b^2-5b+3)\div(-1)$
3. $(ax+bx)\div(x)$
4. $(2x-4x^2)\div(2x)$
5. $(\pi r^2-2\pi r)\div(\pi r)$
6. $(9cd^2-12c^2d)\div(-3cd)$
7. $(7ab-14ac)\div(7a)$
8. $(-9x^2-18x^3y^2)\div(-9x^2)$
9. $(4a^2b^2c-20a^2bc^2+8ab^2c^2)\div(4abc)$
10. $(25c^2x-15c^3y+10c^4z)\div(-5c^2)$

SET 17

1. Divide $3r-9$ by 3.
2. Divide $-8xy+16yz$ by -4.
3. Divide x^3-x^2+x by $-x$.
4. Divide $5a^3-10a^2-15a$ by $5a$.
5. Divide $12a^2b^2+15ab^3$ by $-3ab^2$.
6. Divide $5m^3n^2x-3mn^2x^3$ by $-mnx$.
7. Divide $36axyz^2-24bxy^2z$ by $4xyz$.
8. Divide $9d^4x^2-6d^2x^2+12d^2x^4$ by $-3d^2x^2$.
9. Divide $8x^3y^2z-12xyz^2+10xy^2$ by $2xy$.
10. Divide $7c^4y-14c^3y^2+35c^2y^3-49cy^4$ by $-7cy$.

EXERCISE 35

A Polynomial by a Polynomial

I. Aim: To divide a polynomial by a polynomial.

II. Procedure

1. Arrange the terms of both the dividend and the divisor in either descending or ascending powers of some common letter.

2. Divide the first term of the dividend by the first term of the divisor. Write the answer as the first term of the quotient.

3. Multiply the entire divisor by the first term of the quotient. Write this product under the dividend, keeping similar terms under each other.

4. Subtract this product from the dividend.

5. Considering the remainder and any additional terms of the original dividend as a new dividend, repeat steps, 2, 3, and 4 until the remainder is no longer divisible.

6. Check by numerical substitution or by multiplication.

III. Sample Solutions

Divide:

1. $x^2 + 7x + 12$ by $x + 3$

STEP 1	STEP 2	STEP 3	STEP 4

$$\text{STEP 1: } x+3\overline{)x^2+7x+12}$$

$$\text{STEP 2: } \begin{array}{r} x \\ x+3\overline{)x^2+7x+12} \end{array}$$

$$\text{STEP 3: } \begin{array}{r} x \\ x+3\overline{)x^2+7x+12} \\ x^2+3x \end{array}$$

$$\text{STEP 4: } \begin{array}{r} x \\ x+3\overline{)x^2+7x+12} \\ x^2+3x \\ \hline +4x \end{array}$$

STEP 5

a) Repeat step 2
$$\begin{array}{r} x+4 \\ x+3\overline{)x^2+7x+12} \\ x^2+3x \\ \hline +4x \end{array}$$

Answer, $x+4$

b) Repeat step 3
$$\begin{array}{r} x+4 \\ x+3\overline{)x^2+7x+12} \\ x^2+3x \\ \hline +4x+12 \\ +4x+12 \end{array}$$

c) Repeat step 4
$$\begin{array}{r} x+4 \\ x+3\overline{)x^2+7x+12} \\ x^2+3x \\ \hline 4x+12 \\ 4x+12 \\ \hline \end{array}$$

2. Divide $x^2 - 9x + 20$ by $x - 4$

$$\begin{array}{r} x-5 \\ x-4\overline{)x^2-9x+20} \\ x^2-4x \\ \hline -5x+20 \\ -5x+20 \\ \hline \end{array}$$

Answer, $x-5$

3. Divide $x^2 - 3xy - 10y^2$ by $x - 5y$

$$\begin{array}{r} x+2y \\ x-5y\overline{)x^2-3xy-10y^2} \\ x^2-5xy \\ \hline +2xy-10y^2 \\ +2xy-10y^2 \\ \hline \end{array}$$

Answer, $x+2y$

4. Divide $15b^3 + 41b^2 + 2b - 28$ by $3b + 7$

$$\begin{array}{r} 5b^2+2b-4 \\ 3b+7\overline{)15b^3+41b^2+\ 2b-28} \\ 15b^3+35b^2 \\ \hline +\ 6b^2+\ 2b \\ +\ 6b^2+14b \\ \hline -12b-28 \\ -12b-28 \\ \hline \end{array}$$

Answer, $5b^2 + 2b - 4$

5. Divide $3a^2 - 11a - 18$ by $a - 5$

$$
\begin{array}{r}
3a + 4 \\
a - 5 \overline{)\,3a^2 - 11a - 18} \\
\underline{3a^2 - 15a} \\
+4a - 18 \\
\underline{+4a - 20} \\
+2
\end{array}
$$

Answer, $3a + 4 + \dfrac{2}{a - 5}$

6. Divide $a^4 - b^4$ by $a - b$

$$
\begin{array}{r}
a^3 + a^2b + ab^2 + b^3 \\
a - b \overline{)\,a^4 \qquad\qquad\qquad - b^4} \\
\underline{a^4 - a^3b} \\
+a^3b \\
\underline{+a^3b - a^2b^2} \\
+a^2b^2 \\
\underline{+a^2b^2 - ab^3} \\
+ab^3 - b^4 \\
\underline{+ab^3 - b^4}
\end{array}
$$

Answer, $a^3 + a^2b + ab^2 + b^3$

DIAGNOSTIC TEST

Divide:

1. $c^2 + 10c + 21$ by $c + 3$.
2. $x^2 + 3x - 10$ by $x - 2$.
3. $m^2 - 4m - 12$ by $m - 6$.
4. $b^2 - 2b - 63$ by $b + 7$.
5. $s^2 + 2s - 15$ by $s + 5$.
6. $a^2 - 10a + 24$ by $a - 4$.
7. $x^2 + x - 6$ by $x + 3$.
8. $8 + 2b - b^2$ by $2 + b$.
9. $18c^2 - 34c - 4$ by $9c + 1$.
10. $8b^6 + 22b^3 + 15$ by $2b^3 + 3$.

11. $a^2 - 2ax + x^2$ by $a - x$.
12. $42m^2 + 16mn - 8n^2$ by $6m + 4n$.
13. $a^2 - 3b^2 + 2ab$ by $3b + a$.
14. $8a^4b^2 + 16a^2bx - 10x^2$ by $4a^2b - 2x$.
15. $n^3 + 4n^2 - 27n + 18$ by $n - 3$.
16. $9c^3 - 21c^2d + 16cd^2 - 4d^3$ by $3c - 2d$.
17. $a^2 + ab - ac - bc$ by $a + b$.
18. $x^4 - x^3 - 8x^2 + 16x - 8$ by $x^2 + 2x - 4$.
19. $b^4 - 16$ by $b + 2$.
20. $m^2 + 11m + 32$ by $m + 5$.

Related Practice Examples

Divide:

SET 1

1. $x^2 + 4x + 4$ by $x + 2$.
2. $y^2 + 8y + 15$ by $y + 5$.
3. $a^2 + 4a + 3$ by $a + 1$.
4. $m^2 + 20m + 96$ by $m + 8$.
5. $r^2 + 21r + 80$ by $r + 16$.

SET 2

1. $b^2 + 2b - 15$ by $b - 3$.
2. $x^2 + 5x - 84$ by $x - 7$.
3. $d^2 + 3d - 28$ by $d - 4$.
4. $t^2 + 7t - 18$ by $t - 2$.
5. $z^2 + 8z - 9$ by $z - 1$.

SET 3

1. $c^2 - 5c - 24$ by $c - 8$.
2. $s^2 - 6s - 27$ by $s - 9$.
3. $v^2 - 4v - 5$ by $v - 5$.
4. $x^2 - 3x - 108$ by $x - 12$.
5. $a^2 - 20a - 96$ by $a - 24$.

SET 4

1. $x^2 - 5x - 36$ by $x + 4$.
2. $d^2 - 2d - 48$ by $d + 6$.
3. $s^2 - 15s - 54$ by $s + 3$.
4. $r^2 - 10r - 75$ by $r + 5$.
5. $y^2 - 2y - 120$ by $y + 10$.

SET 5

1. $m^2 + 5m - 14$ by $m + 7$.
2. $y^2 + 7y - 8$ by $y + 8$.
3. $c^2 + 13c - 48$ by $c + 16$.
4. $h^2 + 7h - 60$ by $h + 12$.
5. $t^2 + 6t - 135$ by $t + 15$.

SET 6

1. $x^2 - 11x + 24$ by $x - 8$.
2. $h^2 - 8h + 16$ by $h - 4$.
3. $n^2 - 14n + 45$ by $n - 9$.
4. $b^2 - 24b + 143$ by $b - 11$.
5. $z^2 - 20z + 100$ by $z - 10$.

SET 7

1. $a^2 - a - 2$ by $a + 1$.
2. $r^2 + r - 30$ by $r - 5$.
3. $m^2 - m - 56$ by $m - 8$.
4. $g^2 - g - 90$ by $g + 9$.
5. $v^2 - v - 132$ by $v - 12$.

SET 8

1. $9 + 6x + x^2$ by $3 + x$.
2. $12 + 7y + y^2$ by $4 + y$.
3. $24 - 10b - b^2$ by $2 - b$.
4. $21 - 4a - a^2$ by $7 + a$.
5. $20 + w - w^2$ by $5 - w$.

SET 9

1. $2b^2+13b+6$ by $b+6$.
2. $25x^2-5x-6$ by $5x-3$.
3. $6y^2-13y-28$ by $3y+4$.
4. $28a^2+22a-30$ by $7a-5$.
5. $12x^2-22x+8$ by $4x-2$.

SET 10

1. x^4+9x^2+20 by x^2+4.
2. a^4-2a^2-8 by a^2+2.
3. c^6-2c^3+1 by c^3-1.
4. $6y^4+9y^2-42$ by $3y^2-6$.
5. $10b^6+b^3-24$ by $5b^3+8$.

SET 11

1. $x^2+2xy+y^2$ by $x+y$.
2. $a^2+2ab+b^2$ by $a+b$.
3. $c^2-2cd+d^2$ by· $c-d$.
4. $m^4+2m^2n^2+n^4$ by m^2+n^2.
5. $r^6-2r^3s^2+s^4$ by r^3-s^2.

SET 12

1. $4x^2+12xy+9y^2$ by $2x+3y$.
2. $3b^2-13bc+4c^2$ by $b-4c$.
3. $20a^2-2ad-6d^2$ by $5a-3d$.
4. $35c^2+37cx-6x^2$ by $7c-x$.
5. $16m^4-26m^2n^2-35n^4$ by $8m^2+7n^2$.

SET 13

1. $2cd+d^2+c^2$ by $c+d$.
2. $10+x^2-7x$ by $x-2$.
3. $14y-8+15y^2$ by $4+3y$.
4. $15a^2-32b^2-28ab$ by $4b+5a$.
5. $35y^2-62xy+24x^2$ by $6x-5y$.

SET 14

1. $c^2d^2-2cdx+x^2$ by $cd-x$.
2. $4x^2+17xyz+15y^2z^2$ by $4x+5yz$.
3. $6b^2c^2+13bcmx-28m^2x^2$ by $2bc+7mx$.
4. $14a^4m^2-64a^2my+32y^2$ by $7a^2m-4y$.
5. $20d^6r^4-14d^3r^2tx^2-24t^2x^4$ by $5d^3r^2+4tx^2$.

SET 15

1. x^3-2x^2+2x-1 by $x-1$.
2. $c^3-2c^2-13c+20$ by $c-4$.
3. $a^3-3a^2b+3ab^2-b^3$ by $a-b$.
4. $m^3-6m^2n+2mn^2+3n^3$ by $m-n$.
5. $a^3b^3+3a^2b^2c-6abc^2+2c^3$ by $ab-c$.

SET 16

1. $3r^3-19r^2+27r+4$ by $r-4$.
2. $6m^3-4m^2-7m+12$ by $3m+4$.
3. $8b^3-18b^2c+25bc^2-12c^3$ by $4b-3c$.
4. $3a^3x^3-18a^2x^2y+9axy^2+6y^3$ by $3ax-3y$.
5. $4a^3x^2+3a^3x-a^2x^2-4a^2x^3-2ax^3$ by $a-x$.

SET 17

1. $c^2+cx+cy+xy$ by $c+x$.
2. $m^2-mr+ms-rs$ by $m-r$.
3. $bd+cd+bx+cx$ by $b+c$.
4. $x^2y^2-x^2y-xy^2+xy$ by x^2-x.
5. $ab^2c-4ac+4d-b^2d$ by $ac-d$.

SET 18

1. $c^3-7c^2+3c+14$ by c^2-5c-7.
2. b^3-4b^2+7b-6 by b^2-2b+3.
3. $a^4+2a^3-4a^2-5a+6$ by a^2+a-2.
4. $3x^4-14x^3+12x^2-26x-7$ by x^2-4x-1.
5. $8m^4-10m^3n-13m^2n^2+13mn^3-10n^4$ by $2m^2-mn-5n^2$.

SET 19

1. b^2-16 by $b+4$.
2. x^2-y^2 by $x-y$.
3. a^3-8 by $a-2$.
4. c^3+d^3 by $c+d$.
5. x^4-y^4 by $x+y$.
6. a^4-81 by $a-3$.
7. x^5+1 by $x+1$.
8. m^6-n^6 by $m-n$.
9. r^6-64 by $r+2$.
10. a^8-b^3 by $a-l$.

SET 20

1. x^2+3x+7 by $x+2$.
2. x^2+6x-9 by $x+3$.
3. a^2+ab+b^2 by $a+b$.
4. $3c^2+4c-5$ by $c+4$.
5. $5a^2+6a-4$ by $a-5$.
6. $4x^2-4xy+6y^2$ by $2x-3y$.
7. $12c^2-4cd-3d^2$ by $2c-5d$.
8. $5y^3-2y^2+5y-9$ by $5y-2$.
9. $6b^4+4b^3-4b^2+4b+7$ by $3b^2-4b+3$.
10. x^4+16 by $x+2$.

REVIEW OF UNIT SIX

A. Addition—Add the following:

1. $-8a^2x$ **2.** $6x^2-5xy-y^2$ **3.** $3b^2-4b+6$ **4.** Find the sum of: $2a^2-8b^2$; $5a^2-4ab-3b^2$; $4b^2-5ab$.

    $+2a^2x$ $-x^2+8xy-5y^2$ $-5b^2-3b-2$ **5.** Combine: $5c^2-3cd-4d^2-cd+2d^2-3c^2+d^2-2c^2$

B. Subtraction—Subtract the lower term from the upper term:

1. $8c$ **2.** $-7b^2c^5y$ **3.** $9x^2-3x+2$ **4.** From $4a-5b$ subtract $6a+9b$.

   $17c$ $4b^2c^5y$ $9x^2-5x-3$ **5.** Take $3c-4$ from $2c^2-c$.

C. Multiplication—Multiply the following:

1. $-6b^2x$ **2.** $7r^2-2rt+6t^2$ **3.** $-4x^2y(2x^2-3xy+y^2)$ **4.** $5a-7d$ **5.** $(9m+7n)(3m-8n)$

   $-2b^3x^2$ $-4r^2t^3$ $3a-4d$

D. Parentheses—Remove parentheses and, if possible, add like terms:

1. $9b^2+(b^2-4b)-3b$ **2.** $6x+2x(-3x+2)+5x^2$ **3.** $8a(a+1)-3a(a-7)-(a+6)(a-9)$

4. Inclose the last three terms in parentheses preceded by a minus sign: $4a^2-4ab+b^2-c^2+2cd-d^2$

E. Division—Divide the following:

1. $\dfrac{-56c^5d^2x^4}{-8c^3d^2x}$ **2.** $\dfrac{18a^4x^2-24ax^5}{6ax^2}$ **3.** $\dfrac{24m^6x^4-9m^5x^3+3m^4x^3}{-3m^4x^3}$ **4.** $x^2-13x+42$ by $x-7$.

                                                    5. $6c^3-17c^2d+15cd^2-4d^3$ by $3c-4d$.

F. Applications

1. Transform the following formulas by removing parentheses: **2.** Simplify: $\dfrac{10^{17}\times 10^{13}}{10^{18}}$

   (a) $A=p(1+rt)$ (b) $B=180-(A+C)$ (c) $A=2\pi r(r+h)$

3. Find the value of the expression x^2+5x+9 when $x=3$. Determine whether this value equals the remainder when x^2+5x+9 is divided by $x-3$?

4. The sum of the angles of a triangle equals $180°$. If one angle of a triangle measures $n+16$ degrees and a second angle measures $2n-4$ degrees, find the literal angular measure of the third angle.

5. Find the radius of a circle having a circumference of 24π inches.

CUMULATIVE ALGEBRA REVIEW

1. Add: $5c^2-8c-4$ **2.** Subtract: $2b^2-6bx-x^2$ **3.** Multiply: $6a-3y$ **4.** Divide:

     $2c^2-7c+5$ $3b^2+7bx-x^2$ $2a+9y$ $8m+n\overline{)24m^2-13mn-2n^2}$

5. Remove parentheses and, if possible, add like terms: $10a-7a(2a-4)+(a-5)(a+2)$

6. Solve and check: $7s-24=18$ **7.** Combine: $5x-2y-8z-9y+6z-x-2z-y$

8. Find the value of n when $S=360$, using the formula $S=180n-360$.

9. What algebraic expression represents the perimeter of a rectangle with a length of $a+b$ and a width of $a-b$?   **10.** Find the cost of n articles at c cents per article.

KEYED ACHIEVEMENT TEST

1. Combine like terms: $8r^2-2rs-7s^2-s^2+2rs-3r^2$ ㉔ **3.** Multiply $a-5c$ by $7a-9c$. ㉛

2. Subtract $8n^2-5$ from $4n^2-6n$ ㉖   **4.** Divide $27b^3-64x^3$ by $3b-4x$. ㉟

Remove parentheses and, if possible, add like terms:

5. $10x-(5x-2)+6+(-x+7)$ ㉗   **7.** Solve and check: $9d+3=75$ ⑪

6. $12b-4b(3b-6)+2b^2$ ㉜   **8.** Divide: $\dfrac{10m^4-15m^3+5m^2}{-5m^2}$ ㉞

9. Find the value of I if $E=110$, $r=7$, and $R=15$, using the formula $E=Ir+IR$. ⑫

10. A hand bag with a 10% tax included sells for $\$7.59$. What is the selling price of the bag without the tax? ⑬

INTRODUCTION TO UNIT SEVEN

Both equations and verbal problems have been studied in preceding units. However, with the additional knowledge of the fundamental operations in algebra, students may now study more difficult equations and problems.

An equation is a statement that two expressions are equal. Thus, $x+6=14$ and $2(x+y)=2x+2y$ are equations.

In some equations one expression is equal to the second expression for all values of the variables while in other equations for only particular values of the variables.

The equation $x+6=14$, indicating that a certain number plus 6 equals 14, is satisfied when $x=8$ and only then. That is, $x+6$ is equal to 14 only on the condition that x equals 8. An equation which is satisfied only by particular values of the variables is called a *conditional equation* or usually just an *equation*.

The equation $2(x+y)=2x+2y$, indicating that 2 times the sum of two numbers equals the sum of twice the first number and twice the second number, is satisfied by all values of x and y. An equation which is satified by all values of the variables is called an *identical equation* or an *identity*.

An *equation of the first degree*, sometimes called a *simple* equation or *linear* equation, is one having the variable raised to the first power only or, if it contains fractions, the variable does not appear in the denominator.

Solving an equation means finding the number represented by the variable. This number which will satisfy the conditions of the equation is called the *root* of the equation.

Checking an equation means testing whether the value found representing the variable will satisfy the conditions of the equation. To check, substitute the value of the variable in the given equation. If the resulting answers of the two members are the same, the value is the root.

In exercises 7, 8, 9, and 10 the four basic types of equations were solved by axioms. To solve the equation $x+4=12$, we subtracted 4 from each side. In a similar manner we added 4 to both sides of the equation $x-4=12$, divided both sides of the equation $4x=12$ by 4, and multiplied both sides of the equation $\frac{x}{4}=12$ by 4. Thus, to solve for the value of the unknown by eliminating an unwanted arithmetic number, the operation indicated by the relationship of the unknown and its connected numeral is undone by using the opposite or inverse operation. The balance of the equation is maintained when the operation is performed on both sides, for if equals are increased or decreased or multiplied or divided by equals, the results are equal.

Comparing the two solutions of equation $3x+8=20$, we see that subtracting 8 from the left side of the equation eliminates the $+8$ on that side so that $3x+8-8=20-8$ may be simplified to $3x=20-8$. However, the same result may be obtained directly from the given equation by moving the $+8$ from the left side to the right side and changing its sign. In a similar manner, moving the -6 from the left side of equation $7x-6=15$ to the right side and changing its sign produces the same result as adding 6 to each side.

Thus, moving a number from one side of an equation to the other side and changing its sign is another, and shorter, way of applying the addition and subtraction axioms. Equations are solved also by the additive and multiplicative inverses. See pages 10S and 37S.

Solve: $3x+8=20$

$$3x+8=20$$
$$3x+8-8=20-8$$
$$3x=20-8$$
$$3x=12$$
$$\frac{3x}{3}=\frac{12}{3}$$
$$x=4$$

$$3x+8=20$$
$$3x=20-8$$
$$3x=12$$
$$\frac{3x}{3}=\frac{12}{3}$$
$$x=4$$

Solve: $7x-6=15$

$$7x-6=15$$
$$7x-6+6=15+6$$
$$7x=15+6$$
$$7x=21$$
$$\frac{7x}{7}=\frac{21}{7}$$
$$x=3$$

$$7x-6=15$$
$$7x=15+6$$
$$7x=21$$
$$\frac{7x}{7}=\frac{21}{7}$$
$$x=3$$

UNIT SEVEN—EQUATIONS AND WORD PROBLEMS

EQUATIONS

EXERCISE 36

Simple Equations

I. **Aim**: To solve simple equations.

I. **Procedure**

1. Use the addition and subtraction axioms to get all terms containing the unknown term on one member of the equation and all the known terms on the other member.

   Note: a) If the teacher or student desires to use the mechanical short rule to accomplish the same objective, then: Any term may be moved from one member of an equation to the other member provided its sign is changed. See sample solution 1. See also pages 10S and 37S.

   b) In solving equations in sets 1 to 11 inclusive, the negative sign difficulty may be avoided if the unknown term with the greater positive coefficient is kept on its original side and the other terms are moved accordingly. See sample solution 2.

2. Combine the similar terms of each member.

3. Solve for the unknown term, using either the division or multiplication axiom.

4. In equations involving negative signs, use the operation rules for signed numbers in addition to above steps 1 to 3. See sample solution 3.
   Note: Always solve for a positive unknown term. See sample solution 4.

5. In equations involving parentheses, first remove parentheses and then follow above steps 1 to 4. See sample solutions 5 and 6.

6. In checking equations, substitute the root in the original equation.

III. **Sample Solutions**

Axiom Method   Short Method

1. $5x - 3 = 2x + 9$

$$\begin{aligned} 5x - 3 &= 2x + 9 \\ 3 &= 3 \\ \hline 5x &= 2x + 12 \\ 2x &= 2x \\ \hline 3x &= 12 \\ x &= 4 \end{aligned}$$

Answer, $x = 4$

$$\begin{aligned} 5x - 3 &= 2x + 9 \\ 5x - 2x &= 9 + 3 \\ 3x &= 12 \\ x &= 4 \end{aligned}$$

Check:
$$\begin{aligned} 20 - 3 &= 8 + 9 \\ 17 &= 17 \end{aligned}$$

3. $-6x = 30$
$$x = -5$$
Answer, $x = -5$

Check:
$$30 = 30$$

Inverses
$$\begin{aligned} 5x - 3 &= 2x + 9 \\ 5x + (-3) &= 2x + 9 \\ 5x + (-2x) + (-3) + 3 &= 2x + (-2x) + 9 + (3) \\ 3x &= 12 \\ \tfrac{1}{3} \cdot 3x &= \tfrac{1}{3} \cdot 12 \\ x &= 4 \end{aligned}$$

2. $2x + 15 = 5x$
$$\begin{aligned} 2x &= 2x \\ \hline 15 &= 3x \\ 5 &= x \\ x &= 5 \end{aligned}$$
Answer, $x = 5$

Check:
$$\begin{aligned} 10 + 15 &= 25 \\ 25 &= 25 \end{aligned}$$

4. $-x = 8$
$$x = -8$$
Answer, $x = -8$

Check:
$$8 = 8$$

5. $5x + 10(14 - x) = 95$
$$\begin{aligned} 5x + 140 - 10x &= 95 \\ 5x - 10x &= 95 - 140 \\ -5x &= -45 \\ x &= 9 \end{aligned}$$
Answer, $x = 9$

Check:
$$\begin{aligned} 45 + 10(14 - 9) &= 95 \\ 45 + 10(5) &= 95 \\ 45 + 50 &= 95 \\ 95 &= 95 \end{aligned}$$

6. $(x+6)(x-4) = (x+2)(x-3)$
$x^2 + 2x - 24 = x^2 - x - 6$
$x^2 - x^2 + 2x + x = 24 - 6$
$3x = 18$
$x = 6$ Answer, $x = 6$

Check:
$(6+6)(6-4) = (6+2)(6-3)$
$(12)(2) = (8)(3)$
$24 = 24$

Review

Solve and check:

SET 1	SET 2	SET 3	SET 4	SET 5
1. $x+3=5$	1. $3s=15$	1. $5m=8$	1. $2x+4=10$	1. $25=8c+1$
2. $6+x=9$	2. $8=2d$	2. $4x=6$	2. $5x+3=8$	2. $16=7y+9$
3. $7=x+2$	3. $\dfrac{x}{5}=10$	3. $3y=2$	3. $6d+5=17$	3. $26=3w+5$
4. $a-4=6$	4. $\frac{1}{2}b=7$	4. $6b=3$	4. $8r+3=43$	4. $33=8+5b$
5. $9=r-1$	5. $2=\dfrac{c}{4}$	5. $4x=0$	5. $2+4m=26$	5. $18=6+3x$

SET 6	SET 7	SET 8	SET 9	SET 10
1. $4x-5=7$	1. $9=7x-5$	1. $3x-15=0$	1. $2x=5+3$	1. $4y+2y=6$
2. $6y-14=10$	2. $7=9y-2$	2. $7b-63=0$	2. $3w=8+13$	2. $5x+3x=24$
3. $3t-3=24$	3. $38=10a-12$	3. $8m-56=0$	3. $6c=15-3$	3. $7x-5x=8$
4. $2d-8=22$	4. $18=6x-6$	4. $0=9x-45$	4. $7+9=4x$	4. $15=3x+2x$
5. $7n-12=16$	5. $12=4n-8$	5. $0=6y-42$	5. $15-8=7b$	5. $21=6t-3t$

DIAGNOSTIC TEST

Solve and check:

1. $5t=15+2t$
2. $8m-35=3m$
3. $4x+6=6x$
4. $3z=9z-24$
5. $8x=3x+2x$
6. $7x+5=9+3x$
7. $9m-12=7m-6$
8. $3y+15=31-y$

9. $25-3s=3s+1$
10. $6y+2=17-9$
11. $9t-4t=10-5t$
12. $3x-5x+9=29-4x-12$
13. $5x+7x-2=6-14x+2x$
14. $8x+6-x=4+3x+2$
15. $2x=-10$
16. $-4x=12$

17. $-3x=-15$
18. $-x=6$
19. $4a+33=12-3a$
20. $x+x+2+x+4=39$
21. $18-(x-4)=9+(x+3)$
22. $30x+40(15-x)=520$
23. $(b+2)(b-2)=(b+8)(b-3)$

Related Practice Examples

Solve and check:

SET 1	SET 2	SET 3	SET 4
1. $4x=8+2x$	1. $6a-20=2a$	1. $3a+10=8a$	1. $2b=7b-15$
2. $7a=12+a$	2. $9x-18=3x$	2. $5x+6=7x$	2. $5a=9a-32$
3. $6b=36-3b$	3. $5b-48=b$	3. $4b+7=5b$	3. $x=7x-78$
4. $9y=4y+30$	4. $12y-35=7y$	4. $9m+24=11m$	4. $8d=11d-36$
5. $8x=65-5x$	5. $15x-36=11x$	5. $c+28=8c$	5. $3x=15x-84$

SET 5	SET 6	SET 7	SET 8
1. $2x+5x=4x$	1. $2x+1=4+x$	1. $6r-4=20-2r$	1. $3x-2=3+2x$
2. $8b+2b=3b$	2. $5x+3=15+2x$	2. $5x-2=28-x$	2. $9y-5=7y+3$
3. $7y-2y=4y$	3. $3+9y=11+7y$	3. $4d-3=3d-1$	3. $z+2=34-3z$
4. $9x=3x+5x$	4. $9+6z=z+34$	4. $10x-22=8x-10$	4. $2x-6=x+3$
5. $8a=4a-a$	5. $5x+2=3x+8$	5. $6x-3=15-3x$	5. $2+7x=11-2x$

SET 9

1. $25 - 4x = 4x + 1$
2. $18 - 5x = 2x + 4$
3. $5n + 2 = 8n - 7$
4. $8 + 2w = 5w - 13$
5. $17 - x = 4x + 2$

SET 10

1. $2x + 3 = 7 + 6$
2. $5y - 2 = 17 - 4$
3. $8 + 7y = 12 + 24$
4. $20 - 10 = 6b - 8$
5. $13 - 4 = 10x - 11$

SET 11

1. $4r + 2r = 18 + 3r$
2. $7x + 2x = 8x + 4$
3. $3a - a = a + 6$
4. $3x - 2x = 24 - x$
5. $4b - 3b = 5b - 28$

SET 12

1. $3x + 5x + 3 = 5 + 7x$
2. $4y - y + 5 = 35 - 2y$
3. $8h + 5 - 2 = 6h + 17$
4. $7x - 8 - 2x = 64 - 3x$
5. $5x + 6 - 2x - 15 - x + 5 = 0$
6. $4b + 2 + 3b - 4 = 21 + 5b - 17$
7. $6r - 4 + 2r + 8 = 18 - 3r - 8 + 9r$
8. $2y + 23 - 6 + y = 4y + 13 - 3y + 14$
9. $60 + 3x - 5x + 2 = 7x + 2x - 15 - 22$
10. $8y - 3y + 7 - 4y - 2 = 15 - 9y - 5y + 5$

SET 13

1. $6x + 2 = 5$
2. $4 = 8g - 2$
3. $4r - 2r = 3$
4. $6b + 7 = 2b + 8$
5. $4 + 5m = 12m - 6$
6. $3x + x - 2 = 7 - 2x$
7. $5c - 3 + 4 = 9 - 2c + c$
8. $7y + y + 7 = 9 - y + 3y + 13$
9. $11a - 5a + 8 - 19 + 6a - 7 = 0$
10. $0 = 3x - 4 - x - 3 + 2x + 5 - 1$

SET 14

1. $2x + 6 = 6$
2. $4m - 3 = 5m - 3$
3. $2 + 5x = x + 2$
4. $3b - 5 = 2 - 7$
5. $7x + 6 = 8 - x - 2$
6. $4x + 2 = 3 + 2x - 1$
7. $8 + 3m - 5 + m - 3 = 0$
8. $x + 3x - 2 = 2x - 8 + 3x + 6$
9. $2x + 7x + 5 - 3x = 3 + 4x + 2$
10. $9y - 4 + 2y - 3 + 2 - y + 5 = 0$

SET 15

1. $4x = -8$
2. $3y = -6$
3. $7b = -28$
4. $2m = -10$
5. $5z = -23$
6. $8y = -4$
7. $3x = -1$
8. $-21 = 3x$
9. $-54 = 6y$
10. $-11 = 4r$

SET 16

1. $-2m = 12$
2. $-5s = 35$
3. $-4x = 36$
4. $-9t = 12$
5. $-3b = 5$
6. $-8y = 3$
7. $-12x = 8$
8. $24 = -6x$
9. $2 = -3y$
10. $15 = -4b$

SET 17

1. $-7b = -21$
2. $-3a = -36$
3. $-5x = -45$
4. $-10s = -40$
5. $-8z = -9$
6. $-4x = -1$
7. $-15r = -3$
8. $-32 = -4y$
9. $-4 = -9z$
10. $-13 = -3x$

SET 18

1. $-x = 7$
2. $-x = 4$
3. $-b = 3$
4. $-y = 1$
5. $-a = -2$
6. $-x = -5$
7. $-m = -4$
8. $6 = -x$
9. $-1 = -y$
10. $-9 = -n$

SET 19

1. $3x + 9 = 3$
2. $2 + 5x = -3$
3. $6y + 9 = 3y$
4. $3a = 10 + 5a$
5. $9x - 2 = 3x - 10$
6. $3b + 12 = 9 - 6b$
7. $24 - 5t = 19 - 10t$
8. $5y = -6 - 4y$
9. $5 - m + 2m = 14 + 4m$
10. $3z + 6z + 25 = 4z - 31 - 2z$

SET 20

1. $2x + 5x + 5 = 40$
2. $x + x + 10 = 20$
3. $y + 2y + 3y + 30 = 360$
4. $x + x + 1 + x + 2 = 21$
5. $77 - x - 2x - 6x - 5 = 0$
6. $s + s + 4 + s + s + 4 = 40$
7. $x + x + 2 + 2x = 30$
8. $x + 3x + x + 3x = 32$
9. $0 = y + y + 2 - 3y + 5$
10. $a + a + 2 + a + 4 = 42$

SET 21

1. $3x + (x + 2) = 10$
2. $6x - (x - 3) = 18$
3. $y - (8 - y) = 2$
4. $(50 - b) - (3b + 2) = 0$
5. $12 + (4 - z) = 20 + z$
6. $x + (x + 1) + (x + 2) = 12$
7. $20 - (8 + y) - (y - 1) = 29$
8. $5m - (m + 3) = 7 + (m + 2)$
9. $x + (2x + 3) = (x + 3) + (x + 4)$
10. $(x - 1) - (x + 2) - (x - 3) = x$

SET 22

1. $4(2x + 6) = 48$
2. $2(x + 5) = x + 15$
3. $2(s + s + 3) = 14$
4. $5(x + 4) = 7(x + 2)$
5. $4(a - 1) = 5(a - 2)$
6. $5y + 10(8 - y) = 65$
7. $3b + 2(50 - b) = 110$
8. $8 - 4(x - 1) = 2 + 3(4 - x)$
9. $3x + 2(x + 2) = 13 - (2x - 5)$
10. $4x + 5 - 3(2x - 5) = 9 - (8x - 1) + x$

SET 23

1. $x(x + 3) = x^2 + 9$
2. $x(x - 1) = x^2 - 2(x - 2)$
3. $2w(3w + 1) = 3w(2w + 1) - 2$
4. $(x + 2)(x + 2) = x^2 + 8$
5. $(a + 3)(a - 3) = a^2 + 2a - 35$
6. $(y - 4)(y - 1) - y^2 = 9$
7. $(x + 2)(x + 4) = x(x + 8)$
8. $(y - 6)(y - 2) = (y - 4)(y - 5)$

WORD PROBLEMS

EXERCISE 37

Representing Word Phrases as Algebraic Expressions

Review: For procedure see UNIT ONE.

Practice Examples

Represent each of the following phrases by an algebraic expression:

1. x plus 4.
2. The sum of b and $3b$.
3. 6 added to x.
4. 15 more than y.
5. x increased by 7.
6. d exceeded by x.
7. 5 subtracted from m.
8. Subtract x from 4.
9. y minus 6.
10. 8 less than x.
11. 18 less n.
12. The difference between x and 9.
13. $3x$ diminished by x.
14. 7 times x.
15. y multiplied by 6.
16. The product of 9 and x.
17. Twice x.
18. a divided by 5.
19. The quotient of x by 10.
20. Divide $3x$ by $2y$.
21. Five times x subtracted from three times $2x$.
22. The difference between twice $3x$ and three times x.
23. The sum of five times $2x$ and four times $2x - 5$.
24. The product of 3 and x added to 5 times a decreased by 2 multiplied by y.

EXERCISE 38

Representing Unknown Numbers

I. **Aim:** To represent unknown numbers.

II. **Procedure**

1. Whenever possible, represent the smaller unknown quantity by some letter.

2. Then represent the larger unknown quantity in terms of that letter.
   Important note: There are 3 types of representations:
   Type 1. One quantity is some number times a second quantity.
   Type 2. One quantity is some number more than or less than a second quantity.
   Type 3. The sum of two quantities is given.

III. **Sample Solutions**

   Type 1. One number is 8 times a second number.
         Answer: Let x = second number
                 then $8x$ = first number
   Type 2. One number is 8 more than a second number.
         Answer: Let x = second number
                 then $x + 8$ = first number
   Type 3. The sum of two numbers is 8.
         Answer: Let x = first number
                 then $8 - x$ = second number

Note: Since the smaller of the two numbers is not known in type 3, either number can be represented by the letter.

Practice Problems

Type 1. Find the missing numbers or representations:

1. One number is 5 times a second number.

First number	Second number
?	4
?	8
?	10
?	x
?	$2x$

2. John is 4 times as old as Tom.

Tom's Age	John's Age
3 years	?
9 years	?
x year	?
$3x$ years	?
$x+3$ years	?

3. The length of a rectangle is 3 times its width.

Width	Length
6 ft.	?
x ft.	?
?	3 ft.
?	12 ft.
?	x ft.

4. There are 6 times as many nickels as dimes.

No. Dimes	No. Nickels
5	?
x	?
$10x$	?
?	6
?	x

5. Mary weighs twice as much as Joan.

Joan's weight	Mary's weight
25 pounds	?
x pounds	?
$4x$ pounds	?
$5(x-4)$ pounds	?
?	x pounds

6. Car *A* travels $\frac{1}{4}$ as fast as Car *B*.

Car *A* Speed	Car *B* Speed
10 m.p.h.	?
15 m.p.h.	?
x m.p.h.	?
$2(x-3)$ m.p.h.	?
?	x m.p.h.

7. Represent all the unknowns in each of the following statements as algebraic expressions:
   1. One number is 7 times a second number.
   2. David weighs 5 times as much as his baby brother.
   3. There are 10 times as many 50¢ admission tickets as 25¢ admission tickets.
   4. One side of a triangle is 8 times as long as a second side.
   5. The speed of an airplane is 3 times that of a train.
   6. Mrs. Jones is 4 times her daughter's age.
   7. There are twice as many $5 bills as $1 bills.
   8. The base of a rectangle is 4 times its altitude.
   9. Bill is $\frac{1}{3}$ John's age.
   10. There are $\frac{1}{8}$ as many 3¢ stamps as 2¢ stamps.

Type 2. Find the missing numbers or representations:

1. One number is 5 more than a second number.

First number	Second number
?	4
?	8
?	10
?	x
?	$2x$

2. Charlotte weighs 3 pounds more than Nina.

Nina's weight	Charlotte's weight
34 pounds	?
42 pounds	?
x pounds	?
?	50
?	x

3. One airplane travels 40 miles faster than a second airplane.

1st plane	2nd plane
?	100 m.p.h.
?	x m.p.h.
?	$x+5$ m.p.h.
180 m.p.h.	?
x m.p.h.	?

4. One side of a triangle is 6 inches longer than a second side.

1st side	2nd side
?	15 inches
?	x inches
?	$x-8$ inches
28 inches	?
x inches	?

5. Joseph has $5 less than Robert.

Robert	Joseph
$15	?
$21	?
$ x	?
$ $x+8$	?
$ $x-2$	?

6. Elaine is 2 years younger than Florence.

Florence's age	Elaine's age
18 years	?
x years	?
$3x$ years	?
?	27 years
?	x years

7. Represent all the unknowns in each of the following statements as algebraic expressions:
  1. The length of a rectangle is 7 inches greater than the width.
  2. There are 3 more dimes than quarters.
  3. Charles is 7 years older than Jean.
  4. One number is 15 more than a second number.
  5. The area of a rectangle is 8 sq. inches greater than the area of a square.
  6. There are 10 pounds more of the 60¢ candy than of the 50¢ candy.
  7. Bill has 4 cents more than Sue.
  8. Richard is 2 years younger than Carl.
  9. John weighs 40 pounds less than his dad.
  10. Yale scored 25 points more than Harvard.

Type 3. Find the missing numbers or representations:

1. The sum of two numbers is 5.

One number	Second number
1	?
3	?
x	?
?	4
?	x

4. There are 38 stamps; some 1¢ stamps and the rest 2¢ stamps.

No. 1¢ stamps	No. 2¢ stamps
7 stamps	?
x stamps	?
?	14 stamps
?	x stamps
?	$x+3$ stamps

2. A board 15 ft. long is divided into 2 parts.

1st part	2nd part
3 ft.	?
8 ft.	?
x ft.	?
$2x$ ft.	?
?	x ft.

5. Boat *A* and Boat *B* traveled 60 miles.

Distance covered by	
Boat *A*	Boat *B*
20 miles	?
x miles	?
$4x$ miles	?
?	x miles
?	$3x-4$ miles

3. John's and Anna's ages totaled 30 years.

Anna's age	John's age
6 years	?
x years	?
$x+2$ years	?
$x-5$ years	?
$4x$ years	?

6. Paul and James together weigh 190 pounds.

Paul's weight	James' weight
60 pounds	?
x pounds	?
$x-5$ pounds	?
?	$3x$ pounds
?	$5x-7$ pounds

7. Represent all the unknowns in each of the following statements as algebraic expressions:
  1. The sum of two numbers is 25.
  2. Two trains traveled a total distance of 150 miles.
  3. There were 46 boys and girls in the algebra class.
  4. John and Paul together weigh 240 pounds.
  5. The sum of the ages of Joe and Tom is 33 years.
  6. There were 200 pounds of 85¢ and 95¢ coffee.
  7. A man left $1,500 to his son and daughter.
  8. A 2-ton truck and 5-ton truck moved 40 tons.
  9. The heights of Joan and Virginia add up to 128 inches.
  10. Harry and Dick together sold 125 magazines.

EXERCISE 39
Changing Statements Into Equations

I. Aim: To change word statements into equations.

II. Procedure

Using the given algebraic expressions for the unknown, translate the given word statement into an equation.

III. Sample Solutions

If x = Tom's age in years and $x+6$ = Joan's age in years, write an equation for each of the following statements:
1. The sum of Tom's and Joan's ages is 30 years.
   Answer, $x+x+6=30$
2. Three times Tom's age equals twice Joan's age.
   Answer, $3x=2(x+6)$
3. The difference between Joan's age increased by 9 years and twice Tom's age is 3 years.
   Answer, $x+6+9-2x=3$

Practice Problems

Write an equation for each of the following statements:

A. Letting x = first number and $2x$ = second number.
   1. The sum of the first number and the second number is 15.
   2. Three times the first number equals the second number increased by 12.
   3. If four times the first number is subtracted from three times the second number, the result is 8.

B. Letting x = John's age in years and $x+3$ = Mary's age in years.
   1. The sum of John's and Mary's ages equals 17 years.
   2. Twice John's age decreased by 5 years equals Mary's age increased by 2 years.
   3. The difference between three times John's age and twice Mary's age is 10 years.

C. Letting x = number of nickels and $2x+5$ = number of dimes.
   1. Three times the number of nickels equals the number of dimes.
   2. Twice the number of dimes plus the number of nickels equals 20.
   3. The total number of nickels and dimes is 23.

D. Letting x = number of pounds of 40¢ grass seed and $50-x$ = number of pounds of 30¢ grass seed.
   1. The number of pounds of 40¢ seed and twice the number of pounds of 30¢ seed equals 90 pounds.
   2. Twice the number of pounds of 40¢ seed less the number of pounds of 30¢ seed equals 40 pounds.
   3. Six times the number of pounds of 40¢ seed equals four times the number of pounds of 30¢ seed.

E. Letting x = width in feet and $2x+4$ = length in feet.
   1. Twice the length plus twice the width equals 38 feet.
   2. Five times the width is the same as twice the length plus 10 feet.
   3. The length minus the width is equal to double the width.

F. Letting $3x+7$ = speed of train A in m.p.h. and $2x-5$ = speed of train B in m.p.h.
   1. Train A travels twice as fast as train B.
   2. The difference in the speeds of the two trains is the same as the sum of their speeds less 54 m.p.h.
   3. The speed of train A increased by 14 m.p.h. is equal to 3 times the speed of train B.

EXERCISE 40
General Problems

I. Aim: To solve general word problems.

II. Procedure

1. Read the problem carefully to determine:
   a) the unknown.
   b) any known facts which are related to the unknown.

2. Represent the unknown quantities by algebraic expressions.
   a) If there is only one unknown term, represent it by some letter.
   b) If there are 2 or more unknown terms, represent the smallest unknown term by some letter. Then express the other unknown quantities in terms of that letter.

3. Form an equation, using two equal facts with at least one containing the unknown.

4. Solve the equation.

5. Check the problem—not the equation.

III. Sample Solutions

1. Number problem: One number is five times a second number. The sum of the two numbers is 36. Find the numbers.

Let $x =$ second number
Then $5x =$ first number
$$*5x + x = 36$$
$$6x = 36$$
$$x = 6 \text{ second number}$$
$$5x = 30 \text{ first number}$$
Answer, 30 and 6

* The equation is determined by the following fact:

The first number plus the second number is equal to 36.

Check: $30 = 5 \times 6$.

```
 30 first no.
+ 6 second no.
 36 sum
```

2. Geometry problem: The length of a rectangle is 4 feet more than the width. The perimeter of the rectangle is 40 feet. Find the length and the width.

Let $x =$ width in feet
Then $x + 4 =$ length in feet
$$*2(x+4) + 2x = 40$$
$$2x + 8 + 2x = 40$$
$$4x + 8 = 40$$
$$4x = 40 - 8$$
$$4x = 32$$
$$x = 8 \text{ ft. (width)}$$
$$x + 4 = 12 \text{ ft. (length)}$$
Answer, length 12 ft.
width 8 ft.

* The equation is determined by the following fact:

The perimeter of a rectangle is equal to twice the length plus twice the width.

Check:

```
  12 ft. length
-  8 ft. width
   4 ft. difference
  24 ft. twice the length
+ 16 ft. twice the width
  40 ft. perimeter
```

Practice Problems

Solve the following problems:

a) Number problems:

1. One number is 4 times a second number. The sum of the two numbers is 30. Find the numbers.
2. One number is 6 more than a second number. The sum of the two numbers is 16. Find the numbers.
3. One number is twice a second number. Five more than the second number is the same as the first number less 3. Find the numbers.
4. The sum of two numbers is 15. Twice the first number is the same as 4 times the second number. Find the numbers.
5. The first number is 8 more than a second number. Three times the second number plus twice the first number is equal to 26. Find the first number.

b) Weight and age problems:

1. Tom weighs 30 pounds more than Clare. Together they weigh 150 pounds. How much does Clare weigh?
2. A man is twice as old as his son. Together the sum of their ages is 63. What are their ages?
3. Richard is 5 years older than Sheila. Four times Sheila's age increased by 3 years equals three times Richard's age diminished by 2 years. Find Richard's age.
4. June and John together weigh 180 pounds. The difference between twice John's weight and three times June's weight is 60 pounds. Find the weight of each.
5. The difference in ages of two girls is 1 year. The sum of their ages is 27 years. Find their ages.

c) Coin and mixture problems:

1. Mrs. Wade has 41 coins. She has 3 more nickels than pennies. How many nickels and how many pennies has she?
2. There are 5 times as many $1 bills as $5 bills. The entire number of bills is 48. How many $1 bills are there?
3. Among 580 admission tickets sold, there were 3 times as many 50¢ tickets sold as 25¢ tickets. Find the number of each.
4. There were 70 pounds of 97¢ coffee and 83¢ coffee sold. For each pound of 97¢ coffee, 4 times as many pounds of 83¢ coffee were sold. How many pounds of 83¢ coffee were sold?
5. Among 35 coins there are 5 more dimes than nickels and 3 fewer nickels than pennies. Find the number of each kind of coin.

d) Geometry problems:

1. A rectangle's length is 14 cm more than its width. The perimeter is 264 cm. Find the dimensions.
2. The perimeter of a rectangle is 168 cm. Its length is 5 times its width. Find the length and width.
3. If two opposite sides of a square are each increased by 12 cm and the other two sides are each decreased by 4 cm, a rectangle is formed having the same area. How long is each side of the square?
4. Side a of a triangle is 2 inches longer than side b. Side b is three times as long as side c. The perimeter of the triangle is 37 inches. Find the length of each side.
5. Complementary angles are two angles whose sum is 90°. If one of two complementary angles is 40° greater than the other, how many degrees are in each angle?
6. Supplementary angles are two angles whose sum is 180°. If one of two supplementary angles is 52° smaller than the other, how large is each angle?
7. The sum of the angles of a triangle is 180°. Find the angles of a triangle if the first angle is 31° more than the second, and the third is 5° less than twice the first.

e) Consecutive integer problems:

Consecutive integers are whole numbers that follow each other in succession, as 3, 4, 5, etc.

1. Find two consecutive integers whose sum is 139.
2. Find three consecutive integers whose sum is 81.
3. What three consecutive odd integers have a sum of 45?
4. Find three consecutive even integers such that 3 times the first equals the sum of the other two.
5. Find four consecutive integers such that the sum of the first and fourth is 53.

EXERCISE 41

Age Problems

I. **Aim**: To solve age problems.

II. **Procedure**: Follow steps outlined in the procedure for general word problems. Represent both the present ages and the ages at the other stated time.

III. **Sample Solution**

Mr. Jones is 4 times as old as his son. In 16 years he will be only twice as old. What are their ages now?

Solution:

Let x = son's present age in yr.

Then $4x$ = father's present age in yr.

$x + 16$ = son's age in yr. 16 yr. hence

$4x + 16$ = father's age in yr. 16 yr. hence

*$4x + 16 = 2(x + 16)$

$4x + 16 = 2x + 32$

$4x - 2x = 32 - 16$

$2x = 16$

$x = 8$ yr., son's present age

$4x = 32$ yr., father's present age

Answer, Father is 32 yr. old and his son is 8 yr. old

* The equation is determined by the following fact:

Father's age 16 yr. hence is equal to twice the son's age at that time.

Check:

Father's age	Son's age
	present
32 yr. = 4 ×	8 yr.
	16 yr. hence
48 yr. = 2 ×	24 yr.

Practice Problems

A. Representations

Find the missing numbers or representations:

1. John is 3 times as old as Tom.

	Now	4 yr. ago	5 yr. from now
a) Tom's age	12 yr.	?	?
John's age	?	?	?
b) Tom's age	x yr.	?	?
John's age	?	?	?

2. Joan is 4 years older than Mary.

	Now	3 yr. ago	7 yr. ago	6 yr. from now
a) Mary's age	10 yr.	?	?	?
Joan's age	?	?	?	?
b) Mary's age	x yr.	?	?	?
Joan's age	?	?	?	?

3. The sum of Charlotte's age and Elaine's age is 40 years.

	Now	5 yr. ago	10 yr. from now
a) Charlotte's age	8 yr.	?	?
Elaine's age	?	?	?
b) Charlotte's age	x yr.	?	?
Elaine's age	?	?	?

B. Problems:

1. Mr. Dix is three times as old as his son. In 12 years he will be only twice as old. Find their ages.

2. Richard is twice as old as his brother. Four years ago he was four times as old. Find their ages.

3. Joe is one fifth as old as Harry. Four years hence three times Joe's age will equal Harry's age. Find Harry's age.

4. Peggy is 6 years older than Rosalie. In 2 years Peggy will be twice as old as Rosalie. Find their ages.

5. Arthur is 12 years younger than Robert. Three years ago Robert was five times as old as Arthur. How old is Robert now?

6. June is 5 years older than Dorothy. Four years ago 8 times Dorothy's age equaled 3 times June's age. Find June's age now.

7. Henry is 4 times as old as George. Six years ago he was 10 times as old as George. Find Henry's age.

8. The sum of the ages of David and Bernice is 48 years. Eight years hence David will be 3 times Bernice's age. Find their ages.

9. The sum of the ages of a mother and daughter is 45 years. Five years ago the mother was 6 times the daughter's age. Find their ages.

10. The sum of the ages of a father and son is 46 years. In two years four times the son's age will equal the father's age. Find their ages.

EXERCISE 42

Coin and Mixture Problems

I. Aim: To solve coin and mixture problems.

II. Procedure

1. Coin problems: Follow steps outlined in procedure for general word problems. Represent the number of each kind of coin; also their values in some common denomination.

2. Mixture problems: Follow the steps outlined in procedure for general word problems. Represent the quantity of each commodity; also their cost in some common denomination.

III. Sample Solutions

1. John has $1.55 in nickels and dimes. He has 7 more nickels than dimes. Find the number of each.

Solution:

Let $x =$ no. of dimes
Then $x + 7 =$ no. of nickels
$10x =$ value of all dimes in cents
$5(x + 7) =$ value of all nickels in cents
*$10x + 5(x + 7) = 155$
$10x + 5x + 35 = 155$
$10x + 5x = 155 - 35$
$15x = 120$
$x = 8$ dimes
$x + 7 = 15$ nickels
Answer, 8 dimes and 15 nickels

* The equation is determined by the following fact:

The number of cents in all dimes plus the number of cents in all nickels equals the total number of cents.

$$\$1.55 = 155 \text{ cents}$$

Check:

15	nickels	$ .75 value of nickels
− 8	dimes	+ .80 value of dimes
7	difference	$1.55

2. A grocer mixes coffee worth 80¢ a pound with coffee worth 95¢ a pound making a blend to sell at 85¢ a pound. If he blends 60 pounds, how many pounds of each kind does he use?

Solution:

Let $n =$ no. of lb. of 80¢ coffee.
Then $60 - n =$ no. of lb. of 95¢ coffee.
$80n =$ cost of all the 80¢ coffee in cents
$95(60 - n) =$ cost of all the 95¢ coffee in cents
*$80n + 95(60 - n) = 85 \times 60$
$80n + 5700 - 95n = 5100$
$80n - 95n = 5100 - 5700$
$-15n = -600$
$n = 40$ lb. of 80¢ coffee
$60 - n = 20$ lb. of 95¢ coffee
Answer, 40 lb. of 80¢ coffee and 20 lb. of 95¢ coffee.

*The equation is determined by the following fact:

The cost of all 80¢ coffee plus the cost of all 95¢ coffee equals the cost of 60 lb. of 85¢ coffee.

Check: 40 lb. + 20 lb. = 60 lb.

40 lb.	20 lb.	60 lb.
×$.80	×$.95	×$.85
$32.00	+ $19.00	= $51.00

Practice Problems

A. Representations

Find the missing numbers or representations:

1. There are twice as many $10 bills as $5 bills.

	(1)	(2)	(3)	(4)
Number of $5 bills	4	10	12	x
Number of $10 bills	?	?	?	?
Value of the $5 bills in dollars	?	?	?	?
Value of the $10 bills in dollars	?	?	?	?

2. There are 3 more nickels than dimes.

	(1)	(2)	(3)	(4)
Number of dimes	8	15	20	x
Number of nickels	?	?	?	?
Value of the dimes in cents	?	?	?	?
Value of the nickels in cents	?	?	?	?

3. A grocer mixes coffee worth 98¢ a pound with coffee worth 79¢ a pound, blending 70 pounds in all.

	(1)	(2)	(3)	(4)
Number of pounds of 98¢ coffee	40	30	10	x
Number of pounds of 79¢ coffee	?	?	?	?
Cost in cents of all the 98¢ coffee	?	?	?	?
Cost in cents of all the 79¢ coffee	?	?	?	?

B. Problems:

1. James has $1.25 in nickels and dimes. He has 3 times as many nickels as dimes. Find the number of each.

2. Mr. Bennett had 4 times as many $5 bills as $1 bills, the total amounting to $84. How many bills of each kind did he have?

3. Joe, in changing a $10 bill, received 2 more dimes than quarters. How many dimes did he receive?

4. Harry has 4 more nickels than half-dollars; their value is $1.85. Find the number of nickels.

5. Elaine has 16 coins, some quarters and the rest nickels. The total value of all the coins is $1.40. Find the number of each kind of coin.

6. Ms. Sullivan has $2.34. She has three times as many dimes as nickels and 6 more pennies than dimes. Find the number of each kind of coin.

7. Stewart has 18 stamps; some 6¢ stamps and the rest 8¢ stamps. The value of all the stamps is $1.30. How many stamps of each kind does he have?

8. Mr. Ford bought stamps costing $1.12. He received the same number of 6¢ stamps as 8¢ stamps, but as many 1¢ stamps as the sum of the other two. How many stamps of each kind did he have?

9. There were 3,000 persons at a football game. Some paid $2 for their tickets while the rest paid $1. The total receipts amounted to $4,850. How many tickets of each kind were sold?

10. A grocer mixes coffee worth 89¢ a pound with coffee worth 99¢ a pound making a blend to sell at 93¢ a pound. If he blends 50 pounds, how many pounds of each kind does he use?

11. A confectioner wishes to make 80 pounds of mixed candy to sell at 50¢ a pound. If he mixes candy worth 38¢ a pound with candy worth 70¢ a pound, how many pounds of each kind does he use?

12. How many pounds of tea worth $1.54 a pound should be blended with tea worth $1.70 a pound to make 40 pounds of blended tea to sell at $1.60 a pound?

13. How many pounds of cookies worth 16¢ a pound must be mixed with 25 pounds of cookies worth 28¢ a pound to get a mixture worth 26¢ a pound?

14. Walnuts cost 20¢ a pound more than peanuts. If Ms. Bailey paid $5.10 for 4 pounds of peanuts and 6 pounds of walnuts, what did she pay per pound for each?

15. A farmer sent 100 bags of potatoes to a commission merchant; some at 90¢ a bag and the rest at 50¢ a bag. If he received $78.80 in payment, how many bags of each did he send?

EXERCISE 43

Motion Problems

I. Aim: To solve motion problems.

II. Procedure: Follow steps outlined in procedure for general word problems. Use the motion formula to relate given facts and to form the equation.

III. Sample Solution

Two trains leave a station, one traveling north at the rate of 60 m.p.h. and the other south at the rate of 54 m.p.h. In how many hours will they be 342 miles apart?

Solution:

Let x = no. of hours each train traveled
$60x$ = no. of miles traveled by train going north
$54x$ = no. of miles traveled by train going south
*$60x + 54x = 342$
$114x = 342$
$x = 3$ hours

Answer, 3 hours

* The equation is determined by the following fact:

The distance traveled by one train plus the distance traveled by the other train equal the total distance.

Check:

60 m.p.h.	54 m.p.h.	180 mi.
× 3 hr.	× 3 hr.	+162 mi.
180 mi.	162 mi.	342 mi.

Practice Problems

A. Representations

Find the missing numbers or representations:

1. (a) Find how many miles a car will go at a given speed for a given time.

Rate of Speed	Time
1. 8 m.p.h.	4 hours
2. 27 m.p.h.	8 hours
3. 40 m.p.h.	x hours
4. 50 m.p.h.	$5x$ hours
5. x m.p.h.	3 hours

(b) Write a formula for the distance covered (d) by a car if the rate of speed (r) and time (t) are given.

2. (a) Find the number of hours it will take a car to travel a given distance at a given speed.

Distance	Rate of Speed
1. 80 miles	20 m.p.h.
2. 210 miles	35 m.p.h.
3. 550 miles	x m.p.h.
4. x miles	25 m.p.h.
5. $200-x$ miles	10 m.p.h.

(b) Write a formula for the time (t) it takes a car to cover a given distance (d) at a given rate of speed (r).

3. (a) Find the rate of speed at which a train travels if it covers a given distance in a given time.

Distance	Time
1. 60 miles	4 hours
2. 130 miles	2 hours
3. 200 miles	x hours
4. 150 miles	$x+2$ hours
5. x miles	3 hours

(b) Write a formula for the rate of speed (r) at which a train travels in covering a given distance (d) in a given time (t).

4. General—Represent the missing term:

	d	r	t
1.	?	30	x
2.	?	x	5
3.	x	40	?
4.	x	?	3
5.	90	?	x
6.	160	x	?
7.	?	20	$x+3$
8.	?	$3x$	7
9.	$140-x$	40	?
10.	?	$x-5$	6

B. Problems:

1. One car, traveling at an average speed of 35 m.p.h., leaves Philadelphia for Washington, a distance of 150 miles. At the same time another car, traveling at an average speed of 40 m.p.h., leaves Washington for Philadelphia. In how many hours will they meet? How far from Philadelphia will they meet?

2. Two trains leave West Philadelphia station, one traveling north at the rate of 50 m.p.h., and the other south at the rate of 55 m.p.h. In how many hours will they be 735 miles apart?

3. Two boys on bicycles start from the same place but ride in opposite directions. Joe rides twice as fast as Tom, and in 4 hours they are 24 miles apart. What is the rate of speed of each boy?

4. How fast did a car go to overtake a bus in 5 hours if the bus averaged 30 m.p.h. and left 3 hours before the car?

5. Three hours after a plane left Newark for San Francisco at a speed of 175 m.p.h., another plane left traveling at a speed of 280 m.p.h. How many hours will it take the second plane to overtake the first plane?

6. Two salesmen leave a hotel at the same time but travel by automobile in opposite directions. Mr. Smith's average rate of speed is 3 miles per hour faster than Mr. White's. Find their rates of speed if, after 5 hours, they are 435 miles apart.

7. A passenger train traveling at the rate of 50 miles per hour leaves a station 6 hours after a freight train and overtakes it in 4 hours. Find the rate of speed of the freight train.

8. Two trucks leave a warehouse at the same time but travel in opposite directions. If the first truck travels at a speed of 28 miles per hour and the other truck travels 8 miles per hour faster, in how many hours will they be 384 miles apart?

9. Two neighboring families left a summer resort for home, a distance of 180 miles, one starting 2 hours ahead of the other and traveling at an average speed of 30 miles per hour. How fast must the second automobile travel to reach home at the same time as the first automobile?

10. Two groups of girl scouts, living in towns 17 miles apart, decide to pitch camp along the road joining the two towns. If the group from one town leaves at 7 A.M. and the group from the second town leaves at 8 A.M. but walks 1 mile per hour faster than the first group, they will meet at 10 A.M. How fast is each group walking?

Radius of Action — Interception

1. How long will it take an airplane, flying at an average speed of 380 m.p.h. to intercept an airplane, observed 84 miles away, flying directly toward it at an estimated speed of 250 m.p.h.?

2. How far from an airport can an airplane fly and yet return (radius of action) in 5 hours if its outgoing speed is 400 m.p.h. and its return speed is 600 m.p.h.?

3. If its outgoing speed is 270 m.p.h. and its return speed is 360 m.p.h., how far from an aircraft carrier can an airplane fly and yet return in 7 hours.?

4. An unknown aircraft is sighted 194 miles from an airbase, flying at an estimated speed of 300 m.p.h. toward the base. If it takes an interceptor plane 2 minutes to take off, flying at an average speed of 420 m.p.h., how far from the base will it intercept the first airplane?

5. How far from an airbase can an airplane fly and yet return in 4 hours if its out going air speed is 425 m.p.h. with a tailwind of 30 m.p.h. and its return air speed is 360 m.p.h. with a head wind of 35 m.p.h.?

REVIEW OF UNIT SEVEN

Solve and check:

1. $9c = 8 + 5c$
2. $6x + 3 = 4x + 27$
3. $8y - 9 = 35 - 3y$
4. $a + .03a = 618$

5. $n + n + 2 + n + 4 = 45$
6. $2s - 3s = -6$
7. $3m = 12m - 54$
8. $8t - 7 = 2t + 6$

9. $5d - 8 + 4d = 5 - 3d - 13$
10. $23 + 6b + 9 = 4b + 20 - 6b$
11. $10x + 25(17 - x) = 215$
12. $(n - 4)(n + 5) = (n + 2)(n - 3)$

13. John is $x + 4$ years old now. How old was he 7 years ago?

14. There are 148 students in the graduating class. If n represents the number of girls, how can the number of boys be represented?

15. If $x =$ first number and $x + 6 =$ second number, write an equation for the statement: Three times the sum of the two numbers is equal to 22 more than the second number.

16. The length of a rectangle is 7 times its width. If the perimeter is 208 inches, what is the length?

17. Charlotte is 9 years older than Marilyn. In 1 year Charlotte will be four times as old as Marilyn. What are their ages now?

18. Kenny has 24 coins, some nickels and the rest dimes. If he has $1.50 in all, how many coins of each kind does he have?

19. How long will it take an airplane flying at an average speed of 500 m.p.h. to intercept an airplane, 420 miles away, flying directly toward it at a speed of 350 m.p.h.?

20. How many pounds of coffee worth 96¢ a pound must be mixed with 60 pounds of coffee worth 70¢ a pound to make a blend to sell at 90¢ a pound?

CUMULATIVE ALGEBRA REVIEW

1. Combine: $6b^3 - 4b^2 - 2b + 8 - 3b^2 - 4b - b^3 + 6b$
2. From $2n^2 - 4nx + x^2$ subtract $8n^2 - x^2$.
3. Multiply: $-5c^2d^3(c^2 - 4cd + 2d^2)$

4. Multiply $5m^2 - 2m + 6$ by $2m - 9$.
5. Divide $16d^2y^4 - 8dy^3 + 4y^2$ by $-2y^2$.
6. Divide $27b^3 + 64c^3$ by $3b + 4c$.

7. Remove parentheses and, if possible, add like terms: $(x - 9)(x + 2) - (x - 5)(x - 7)$

8. Solve and check: $4n - 54 = 90 - 2n$.

9. Solve and check: $14 - (2x - 7) = 6x - 5(4x - 9)$.

10. Find the value of C if $F = 14$, using the formula $C = \frac{5}{9}(F - 32)$ 11. $37\frac{1}{2}\%$ of what number is 645?

12. Using the formula $A = p + prt$, find the value of p when $A = 195$, $r = .08$, and $t = 7$.

13. The aspect ratio of an airplane wing is the ratio of its length to its width. If the area of a rectangular wing is 252 square feet and its length is 42 feet, find its aspect ratio.

14. Richard has $6.15 in quarters and nickels. He has 9 more quarters than nickels. Find the number of each.

15. Angle A in triangle ABC is twice angle B. Angle C is 10 degrees more than angle A. Find the size of each angle. The sum of the angles of any triangle is 180°.

KEYED ACHIEVEMENT TEST

1. Add: $6n^2 - 3n + 9$; $2n^2 - 7$; $8 - 5n - n^2$ ㉔
2. Subtract: $6b^4 - 4b^2 - 9$
   $\underline{\qquad 2b^2 - 1\qquad}$ ㉖

3. Multiply: $(-3x^2)(-6xy)(-2y^2)$ ㉙
4. Divide: $2n - 5)\overline{8n^3 - 26n^2 + 27n - 30}$ �35
5. Solve and check: $25x + 5(30 - x) = 530$ ㊱

6. Remove parentheses and, if possible, add like terms: $4x - (5x - 1) - 3(2x - 5) + (x - 6)(x + 3)$ �32

7. Find the value of l if $p = 82$ and $w = 19$, using the formula $p = 2l + 2w$.   ⑫

8. The sum of two numbers is 17. If one number is n, what is the other number?   ㊳

9. If $x =$ speed of car A in m.p.h. and $x + 10 =$ speed of car B in m.p.h., write an equation for the statement: The difference in the speeds of the two cars increased by 80 m.p.h. is equal to the sum of their speeds.   ㊴

10. There were 900 persons attending the school play. Some paid 75 cents for their tickets and the rest paid 50 cents. If the total receipts amounted to $520, how many tickets of each kind were sold?   ㊷

INTRODUCTION TO UNIT EIGHT

In order to save time when multiplying binomials, special rules are developed so that products may be found mentally. This study of finding products of binomals by short methods is called *special products*.

A complete study of algbraic fractions, fractional equations, formulas, and quadratic equations involves the process of finding two or more expressions whose product is the given expression. This process is called *factoring*. Factoring is the direct reverse of multiplication. In multiplication the factors are given and we are required to find the product. In factoring the product is given and we are required to find the factors. Division and factoring are not the same process. In division the product and a factor are given and we are required to find the other factor. In factoring only the product is given.

When we solve the equation $2x + 3x = 15$, we combine $2x$ and $3x$ to obtain $5x$. However, when solving the equation $ax + bx = c$, we cannot add ax and bx to get a single term. Thus, to solve for x we factor the expression $ax + bx$, selecting x as one of the factors. This process of finding the common monomial factor is also useful when dealing with formulas like $A = p + prt$ and $E = IR + Ir$. Students will find the process of factoring the difference of two squares helpful when formulas like $a = \sqrt{c^2 - b^2}$, $b = \sqrt{c^2 - a^2}$ and $A = \pi R^2 - \pi r^2$ occur. On page 268 factoring is used in the solution of quadratic equations. It is also used to develop the quadratic formula and in the solution of quadratic equations by completing the square.

❖❖

ARITHMETIC MAINTENANCE DRILL

1. Add:
$43 + 5,826 + 63,095 + 24$

2. Subtract:
$80,000 - 8,063$

3. Multiply:
6080×35

4. Divide:
$29304 \div 72$

5. Add:
$5\frac{3}{8} + 1\frac{11}{16} + 2\frac{3}{4}$

6. Subtract:
$5 - 4\frac{7}{8}$

7. Multiply:
$8 \times 2\frac{9}{16}$

8. Divide:
$1\frac{3}{5} \div 2\frac{2}{3}$

9. Add: $59.26
8.09
283.87
6.94
.85$

10. Subtract:
$260.52
89.75$

11. Multiply:
$.05 \times .004$

12. Divide
$.008)\overline{.4}$

13. Round off to the nearest hundredth: 43.1983

14. Change .75 to a common fraction.

15. Divide by short method:
$87.2 \div 100$

16. Find 40% of $142

17. 15 is what % of 25?

18. 27 is $\frac{3}{8}$ of what number?

19. Find the square root of 155236.

20. Change 3 lb. 4 oz. to oz.

UNIT EIGHT—SPECIAL PRODUCTS AND FACTORING

EXERCISE 44

Factoring Polynomials Having a Common Monomial Factor

I. Aim: To factor a polynomial whose terms have a common monomial factor.

II. Procedure

1. Find the highest common factor of its terms.

2. Divide the polynomial by this factor.

3. Indicate the product of the two factors by writing the common factor in front of the quotient found in step 2.

III. Sample Solutions

Factor the following polynomials:

1. $8x - 8y$ Answer, $8(x - y)$
2. $ac - bc + c$ Answer, $c(a - b + 1)$
3. $6a^2xy^2 - 9ax^2y^2 + 12a^3x^2y^3$ Answer, $3axy^2(2a - 3x + 4a^2xy)$
4. $-2ax^4 - 6b^2x^5 - 4c^2x^3$ Answer, $-2x^3(ax + 3b^2x^2 + 2c^2)$
5. $b(b + d) - d(b + d)$ Answer, $(b + d)(b - d)$

Preliminary Examples

Given a product and one factor, find the other factor:

	Product	First factor	Second factor
1.	18	6	?
2.	24	3	?
3.	$4x$	4	?
4.	$35y^3$	$5y$	?
5.	$2x^2 + x$	x	?
6.	$4ab - 2ac$	$2a$	?
7.	$3x^2y - 12xy^2$	$3xy$	?
8.	$9a^3 - 6a^2 + 3a$	$3a$	?
9.	$7a^2x + 14ax - 21ax^2$	$7ax$	?
10.	$16ac^2x^2 - 8a^2cx^2 - 64acx^2$	$-8acx^2$	?

·DIAGNOSTIC TEST

Factor the following polynomials:

1. $5a - 5x$
2. $ar + rl$
3. $ax - bx + x$
4. $8x + 16$
5. $a^4 + 2a^3b$
6. $a^2bx + ab^2x - abx^2$
7. $12a^3x - 8a^2x^2 + 24a^2x^3$
8. $-3b^3 - 6b^2 - 9b$
9. $a(a - b) + b(a - b)$
10. $\frac{1}{2}c^2d - \frac{1}{2}cd^2$
11. $1.2x^2y - 3.6xy - 1.8xy^2$

Related Practice Examples

Factor the following polynomials. Check by multiplying factors:

SET 1

1. $4x + 4y$
2. $3c + 3d$
3. $8a - 8b$
4. $2c - 2x$
5. $ax + ay$
6. $cm + cn$
7. $by - bz$
8. $dx - dy$
9. $ax + ay + az$
10. $dr - ds + dt$

SET 2

1. $ax + bx$
2. $cy - dy$
3. $ab - bc$
4. $xy - yz$
5. $rl + ar$
6. $cx + dx + 3x$
7. $ab + bc + bd$
8. $mx - nx - rx$
9. $am + mx - 2m$
10. $2cd + 2dr - 2dt$

SET 3

1. $5x + 5$
2. $4a + 4$
3. $8r - 8$
4. $3d - 3$
5. $ab + a$
6. $xy + y$
7. $cd - d$
8. $mx + nx + x$
9. $cr - rt - r$
10. $6xy - 6xz - 6x$

SET 4

1. $3x + 6$
2. $8c + 24$
3. $2a - 18$
4. $4y - 40$
5. $6x + 9$
6. $10b - 15$
7. $24d + 8$
8. $20 + 12z$
9. $8a + 16b + 24c$
10. $15x - 12y - 6z$

SET 5

1. $a^2 + ab$
2. $x^3 - xy$
3. $c^3 + c^2d$
4. $m^4 + m^2n$
5. $d^5 + bd^3$
6. $a^3x + a^2y$
7. $c^8m - c^5n$
8. $a^3 + a^2 + 2a$
9. $4x^6 - 3x^4 - 5x^2$
10. $12m^7 - 5m^6 + 3m^4$

SET 6

1. $a^2b^2 + ab^3$
2. $x^4y^2 - x^2y^4$
3. $m^2x^3 - mx^4$
4. $c^2n^4 - cn^2$
5. $x^2y^2 - x^3yz$
6. $a^2bc + abc^2 + ab^2c$
7. $x^3y^2z - xy^3z^2 - x^2yz^3$
8. $mnx^2 - nx^2 + m^3x$
9. $ar + ar^2 + ar^3 + ar^4$
10. $bxy - by - aby - bcy$

SET 7

1. $5a^3 + 10a^2 + 15$
2. $3x^6 - 9x^4 - 6x^2$
3. $4a^2b + 8ab - 12ab^2$
4. $6c^3d - 18c^2d^3 + 30c^2d^4$
5. $2d^2r^2 + 10d^3r^3 - 8d^4r^4$
6. $20ad^3 + 15ad^2 + 10ad$
7. $9a^3c^3 - 15a^3c + 3a^3$
8. $30bx + 10b^2 - 20b^3$
9. $4a^3b^4 - 2a^3b^3c^2 - 6a^2bc^2$
10. $27bc^2d^3 - 36b^2cd^2 - 18bc$

SET 8

1. $-ab - ac - ad$
2. $-x^3 - x^2 - x$
3. $-a^2y^2 - a^2y - ay^2$
4. $-2c^3 - 4c^2 - 6c$
5. $-15bx^3 - 10b^2x^2 - 25b^3x^2$

SET 9

1. $a(x+y) + b(x+y)$
2. $x(x-y) - y(x-y)$
3. $c(c-3) + 3(c-3)$
4. $b(a+2) - 2(a+2)$
5. $x^2(x-5) + 6(x-5)$

SET 10

1. $\frac{1}{2}bx + \frac{1}{2}by$
2. $\frac{1}{4}x^2y - \frac{1}{4}xy^2$
3. $\frac{2}{3}ab^2 + \frac{1}{3}ab^3$
4. $\frac{3}{4}c^3xy + \frac{3}{8}c^2x^2y^2$
5. $\frac{1}{2}a^4m^2x - \frac{1}{4}amx^2 - \frac{3}{4}a^2m^2x$

SET 11

1. $.3x + .9y$
2. $.2a^3 + .6b^3 - .8c^3$
3. $1.5x^2y + 4.5xy + 7.5xy^2$
4. $1.8bx^3 + 1.2b^2x - .6b^3x^2$
5. $-2.1ab^2c - .7abc^2 - 1.4a^2bc$

EXERCISE 45

Squaring a Monomial

I. Aim: To square a monomial.

II. Procedure

1. Multiply the numerical coefficient by itself.

2. Multiply the exponent of each of its letters by 2.

III. Sample Solutions

1. 6   Answer, 36
2. x^4y Answer, x^8y^2
3. $3a^3$ Answer, $9a^6$
4. $\frac{2}{3}a^2m^5$ Answer, $\frac{4}{9}a^4m^{10}$
5. $0.2b$ Answer, $0.04b^2$

DIAGNOSTIC TEST

Square the following monomials:

1. 7   3. $4x$ 5. b^2 7. $\frac{1}{2}$ 9. 0.3

2. a 4. ac 6. $5x^3$ 8. $\frac{3}{4}t$ 10. $0.7mx$

Related Practice Examples

Square the following monomials:

SET 1	SET 2	SET 3	SET 4	SET 5
1. 3	1. b	1. $3x$	1. xy	1. a^2
2. 5	2. x	2. $7y$	2. ax	2. x^2
3. 8	3. y	3. $9a$	3. bc	3. b^3
4. 10	4. c	4. $4c$	4. cd	4. x^4
5. 1	5. m	5. $12b$	5. mn	5. y^5

SET 6	SET 7	SET 8	SET 9	SET 10
1. $6y^2$	1. $\frac{1}{3}$	1. $\frac{2}{3}x$	1. 0.2	1. $0.6x$
2. $2b^3$	2. $\frac{2}{5}$	2. $\frac{1}{4}t^2$	2. 0.8	2. $0.4xy$
3. $7a^2b$	3. $\frac{3}{7}$	3. $\frac{1}{2}at$	3. 1.3	3. $1.2a^2$
4. $3x^2y^2$	4. $\frac{5}{6}$	4. $\frac{4}{5}x^2y$	4. 1.4	4. $3.2ab^2$
5. $4a^2bc^3$	5. $\frac{3}{4}$	5. $\frac{3}{10}a^2b$	5. 2.5	5. $0.02x^2y^3$

EXERCISE 46

Square Root of a Monomial

I. Aim: To find the square root of a monomial.

II. Procedure

1. Take the square root of its numerical coefficient.

2. Divide the exponent of each of its letters by 2.

III. Sample Solutions

Find the square roots of the following:

1. 64   Answer, 8
2. a^4x^6 Answer, a^2x^3
3. $49m^2n^8$ Answer, $7mn^4$
4. $\frac{4}{25}b^2$ Answer, $\frac{2}{5}b$
5. $0.09c^6x^2$ Answer, $0.3c^3x$

DIAGNOSTIC TEST

Find the square roots of the following monomials:

1. 9   3. $64x^2$ 5. $49b^6$ 7. $\frac{1}{4}$ 9. 0.04

2. b^2 4. a^4x^2 6. $25c^4d^2x^6$ 8. $\frac{4}{9}a^2$ 10. $0.81b^2x^4$

Related Practice Examples

Find the square roots of the following monomials:

SET 1	SET 2	SET 3	SET 4	SET 5
1. 4	1. x^2	1. $9c^2$	1. x^2y^2	1. $81x^4$
2. 64	2. a^2	2. $36m^2$	2. b^2x^2	2. $16b^4$
3. 25	3. b^4	3. $81x^2$	3. a^4y^2	3. $49y^6$
4. 49	4. y^6	4. $100b^2$	4. c^4d^6	4. $9a^8$
5. 144	5. c^{10}	5. $16x^2$	5. x^8y^4	5. $121c^{10}$

SET 6	SET 7	SET 8	SET 9	SET 10
1. $36a^2b^2$	1. $\frac{1}{9}$	1. $\frac{1}{4}b^2$	1. 0.01	1. $0.04b^2$
2. $25x^4y^{10}$	2. $\frac{4}{25}$	2. $\frac{4}{81}x^2$	2. 0.16	2. $0.25x^2$
3. $144a^2b^2c^4$	3. $\frac{16}{49}$	3. $\frac{9}{25}a^4$	3. 0.49	3. $0.36a^2c^2$
4. $4m^4n^2x^6$	4. $\frac{36}{81}$	4. $\frac{100}{121}m^2x^2$	4. 0.09	4. $0.81c^2x^4$
5. $100a^6x^8y^4$	5. $\frac{9}{100}$	5. $\frac{49}{144}c^2x^4$	5. 0.81	5. $0.49a^2b^4y^6$

EXERCISE 47

Product of the Sum and Difference of the Same Two Terms

I. Aim: To find the product of the sum and the difference of the same two terms.

II. Procedure

1. Square the first term to find the first term of the product.

2. Square the second term to find the second term of the product.

3. Subtract the second square from the first by placing a minus sign between the two squares.
   Note: There are only two terms in the product.

III. Sample Solutions

Find the following products mentally:

1. $(a+6)(a-6)$ Answer, a^2-36
2. $(4-x)(4+x)$ Answer, $16-x^2$
3. $(2b+3c)(2b-3c)$ Answer, $4b^2-9c^2$
4. $(\frac{1}{2}ab-x^2)(\frac{1}{2}ab+x^2)$ Answer, $\frac{1}{4}a^2b^2-x^4$
5. $(x+3)(x-3)(x^2+9)$ Answer, x^4-81

Note: Solution of example 5.
$$(x+3)(x-3)(x^2+9)$$
$$= (x^2-9)(x^2+9)$$
$$= x^4-81$$
Answer, x^4-81

DIAGNOSTIC TEST

Find the following products mentally:

1. $(x+3)(x-3)$
2. $(2+a)(2-a)$
3. $(a-b)(a+b)$
4. $(x^2-y^2)(x^2+y^2)$

5. $(ab^2+x)(ab^2-x)$
6. $(3b+2)(3b-2)$
7. $(4a-3b)(4a+3b)$

8. $(\frac{2}{3}ax-y)(\frac{2}{3}ax+y)$
9. $(.4x+.3y)(.4x-.3y)$
10. $(x+2)(x-2)(x^2+4)$

Related Practice Examples

Find the following products mentally:

SET 1

1. $(x+2)(x-2)$
2. $(x+1)(x-1)$
3. $(x+5)(x-5)$
4. $(y+7)(y-7)$
5. $(b+4)(b-4)$
6. $(c-10)(c+10)$
7. $(m-6)(m+6)$
8. $(d-8)(d+8)$
9. $(n-12)(n+12)$
10. $(r-3)(r+3)$

SET 2

1. $(1+a)(1-a)$
2. $(6+b)(6-b)$
3. $(8+x)(8-x)$
4. $(7-s)(7+s)$
5. $(5-t)(5+t)$

SET 3

1. $(x+y)(x-y)$
2. $(c+d)(c-d)$
3. $(m-n)(m+n)$
4. $(b-a)(b+a)$
5. $(y+x)(y-x)$

SET 4

1. $(a^2+b^2)(a^2-b^2)$
2. $(c^2+d^2)(c^2-d^2)$
3. $(m^2-n^2)(m^2+n^2)$
4. $(b^3+c^3)(b^3-c^3)$
5. $(r^4-s^4)(r^4+s^4)$

SET 5

1. $(ab+x)(ab-x)$
2. $(c+xy)(c-xy)$
3. $(r-st)(r+st)$
4. $(a^2x+y)(a^2x-y)$
5. $(bx^2-cy^2)(bx^2+cy^2)$

SET 6

1. $(2a+5)(2a-5)$
2. $(3b-2)(3b+2)$
3. $(7x-4)(7x+4)$
4. $(6r+5)(6r-5)$
5. $(2r-1)(2r+1)$
6. $(8x-3)(8x+3)$
7. $(4+9m)(4-9m)$
8. $(3-10x)(3+10x)$
9. $(ab+9)(ab-9)$
10. $(x^2-7)(x^2+7)$

SET 7

1. $(3x+2y)(3x-2y)$
2. $(2a-5b)(2a+5b)$
3. $(7y+z)(7y-z)$
4. $(5m-2n)(5m+2n)$
5. $(10d+11r)(10d-11r)$
6. $(9x-2y)(9x+2y)$
7. $(3b^2+7c)(3b^2-7c)$
8. $(2ax+9y)(2ax-9y)$
9. $(4b^2c-d^4)(4b^2c+d^4)$
10. $(11cx^3+2dy)(11cx^3-2dy)$

SET 8

1. $(b+\frac{1}{2})(b-\frac{1}{2})$
2. $(\frac{3}{4}+a)(\frac{3}{4}-a)$
3. $(\frac{2}{5}ab-c)(\frac{2}{5}ab+c)$
4. $\left(\dfrac{b}{2}+\dfrac{c}{5}\right)\left(\dfrac{b}{2}-\dfrac{c}{5}\right)$
5. $\left(\dfrac{2}{b}-\dfrac{5}{c}\right)\left(\dfrac{2}{b}+\dfrac{5}{c}\right)$

SET 9

1. $(.2x+y)(.2x-y)$
2. $(.7a-.2b)(.7a+.2b)$
3. $(.8+y^2)(.8-y^2)$
4. $(.3a-1.2x)(.3a+1.2x)$
5. $(.4a^2b+.5x^2)(.4a^2b-.5x^2)$

SET 10

1. $(a+1)(a-1)(a^2+1)$
2. $(a-3)(a+3)(a^2+9)$
3. $(a+x)(a-x)(a^2+x^2)$
4. $(b^2+4c^2)(b-2c)(b+2c)$
5. $(2b-3x)(4b^2+9x^2)(2b+3x)$

EXERCISE 48

Factoring—Difference of Two Squares

I. Aim: To factor the difference of two squares.

II. Procedure

1. Find the square roots of the two square terms.

2. Write the sum of the two square roots (see step 1) as one of the factors.

3. Write the difference of the two square roots (see step 1) as the other factor.
   Note: Two square terms with a plus sign between them is the sum of two squares and cannot be factored by the above method.

III. Sample Solutions

Factor the following binomials:

1. $b^2 - 25$ Answer, $(b+5)(b-5)$
2. $1 - x^2$ Answer, $(1+x)(1-x)$
3. $64a^6 - 49b^2c^4$ Answer, $(8a^3 + 7bc^2)(8a^3 - 7bc^2)$
4. $\frac{16}{81}m^2 - 121$ Answer, $(\frac{4}{9}m + 11)(\frac{4}{9}m - 11)$
5. $b^4 - x^4$ Answer, $(b^2 + x^2)(b+x)(b-x)$

Note: Solution of example 5.
$b^4 - x^4$
$= (b^2 + x^2)(b^2 - x^2)$
$= (b^2 + x^2)(b+x)(b-x)$
Answer, $(b^2 + x^2)(b+x)(b-x)$

DIAGNOSTIC TEST

Factor the following binomials:

1. $a^2 - 4$
2. $25 - x^2$
3. $9b^2 - 16$
4. $a^2 - b^2$
5. $a^2x^2 - y^2$
6. $49c^2 - 25d^2$
7. $100b^2c^2 - 81m^2$
8. $a^4 - b^4$
9. $\frac{1}{4}b^2 - 49$
10. $c^2 - 0.36$

Related Practice Examples

Factor the following binomials:

SET 1	SET 2	SET 3	SET 4	SET 5
1. $b^2 - 9$	1. $4 - a^2$	1. $4x^2 - 25$	1. $x^2 - y^2$	1. $a^2b^2 - y^2$
2. $x^2 - 25$	2. $100 - r^2$	2. $49a^2 - 1$	2. $c^2 - d^2$	2. $c^2d^2 - x^2$
3. $a^2 - 49$	3. $81 - y^2$	3. $9y^2 - 16$	3. $r^2 - s^2$	3. $b^2 - x^2y^2$
4. $c^2 - 100$	4. $36 - x^2$	4. $100b^2 - 81$	4. $b^4 - a^2$	4. $a^4x^2 - y^2$
5. $d^2 - 144$	5. $16 - c^2$	5. $36 - 25c^2$	5. $c^2 - d^4$	5. $b^2c^6 - x^4y^8$
6. $y^2 - 1$	6. $9 - m^2$	6. $121 - 64b^2$		
7. $x^2 - 16$	7. $121 - b^2$	7. $x^2y^2 - 4$		
8. $x^2 - 4$	8. $49 - x^2$	8. $b^4 - 100$		
9. $m^2 - 64$	9. $25 - a^2$	9. $25 - a^2x^2$		
10. $a^2 - 36$	10. $1 - d^2$	10. $144 - a^6$		

SET 6	SET 7	SET 8	SET 9	SET 10
1. $4a^2 - 9b^2$	1. $64a^2b^2 - x^2$	1. $a^4 - 81$	1. $x^2 - \frac{1}{9}$	1. $b^2 - 0.16$
2. $25x^2 - 16y^2$	2. $4a^4x^2 - 49b^2y^4$	2. $x^4 - y^4$	2. $\frac{1}{4}a^2 - 25$	2. $x^2 - 0.01$
3. $b^2 - 36d^2$	3. $121b^6 - 16m^4$	3. $a^4 - 16x^4$	3. $\frac{4}{25}m^2 - 64$	3. $0.64 - a^2$
4. $49m^2 - 4n^2$	4. $81m^4x^2y^2 - 25a^2$	4. $a^8 - b^8$	4. $\frac{x^2}{9} - \frac{y^2}{4}$	4. $49 - 0.81m^2n^4$
5. $144c^2 - 121d^2$	5. $a^2b^2x^2 - 4c^2d^2y^2$	5. $c^8 - 1$	5. $\frac{36}{a^2} - \frac{25}{b^2}$	5. $0.25c^2 - 0.36d^2$

EXERCISE 49

The Square of a Binomial

I. Aim: To square a binomial.

II. Procedure

There are three terms in the answer.

1. To find the first term, square the first term of the binomial.

2. To find the second term, first find the product of the two terms of the binomial. Then multiply this product by 2.

3. To find the third term, square the second term of the binomial.

4. The signs of the first and third terms are always plus. The sign of the second term is the same as the sign between the two terms of the binomial.

III. Sample Solutions

Find the following products mentally:

1. $(a+4)(a+4)$ Answer, $a^2+8a+16$ 4. $(\frac{1}{2}m^2+xy)^2$ Answer, $\frac{1}{4}m^4+m^2xy+x^2y^2$
2. $(b-c)(b-c)$ Answer, $b^2-2bc+c^2$ 5. $(.2b+7)(.2b+7)$ Answer, $.04b^2+2.8b+49$
3. $(5b-3x)(5b-3x)$ Answer, $25b^2-30bx+9x^2$ 6. $(x+2)(x-2)(x^2-4)$ Answer, x^4-8x^2+16

Note—Solution of example 6.
$$(x+2)(x-2)(x^2-4)$$
$$=(x^2-4)(x^2-4)$$
$$=x^4-8x^2+16$$
Answer, x^4-8x^2+16

Preliminary Examples

Finding the middle term.

	First term	Second term	Twice the product of the two terms		First term	Second term	Twice the product of the two terms
1.	x	3	?	6.	$7x$	$2y$	?
2.	b	1	?	7.	$9c$	$7d$	?
3.	a	b	?	8.	$10r$	$3s$	?
4.	x	y	?	9.	x	$\frac{1}{2}$	?
5.	$5a$	4	?	10.	$4m$	$.3$	?

DIAGNOSTIC TEST

Find the following products mentally:

1. $(x+3)(x+3)$ 6. $(b+8)^2$ 11. $(5c^2d-4y)(5c^2d-4y)$
2. $(a-5)(a-5)$ 7. $(a^2+c^2)(a^2+c^2)$ 12. $(\frac{1}{2}x+4)(\frac{1}{2}x+4)$
3. $(6+b)(6+b)$ 8. $(ab-x)^2$ 13. $(.5x+.3y)^2$
4. $(x+y)(x+y)$ 9. $(4a+3)(4a+3)$ 14. $(b+1)(b-1)(b^2-1)$
5. $(c-d)(c-d)$ 10. $(3x-2y)^2$

Related Practice Examples

Find the following products mentally:

SET 1	SET 2	SET 3	SET 4
1. $(x+2)(x+2)$	1. $(b-3)(b-3)$	1. $(5+a)(5+a)$	1. $(a+b)(a+b)$
2. $(b+5)(b+5)$	2. $(d-6)(d-6)$	2. $(4+x)(4+x)$	2. $(c+d)(c+d)$
3. $(c+8)(c+8)$	3. $(m-2)(m-2)$	3. $(7-b)(7-b)$	3. $(m+n)(m+n)$
4. $(a+1)(a+1)$	4. $(x-12)(x-12)$	4. $(1-x)(1-x)$	4. $(r+s)(r+s)$
5. $(x+10)(x+10)$	5. $(x-9)(x-9)$	5. $(8+c)(8+c)$	5. $(u+v)(u+v)$

SET 5	SET 6	SET 7	SET 8
1. $(b-x)(b-x)$	1. $(a+4)^2$	1. $(a^2+b^2)(a^2+b^2)$	1. $(ac-d)^2$
2. $(a-d)(a-d)$	2. $(b+y)^2$	2. $(x^2-y^2)(x^2-y^2)$	2. $(b+cd)(b+cd)$
3. $(x-a)(x-a)$	3. $(x-9)^2$	3. $(m^2-n^2)^2$	3. $(mx-ny)(mx-ny)$
4. $(s-c)(s-c)$	4. $(c-r)^2$	4. $(a^3-x^3)(a^3-x^3)$	4. $(b^2c+d^2)(b^2c+d^2)$
5. $(s-b)(s-b)$	5. $(3-m)^2$	5. $(b^2+x)(b^2+x)$	5. $(a^3b-xy^3)^2$

SET 9	SET 10	SET 11
1. $(3a+5)(3a+5)$	1. $(2a+3b)(2a+3b)$	1. $(3ab+x)(3ab+x)$
2. $(5x-1)(5x-1)$	2. $(5x+4y)(5x+4y)$	2. $(8xy^2-7a)(8xy^2-7a)$
3. $(9c+4)^2$	3. $(8m+3n)^2$	3. $(r^3-3mn)(r^3-3mn)$
4. $(2d-7)^2$	4. $(7c+10d)^2$	4. $(3a^2b+x)^2$
5. $(8y+3)(8y+3)$	5. $(3x-4y)(3x-4y)$	5. $(6b^2y^4-4c^2)^2$
6. $(4b-6)(4b-6)$	6. $(9r-5t)(9r-5t)$	
7. $(10x-9)^2$	7. $(12b-7x)^2$	SET 12
8. $(6m+5)^2$	8. $(4c-d)^2$	1. $(\frac{1}{4}x+2)(\frac{1}{4}x+2)$
9. $(4+3x)(4+3x)$	9. $(3x^2+8y^2)(3x^2+8y^2)$	2. $(\frac{2}{5}a-10)(\frac{2}{5}a-10)$
10. $(5-4x)^2$	10. $(2ax-9y)^2$	3. $(\frac{1}{3}b-3c)^2$
		4. $(\frac{3}{4}xy+6)(\frac{3}{4}xy+6)$
SET 13	SET 14	5. $(\frac{5}{6}b^2-12y)(\frac{5}{6}b^2-12y)$
1. $(.3x+4)^2$	1. $(x+3)(x-3)(x^2-9)$	
2. $(.5x-.2y)^2$	2. $(a-b)(a+b)(a^2-b^2)$	
3. $(.4a-.1b)(.4a-.1b)$	3. $(5m+4)(25m^2-16)(5m-4)$	
4. $(1.2r+.5s)(1.2r+.5s)$	4. $(2c-3d)(4c^2-9d^2)(2c+3d)$	
5. $(.6m-.4x^2)(.6m-.4x^2)$	5. $(4b+xy)(4b-xy)(16b^2-x^2y^2)$	

EXERCISE 50

Factoring—Perfect Trinomial Squares

I. Aim: To factor a perfect trinomial square.

II. Procedure

1. Determine whether the trinomial is a perfect square trinomial by the following rule:
   a) Two terms must be perfect squares (usually the first and third terms) and must be preceded by plus signs.
   b) The remaining term must be twice the product of the square roots of the perfect square terms.

2. If the trinomial is a perfect trinomial square, factor as follows:
   a) Find the square roots of the two perfect square terms.
   b) Connect them with the sign of the remaining term.
   c) Indicate that the binomial is to be used twice as a factor.

III. Sample Solutions

Factor the following trinomials:

1. $x^2 + 6x + 9$ Answer, $(x+3)(x+3)$ or $(x+3)^2$
2. $c^2 - 2cd + d^2$ Answer, $(c-d)(c-d)$ or $(c-d)^2$
3. $4x^2 + 20xy + 25y^2$ Answer, $(2x+5y)(2x+5y)$
4. $49a^6 - 56a^3xy^2 + 16x^2y^4$ Answer, $(7a^3 - 4xy^2)^2$
5. $m^2 + 3m + \frac{9}{4}$ Answer, $(m + \frac{3}{2})(m + \frac{3}{2})$

Preliminary Examples

A. Which are perfect trinomial squares?

1. $a^2 + 10a + 16$
2. $b^2 + 14b - 49$
3. $x^2 - 5x + 4$
4. $x^2 + 10x + 25$
5. $c^2 - 2cd - d^2$
6. $36d^2 + 13dx + x^2$
7. $81a^2 - 72ab + 16b^2$
8. $4x^2 + 4x + 1$
9. $49m^2 + 140mn + 100n^2$
10. $16b^2 - 20by + 25y^2$

B. Fill in the missing term making a perfect trinomial square.

1. $a^2 + ? + 9$
2. $x^2 + ? + 25$
3. $b^2 + ? + x^2$
4. $c^2 - ? + d^2$
5. $m^2 + 8m + ?$
6. $? + 2ax + x^2$
7. $81c^2 + ? + 36$
8. $9b^2 - ? + 49y^2$
9. $64a^2b^2 + 80abx + ?$
10. $? - 240a^2b^2xy + 144b^4y^2$

DIAGNOSTIC TEST

Factor the following trinomials:

1. $x^2 + 8x + 16$
2. $c^2 - 14c + 49$
3. $36 + 12b + b^2$
4. $m^2 + 2mn + n^2$
5. $a^4 + 2a^2b^2 + b^4$
6. $16x^2 + 40x + 25$
7. $81 - 36x + 4x^2$
8. $9a^2b^2 + 12ab + 4$
9. $49x^2 - 84xy + 36y^2$
10. $64b^2c^2 + 144bcx + 81x^2$
11. $m^2 + 9m + \frac{81}{4}$
12. $a^2 - 1.2a + 0.36$

Related Practice Examples

Factor the following trinomials:

SET 1

1. $a^2 + 2a + 1$
2. $x^2 + 10x + 25$
3. $x^2 + 16x + 64$
4. $c^2 + 20c + 100$
5. $b^2 + 4b + 4$

SET 2

1. $b^2 - 2b + 1$
2. $y^2 - 8y + 16$
3. $x^2 - 12x + 36$
4. $d^2 - 18d + 81$
5. $a^2 - 6a + 9$

SET 3

1. $25 + 10b + b^2$
2. $9 + 6x + x^2$
3. $144 + 24x + x^2$
4. $64 - 16y + y^2$
5. $1 - 2m + m^2$

SET 4

1. $c^2 + 2cd + d^2$
2. $x^2 - 2xy + y^2$
3. $a^2 - 2ab + b^2$
4. $d^2 - 2dy + y^2$
5. $a^2 + 2ab + b^2$

SET 5

1. $x^4 + 2x^2y^2 + y^4$
2. $m^4 + 2m^2n^2 + n^4$
3. $r^2 - 2rs^2 + s^4$
4. $a^4 + 2a^2t^3 + t^6$
5. $x^6 - 2x^3y^2 + y^4$

SET 6

1. $4x^2 + 4x + 1$
2. $25b^2 + 20b + 4$
3. $49y^2 - 56y + 16$
4. $100a^2 - 180a + 81$
5. $36m^2 + 60m + 25$

SET 7

1. $9 + 12y + 4y^2$
2. $64 - 176b + 121b^2$
3. $144 + 72c + 9c^2$
4. $25 - 40x + 16x^2$
5. $100 + 140a + 49a^2$

SET 8

1. $a^2x^2 + 10ax + 25$
2. $c^2x^2 - 16cx + 64$
3. $25b^2x^2 + 70bx + 49$
4. $121c^4y^2 - 132c^2y + 36$
5. $144x^2y^4 - 120xy^2 + 25$

SET 9

1. $16a^2 + 8ab + b^2$
2. $36x^2 + 60xy + 25y^2$
3. $49c^2 - 28cd + 4d^2$
4. $64m^2 - 80mn + 25n^2$
5. $121a^2 - 220ar + 100r^2$

SET 10

1. $25a^2d^2 + 20acd + 4c^2$
2. $100x^4 - 140x^2y^2 + 49y^4$
3. $4a^4x^2 + 12a^2b^3x + 9b^6$
4. $9m^4 - 42m^2n^3x^2 + 49n^6x^4$
5. $81b^2x^2 - 90bcxy + 25c^2y^2$

SET 11

1. $x^2 + x + \frac{1}{4}$
2. $a^2 - 5a + \frac{25}{4}$
3. $x^2 + 7x + \frac{49}{4}$
4. $9b^2 - 4b + \frac{4}{9}$
5. $36a^2 - 15ab + \frac{25}{16}b^2$

SET 12

1. $x^2 + 0.8x + 0.16$
2. $a^2 + 0.2a + 0.01$
3. $y^2 - 0.4y + 0.04$
4. $4b^2 + 2.8b + 0.49$
5. $0.16a^2 - 0.72a + 0.81$

EXERCISE 51

Product of Two Binomials Having a Common Term

I. Aim: To find the product of two binomials having a common term.

II. Procedure

1. To find the first term of the product, square the common term.

2. To find the second term of the product, find the algebraic sum of the second terms of the binomials and multiply it by the common term.

3. To find the third term of the product, multiply the second terms of the binomials algebraically.

III. Sample Solutions

Find the following products mentally:

1. $(b+4)(b+2)$ Answer, b^2+6b+8
2. $(x-2)(x-5)$ Answer, $x^2-7x+10$
3. $(y+3)(y-1)$ Answer, y^2+2y-3

4. $(c-7)(c+6)$ Answer, c^2-c-42
5. $(3x+1)(3x-4)$ Answer, $9x^2-9x-4$

Preliminary Examples

A. Add the second and third terms algebraically and then multiply the sum by the first term:

	SET 1					SET 2		
	First	Second	Third			First	Second	Third
1.	x	$+2$	$+3$		1.	$3x$	$+5$	$+3$
2.	a	$+7$	$+1$		2.	$8y$	-4	-7
3.	b	$+6$	$+4$		3.	$4a$	-3	$+2$
4.	m	-2	$+5$		4.	s	-5	-5
5.	y	-4	$+3$		5.	w	$+6$	-6
6.	d	$+7$	-4		6.	x	$+2y$	$+y$
7.	x	$+2$	-6		7.	b	$-3x$	$-4x$
8.	r	-4	-3		8.	c	$-8d$	$+7d$
9.	b	-8	-9		9.	$3a$	$+5m$	$-9m$
10.	x	-5	$+11$		10.	x^2	$-3y^2$	$-5y^2$

B. Find the product of the second and third terms, using examples in Part A.

DIAGNOSTIC TEST

Find the following products mentally:

1. $(a+3)(a+2)$
2. $(x-5)(x-3)$
3. $(b+6)(b-4)$
4. $(m+4)(m-7)$

5. $(c-4)(c+2)$
6. $(r-1)(r+5)$
7. $(a-3)(a+2)$
8. $(x-4)(x+4)$

9. $(5a+2)(5a+4)$
10. $(a^2+6)(a^2-3)$
11. $(3xy-7)(3xy-2)$
12. $(4+2a)(4-3a)$

13. $(3-a)(7-a)$
14. $(\frac{1}{2}x+5)(\frac{1}{2}x-3)$
15. $(a-.8)(a+.3)$
16. $(2a-5b)(2a+7b)$

Related Practice Examples

Find the following products mentally:

SET 1	SET 2	SET 3	SET 4
1. $(a+2)(a+1)$	**1.** $(b-4)(b-2)$	**1.** $(x+8)(x-3)$	**1.** $(b+2)(b-9)$
2. $(x+4)(x+6)$	**2.** $(x-7)(x-9)$	**2.** $(b+10)(b-5)$	**2.** $(a+7)(a-12)$
3. $(x+9)(x+2)$	**3.** $(d-6)(d-1)$	**3.** $(y+3)(y-1)$	**3.** $(r+1)(r-4)$
4. $(y+3)(y+4)$	**4.** $(a-2)(a-7)$	**4.** $(m+12)(m-2)$	**4.** $(t+5)(t-8)$
5. $(m+5)(m+8)$	**5.** $(a-3)(a-3)$	**5.** $(a+11)(a-5)$	**5.** $(v+10)(v-12)$

SET 5	SET 6	SET 7	SET 8
1. $(x-3)(x+1)$	**1.** $(c-2)(c+8)$	**1.** $(a+4)(a-3)$	**1.** $(x+2)(x-2)$
2. $(m-9)(m+4)$	**2.** $(r-7)(r+10)$	**2.** $(b-5)(b+6)$	**2.** $(a-5)(a+5)$
3. $(s-5)(s+2)$	**3.** $(d-4)(d+6)$	**3.** $(x+8)(x-9)$	**3.** $(b-8)(b+8)$
4. $(u-15)(u+4)$	**4.** $(k-3)(k+10)$	**4.** $(y-2)(y+1)$	**4.** $(x+9)(x-9)$
5. $(y-18)(y+3)$	**5.** $(b-5)(b+15)$	**5.** $(m+10)(m-9)$	**5.** $(y-12)(y+12)$

SET 9		SET 10	SET 11
1. $(2x+3)(2x+1)$	**6.** $(3x+4)(3x-2)$	**1.** $(b^2+4)(b^2+1)$	**1.** $(ab+3)(ab+5)$
2. $(5a+4)(5a+5)$	**7.** $(8x+3)(8x-9)$	**2.** $(x^2+5)(x^2-7)$	**2.** $(bx-8)(bx-4)$
3. $(3y+8)(3y+2)$	**8.** $(10m-5)(10m+6)$	**3.** $(a^3+2)(a^3+3)$	**3.** $(2xy-9)(2xy-3)$
4. $(6b-1)(6b-7)$	**9.** $(2x-8)(2x+5)$	**4.** $(y^3-6)(y^3+5)$	**4.** $(5bd+1)(5bd-2)$
5. $(4c-9)(4c-3)$	**10.** $(11x+8)(11x-12)$	**5.** $(h^3-5)(h^3-10)$	**5.** $(3a^2x-8)(3a^2x+2)$

SET 12	SET 13	SET 14	SET 15
1. $(3+a)(3+2a)$	**1.** $(4+c)(5+c)$	**1.** $(\frac{1}{3}b+9)(\frac{1}{3}b+3)$	**1.** $(x+.5)(x+.9)$
2. $(5+4x)(5-3x)$	**2.** $(1-b)(3-b)$	**2.** $(\frac{3}{4}x-4)(\frac{3}{4}x+8)$	**2.** $(y-.1)(y-.6)$
3. $(7-2b)(7-3b)$	**3.** $(7+2a)(4+2a)$	**3.** $(\frac{2}{5}a-5)(\frac{2}{5}a-10)$	**3.** $(a-3.1)(a+.4)$
4. $(11-7x^2)(11+5x^2)$	**4.** $(2x+3)(x+3)$	**4.** $(\frac{7}{8}y^2+8)(\frac{7}{8}y^2-16)$	**4.** $(2b-.6)(2b-.3)$
5. $(10+2xy)(10-xy)$	**5.** $(9a-4)(7a-4)$	**5.** $(x+\frac{1}{4})(x+8)$	**5.** $(.5x-.9)(.5x-.2)$

SET 16	
1. $(x+2y)(x+3y)$	**6.** $(4x+3y)(4x+7y)$
2. $(b-6x)(b-5x)$	**7.** $(2a-b)(2a-5b)$
3. $(m-4n)(m+7n)$	**8.** $(3m^2+4r)(3m^2-6r)$
4. $(c+8d)(c-9d)$	**9.** $(8rs-7t)(8rs-3t)$
5. $(3x-2y)(3x+5y)$	**10.** $(10ab+5xy)(10ab-8xy)$

EXERCISE 52

Factoring—Factors Are Binomials Having a Common Term

I. Aim: To factor a trinomial whose factors are two binomials having a common term.

II. Procedure

1. Find the common term by extracting the square root of the perfect square term (usually the first term of the trinomial).

2. Find two terms whose product is one of the terms of the trinomial (usually the third term) and whose algebraic sum multiplied by the square root of the perfect square term is the remaining term of the trinomial (usually the second term).

3. Use as one factor the binomial consisting of the common term and one term found in step 2. Use as the second factor the binomial consisting of the common term and the other term found in step 2.

III. Sample Solutions

Factor the following trinomials:

1. $x^2+9x+20$ Answer, $(x+5)(x+4)$
2. $b^2-11b+18$ Answer, $(b-9)(b-2)$
3. $m^2-6m-16$ Answer, $(m-8)(m+2)$
4. s^2+s-12 Answer, $(s+4)(s-3)$
5. $4x^2-8x-5$ Answer, $(2x+1)(2x-5)$

Preliminary Examples

Find two numbers which, when added, will give the following sum, and which, when multiplied, will give the following product:

	Sum	Product		Sum	Product		Sum	Product		Sum	Product
1.	+6	+8	6.	−11	+18	11.	−8	−20	16.	−14	−72
2.	+5	+6	7.	+4	−5	12.	−1	−12	17.	+11	−60
3.	+8	+7	8.	+10	−24	13.	+25	+24	18.	−1	−30
4.	−3	+2	9.	+1	−42	14.	−6	−16	19.	+23	+22
5.	−10	+21	10.	−3	−18	15.	−20	+36	20.	−29	+54

DIAGNOSTIC TEST

Factor the following trinomials:

1. a^2+5a+6
2. x^2-6x+8
3. $b^2+10b-24$
4. $y^2-7y-18$
5. x^2+x-20
6. $x^2+8xy+15y^2$
7. $16a^2-16a-5$
8. $9a^2+9ab-4b^2$

Related Practice Examples

Factor the following trinomials:

SET 1	SET 2	SET 3	SET 4
1. x^2+4x+3	1. x^2-5x+6	1. x^2+5x-6	1. x^2-2x-8
2. $b^2+7b+10$	2. x^2-9x+8	2. $c^2+9c-10$	2. $n^2-5n-24$
3. $t^2+7t+12$	3. $a^2-8a+12$	3. $a^2+2a-35$	3. $b^2-19b-20$
4. $y^2+16y+28$	4. $b^2-9b+18$	4. $x^2+8x-20$	4. $d^2-4d-12$
5. $m^2+12m+27$	5. $d^2-30d+56$	5. $b^2+2b-24$	5. $s^2-9s-90$
6. $a^2+15a+50$	6. $m^2-11m+28$	6. s^2+3s-4	6. $y^2-4y-21$
7. $x^2+12x+36$	7. $r^2-18r+72$	7. $y^2+13y-48$	7. $x^2-15x-54$
8. $s^2+18s+45$	8. $b^2-52b+100$	8. $x^2+11x-80$	8. $m^2-11m-42$
9. $c^2+16c+39$	9. $y^2-16y+64$	9. $x^2+43x-90$	9. $x^2-4x-32$
10. $d^2+20d+64$	10. $x^2-18x+81$	10. $b^2+7b-98$	10. $x^2-5x-14$

SET 5	SET 6	SET 7	SET 8
1. a^2+a-6	1. $x^2+6xy+5y^2$	1. $16x^2-16x+3$	1. $4x^2+16xy+15y^2$
2. x^2-x-2	2. $a^2+12ab+20b^2$	2. $25b^2+20b-12$	2. $25c^2+10cd-8d^2$
3. y^2+y-56	3. $a^2-6ax+8x^2$	3. $49m^2-7m-30$	3. $9m^2-3mn-2n^2$
4. x^2-x-30	4. $c^2+10cd-24d^2$	4. $64x^2-64x+15$	4. $49a^2-21ax-10x^2$
5. b^2-b-42	5. $x^2-10xy-11y^2$	5. $9a^2-21a-8$	5. $81s^2-99st+28t^2$

EXERCISE 53
General Types—Special Products

I. Aim: To find the product of two binomials using the general method.

II. Procedure

1. To find the first term of the product, multiply the first terms of the two binomials algebraically.

2. To find the second term of the product, find the algebraic sum of the cross products.

3. To find the third term of the product, multiply the second terms of the two binomials algebraically.

III. Sample Solutions

Find the following products mentally:

1. $(3x+2)(4x+3)$ Answer, $12x^2+17x+6$
2. $(2a-5c)(6a-7c)$ Answer, $12a^2-44ac+35c^2$
3. $(5b-3)(4b+2)$ Answer, $20b^2-2b-6$
4. $(4m+9nx)(2m-3nx)$ Answer, $8m^2+6mnx-27n^2x^2$

DIAGNOSTIC TEST

Find the following products mentally:

1. $(2x+3)(3x+5)$ 4. $(4c-3)(7c+6)$ 8. $(5ab+x)(7ab-4x)$
2. $(3b-2)(4b-1)$ 5. $(a+5)(2a-7)$ 9. $(2c^2+5)(4c^2+9)$
3. $(5x+4)(2x-3)$ 6. $(4-3x)(6-5x)$ 10. $(2b-c)(x+2y)$
                          7. $(2a+5b)(4a-3b)$

Related Practice Examples

Find the following products mentally:

SET 1	SET 2	SET 3	SET 4
1. $(3x+4)(2x+3)$	1. $(5d-1)(3d-5)$	1. $(4x+1)(5x-6)$	1. $(2x-5)(3x+10)$
2. $(4b+5)(7b+2)$	2. $(6t-3)(2t-7)$	2. $(8m+5)(3m-4)$	2. $(7a-8)(5a+3)$
3. $(9m+2)(5m+6)$	3. $(9n-4)(7n-8)$	3. $(3a+2)(9a-5)$	3. $(5s-6)(2s+7)$
4. $(2r+3)(4r+7)$	4. $(3y-2)(8y-3)$	4. $(9x+8)(7x-10)$	4. $(10b-9)(4b+1)$
5. $(7t+6)(8t+5)$	5. $(4x-3)(2x-9)$	5. $(11c+7)(3c-2)$	5. $(12y-7)(5y+4)$

SET 5	SET 6	SET 7(a)	SET 7(b)
1. $(b+8)(2b+5)$	1. $(3+4x)(1+5x)$	1. $(5x+2y)(6x+5y)$	1. $(2c+d)(c+3d)$
2. $(x-2)(3x+4)$	2. $(8-7y)(5-2y)$	2. $(3a+7b)(a+4b)$	2. $(8x-3y)(9x-5y)$
3. $(5c+3)(c+7)$	3. $(7+6a)(4-3a)$	3. $(4m-3n)(7m-2n)$	3. $(5s-8t)(s+6t)$
4. $(9y-8)(y+1)$	4. $(2-5b)(9+11b)$	4. $(9r+4s)(4r-3s)$	4. $(3a+7b)(8a-12b)$
5. $(s-5)(8s-3)$	5. $(5-x)(2-4x)$	5. $(8x-5y)(3x+7y)$	5. $(10b-3d)(4b+5d)$

SET 8	SET 9	SET 10
1. $(3ab+4c)(2ab+5c)$	1. $(5x^2+2)(3x^2+6)$	1. $(a+2b)(3a-c)$
2. $(7xy-3z)(5xy+4z)$	2. $(2b^3-7)(4b^3+1)$	2. $(2x+y)(m-n)$
3. $(6b-5dx)(b-2dx)$	3. $(4+9y^3)(8-3y^3)$	3. $(5r-2t)(4s-3)$
4. $(5a+4xy)(7a-9xy)$	4. $(7x^2-y)(5x^2-4y)$	4. $(7x^2+5y)(3x-2y)$
5. $(4ab-3xy)(7ab+5xy)$	5. $(3a^2y-5x)(4a^2y-3x)$	5. $(2ab-7c)(b+5ac)$

EXERCISE 54

General Type—Factoring

I. Aim: To factor a trinomial using the general method. This method excludes common factoring.

II. Procedure

1. Find two terms whose product is a term of the trinomial (usually the first term). These terms are the first terms of the two binomial factors.

2. Find two terms whose product is another term of the trinomial (usually the third term). These terms are the second terms of the two binomial factors.

3. Add algebraically the cross products of these terms to obtain the remaining term of the trinomial (usually the second term).

   If the algebraic sum of the cross products does not equal the remaining term, try all pairs of terms which give the products represented by two terms (usually the first and third terms) of the trinomial until the proper combination is found. If all fail, then the trinomial cannot be factored.

III. Sample Solutions

Factor the following trinomials:

1. $20x^2 + 21x + 4$ Answer, $(5x+4)(4x+1)$
2. $12a^2 - 52a + 35$ Answer, $(2a-7)(6a-5)$
3. $32b^2 + 28b - 15$ Answer, $(4b+5)(8b-3)$
4. $6y^2 - 7y - 24$ Answer, $(3y-8)(2y+3)$
5. $30x^2 - xy - 42y^2$ Answer, $(6x+7y)(5x-6y)$

DIAGNOSTIC TEST

Factor the following trinomials:

1. $8x^2 + 26x + 15$
2. $15c^2 - 41c + 28$
3. $12a^2 + 17a - 5$
4. $24b^2 - 50b - 9$
5. $20 + 7m - 6m^2$
6. $6x^2 + 5xy - 21y^2$
7. $24b^2d^2 - 2bcd - 15c^2$
8. $16d^4 - 42d^2 + 5$

Related Practice Examples

Factor the following trinomials:

SET 1	SET 2	SET 3	SET 4
1. $6b^2 + 23b + 7$	1. $15x^2 - 26x + 8$	1. $10x^2 + 3x - 4$	1. $16x^2 - 6x - 27$
2. $10x^2 + 51x + 27$	2. $8y^2 - 26y + 21$	2. $18b^2 + 55b - 28$	2. $2t^2 - 3t - 14$
3. $24y^2 + 47y + 20$	3. $28m^2 - 39m + 8$	3. $84d^2 + d - 15$	3. $15m^2 - 17m - 4$
4. $42a^2 + 19a + 2$	4. $12s^2 - 44s + 35$	4. $5x^2 + 33x - 56$	4. $56a^2 - 33a - 108$
5. $4d^2 + 21d + 27$	5. $24x^2 - 43x + 18$	5. $80s^2 + 66s - 27$	5. $44b^2 - 47b - 10$

SET 5	SET 6	SET 7	SET 8
1. $28 + 71b + 18b^2$	1. $40x^2 + 31xy + 6y^2$	1. $15x^2y^2 - 23xy - 28$	1. $24a^4 + 23a^2 + 5$
2. $6 - 23a + 20a^2$	2. $18m^2 + 17mn - 15n^2$	2. $6a^2b^2 - abc - 40c^2$	2. $18x^6 - 35x^3 + 12$
3. $20 - 19y - 6y^2$	3. $12b^2 - 19bd - 21d^2$	3. $35m^2 + 43mrs + 12r^2s^2$	3. $12 + 32y^2 - 35y^4$
4. $28 + 43x - 45x^2$	4. $70x^2 - 83xy + 18y^2$	4. $36c^2 - 37cdx + 7d^2x^2$	4. $21c^4 + 19c^2d - 12d^2$
5. $2 - 11t + 12t^2$	5. $60a^2 - 59ab - 20b^2$	5. $12a^2b^2 + 8abxy - 15x^2y^2$	5. $45b^4c^2 + 71b^2cx + 28x^2$

EXERCISE 55

Factoring—Prime Factors and Miscellaneous Types

I. **Aim:** To find prime factors of polynomials.

II. **Procedure**

    1. Factor the given expression by some method. (Try the common factor method first.)

    2. If possible, factor the resulting factors.

    3. Repeat step 2 until the resulting factors cannot be factored further.

III. **Sample Solutions**

1. $cx^2 - c$
$= c(x^2 - 1)$
$= c(x+1)(x-1)$
Answer, $c(x+1)(x-1)$

2. $ar^5 - a^5r^5$
$= ar^5(1 - a^4)$
$= ar^5(1 + a^2)(1 - a^2)$
$= ar^5(1 + a^2)(1 + a)(1 - a)$
Answer, $ar^5(1 + a^2)(1 + a)(1 - a)$

3. $2x^2y - 4xy - 30y$
$= 2y(x^2 - 2x - 15)$
$= 2y(x - 5)(x + 3)$
Answer, $2y(x - 5)(x + 3)$

4. $x^2(x^2 - 9) - 4(x^2 - 9)$
$= (x^2 - 9)(x^2 - 4)$
$= (x+3)(x-3)(x+2)(x-2)$
Answer, $(x+3)(x-3)(x+2)(x-2)$

5. $a^2 + 2ab + b^2 - c^2$
$= (a+b)^2 - c^2$
$= (a+b+c)(a+b-c)$
Answer, $(a+b+c)(a+b-c)$

DIAGNOSTIC TEST

Factor the following polynomials:

1. $ax^2 - a$
2. $5x^2 - 20y^2$
3. $ab^4 - ac^4$
4. $3x^2 + 12x + 12$
5. $2b^2 - 8b - 10$
6. $a^2(a+2) - 9(a+2)$
7. $b^2 - 2bc + c^2 - d^2$

Related Practice Examples

Factor the following polynomials:

SET 1
1. $bx^2 - b$
2. $9x^3 - 9x$
3. $s^3 - s$
4. $a - ar^2$
5. $ar - a^3r^3$

SET 2
1. $5x^2 - 5y^2$
2. $3a^2 - 75d^2$
3. $25m^2 - 100n^2$
4. $2a^2 - 72b^2$
5. $\pi R^2 - \pi r^2$

SET 3
1. $ab^4 - ax^4$
2. $6m^5 - 6m$
3. $2b^4 - 32x^4$
4. $5x^8 - 5y^8$
5. $a^5r^5 - ar^5$

SET 4
1. $2x^2 + 12x + 18$
2. $a^3 - 8a^2 + 16a$
3. $9a^2 + 18ab + 9b^2$
4. $2ab^2 + 20ab + 50a$
5. $4bx^2 - 8bxy + 4by^2$

SET 5
1. $3b^2 + 21b + 36$
2. $y^3 - y^2 - 2y$
3. $5c^2 - 25c + 30$
4. $3cd^2 - 3cd - 126c$
5. $4a^2b + 12ab - 72b$

SET 6
1. $a(a+b) + b(a+b)$
2. $x(x^2 - 4) + 2(x^2 - 4)$
3. $x^2(x-3) - 4(x-3)$
4. $a^2(a^2 - c^2) - b^2(a^2 - c^2)$
5. $x^2(x^2 - 9) - 16(x^2 - 9)$

SET 7
1. $x^2 + 2xy + y^2 - 4$
2. $a^2 + 6a + 9 - b^2$
3. $c^2 - 2cd + d^2 - x^2$
4. $a^2 - b^2 - 2bc - c^2$
5. $d^2 - x^2 + 2xy - y^2$
6. $9 - m^2 - 2mn - n^2$
7. $16c^2 - r^2 + 2rs - s^2$
8. $4x^2 + 12xy + 9y^2 - 25z^2$
9. $36a^2 - 9b^2 + 24bc - 16c^2$
10. $a^2 + b^2 - 4 - 2ab$

EXERCISE 56

APPLICATIONS

I. Formulas

Rewrite the following formulas with the right member arranged in factored form:

1. $p = 2l + 2w$ 2. $S = 180n - 360$ 3. $E = Ir + IR$ 4. $A = p + prt$ 5. $a = S - Sr$

6. $A = \pi r^2 + \pi r l$ 7. $A = 2\pi rh + 2\pi r^2$ 8. $S = \frac{1}{2}an + \frac{1}{2}ln$ 9. $A = \frac{1}{2}bh + \frac{1}{2}b'h$ 10. $A = \pi dh + \frac{1}{2}\pi d^2$

11. $A = S^2 - s^2$ 12. $A = \pi R^2 - \pi r^2$ 13. $A = \frac{1}{4}\pi D^2 - \frac{1}{4}\pi d^2$ 14. $a = \sqrt{c^2 - b^2}$ 15. $b = \sqrt{c^2 - a^2}$

II. Arithmetic

Special products may be used to compute examples like: 1) $18 \times 26 + 12 \times 26$; 2) 42×38; 3) $(23)^2$.

1. $18 \times 26 + 12 \times 26$. Just as $ac + bc = c(a+b)$, so $18 \times 26 + 12 \times 26 = 26(18+12) = 26(30) = 780$. Answer, 780.

2. 42×38. Since $42 = 40 + 2$ and $38 = 40 - 2$, 42×38 may be written as $(40+2)(40-2)$. Just as $(a+b)(a-b) = a^2 - b^2$, so $(40+2)(40-2) = 40^2 - 2^2 = 1600 - 4 = 1596$. Answer, 1596.

3. $(23)^2$. Since $23 = 20 + 3$ or $30 - 7$, $(23)^2$ may be written as $(20+3)^2$ or $(30-7)^2$. Just as $(a+b)^2 = a^2 + 2ab + b^2$ so $(20+3)^2 = 20^2 + 2 \cdot 20 \cdot 3 + 3^2 = 400 + 120 + 9 = 529$. Answer, 529. Since $(a-b)^2 = a^2 - 2ab + b^2$, $(30-7)^2 = 30^2 - 2 \cdot 30 \cdot 7 + 7^2 = 900 - 420 + 49 = 529$. Answer, 529.

Compute the following examples, using the principles studied in special products:

SET 1		SET 2		SET 3	
1. $7 \times 19 + 3 \times 19$	6. $27 \times 45 - 7 \times 45$	1. 21×19	6. 84×76	1. $(34)^2$	6. $(1.5)^2$
2. $24 \times 35 + 16 \times 35$	7. $89 \times 33 - 19 \times 33$	2. 52×48	7. 92×88	2. $(42)^2$	7. $(7\frac{1}{2})^2$
3. $18 \times 14 + 32 \times 14$	8. $13 \times \frac{1}{2} + 17 \times \frac{1}{2}$	3. 37×43	8. 49×51	3. $(21)^2$	8. $(3.5)^2$
4. $71 \times 27 + 29 \times 27$	9. $56 \times 9 - 16 \times 9$	4. 18×22	9. 26×34	4. $(63)^2$	9. $(96)^2$
5. $42 \times 58 + 28 \times 58$	10. $35 \times 51 + 55 \times 51$	5. 63×57	10. 73×67	5. $(2\frac{1}{2})^2$	10. $(57)^2$

III. Evaluation

Using the factored form, find the value of:

1. S when $n = 7$. Formula: $S = 180n - 360$ 2. p when $l = 29$ and $w = 15$. Formula: $p = 2l + 2w$

3. A when $p = 60$, $r = .03$, and $t = 8$. Formula: $A = p + prt$

4. E when $I = 4$, $r = 67$, and $R = 23$. Formula: $E = Ir + IR$

5. A when $\pi = \frac{22}{7}$, $r = 28$, and $l = 9$. Formula: $A = \pi r^2 + \pi r l$

6. A when $b = 16$, $b' = 12$, and $h = 6$. Formula: $A = \frac{1}{2}bh + \frac{1}{2}b'h$

7. A when $\pi = 3.14$, $r = 5$, and $h = 15$. Formula: $A = 2\pi rh + 2\pi r^2$

8. A when $S = 18$ and $s = 12$. Formula: $A = S^2 - s^2$

9. A when $\pi = 3.14$, $R = 24$, and $r = 8$. Formula: $A = \pi R^2 - \pi r^2$

10. A when $\pi = \frac{22}{7}$, $D = 42$, and $d = 28$. Formula $A = \frac{1}{4}\pi D^2 - \frac{1}{4}\pi d^2$

IV. Literal Representations

Express in factored form the representations of the following:

1. The difference in areas of two circles. The larger circle has a radius of b units and the smaller circle has a radius of c units.

2. The difference in areas of two squares. The side of the larger square is m units long and the side of the smaller square is n units long.

3. The cross-sectional area of tubing. The outside diameter is h units and the inside diameter is k units.

4. The area of the surface of the tin remaining when a small square with side l is cut from each corner of a square piece of tin with side s.

5. The area of the surface remaining when nine circular holes each having a diameter of t units are drilled in a circular metal plate with a diameter of a units.

REVIEW OF UNIT EIGHT

Find the following products by inspection :   Factor the following polynomials:

SET 1	SET 2	SET 3	SET 4
1. $(r+s)(r+s)$	**1.** $(4b-7d)(4b-7d)$	**1.** x^2-81	**1.** $d^2+2dy+y^2$
2. $(3a-4)(3a+4)$	**2.** $(\frac{3}{4}m-5)(\frac{3}{4}m+5)$	**2.** $4c^2+16$	**2.** a^2+5a-6
3. $(2m-3)(2m-3)$	**3.** $(5mn-12y)^2$	**3.** $y^2+11y+28$	**3.** $144-49x^2$
4. $(4a+9b)^2$	**4.** $(t+9)(t-8)$	**4.** $m^2+16m+64$	**4.** $9x^2-48xy+64y^2$
5. $(x-3)(x-7)$	**5.** $(2m^2x+11ny^2)^2$	**5.** $9a^2-30ab+25b^2$	**5.** $16b^6x^2-12b^4x^4+8b^2x^6$
6. $(7+b)(7-b)$	**6.** $(1+c^3)(1-c^3)$	**6.** b^2-b-56	**6.** $81m^2+36m+4$
7. $(x-8y)(x-8y)$	**7.** $(a^2+b^2)(a^2+b^2)$	**7.** $t^2+10t+16$	**7.** $2y^2+4y-96$
8. $(3ab+5x^2)(3ab+5x^2)$	**8.** $(9x-6y)(4x-7y)$	**8.** $m^2+10m+9$	**8.** $36r^2+11r-12$
9. $(d-4)(d+3)$	**9.** $(2a-b)(2a+b)(4a^2+b^2)$	**9.** $25c^2d^4-36x^2$	**9.** c^4-81d^4
10. $(6m-7)(9m+5)$	**10.** $(4c+3d)(4c-3d)(16c^2-9d^2)$	**10.** $5x^3y-3x^2y+xy$	**10.** $\frac{4}{9}a^2-x^4y^4$

CUMULATIVE ALGEBRA REVIEW

1. Express as a formula: The rate of discount (r) equals the discount (d) divided by the list price (l).

2. What is the value of the expression $5b^2-4bc-c^2$ when $b=8$ and $c=-2$?

3. Find the value of H when $F=38,400$, $A=30$, and $D=64$, using the formula $F=AHD$.

4. What is the perimeter of a triangle with sides measuring $3n+2$, $4n-5$, and $2n-7$?

5. How much less than $m^2+2mn+n^2$ is $m^2-2mn+n^2$?

6. A rectangular floor is $(7n+3)$ feet long and $8n$ feet wide. How many sq. ft. of floor space does it contain?

7. What is the factor which when multiplied by $5r-9s$ will give the product of $15r^2-67rs+72s^2$?

8. Transform the following formula by removing parentheses: $A=\pi r(r+l)$.

9. Remove parentheses and, if possible, add like terms: $9x^2-x+(-4x+5)-3x(8x-6)$.

10. Solve and check: $9x-7=28+2x$ **11.** Solve and check: $6a-2=8(a-2)$

12. At what price must a merchant sell a rug which costs \$273 to make a profit of 30% on the selling price?

13. In an algebra class of 41 pupils there are 5 more girls than boys. How many girls are in the class?

14. Multiply by inspection: a) $(\frac{1}{2}xy-9)(\frac{1}{2}xy+9)$ b) $(6c-5d)(6c-5d)$ c) $(12b+1)^2$ d) $(b-3)(b+2)$

15. Factor: a) $8b^4c^5d-24b^3c^7$ b) x^4-9y^2 c) $m^2-15m-54$ d) $81b^2-90bd+25d^2$ e) x^4-16a^8

ooooooooooooooooooooooooooooooooooooooooooooooooooooooooooooooooooooooooo

KEYED ACHIEVEMENT TEST

1. Express as a formula: Work (W) is the product of force (F) and distance (d).   ①

2. Find the value of M when $N=84$, using the formula $M+N=180$.   ⑫

3. According to rocket readings the temperature at an altitude of 8 miles above the earth's surface is 70° below zero and at an altitude of 35 miles rises to 180° above zero. Express the two temperature readings using signed numbers.   ⑭

4. Add: $4x^2-3x+8$, $5x^2-4x-5$, and $3-7x^2$.   ㉔   **5.** From $8y-z$ take $2x+z$.   ㉖

6. Multiply: $-6b^3c(4b^3-2b^2c+bc^2-5c^3)$ ㉚   **7.** Divide $6a^2-3ab-8ac+4bc$ by $3a-4c$.   ㉟

8. Remove parentheses and, if possible, add like terms: $6-(x-8)+2(-x+4)$ ㉜

9. Solve and check: $(n-4)(n+4)=(n+20)(n-8)$ ㊱

10. Charlotte is now 8 years older than her sister. A year ago she was five times as old as her sister. What are their ages now?   ㊶

Multiply by inspection:
11. $(ab+x)(ab-x)$ ㊼   **13.** $(c-12)(c+11)$ ㋑
12. $(10x-7y)^2$ ㊾   **14.** $(8y-3)(5y-6)$ ㋓

Factor:
15. $24x^3y^2-16x^2y^2-32x^2y^3$ ㊽   **17.** $49r^2-112rs+64s^2$ ㋀   **19.** $12a^2-23ax-24x^2$ ㋔
16. $36b^4x^2-25y^6$ ㊽   **18.** $n^2+14n-72$ ㋒   **20.** $3b^5-243bc^4$ ㋕

INTRODUCTION TO UNIT NINE

Since algebraic fractions are sometimes found in formulas and equations, it is necessary to learn to operate with them. We shall find that the principles used in the study of arithmetic fractions are generalized in the work with algebraic fractions.

A fraction is an indicated division. The fraction $\frac{c}{d}$ means c divided by d and is often read "c over d." In this fraction c is the *numerator* or the quantity which is divided and d is the *denominator* or the quantity by which you divide. Since division by zero is excluded, the denominator d can be any number except zero.

In arithmetic we learned that the value of a fraction does not change if the numerator and denominator are both divided by the same number. We continue to use this principle in algebra when reducing fractions to lower terms and in multiplication and division.

Fractions which have the same value but differ in form are called *equivalent fractions*. $\frac{36}{48}, \frac{18}{24}, \frac{9}{12}, \frac{6}{8}$, and $\frac{3}{4}$ are equivalent fractions.

Fractions can be combined only when they have the same denominator. In the addition and subtraction of fractions with unlike denominators the fractions must be changed to equivalent fractions with a common denominator. We found in arithmetic that the value of a fraction does not change if the numerator and denominator are multiplied by the same number. Therefore, to change a fraction to higher terms we divide the common denominator by the denominator of the given fraction and then multiply both numerator and denominator of the given fraction by this quotient. For example, when changing $\frac{2}{3}$ to 12ths, we get $\frac{2}{3} = \frac{2 \times 4}{3 \times 4} = \frac{8}{12}$. Or, since we know the denominator of the equivalent fraction, we can find its numerator by dividing this denominator by the denominator of the given fraction and then multiplying the numerator of the given fraction by the quotient. Thus, $\frac{2}{3} = \frac{?}{12}$ becomes $\frac{2}{3} = \frac{8}{12}$ since $12 \div 3 = 4$ and $4 \times 2 = 8$.

Sometimes we are required to change signs in fractions. Every fraction has signs in three places: the sign of the fraction, the sign of the numerator, and the sign of the denominator. We shall see that the change in signs of any two of the three places will not change the value of the fraction.

A *complex fraction* is one which has one or more fractions in either its numerator or denominator or both. The simplification of complex fractions and mixed expressions provides practice in the operational skills used in algebraic fractions. These techniques will be employed in the study of trigonometry and engineering formulas.

ARITHMETIC PRACTICE

1. Reduce to lowest terms:

    a) $\frac{3}{12}$ b) $\frac{9}{54}$ c) $\frac{10}{25}$ d) $\frac{24}{32}$ e) $\frac{52}{91}$ f) $\frac{96}{192}$ g) $\frac{60}{200}$ h) $\frac{148}{365}$ i) $\frac{440}{1760}$ j) $\frac{3600}{5280}$

2. Change to higher terms:

    a) $\frac{1}{8} = \frac{}{32}$ b) $\frac{2}{3} = \frac{}{18}$ c) $\frac{3}{5} = \frac{}{100}$ d) $\frac{7}{9} = \frac{}{72}$ e) $\frac{13}{16} = \frac{}{80}$ f) $\frac{11}{12} = \frac{}{84}$ g) $\frac{5}{6} = \frac{}{96}$

3. Find the lowest common denominator:

    a) $\frac{1}{4}$ and $\frac{1}{8}$ b) $\frac{1}{4}$ and $\frac{1}{3}$ c) $\frac{1}{4}$ and $\frac{1}{6}$ d) $\frac{1}{3}, \frac{1}{12}$ and $\frac{1}{6}$ e) $\frac{1}{10}, \frac{1}{8}$ and $\frac{1}{12}$

4. Multiply:

    a) $\frac{1}{8} \times \frac{1}{6}$ b) $\frac{1}{3} \times \frac{3}{10}$ c) $\frac{4}{35} \times \frac{7}{8}$ d) $\frac{5}{6} \times \frac{4}{5}$ e) $\frac{2}{3} \times 72$ f) $4 \times \frac{9}{16}$ g) $\frac{5}{8} \times 3$ h) $\frac{3}{4} \times \frac{7}{8}$

5. Divide:

    a) $\frac{1}{4} \div \frac{4}{5}$ b) $\frac{7}{8} \div \frac{2}{3}$ c) $\frac{3}{8} \div \frac{3}{4}$ d) $\frac{5}{12} \div \frac{3}{16}$ e) $\frac{2}{5} \div 8$ f) $10 \div \frac{5}{12}$ g) $18 \div \frac{27}{32}$ h) $\frac{5}{8} \div \frac{22}{7}$

6. Add:

    a) $\frac{2}{5} + \frac{1}{5}$ b) $\frac{9}{16} + \frac{3}{16}$ c) $\frac{5}{8} + \frac{1}{2}$ d) $\frac{3}{4} + \frac{2}{5}$ e) $\frac{5}{8} + \frac{7}{8}$ f) $\frac{1}{2} + \frac{5}{8} + \frac{3}{16}$ g) $\frac{7}{10} + \frac{5}{6} + \frac{1}{8}$ h) $\frac{11}{12} + \frac{2}{3} + \frac{5}{6}$

7. Subtract:

    a) $\frac{2}{3} - \frac{1}{3}$ b) $\frac{13}{16} - \frac{7}{16}$ c) $\frac{7}{8} - \frac{25}{32}$ d) $\frac{11}{16} - \frac{2}{3}$ e) $\frac{1}{4} - \frac{1}{10}$ f) $\frac{5}{8} - \frac{1}{2}$ g) $\frac{15}{16} - \frac{17}{20}$ h) $\frac{11}{12} - \frac{3}{8}$

UNIT NINE—FRACTIONS

EXERCISE 57

Changing Fractions to Lowest Terms

I. Aim : To change algebraic fractions to lowest terms.

II. Procedure

1. Find the largest common factor of both numerator and denominator. If the numerator, or denominator, or both are polynomials, factor them if possible.

2. Divide both numerator and denominator by the largest common factor.

3. Do not cancel term with term. See sample solutions 6, 7, and 8.

4. Check by going over the work again or by numerical substitution.

III. Sample Solutions

1. $\dfrac{3}{9} = \dfrac{1}{3}$

   Divide numerator and denominator by 3.

   Answer, $\dfrac{1}{3}$

2. $\dfrac{4ab}{5ac} = \dfrac{4b}{5c}$

   Divide numerator and denominator by a.

   Answer, $\dfrac{4b}{5c}$

3. $\dfrac{a^5}{a^8} = \dfrac{1}{a^3}$

   Divide numerator and denominator by a^5.

   Answer, $\dfrac{1}{a^3}$

4. $\dfrac{8x^3y^2}{12x^5y} = \dfrac{2y}{3x^2}$

   Divide numerator and denominator by $4x^3y$.

   Answer, $\dfrac{2y}{3x^2}$

5. $\dfrac{b(x-y)}{c(x-y)} = \dfrac{b}{c}$

   Divide numerator and denominator by $x-y$.

   Answer, $\dfrac{b}{c}$

6. $\dfrac{3x}{3(x+y)} = \dfrac{x}{x+y}$

   Divide numerator and denominator by 3.
   Do not cancel x in answer.
   Remove parentheses from $x+y$ in answer.

   Answer, $\dfrac{x}{x+y}$

7. $\dfrac{3x(x+2)(x-4)}{(x-4)(x-2)} = \dfrac{3x(x+2)}{x-2}$

   Divide numerator and denominator by $x-4$.

   Answer, $\dfrac{3x(x+2)}{x-2}$

8. $\dfrac{x^2+6x+9}{x^2-9} = \dfrac{(x+3)(x+3)}{(x+3)(x-3)} = \dfrac{x+3}{x-3}$

   Factor; then divide numerator and denominator by $x+3$.
   Do not cancel x or 3 in answer.

   Answer, $\dfrac{x+3}{x-3}$

DIAGNOSTIC TEST

Change each of the following fractions to lowest terms:

1. $\dfrac{24}{32}$

2. $\dfrac{ax}{ay}$

3. $\dfrac{c}{c^3}$

4. $\dfrac{a^2b^3c^4}{ab^2c^6}$

5. $\dfrac{x^4y^2z}{x^2y^2z^2}$

6. $\dfrac{a^3x^2}{ay}$

7. $\dfrac{18a^4b}{30ab^2}$

8. $\dfrac{10c^2d^3}{cd^4}$

9. $\dfrac{6b}{18ab}$

10. $\dfrac{-9x^2y}{18xy^2}$

11. $\dfrac{5a^2(x+y)}{15a(x+y)}$

12. $\dfrac{12ab^2}{6b^4(a-b)}$

13. $\dfrac{3x^2y^3(a-3)(a+7)}{6xy^4(a+4)(a-3)}$

14. $\dfrac{b+3}{(b+3)^2}$

15. $\dfrac{ax-a^2x^2}{bx-abx^2}$

16. $\dfrac{2ab^2c}{2ab+4ac}$

17. $\dfrac{2x^2+2xy}{x^2-y^2}$

18. $\dfrac{a^2-16}{a^2-8a+16}$

19. $\dfrac{x^2+4x-5}{x^2+8x+15}$

20. $\dfrac{2x^2+4x-30}{3x^2+21x+30}$

Related Practice Examples

Change each of the following fractions to lowest terms:

A	B	C	D	E
1. $\dfrac{4}{12}$	1. $\dfrac{6}{9}$	1. $\dfrac{25}{40}$	1. $\dfrac{49}{56}$	1. $\dfrac{48}{72}$
2. $\dfrac{bc}{bd}$	2. $\dfrac{mx}{nx}$	2. $\dfrac{5ax}{8ax}$	2. $\dfrac{7cd}{4ac}$	2. $\dfrac{3a}{10a}$
3. $\dfrac{x}{x^2}$	3. $\dfrac{b^2}{b^7}$	3. $\dfrac{cd}{c^2d^2}$	3. $\dfrac{c}{3c^4}$	3. $\dfrac{d^4}{d^6}$
4. $\dfrac{c^4d^3}{c^2d^6}$	4. $\dfrac{a^8b^3c^5}{a^3b^7c^2}$	4. $\dfrac{m^5n^2x^5}{m^2nx^6}$	4. $\dfrac{c^8xy^6}{c^9x^4y^4}$	4. $\dfrac{r^4s^2t^6}{r^7st^2}$
5. $\dfrac{m^3}{m^3}$	5. $\dfrac{ab^4}{a^2b^4}$	5. $\dfrac{c^2d^3x^2}{c^2d^3x}$	5. $\dfrac{m^5xy^2}{m^3xy^5}$	5. $\dfrac{acy^3}{ac^2y}$
6. $\dfrac{a^5b^2c}{a^4b^3}$	6. $\dfrac{amx^2}{m^3xy^2}$	6. $\dfrac{c^2d^2m^2}{cd^7n}$	6. $\dfrac{r^9s^2t}{m^2s^8x^2}$	6. $\dfrac{a^2b^2c^3d^8}{b^5cd^4e}$
7. $\dfrac{6a^2b^5}{12ab}$	7. $\dfrac{5x^3y^2}{15xy}$	7. $\dfrac{4a^3x}{10a^6x^2}$	7. $\dfrac{12a^2x}{3ax^3}$	7. $\dfrac{4m^3n^3}{6m^2n^4}$
8. $\dfrac{8a^4}{a^7}$	8. $\dfrac{b^3c^5}{3b^5c^2}$	8. $\dfrac{a^4x^3y^2}{5x^2y^4}$	8. $\dfrac{14a^3x}{xy^5}$	8. $\dfrac{4\pi r^2}{\pi r^3}$
9. $\dfrac{5c}{10bc}$	9. $\dfrac{16a^2x}{48a^4x^2}$	9. $\dfrac{25b^3c^2}{50b^8c^5}$	9. $\dfrac{10m^2x}{40m^6x^8}$	9. $\dfrac{2x^4z^2}{12x^5z^{10}}$
10. $\dfrac{-8a^3}{-4a^5}$	10. $\dfrac{-2c^3d^7}{6c^2d^9}$	10. $\dfrac{8x^4y^2}{-32x}$	10. $\dfrac{-15c^3m^{12}}{-5c^4m^5}$	10. $\dfrac{18a^5xy^2}{-6a^2xy^5}$
11. $\dfrac{3(x+y)}{4(x+y)}$	11. $\dfrac{8(a+b)}{12(a+b)}$	11. $\dfrac{a(a-c)}{b(a-c)}$	11. $\dfrac{3x^2(x-y)}{9x(x-y)}$	11. $\dfrac{4r(s-2t)}{2r^4(s-2t)}$
12. $\dfrac{a(x-y)}{ax}$	12. $\dfrac{5x}{5(x+y)}$	12. $\dfrac{2b(c+d)}{4b^2}$	12. $\dfrac{9a^6b^3(a-b)}{18ab^4}$	12. $\dfrac{10m^2x^5}{5x^2(m+x)}$

13. $\dfrac{(a+b)(a+b)}{(a+b)(a-b)}$ 13. $\dfrac{(x+3)(x-5)}{(x-2)(x-5)}$ 13. $\dfrac{(c+2)(c-3)}{(c-3)(c+8)}$ 13. $\dfrac{2x(x+y)(x-y)}{6x(x+y)}$ 13. $\dfrac{6a^2b(c-4)(c+2)}{8ab^2(c+2)(c+1)}$

14. $\dfrac{a-b}{(a-b)^2}$ 14. $\dfrac{c+2}{(c+2)(c-2)}$ 14. $\dfrac{x-4}{6(x-4)^3}$ 14. $\dfrac{8b^2(x-y)^4}{16b(x-y)^7}$ 14. $\dfrac{10x^3y^2(x+y)^3}{15xy^3(x+y)^4}$

15a. $\dfrac{3x+3y}{3x-3y}$ 15a. $\dfrac{4a-4b}{8a+8b}$ 15a. $\dfrac{4a-4b}{8a-8b}$ 15a. $\dfrac{2x+4y}{6x+12y}$ 15a. $\dfrac{ax+bx}{cx+dx}$

b. $\dfrac{bc-bd}{cx-dx}$ b. $\dfrac{abc+2ab}{acm+2am}$ b. $\dfrac{cx-c^2x^2}{dx-cdx^2}$ b. $\dfrac{ac+ad+ae}{bc+bd+be}$ b. $\dfrac{ac+ad+ac}{bc+bd+bc}$

16. $\dfrac{12x}{6x^2+9x^3}$ 16. $\dfrac{4a^2-8a}{16a}$ 16. $\dfrac{4abc}{2ab-2ac}$ 16. $\dfrac{6b^3c^2-4bc^3}{8bc^2}$ 16. $\dfrac{15m^2n^2x}{6mnx-18m^2nx}$

17. $\dfrac{x^2-4}{2(x-2)}$ 17. $\dfrac{y^2-1}{2y+2}$ 17. $\dfrac{3x+15}{x^2-25}$ 17. $\dfrac{2a+10}{a^2+10a+25}$ 17. $\dfrac{x^2-4x}{x^2-6x+8}$

18. $\dfrac{x^2-2xy+y^2}{x^2-y^2}$ 18. $\dfrac{x^2-1}{x^2+2x+1}$ 18. $\dfrac{a^2-b^2}{(a-b)^2}$ 18. $\dfrac{x^2-14x+49}{x^2-49}$ 18. $\dfrac{a^2+6a+9}{a^2+2a-3}$

19. $\dfrac{a^2+5a+6}{a^2+6a+9}$ 19. $\dfrac{b^2+b-12}{b^2+2b-15}$ 19. $\dfrac{x^2-12x+36}{x^2+2x-48}$ 19. $\dfrac{b^2+b-6}{b^2-9}$ 19. $\dfrac{a^2-2a+1}{a^2+3a-4}$

20. $\dfrac{ab(x^2-y^2)}{2ab(x-y)^2}$ 20. $\dfrac{x^3-xy^2}{xy(x-y)^2}$ 20. $\dfrac{4c^2+16c+16}{6c^2+18c+12}$ 20. $\dfrac{3ab^3-27ab}{6ab^2+6ab-72a}$ 20. $\dfrac{8b^3+24b^2-32b}{4b^3-16b^2+12b}$

EXERCISE 58

Multiplication of Fractions

I. **Aim:** To multiply algebraic fractions.

II. **Procedure**

1. Divide any numerator and any denominator having a common factor by the largest factor common to both. If any numerator or denominator is a polynomial, factor if possible before dividing by the largest common factor.

2. To find the numerator of the answer, multiply the remaining factors of the numerators.

3. To find the denominator of the answer, multiply the remaining factors of the denominators.

4. Check by going over the work again or by numerical substitution.

III. **Sample Solutions**

1. $\dfrac{3}{10}\cdot\dfrac{4}{9}$

$$\dfrac{\overset{1}{\cancel{3}}}{\underset{5}{\cancel{10}}}\cdot\dfrac{\overset{2}{\cancel{4}}}{\underset{3}{\cancel{9}}}=\dfrac{2}{15}$$

Answer, $\dfrac{2}{15}$

2. $\dfrac{x^2}{y^3}\cdot\dfrac{y^4}{x^5}$

$$\dfrac{\overset{1}{\cancel{x^2}}}{\underset{1}{\cancel{y^3}}}\cdot\dfrac{\overset{y}{\cancel{y^4}}}{\underset{x^3}{\cancel{x^5}}}=\dfrac{y}{x^3}$$

Answer, $\dfrac{y}{x^3}$

3. $*2a^2b\cdot\dfrac{3a-4b}{4a}$

$$\dfrac{\overset{a}{\cancel{2a^2b}}}{1}\cdot\dfrac{3a-4b}{\underset{2}{\cancel{4a}}}=\dfrac{3a^2b-4ab^2}{2}$$

Answer, $\dfrac{3a^2b-4ab^2}{2}$

* A whole number can be written as a fraction with 1 as its denominator.

4. $\dfrac{2a^2(x+4)}{3ab(x-2)}\cdot\dfrac{9b^2(x-2)}{8a(x-4)}$

$$\dfrac{\overset{a}{\cancel{2a^2}}(x+4)}{\underset{1\ \ 1}{\cancel{3ab}(\cancel{x-2})}}\cdot\dfrac{\overset{3b}{\cancel{9b^2}}\overset{1}{(\cancel{x-2})}}{\underset{4}{\cancel{8a}(x-4)}}=\dfrac{3b(x+4)}{4(x-4)}$$

Answer, $\dfrac{3b(x+4)}{4(x-4)}$

5. $\dfrac{(a+x)^2}{a^2-x^2}\cdot\dfrac{a^2-2ax+x^2}{ab-bx}$

$$\dfrac{\overset{a+x}{\cancel{(a+x)^2}}}{\underset{1\quad\ \ 1}{(\cancel{a+x})(\cancel{a-x})}}\cdot\dfrac{\overset{1}{(\cancel{a-x})}\overset{1}{(\cancel{a-x})}}{\underset{1}{b(\cancel{a-x})}}=\dfrac{a+x}{b}$$

Answer, $\dfrac{a+x}{b}$

DIAGNOSTIC TEST

Find the following products:

1. $\dfrac{a^2}{b^2}\cdot\dfrac{b}{a}$

2. $\dfrac{2a}{5x}\cdot\dfrac{4b}{3y}$

3. $\dfrac{5c}{2}\cdot 6$

4. $8x\cdot\dfrac{3x}{4}$

5. $\dfrac{7a^2}{4bc}\cdot\dfrac{8bc^2}{21a^3c}$

6. $\dfrac{a+3}{6a}\cdot 9a^2$

7. $\dfrac{14x^2}{5y}\cdot\dfrac{y^3}{x^3}\cdot\dfrac{15x}{4y^2}$

8. $\dfrac{x+y}{x-y}\cdot\dfrac{x-y}{x+y}$

9. $\dfrac{c+d}{10cd}\cdot\dfrac{5c^3d}{(c+d)^2}$

10. $\dfrac{(a-2)(a-3)}{(a+2)(a+4)}\cdot\dfrac{(a-1)(a+2)}{(a+1)(a-3)}$

11. $\dfrac{10a(a+2)}{3b(b-3)}\cdot\dfrac{6b(b-3)(b+3)}{25a^2(a-2)(a+2)}$

12. $\dfrac{x^2-4}{x^2+4x+4}\cdot\dfrac{2x+4}{x^2+x-6}$

Related Practice Examples

Find the following products:

A

1. $\dfrac{2}{3}\cdot\dfrac{15}{28}$

2. $\dfrac{2}{5}\cdot\dfrac{1}{3}$

3. $\dfrac{4}{5}\cdot 10$

4. $4\cdot\dfrac{3}{8}$

5a. $\dfrac{ab}{3}\cdot\dfrac{6}{a}$

b. $\dfrac{4x^2}{5y}\cdot\dfrac{3y}{4x}$

B

1. $\dfrac{a}{b}\cdot\dfrac{b}{a}$

2. $\dfrac{x}{y}\cdot\dfrac{m}{a}$

3. $\dfrac{1}{2}\cdot 2x$

4. $3x\cdot\dfrac{y}{3}$

5a. $\dfrac{2}{x}\cdot\dfrac{xy}{4}$

b. $\dfrac{5x}{4a^2}\cdot\dfrac{2a}{10x^2}$

C

1. $\dfrac{c}{d^2}\cdot\dfrac{d}{c^2}$

2. $\dfrac{5a}{6}\cdot\dfrac{13}{4}$

3. $\dfrac{x}{y^2}\cdot y$

4. $4a^2\cdot\dfrac{b}{a^3}$

5a. $\dfrac{2b^2}{a^2}\cdot\dfrac{ab}{4}$

b. $\dfrac{4a}{3c}\cdot\dfrac{3cd}{4b}$

D

1. $\dfrac{x^5}{y^2}\cdot\dfrac{y^3}{x^6}$

2. $\dfrac{a}{b}\cdot\dfrac{c}{2d}$

3. $\dfrac{4b}{3}\cdot 9$

4. $c\cdot\dfrac{b}{c}$

5a. $\dfrac{2c}{5d}\cdot\dfrac{10d}{6c}$

b. $\dfrac{16x^2y^3}{9a^3}\cdot\dfrac{27a^2}{8xy}$

A

6. $\dfrac{x+y}{2}\cdot 10$

7. $\dfrac{2x}{5a}\cdot\dfrac{3a^2}{4x}\cdot\dfrac{5}{6ax}$

B

6. $\dfrac{r-d}{3}\cdot 4$

7. $\dfrac{16a^2b^3}{3ac^4}\cdot\dfrac{25c^2}{32ab^4}\cdot\dfrac{9ab^3}{5c}$

C

6. $3x^2y\cdot\dfrac{4x-y}{3x}$

7. $\dfrac{2b^2m^4}{9ad^2}\cdot\dfrac{3a^2c^3}{8bx^3}\cdot\dfrac{6dx^2}{7c^5m}$

8. $\dfrac{a+b}{a-b} \cdot \dfrac{a-b}{a+b}$

8. $\dfrac{x+6}{x-3} \cdot \dfrac{x-3}{x+6}$

8. $\dfrac{m-1}{m+5} \cdot \dfrac{m-5}{m-1}$

9. $\dfrac{a+x}{3ax} \cdot \dfrac{6ax}{(a+x)^2}$

9. $\dfrac{(b-2)^5}{4b} \cdot \dfrac{12b^3}{(b-2)^3}$

9. $\dfrac{3xy}{x-2y} \cdot \dfrac{(x-2y)^4}{4y^2}$

10. $\dfrac{(x-1)(x+5)}{(x-3)(x+5)} \cdot \dfrac{(x-3)(x-2)}{(x+4)(x-3)}$

10. $\dfrac{(a+c)(b+c)}{(c+d)(a+b)} \cdot \dfrac{(c+d)(a+2b)}{(b-c)(a+c)}$

10. $\dfrac{(a-2y)(b+2y)}{(a+2y)(b-2y)} \cdot \dfrac{(a+2y)(b-2y)}{(b-2y)(a-2y)}$

11. $\dfrac{3a(x+2)}{5x(a+5)} \cdot \dfrac{15x(a-5)}{4a(x+2)}$

11. $\dfrac{6c^2d(2c-d)}{5d^3(c-d)} \cdot \dfrac{cd(c-d)}{3c^2(2c-d)}$

11. $\dfrac{12xy(x+y)}{7x^2(x-y)} \cdot \dfrac{35y^3(x-y)}{48x^2y(x-y)(x+y)}$

12a. $\dfrac{6x+6y}{x-y} \cdot \dfrac{5x-5y}{12}$

12a. $\dfrac{4a^2+10}{a-3} \cdot \dfrac{a^2-9}{6a^2+15}$

12a. $\dfrac{4x+8}{6x-24} \cdot \dfrac{9x-36}{2x+4}$

b. $\dfrac{(a+b)^2}{a^2-b^2} \cdot \dfrac{ax-bx}{ay+by}$

b. $\dfrac{4x-4}{a^2-b^2} \cdot \dfrac{a^3b^2-a^2b^3}{abx-ab}$

b. $\dfrac{a^2-8a+16}{a^2+3a-10} \cdot \dfrac{a^2+2a-8}{a^2-16}$

c. $\dfrac{b^2-b-12}{b^2-6b+8} \cdot \dfrac{b^2-4}{b^2+5b+6}$

c. $\dfrac{x^2+x-2}{x^2-7x} \cdot \dfrac{x^2-13x+42}{x^2+2x}$

c. $\dfrac{m^2-7m+12}{m^2-m-6} \cdot \dfrac{m^2+7m+10}{m^2+m-20}$

d. $\dfrac{x^2+5xy+6y^2}{x^2+4xy-5y^2} \cdot \dfrac{x^2+3xy-10y^2}{x^2+xy-6y^2}$

d. $\dfrac{m^2+7mn+10n^2}{m^2+mn-2n^2} \cdot \dfrac{m^2-5mn+4n^2}{m^2+mn-20n^2}$

d. $\dfrac{b^2-4bc+3c^2}{b^2-8bc+15c^2} \cdot \dfrac{b^2+9bc+18c^2}{b^2+5bc-6c^2}$

EXERCISE 59

Division of Fractions

I. Aim: To divide algebraic fractions.

II. Procedure

    1. Invert the divisor (the term directly after the division sign).

    2. Then follow the procedure for the multiplication of algebraic fractions. See exercise 58.

    3. Check by going over the work again or by numerical substitution.

III. Sample Solutions

1. $\dfrac{5}{8} \div \dfrac{3}{4}$

$$= \dfrac{5}{\underset{2}{\cancel{8}}} \times \dfrac{\overset{1}{\cancel{4}}}{3} = \dfrac{5}{6}$$

Answer, $\dfrac{5}{6}$

2. $\dfrac{2a^2c}{3bd^2} \div \dfrac{4ac^2}{6b^2d}$

$$= \dfrac{\overset{a}{\cancel{2a^2c}}}{\underset{d}{\cancel{3bd^2}}} \times \dfrac{\overset{2b}{\cancel{6b^2d}}}{\underset{2c}{\cancel{4ac^2}}} = \dfrac{ab}{cd}$$

Answer, $\dfrac{ab}{cd}$

3. $\dfrac{x^2+2x-8}{x^2-16} \div \dfrac{x^2-6x+8}{x^2-8x+16}$

$$= \dfrac{x^2+2x-8}{x^2-16} \times \dfrac{x^2-8x+16}{x^2-6x+8}$$

$$= \dfrac{\overset{1}{\cancel{(x+4)}}\,\overset{1}{\cancel{(x-2)}}}{\underset{1}{\cancel{(x+4)}}\,\underset{1}{\cancel{(x-4)}}} \times \dfrac{\overset{1}{\cancel{(x-4)}}\,\overset{1}{\cancel{(x-4)}}}{\underset{1}{\cancel{(x-4)}}\,\underset{1}{\cancel{(x-2)}}} = 1$$

Answer, 1

DIAGNOSTIC TEST

Divide as indicated:

1. $\dfrac{2ab^2}{3c^3} \div \dfrac{4a^3b}{9c^2}$

2. $\dfrac{7m^2n^2}{8a^3b^2} \div 21mn^4$

3. $\dfrac{a^2-b^2}{8x^3} \div \dfrac{(a-b)^2}{24x^3}$

4. $\dfrac{a^2+6a+9}{a^2+2a-3} \div \dfrac{a^2-9}{a^2-a-6}$

Related Practice Examples

SET 1

1. $\dfrac{3}{4} \div \dfrac{3}{8}$

2. $\dfrac{2}{x} \div \dfrac{3}{x}$

3. $\dfrac{1}{a^2} \div \dfrac{1}{a}$

4. $\dfrac{b^2}{x^3} \div \dfrac{b}{x^2}$

5. $\dfrac{x}{a} \div \dfrac{y}{b}$

6. $\dfrac{ax}{by} \div \dfrac{x}{y}$

7. $\dfrac{3a^2c}{8bd^2} \div \dfrac{6ac^3}{bd}$

8. $\dfrac{5x^2y}{6ad} \div \dfrac{10xy^2}{3a^2d}$

9. $\dfrac{2m^3x}{11ny^4} \div \dfrac{4mx^2}{33ny^6}$

10. $\dfrac{5b^2c^3d}{7a^2x^2y^2} \div \dfrac{15bc^4}{28a^2xy^3}$

SET 2

1. $\dfrac{3a^2c^4}{4b^2} \div 6ac^2$

2. $\dfrac{2x^4y^2}{5m^2n} \div 8xy^2$

3. $14a^2m^3 \div \dfrac{7a^2m^4}{8bx^2}$

4. $4abc \div \dfrac{2a^2b}{3d^2}$

5. $\dfrac{9c^2m^3x^4}{10by^2} \div 27cx^7$

SET 3

1. $\dfrac{4a-4c}{5a+5c} \div \dfrac{4}{15}$

2. $\dfrac{2a+4x}{3ax} \div \dfrac{6a+12x}{6a^2x}$

3. $\dfrac{c^2-d^2}{4c^2} \div \dfrac{c^2-2cd+d^2}{2d^2}$

4. $\dfrac{4m^2+20m+25}{5m} \div \dfrac{4m^2-25}{4m^2}$

5. $\dfrac{a^2+a-20}{4a^3} \div \dfrac{a^2-16}{6a^2}$

SET 4

1. $\dfrac{5x-5}{x^2-25} \div \dfrac{x-1}{x-5}$

2. $\dfrac{3x+9}{x+5} \div \dfrac{x+3}{3x+15}$

3. $\dfrac{a^2-b^2}{(a+b)^2} \div \dfrac{a-b}{4a+4b}$

4. $\dfrac{x+y}{x^2-xy} \div \dfrac{1}{x^2-y^2}$

5. $\dfrac{(b+2)^2}{bx-by} \div \dfrac{b^2+2b}{b^2x-b^2y}$

6. $\dfrac{ab^2-a^2b}{ab^2-ab} \div \dfrac{b^2-a^2}{ab}$

7. $\dfrac{x^2-xy}{cx^2-cy^2} \div \dfrac{x^3-x^2}{cx^2-cx}$

8. $\dfrac{b^2+4b-12}{b^2+9b+18} \div \dfrac{3b+12}{6b+6}$

9. $\dfrac{c^2+14c+49}{c^2+2c-35} \div \dfrac{c^2+9c+14}{c^2-3c-10}$

10. $\dfrac{x^2+xy}{x^2+y^2} \div \dfrac{x^3y+2x^2y^2+xy^3}{x^4-y^4}$

EXERCISE 60

Addition and Subtraction—Like Denominators

I. Aim: To add and subtract fractions with like or common denominators.

II. Procedure

1. Make one fraction.
   a) For its denominator, use the common denominator.
   b) For its numerator, rewrite the numerators of the given fractions over the common denominator, using the following principles:
      (1) If a fraction is preceded by a plus sign or has no sign at all, rewrite the terms of its numerator without changing their signs. A plus sign may be written before any term in the numerator if its plus sign is understood.
      (2) If a fraction is preceded by a minus sign, rewrite the terms of its numerator, changing their signs.

2. If possible, combine any similar terms found in the numerator.

3. Also if possible, change the resulting fraction to lowest terms.

4. Check by going over the work again or by numerical substitution.

III. Sample Solutions

Exercise A

1. $\dfrac{1}{8} + \dfrac{3}{8}$

$= \dfrac{1+3}{8}$

$= \dfrac{4}{8}$

$= \dfrac{1}{2}$

Answer, $\dfrac{1}{2}$

2. $\dfrac{x}{4} + \dfrac{5x}{4}$

$= \dfrac{x+5x}{4}$

$= \dfrac{6x}{4}$

$= \dfrac{3x}{2}$

Answer, $\dfrac{3x}{2}$

3. $\dfrac{5a}{6x} + \dfrac{7a}{6x}$

$= \dfrac{5a+7a}{6x}$

$= \dfrac{12a}{6x}$

$= \dfrac{2a}{x}$

Answer, $\dfrac{2a}{x}$

4. $\dfrac{2c}{5x} + \dfrac{3d}{5x}$

$= \dfrac{2c+3d}{5x}$

Answer, $\dfrac{2c+3d}{5x}$

5. $\dfrac{5a}{a+b} + \dfrac{5b}{a+b}$

$= \dfrac{5a+5b}{a+b}$

$= \dfrac{5(a+b)}{a+b} = 5$

Answer, 5

Exercise B

1. $\dfrac{3}{4} - \dfrac{1}{4}$

$= \dfrac{3-1}{4}$

$= \dfrac{2}{4} = \tfrac{1}{2}$

Answer, $\dfrac{1}{2}$

2. $\dfrac{5x}{2} - \dfrac{x}{2}$

$= \dfrac{5x-x}{2}$

$= \dfrac{4x}{2} = 2x$

Answer, $2x$

3. $\dfrac{5m}{8} - \dfrac{3n}{8}$

$= \dfrac{5m-3n}{8}$

Answer, $\dfrac{5m-3n}{8}$

4. $\dfrac{3d}{c+d} - \dfrac{d}{c+d}$

$= \dfrac{3d-d}{c+d}$

$= \dfrac{2d}{c+d}$

Answer, $\dfrac{2d}{c+d}$

5. $\dfrac{c^2}{c-2} - \dfrac{4}{c-2}$

$= \dfrac{c^2-4}{c-2}$

$= \dfrac{(c+2)(c-2)}{c-2} = c+2$

Answer, $c+2$

Exercise C

1. $\dfrac{3x+2y}{5}+\dfrac{2x+y}{5}$

   $=\dfrac{3x+2y+2x+y}{5}$

   $=\dfrac{5x+3y}{5}$

   Answer, $\dfrac{5x+3y}{5}$

2. $\dfrac{7a-2y}{3}-\dfrac{a+4y}{3}$

   $=\dfrac{7a-2y-a-4y}{3}$

   $=\dfrac{6a-6y}{3}$

   $=\dfrac{\overset{2}{\cancel{6}}(a-y)}{\cancel{3}}=2(a-y)$

   Answer, $2(a-y)$

3. $\dfrac{9m+2n}{4}-\dfrac{m-2n}{4}$

   $=\dfrac{9m+2n-m+2n}{4}$

   $=\dfrac{8m+4n}{4}$

   $=\dfrac{\overset{1}{\cancel{4}}(2m+n)}{\underset{1}{\cancel{4}}}=2m+n$

   Answer, $2m+n$

4. $\dfrac{2a^2+4a+17}{(a+2)(a+3)}-\dfrac{a^2-4a+2}{(a+2)(a+3)}$

   $=\dfrac{2a^2+4a+17-a^2+4a-2}{(a+2)(a+3)}$

   $=\dfrac{a^2+8a+15}{(a+2)(a+3)}$

   $=\dfrac{\overset{1}{\cancel{(a+3)}}(a+5)}{(a+2)\underset{1}{\cancel{(a+3)}}}=\dfrac{a+5}{a+2}$

   Answer, $\dfrac{a+5}{a+2}$

5. $\dfrac{x^2+xy-y^2}{x^2+2xy+y^2}+\dfrac{x^2+xy+y^2}{x^2+2xy+y^2}$

   $=\dfrac{x^2+xy-y^2+x^2+xy+y^2}{x^2+2xy+y^2}$

   $=\dfrac{2x^2+2xy}{x^2+2xy+y^2}$

   $=\dfrac{2x(x+y)}{(x+y)^2}=\dfrac{2x}{x+y}$

   Answer, $\dfrac{2x}{x+y}$

DIAGNOSTIC TEST A

Add as indicated:

1. $\dfrac{5s}{8}+\dfrac{2s}{8}$

2. $\dfrac{5b}{4}+\dfrac{3b}{4}$

3. $\dfrac{x}{6}+\dfrac{3x}{6}$

4. $\dfrac{x}{3}+\dfrac{y}{3}$

5. $\dfrac{b}{5y}+\dfrac{3b}{5y}$

6. $\dfrac{3}{4a}+\dfrac{1}{4a}$

7. $\dfrac{5r}{10b}+\dfrac{3r}{10b}$

8. $\dfrac{a}{c+d}+\dfrac{b}{c+d}$

9. $\dfrac{5}{x+y}+\dfrac{7}{x+y}$

10. $\dfrac{3c}{c+d}+\dfrac{3d}{c+d}$

Related Practice Examples

Add as indicated:

A

1. $\dfrac{1}{4}+\dfrac{2}{4}$

2. $\dfrac{5}{8}+\dfrac{3}{8}$

B

1. $\dfrac{x}{5}+\dfrac{3x}{5}$

2. $\dfrac{9b}{6}+\dfrac{3b}{6}$

C

1. $\dfrac{3a}{7}+\dfrac{6a}{7}$

2. $\dfrac{7x}{2}+\dfrac{5x}{2}$

3. $\dfrac{3}{10}+\dfrac{5}{10}$

4. $\dfrac{c}{4}+\dfrac{d}{4}$

5. $\dfrac{5}{x}+\dfrac{3}{x}$

6. $\dfrac{7}{5a}+\dfrac{3}{5a}$

7. $\dfrac{1}{8x}+\dfrac{5}{8x}$

8. $\dfrac{4a^2}{y+1}+\dfrac{3b^2}{y+1}$

9. $\dfrac{5}{b+c}+\dfrac{4}{b+c}$

10. $\dfrac{a}{a+b}+\dfrac{b}{a+b}$

3. $\dfrac{3m}{8}+\dfrac{3m}{8}$

4. $\dfrac{2a}{5}+\dfrac{3b}{5}$

5. $\dfrac{4m}{ad}+\dfrac{3m}{ad}$

6. $\dfrac{7d}{8x}+\dfrac{9d}{8x}$

7. $\dfrac{3x}{10y}+\dfrac{x}{10y}$

8. $\dfrac{c}{m+n}+\dfrac{d}{m+n}$

9. $\dfrac{x}{a+b}+\dfrac{2x}{a+b}$

10. $\dfrac{2c}{c+d}+\dfrac{2d}{c+d}$

3. $\dfrac{5c}{12}+\dfrac{3c}{12}$

4. $\dfrac{5x}{8}+\dfrac{3y}{8}$

5. $\dfrac{3a}{x^2}+\dfrac{2a}{x^2}$

6. $\dfrac{5ab}{4c^2}+\dfrac{7ab}{4c^2}$

7. $\dfrac{3m^2}{16x^2}+\dfrac{9m^2}{16x^2}$

8. $\dfrac{3x}{x-y}+\dfrac{2y}{x-y}$

9. $\dfrac{7ac}{d-x}+\dfrac{5ac}{d-x}$

10. $\dfrac{4m}{m+2n}+\dfrac{8n}{m+2n}$

DIAGNOSTIC TEST B

Subtract as indicated:

1. $\dfrac{3x}{5}-\dfrac{2x}{5}$

2. $\dfrac{5b}{4}-\dfrac{b}{4}$

3. $\dfrac{7a}{8}-\dfrac{3a}{8}$

4. $\dfrac{m}{2}-\dfrac{n}{2}$

5. $\dfrac{5}{c}-\dfrac{3}{c}$

6. $\dfrac{12b}{5x}-\dfrac{2b}{5x}$

7. $\dfrac{7b^2}{12x^2}-\dfrac{b^2}{12x^2}$

8. $\dfrac{a}{c-d}-\dfrac{b}{c-d}$

9. $\dfrac{4x}{x+y}-\dfrac{2x}{x+y}$

10. $\dfrac{b^2}{b-3}-\dfrac{9}{b-3}$

Related Practice Examples

Subtract as indicated:

A

1. $\dfrac{7n}{3}-\dfrac{5n}{3}$

2. $\dfrac{6a}{5}-\dfrac{a}{5}$

3. $\dfrac{9x}{10}-\dfrac{3x}{10}$

4. $\dfrac{13a}{6}-\dfrac{7b}{6}$

5. $\dfrac{8}{x}-\dfrac{6}{x}$

B

1. $\dfrac{4a}{6}-\dfrac{3a}{6}$

2. $\dfrac{25h}{8}-\dfrac{9h}{8}$

3. $\dfrac{7m}{12}-\dfrac{m}{12}$

4. $\dfrac{14b}{3}-\dfrac{5c}{3}$

5. $\dfrac{4c}{xy}-\dfrac{2c}{xy}$

C

1. $\dfrac{9c}{11}-\dfrac{4c}{11}$

2. $\dfrac{23x}{7}-\dfrac{2x}{7}$

3. $\dfrac{17b}{32}-\dfrac{5b}{32}$

4. $\dfrac{3bc}{5}-\dfrac{2ad}{5}$

5. $\dfrac{10bx}{ad^2}-\dfrac{7bx}{ad^2}$

6. $\dfrac{9}{2s} - \dfrac{3}{2s}$

7. $\dfrac{4d}{6x} - \dfrac{d}{6x}$

8. $\dfrac{5b^2c}{y+3} - \dfrac{2a^2x}{y+3}$

9. $\dfrac{7}{a+d} - \dfrac{5}{a+d}$

10a. $\dfrac{c}{c-d} - \dfrac{d}{c-d}$

b. $\dfrac{x^2}{x-y} - \dfrac{y^2}{x-y}$

6. $\dfrac{3g}{2z} - \dfrac{g}{2z}$

7. $\dfrac{9x}{10r^2} - \dfrac{5x}{10r^2}$

8. $\dfrac{x}{a+b} - \dfrac{3}{a+b}$

9. $\dfrac{3x}{x-y} - \dfrac{x}{x-y}$

10a. $\dfrac{5m}{m-n} - \dfrac{5n}{m-n}$

b. $\dfrac{b^2}{b+3} - \dfrac{9}{b+3}$

6. $\dfrac{16a}{5c^2} - \dfrac{6a}{5c^2}$

7. $\dfrac{23c^2d^2}{24x^2y} - \dfrac{15c^2d^2}{24x^2y}$

8. $\dfrac{a}{x-y} - \dfrac{b}{x-y}$

9. $\dfrac{8c^2}{c-d} - \dfrac{3d^2}{c-d}$

10a. $\dfrac{x^2}{x+y} - \dfrac{y^2}{x+y}$

b. $\dfrac{b^2}{b-4} - \dfrac{16}{b-4}$

DIAGNOSTIC TEST C

Add or subtract as indicated:

1. $\dfrac{3x-y}{5} + \dfrac{4x+2y}{5}$

2. $\dfrac{a+2b}{3} + \dfrac{2a+b}{3}$

3. $\dfrac{2c-3d}{4} - \dfrac{c+3d}{4}$

4. $\dfrac{4r-s}{6} - \dfrac{2r-7s}{6}$

5. $\dfrac{c+3d}{c+d} + \dfrac{c-d}{c+d}$

6. $\dfrac{3x}{(x-y)(x-y)} - \dfrac{2y}{(x-y)(x-y)}$

7. $\dfrac{a}{(a+b)(a-b)} + \dfrac{b}{(a+b)(a-b)}$

8. $\dfrac{c^2-cd}{(c+d)(c-d)} - \dfrac{cd-d^2}{(c+d)(c-d)}$

9. $\dfrac{b^2}{b^2+2b-15} + \dfrac{25}{b^2+2b-15}$

10. $\dfrac{x^2}{x^2-9} - \dfrac{6x-9}{x^2-9}$

Related Practice Examples

Add or subtract as indicated:

A

1. $\dfrac{5c-3d}{2} + \dfrac{3c+2d}{2}$

2a. $\dfrac{2x+3y}{5} + \dfrac{3x+2y}{5}$

b. $\dfrac{2a-b}{4} + \dfrac{2a+5b}{4}$

3. $\dfrac{8x-2y}{3} - \dfrac{4x-5y}{3}$

4a. $\dfrac{10s+4t}{7} - \dfrac{3s-3t}{7}$

b. $\dfrac{6x+5y}{2x} - \dfrac{4x+y}{2x}$

B

1. $\dfrac{4a+3b}{3a} + \dfrac{a+b}{3a}$

2a. $\dfrac{2c+d}{9} + \dfrac{c+2d}{9}$

b. $\dfrac{5m-2n}{6} + \dfrac{7m-4n}{6}$

3. $\dfrac{7d+4m}{10} - \dfrac{2d+3m}{10}$

4a. $\dfrac{7m-2n}{3} - \dfrac{m+8n}{3}$

b. $\dfrac{4a+3ab}{a^2b^2} - \dfrac{a-2ab}{a^2b^2}$

5. $\dfrac{4a-3x}{a+x}+\dfrac{2a+9x}{a+x}$

6. $\dfrac{5a}{(a+b)(a+b)}+\dfrac{4b}{(a+b)(a+b)}$

7. $\dfrac{x}{(x+y)(x+y)}+\dfrac{y}{(x+y)(x+y)}$

8a. $\dfrac{3x}{2(x+2)}+\dfrac{5x}{2(x+2)}$

b. $\dfrac{b^2+6b+2}{(b+3)(b-2)}-\dfrac{2b-1}{(b+3)(b-2)}$

9. $\dfrac{a^2}{a^2+2ab+b^2}+\dfrac{b^2}{a^2+2ab+b^2}$

10a. $\dfrac{x}{x^2-16}+\dfrac{4}{x^2-16}$

b. $\dfrac{x^2-4x}{x^2-x-6}-\dfrac{x-6}{x^2-x-6}$

5. $\dfrac{5c-4}{c-2}-\dfrac{2c+2}{c-2}$

6. $\dfrac{2x-3}{(x-2)(x+1)}-\dfrac{x}{(x-2)(x+1)}$

7. $\dfrac{2m-3n}{(m-n)(m-n)}-\dfrac{m-2n}{(m-n)(m-n)}$

8a. $\dfrac{c^2+7c+3}{(c+4)(c+5)}-\dfrac{2c+3}{(c+4)(c+5)}$

b. $\dfrac{x^2+x-7}{(x+5)(x-2)}+\dfrac{x^2+5x-13}{(x+5)(x-2)}$

9. $\dfrac{3m^2}{m^2-8m+16}-\dfrac{16}{m^2-8m+16}$

10a. $\dfrac{b^2}{b^2+2b-15}-\dfrac{25}{b^2+2b-15}$

b. $\dfrac{a^2+ab-b^2}{a^2+2ab+b^2}+\dfrac{a^2+ab+b^2}{a^2+2ab+b^2}$

EXERCISE 61

Addition and Subtraction—Monomial Denominators

I. **Aim**: To add and subtract fractions with monomial denominators.

II. **Procedure**

1. Change the given fractions to equivalent fractions having a common denominator as follows:
   a) Find the lowest common denominator of the given fractions by making an algebraic expression which contains all the factors of the given denominators (see sample solutions below).
   Note—The l.c.d. is the smallest algebraic expression which is exactly divisible by all the denominators of the given fractions.
   b) Write the l.c.d. as the denominator of all the equivalent fractions and precede each fraction with the sign of the corresponding given fraction.
   c) Find the numerator of each equivalent fraction by dividing the denominator of the given fraction into the l.c.d. Then multiply this quotient by the numerator of the given fraction. Write the product, thus obtained, as the numerator of the equivalent fraction.

2. To complete the solution, follow the procedure outlined for exercise 60.

3. To change a mixed expression to a fraction, write the integral term as a fraction having the denominator 1. Then follow the procedure for the addition and subtraction of fractions. (See sample solution 8.)

4. Check by going over the work again or by numerical substitution.

III. Sample Solutions

1. $\dfrac{a}{5}+\dfrac{3a}{10}$

l.c.d. $= 10$

$\dfrac{2a}{10}+\dfrac{3a}{10}$

$= \dfrac{2a+3a}{10}$

$= \dfrac{5a}{10}=\dfrac{a}{2}$

Answer, $\dfrac{a}{2}$

2. $\dfrac{2xy}{3}-\dfrac{xy}{4}$

l.c.d. $= 12$

$\dfrac{8xy}{12}-\dfrac{3xy}{12}$

$= \dfrac{8xy-3xy}{12}$

$= \dfrac{5xy}{12}$

Answer, $\dfrac{5xy}{12}$

3. $\dfrac{3a}{4x}+\dfrac{5a}{6x}$

l.c.d. $= 12x$

$\dfrac{9a}{12x}+\dfrac{10a}{12x}$

$= \dfrac{9a+10a}{12x}$

$= \dfrac{19a}{12x}$

Answer, $\dfrac{19a}{12x}$

4. $\dfrac{1}{a}-\dfrac{1}{b}$

l.c.d. $= ab$

$\dfrac{b}{ab}-\dfrac{a}{ab}$

$= \dfrac{b-a}{ab}$

Answer, $\dfrac{b-a}{ab}$

5. $\dfrac{3}{2b^2}-\dfrac{2}{3b^3}+\dfrac{5}{6b}$

l.c.d. $= 6b^3$

$\dfrac{9b}{6b^3}-\dfrac{4}{6b^3}+\dfrac{5b^2}{6b^3}$

$= \dfrac{9b-4+5b^2}{6b^3}$

Answer, $\dfrac{5b^2+9b-4}{6b^3}$

6. $\dfrac{a+3}{10}+\dfrac{a+1}{2}$

l.c.d. $= 10$

$\dfrac{a+3}{10}+\dfrac{5a+5}{10}$

$= \dfrac{a+3+5a+5}{10}$

$= \dfrac{6a+8}{10}$

$= \dfrac{\overset{1}{\cancel{2}}(3a+4)}{\underset{5}{\cancel{10}}}$

$= \dfrac{3a+4}{5}$

Answer, $\dfrac{3a+4}{5}$

7. $\dfrac{c+d}{2cd^2}-\dfrac{c-d}{6c^2d}$

l.c.d. $= 6c^2d^2$

$\dfrac{3c^2+3cd}{6c^2d^2}-\dfrac{cd-d^2}{6c^2d^2}$

$= \dfrac{3c^2+3cd-cd+d^2}{6c^2d^2}$

$= \dfrac{3c^2+2cd+d^2}{6c^2d^2}$

Answer, $\dfrac{3c^2+2cd+d^2}{6c^2d^2}$

Change to a fraction:

8. $\dfrac{a^2-3}{4a}+3a$

$\dfrac{a^2-3}{4a}+\dfrac{3a}{1}$

l.c.d. $= 4a$

$\dfrac{a^2-3}{4a}+\dfrac{12a^2}{4a}$

$= \dfrac{a^2-3+12a^2}{4a}$

$= \dfrac{13a^2-3}{4a}$

Answer, $\dfrac{13a^2-3}{4a}$

Preliminary Examples

In each example find the smallest algebraic expression which is exactly divisible by the given expressions:

SET 1	SET 2	SET 3	SET 4
1. 6 and 12	**1.** a^4 and a^2	**1.** a and x	**1.** $5x$ and $3y$
2. 5 and 4	**2.** m^3 and m^4	**2.** b^2 and y^3	**2.** $6c^2$ and $10c^3$
3. 6 and 8	**3.** a^3b^2 and a^2b^4	**3.** a^2c and ad^2	**3.** $8a^2d$ and $4ad^2$
4. 2, 4, and 6	**4.** c^2d, cd^2, and c^3d	**4.** m^4n^2, mx^2, and m^2y^3	**4.** $2a$, $5a^2$, and $6a^3$
5. 9, 15, and 5	**5.** m^2x^3, m^5x^2, and m^3x^4	**5.** c^3d, d^2x, and x^2y	**5.** $4m$, $2n$, and $3x$

DIAGNOSTIC TEST

Add or subtract as indicated:

1. $\dfrac{a}{3}+\dfrac{a}{6}$

2. $\dfrac{3x}{5}-\dfrac{x}{10}$

3. $\dfrac{5c}{6}+\dfrac{2c}{5}$

4. $\dfrac{c}{2}-\dfrac{d}{3}$

5. $\dfrac{3b}{4}+\dfrac{5c}{6}$

6. $\dfrac{5m}{12}-\dfrac{7m}{30}$

7. $\dfrac{7}{10a}+\dfrac{3}{2a}$

8. $\dfrac{2a}{3b}-\dfrac{a}{4b}$

9. $\dfrac{5a}{6c}+\dfrac{7b}{8c}$

10. $\dfrac{3}{x}+\dfrac{4}{x^2}$

11. $\dfrac{b}{2a^2}+\dfrac{c}{3a^3}$

12. $\dfrac{2}{m}-\dfrac{5}{n}$

13. $\dfrac{3c}{4x}+\dfrac{5c}{8y}$

14. $\dfrac{5a}{12x^2y}-\dfrac{3b}{10xy^2}$

15. $\dfrac{x+4}{6}+\dfrac{1}{2}$

16. $\dfrac{x+2}{4}+\dfrac{x+3}{2}$

17. $\dfrac{x+y}{6}+\dfrac{x+y}{2}$

18. $\dfrac{a+5}{3}-\dfrac{a+2}{4}$

19. $\dfrac{2d-5}{2}-\dfrac{d-4}{5}$

20. $\dfrac{2a+3}{a}+\dfrac{a+2}{2}$

21. $\dfrac{3x+6}{2x}+\dfrac{5y+4}{2y}$

22. $\dfrac{c-d}{cd^2}-\dfrac{3c-3d}{c^2d}$

23. $\dfrac{a+b}{2a}-\dfrac{a-b}{3b}+\dfrac{b-c}{c}$

24. $\dfrac{4(a+2)}{a}-\dfrac{2(a+4)}{3a}+\dfrac{a+1}{6a}$

25. Change to a fraction: $\dfrac{4x^2-7}{3x}+2x$

Related Practice Examples

Add or subtract as indicated:

A

1. $\dfrac{3}{4}+\dfrac{5}{8}$

2. $\dfrac{a}{2}-\dfrac{a}{4}$

3. $\dfrac{4b}{5}+\dfrac{3b}{2}$

4. $\dfrac{7y}{2}-\dfrac{y}{3}$

5. $\dfrac{5a}{6}+\dfrac{a}{4}$

6. $\dfrac{3b}{4}-\dfrac{7b}{10}$

7. $\dfrac{7}{6x}+\dfrac{5}{2x}$

8. $\dfrac{3}{2c}+\dfrac{8}{3c}$

9. $\dfrac{5x}{4a}+\dfrac{7x}{6a}$

10. $\dfrac{2}{b^2}+\dfrac{5}{b}$

B

1. $\dfrac{2b}{5}+\dfrac{3b}{10}$

2. $\dfrac{3x^2}{5}-\dfrac{x^2}{10}$

3. $\dfrac{7a}{8}+\dfrac{5x}{9}$

4. $\dfrac{2ab}{3}-\dfrac{ab}{5}$

5. $\dfrac{3xy}{8}+\dfrac{5xy}{12}$

6. $\dfrac{5ad}{6}-\dfrac{3ad}{8}$

7. $\dfrac{7a}{4b}-\dfrac{7a}{8b}$

8. $\dfrac{7x}{4a}-\dfrac{3x}{5a}$

9. $\dfrac{15b}{8d}-\dfrac{3b}{10d}$

10. $\dfrac{a}{m^2}-\dfrac{2a}{m^5}$

C

1. $\dfrac{5a}{3}+\dfrac{4b}{9}$

2. $\dfrac{5c^2}{6}-\dfrac{c}{3}$

3. $\dfrac{2cd}{3}+\dfrac{3xy}{4}$

4. $\dfrac{3bx}{4}-\dfrac{2cx}{3}$

5. $\dfrac{9a^2}{16}+\dfrac{5b^2}{18}$

6. $\dfrac{11x^2y}{12}-\dfrac{9xy^2}{16}$

7. $\dfrac{9a}{8m}-\dfrac{11a}{16m}$

8. $\dfrac{5c}{2x}+\dfrac{d}{9x}$

9. $\dfrac{7a}{12m}+\dfrac{3b}{8m}$

10. $\dfrac{b^2}{x^4}-\dfrac{bd}{x^3}$

A

11. $\dfrac{3a}{4b^2}+\dfrac{5a}{2b^3}$

12. $\dfrac{1}{x}+\dfrac{1}{y}$

13. $\dfrac{8a}{5x}+\dfrac{2b}{3y}$

14. $\dfrac{7x}{a^2b}+\dfrac{x^2}{ab^2}$

15. $\dfrac{5b+4}{12}+\dfrac{3}{16}$

16a. $\dfrac{r+2}{2}+\dfrac{r+6}{4}$

b. $\dfrac{4b+3}{5}+\dfrac{6y-5}{20}$

17. $\dfrac{2b}{5}+\dfrac{b+5d}{10}$

18. $\dfrac{a-b}{4}-\dfrac{a+b}{8}$

19. $\dfrac{2a+4}{7}-\dfrac{3a-2}{3}$

20. $\dfrac{3}{a}+\dfrac{a+2}{5}$

21. $\dfrac{a+2}{3a}+\dfrac{b+3}{3b}$

22. $\dfrac{2a-2b}{a^2b}+\dfrac{a-b}{ab^2}$

23. $\dfrac{x+y}{2xy^2}-\dfrac{2x-y}{4x^2y}+\dfrac{x^2-2y^2}{3x^2y^2}$

24. $\dfrac{c+d}{3}-\dfrac{c-d}{6}+\dfrac{2(c+d)}{9}$

B

11. $\dfrac{4b}{5x^4}-\dfrac{5c}{3x}$

12. $\dfrac{4}{a}-\dfrac{3}{b}$

13. $\dfrac{3c}{8mx}-\dfrac{5d}{16ny}$

14. $\dfrac{2a}{3c^2}-\dfrac{3b}{4cd}$

15. $\dfrac{3a+5}{4}-\dfrac{7}{8}$

16a. $\dfrac{m-4}{8}+\dfrac{m+2}{4}$

b. $\dfrac{c+d}{4}+\dfrac{3c-2d}{2}$

17. $\dfrac{2b+2x}{5}+\dfrac{b+x}{10}$

18. $\dfrac{b+3}{3}-\dfrac{b+2}{5}$

19. $\dfrac{4x+2y}{3}-\dfrac{x-2y}{10}$

20. $\dfrac{a+3}{a}+\dfrac{a+2}{2}$

21. $\dfrac{ax+1}{a^2}+\dfrac{x+a}{a}$

22. $\dfrac{b-x}{bx}-\dfrac{c-x}{cx}$

23. $\dfrac{4a-3b}{6ab}-\dfrac{a-4c}{8ac}-\dfrac{3b-c}{4bc}$

24. $\dfrac{a(b+c)}{c}-\dfrac{b(a+c)}{a}-\dfrac{c(a+b)}{b}$

C

11. $\dfrac{13ab^2}{6y^4}-\dfrac{7a^2b}{8y^2}$

12. $\dfrac{2a}{c}+\dfrac{5b}{d}$

13. $\dfrac{a}{x}+\dfrac{3}{5}$

14. $\dfrac{5a}{2b^3}-\dfrac{2a^2}{3b^2}-\dfrac{5a^3}{4b}$

15. $\dfrac{2b-3}{5}+\dfrac{9}{10}$

16a. $\dfrac{y+6}{2}+\dfrac{y-3}{3}$

b. $\dfrac{5a+3x}{2}+\dfrac{2a+3y}{5}$

17. $\dfrac{3x+y}{3}+\dfrac{3x-5y}{6}$

18. $\dfrac{x-2}{6}-\dfrac{x+3}{2}$

19. $\dfrac{3a-2b}{4}-\dfrac{3a-2b}{20}$

20. $\dfrac{c-4}{4}-\dfrac{c-4}{c}$

21. $\dfrac{2x-3y}{4x}-\dfrac{3x-2y}{6y}$

22. $\dfrac{b-2x}{12b^2x}-\dfrac{2b+x}{10bx^2}$

23. $\dfrac{m+4n}{5m^3n^2}+\dfrac{3m-2n}{2m^2n^2}-\dfrac{5m+n}{6m^2n^3}$

24. $\dfrac{x^2-y^2}{xy}+\dfrac{y(x-3)}{4x}-\dfrac{x(y-2)}{6y}$

Change to a fraction:

25. $\dfrac{ax+2}{ax}+4$

25. $\dfrac{4cd^2-3}{2cd}-5d$

25. $4m^2+\dfrac{2m-3n}{5mn}$

EXERCISE 62

Addition and Subtraction—Binomial and Trinomial Denominators

I. Aim: To add and subtract fractions having binomial and trinomial denominators.

II. Procedure

1. Find the l.c.d. by making an algebraic expression which contains all the factors of the given denominators (see sample solutions below).

2. Then follow the procedure outlined for exercise 61.

3. To change a mixed expression to a fraction, write the integral term as a fraction having the denominator 1. Then follow the procedure for the addition and subtraction of fractions.

4. Check by going over the work again or by numerical substitution.

III. Sample Solutions

Exercise A

1. $\dfrac{5}{a+3}+\dfrac{2}{a-2}$

l.c.d. $=(a+3)(a-2)$

$\dfrac{5a-10}{(a+3)(a-2)}+\dfrac{2a+6}{(a+3)(a-2)}$

$=\dfrac{5a-10+2a+6}{(a+3)(a-2)}$

$=\dfrac{7a-4}{(a+3)(a-2)}$

Answer, $\dfrac{7a-4}{(a+3)(a-2)}$

2. $\dfrac{4}{b}-\dfrac{3}{b+3}$

l.c.d. $=b(b+3)$

$\dfrac{4b+12}{b(b+3)}-\dfrac{3b}{b(b+3)}$

$=\dfrac{4b+12-3b}{b(b+3)}$

$=\dfrac{b+12}{b(b+3)}$

Answer, $\dfrac{b+12}{b(b+3)}$

3. $\dfrac{3x}{x-5}-\dfrac{x-2}{x+5}$

l.c.d. $=(x+5)(x-5)$

$\dfrac{3x^2+15x}{(x+5)(x-5)}-\dfrac{x^2-7x+10}{(x+5)(x-5)}$

$=\dfrac{3x^2+15x-x^2+7x-10}{(x+5)(x-5)}$

$=\dfrac{2x^2+22x-10}{(x+5)(x-5)}$

$=\dfrac{2(x^2+11x-5)}{(x+5)(x-5)}$

Answer, $\dfrac{2(x^2+11x-5)}{(x+5)(x-5)}$ or $\dfrac{2x^2+22x-10}{x^2-25}$

Exercise B

Note—In each of the following examples only the l.c.d. is found. For the remainder of the solution of this type of example, see completed sample solutions in exercises 62A and 63.

1. $\dfrac{3}{a+4}+\dfrac{2}{3(a+4)}$

l.c.d. $=3(a+4)$

2. $\dfrac{2x}{x+5}-\dfrac{3x}{(x+5)(x-3)}$

l.c.d. $=(x+5)(x-3)$

3. $\dfrac{4b}{(b-2)^2}-\dfrac{b}{b-2}$

l.c.d. $=(b-2)^2$ or $(b-2)(b-2)$

4. $\dfrac{a+5}{2(a+3)}-\dfrac{2a}{3(a+3)}$

l.c.d. $=6(a+3)$

5. $\dfrac{x}{3(x+4y)}+\dfrac{y}{6(4x+y)}$

l.c.d. $=6(x+4y)(4x+y)$

6. $\dfrac{5c}{(c+4)(c+3)}-\dfrac{c+2}{(c+4)(c-1)}$

l.c.d. $=(c+4)(c+3)(c-1)$

Preliminary Examples

In each example find the smallest algebraic expression which is exactly divisible by the given expressions.

SET 1	SET 2	SET 3
1. $a+2$ and $a+4$	**1.** $m+3$ and $2(m+3)$	**1.** $x+6$ and $(x+6)(x-2)$
2. $x-3$ and $x+2$	**2.** $(c-2)^2$ and $c-2$	**2.** $(b+2)(b-5)$ and $(b-5)(b+3)$
3. $x+7$ and $x-7$	**3.** $6(m-n)$ and $3(m-n)$	**3.** $(m+7)(m-2)$ and $(m+7)(m+4)$
4. ab and $a+b$	**4.** $a+b$ and $(a+b)^2$	**4.** $3(b-5)$ and $4(b+2)$
5. $b-4$, $b-1$ and 4	**5.** $4(c-2)$ and $6(c-2)$	**5.** $8(c+2)$ and $12(c-2)$

DIAGNOSTIC TEST A

Add or subtract as indicated:

1. $\dfrac{2}{a+2}+\dfrac{3}{a+3}$ **4.** $\dfrac{6}{x}+\dfrac{2}{x+2}$ **7.** $\dfrac{2}{c-d}+\dfrac{c+d}{cd}$

2. $\dfrac{7}{x+1}-\dfrac{5}{x-1}$ **5.** $\dfrac{5m}{m-2}+\dfrac{2m}{m+4}$ **8.** $\dfrac{3a}{a-5}-\dfrac{a+2}{a+6}$

3. $\dfrac{5}{x-3}-\dfrac{3}{x+3}$ **6.** $\dfrac{3x}{x-3}+\dfrac{x-4}{x-5}$ **9.** $\dfrac{b-x}{b+x}-\dfrac{b+x}{b-x}$

10. $\dfrac{3}{a+3}+\dfrac{2}{a+2}+\dfrac{2}{3}$ **11.** Change to a fraction: $x-y+\dfrac{y^2}{x+y}$

Related Practice Examples

Add or subtract as indicated:

A	B	C
1. $\dfrac{6}{x+5}+\dfrac{3}{x+4}$	**1.** $\dfrac{4}{a+4}+\dfrac{5}{a-2}$	**1.** $\dfrac{9}{c-2}+\dfrac{2}{c-3}$
2. $\dfrac{8}{c+4}-\dfrac{2}{c-6}$	**2.** $\dfrac{9}{b+2}-\dfrac{4}{b-3}$	**2.** $\dfrac{3}{m+1}-\dfrac{5}{m-2}$
3. $\dfrac{7}{y-6}-\dfrac{1}{y+6}$	**3.** $\dfrac{10}{x-3}-\dfrac{2}{x+4}$	**3.** $\dfrac{4}{x-5}-\dfrac{7}{x+2}$
4. $\dfrac{5}{2}+\dfrac{6}{a+3}$	**4.** $\dfrac{3}{y+1}-\dfrac{3}{y}$	**4.** $\dfrac{3}{x}+\dfrac{4}{x+4}$
5. $\dfrac{2c}{c-2}+\dfrac{c}{c-1}$	**5.** $\dfrac{x}{x-y}-\dfrac{y}{x+y}$	**5.** $\dfrac{4}{d+7}-\dfrac{3d}{d-2}$
6. $\dfrac{a+2}{a-4}+\dfrac{2a}{a-2}$	**6.** $\dfrac{x+5}{x-6}+\dfrac{3x}{x+5}$	**6.** $\dfrac{2b}{b+2}+\dfrac{b+2}{b-2}$
7. $\dfrac{4x}{x-3}+\dfrac{x+3}{2x}$	**7.** $\dfrac{x-2}{x-4}-\dfrac{5}{3x}$	**7.** $\dfrac{a}{a-b}+\dfrac{a+b}{ab}$
8. $\dfrac{2x}{x-1}-\dfrac{x+3}{x+2}$	**8.** $\dfrac{3b}{b+2}-\dfrac{b+4}{b-3}$	**8.** $\dfrac{5c}{c-2}-\dfrac{c-1}{c+2}$

9. $\dfrac{a+5}{a-5}+\dfrac{a-5}{a+5}$ 9. $\dfrac{c-d}{c+d}-\dfrac{c+d}{c-d}$ 9. $\dfrac{m-2n}{m+2n}-\dfrac{m+2n}{m-2n}$

10. $\dfrac{4}{x+1}-\dfrac{3}{x+2}+\dfrac{2}{x}$ 10. $\dfrac{1}{b-3}-\dfrac{4}{b-6}+\dfrac{5}{6}$ 10. $\dfrac{3}{x}+\dfrac{2}{x-y}-\dfrac{1}{x+y}$

Change to a fraction:

11a. $\dfrac{a}{1}+\dfrac{a^2}{a-5}$ 11a. $\dfrac{3}{x+y}+\dfrac{4}{1}$ 11a. $\dfrac{a+b}{1}-\dfrac{ab}{a+b}$

b. $\dfrac{a+b}{a-b}+1$ b. $1-\dfrac{x+y}{x-y}$ b. $a+3b-\dfrac{a^2+b^2}{a+3b}$

c. $b-5+\dfrac{3b-7}{b-3}$ c. $x+\dfrac{2x^2}{x-5}-6$ c. $2m-5-\dfrac{3m^2+5}{2m+5}$

DIAGNOSTIC TEST B

Add or subtract as indicated:

1. $\dfrac{5}{b+2}+\dfrac{3}{2(b+2)}$ 3. $\dfrac{3a}{(a-3)^2}-\dfrac{3}{a-3}$ 5. $\dfrac{a}{2(a+2b)}+\dfrac{b}{4(2a-b)}$

2. $\dfrac{2x}{x-2}-\dfrac{6x}{(x+1)(x-2)}$ 4. $\dfrac{x+2}{3(x+5)}-\dfrac{x}{5(x+5)}$ 6. $\dfrac{b-2}{(b+5)(b+1)}-\dfrac{b-2}{(b+5)(b+2)}$

Related Practice Examples

Add or subtract as indicated:

A	B	C

1. $\dfrac{b}{5}+\dfrac{4x^2}{5(b+4x)}$ 1. $\dfrac{c}{2}-\dfrac{cd}{2(c+d)}$ 1. $\dfrac{2a}{a+b}-\dfrac{8b}{3(a+b)}$

2. $\dfrac{6}{(x+5)(x+2)}+\dfrac{2}{x+5}$ 2. $\dfrac{2b-7}{(b+5)(b-2)}+\dfrac{b+5}{b-2}$ 2. $\dfrac{x-y}{x+y}+\dfrac{4xy}{(x+y)(x-y)}$

3a. $\dfrac{5}{x-5}+\dfrac{1}{(x-5)^2}$ 3a. $\dfrac{8}{a+x}-\dfrac{4x}{(a+x)^2}$ 3a. $\dfrac{x}{(x-4)^2}-\dfrac{1}{x-4}$

b. $\dfrac{9}{(a-6)^2}+\dfrac{a+4}{a-6}$ b. $\dfrac{5}{(c-5)^2}-\dfrac{c+5}{c-5}$ b. $\dfrac{a^2}{(a-b)^2}-\dfrac{a+b}{a-b}$

4. $\dfrac{5}{2(a+1)}+\dfrac{2}{3(a+1)}$ 4. $\dfrac{4d}{5(d-2)}-\dfrac{3d}{10(d-2)}$ 4. $\dfrac{x^2}{4(x+y)}+\dfrac{y^2}{6(x+y)}$

5. $\dfrac{3a}{4(a+3)}+\dfrac{3}{5(a-3)}$ 5. $\dfrac{5x}{8(x-y)}-\dfrac{x}{2(x+y)}$ 5. $\dfrac{3c}{10(c+d)}-\dfrac{3d}{16(c-d)}$

6. $\dfrac{4}{(a+4)(a-2)}+\dfrac{2}{(a+4)(a+1)}$ 6. $\dfrac{2x}{(x-1)(x+3)}-\dfrac{x}{(x-1)(x+2)}$ 6. $\dfrac{x-2}{2(x+3)(x-3)}+\dfrac{x+3}{3(x-3)(x+2)}$

EXERCISE 63

Addition and Subtraction—Binomial and Trinomial Denominators Involving Factoring

I. Aim: To add and subtract fractions having binomial and trinomial denominators—Factoring necessary in finding l.c.d.

II. Procedure

1. If possible, factor the denominators of the given fractions.

2. Then follow the procedure outlined for exercise 62.

3. Check by going over the work again or by numerical substitution.

III. Sample Solutions

Note—In some of the solutions below only the l.c.d. is found. For the remainder of the solution of this type of example, see completed sample solutions in exercise 62A and in this exercise.

1. $\dfrac{3}{x+1} + \dfrac{3}{x^2+x}$

$\dfrac{3}{x+1} + \dfrac{3}{x(x+1)}$

l.c.d. $= x(x+1)$

$\dfrac{3x}{x(x+1)} + \dfrac{3}{x(x+1)}$

$= \dfrac{3x+3}{x(x+1)}$

$= \dfrac{3(x+1)}{x(x+1)} = \dfrac{3}{x}$

Answer, $\dfrac{3}{x}$

2. $\dfrac{2b}{b^2-25} + \dfrac{4}{b+5}$

$\dfrac{2b}{(b+5)(b-5)} + \dfrac{4}{b+5}$

l.c.d. $= (b+5)(b-5)$

3. $\dfrac{2x}{x+4} - \dfrac{3x-5}{x^2+8x+16}$

$= \dfrac{2x}{x+4} - \dfrac{3x-5}{(x+4)(x+4)}$

l.c.d. $= (x+4)(x+4)$ or $(x+4)^2$

4. $\dfrac{5c}{3c+6d} - \dfrac{3d}{4c+8d}$

$\dfrac{5c}{3(c+2d)} - \dfrac{3d}{4(c+2d)}$

l.c.d. $= 12(c+2d)$

5. $\dfrac{b-3x}{2b+4x} - \dfrac{x}{4b+2x}$

$\dfrac{b-3x}{2(b+2x)} - \dfrac{x}{2(2b+x)}$

l.c.d. $= 2(b+2x)(2b+x)$

6. $\dfrac{6x}{x^2+5x+6} - \dfrac{2x}{x^2+6x+9}$

$\dfrac{6x}{(x+3)(x+2)} - \dfrac{2x}{(x+3)(x+3)}$

l.c.d. $= (x+3)(x+2)(x+3)$

$\dfrac{6x^2+18x}{(x+3)(x+2)(x+3)} - \dfrac{2x^2+4x}{(x+3)(x+2)(x+3)}$

$= \dfrac{6x^2+18x-2x^2-4x}{(x+3)(x+2)(x+3)}$

$= \dfrac{4x^2+14x}{(x+3)(x+2)(x+3)}$

$= \dfrac{2x(2x+7)}{(x+3)(x+2)(x+3)}$ or $\dfrac{2x(2x+7)}{(x+3)^2(x+2)}$

Answer, $\dfrac{2x(2x+7)}{(x+3)^2(x+2)}$

Preliminary Examples

In each example find the smallest algebraic expression which is exactly divisible by the given expressions. If necessary, first factor the given expressions.

SET 1

1. $b+3$ and $3b+9$
2. $5m+5n$ and $4m+4n$
3. $6c-12$ and $c-2$
4. $4b+4c$ and $6b-6c$
5. $10r-6x$ and $5r+3x$

SET 2

1. $m-6$ and m^2-36
2. b^2-49 and $b+7$
3. $b+1$, $b-1$, and b^2-1
4. $c+6$ and $c^2+12c+36$
5. $a^2-16a+64$ and $a-8$

SET 3

1. $x^2+7x+10$ and $x^2+8x+15$
2. s^2-5s+4 and s^2-2s-8
3. a^2-16 and a^2+6a+8
4. m^2-n^2 and $m^2+2mn+n^2$
5. b^2-9, b^2+6b+9, and b^2-b-6

DIAGNOSTIC TEST

Add or subtract as indicated:

1. $\dfrac{b}{b+2}+\dfrac{b-3}{2b+4}$

2. $\dfrac{6s}{s^2-100}-\dfrac{3}{s-10}$

3. $\dfrac{4m}{m-5}-\dfrac{4m-8}{m^2-10m+25}$

4. $\dfrac{2a+3b}{2a+2b}+\dfrac{2a}{3a+3b}$

5. $\dfrac{a-2x}{4a+2x}-\dfrac{2a-x}{2a+4x}$

6. $\dfrac{a+3}{a^2+9a+14}+\dfrac{a-2}{a^2+4a-21}$

Add or subtract as indicated:

A	B	C
1a. $\dfrac{2}{x+3}+\dfrac{3}{2x+6}$	**1a.** $\dfrac{5}{a+5}-\dfrac{2}{3a+15}$	**1a.** $\dfrac{b}{3}+\dfrac{2b}{3b-6}$
b. $\dfrac{2}{a^2+a}+\dfrac{2}{a+1}$	**b.** $\dfrac{c^2}{3c-3d}-\dfrac{c+d}{3}$	**b.** $\dfrac{x+3}{x-3}-\dfrac{x+3}{4x-12}$
2a. $\dfrac{5}{x^2-4}+\dfrac{3}{x+2}$	**2a.** $\dfrac{6}{a^2-9}-\dfrac{2}{a+3}$	**2a.** $\dfrac{2r}{r-9}-\dfrac{20}{r^2-81}$
b. $\dfrac{5x}{25x^2-4}+\dfrac{3}{5x+2}$	**b.** $\dfrac{t+7}{t-7}-\dfrac{14t}{t^2-49}$	**b.** $\dfrac{11x-14}{x^2-4}+\dfrac{x-2}{x+2}$
c. $\dfrac{6a^2}{a^2-9}-\dfrac{3a}{a+3}-\dfrac{2a}{a-3}$	**c.** $\dfrac{c-2}{c+2}+\dfrac{10c-4}{c^2-4}-\dfrac{c+2}{c-2}$	**c.** $\dfrac{3x}{x-1}+\dfrac{4x^2+8}{x^2-1}-\dfrac{6x}{x+1}$
d. $\dfrac{4}{c^2-6c+8}+\dfrac{2}{c-2}$	**d.** $\dfrac{3a}{a^2+6a-16}+\dfrac{3}{a+8}$	**d.** $\dfrac{m-4}{m-6}-\dfrac{3m}{m^2-3m-18}$
e. $\dfrac{5}{x+2}+\dfrac{8x+1}{x^2+7x+10}$	**e.** $\dfrac{2x^2+5x}{x^2-8x-20}-\dfrac{x-2}{x-10}$	**e.** $\dfrac{2t^2+7}{t^2+t-2}-\dfrac{t-3}{t+2}$
3a. $\dfrac{3}{x^2+6x+9}+\dfrac{3}{x+3}$	**3a.** $\dfrac{5a}{a+5}-\dfrac{5}{a^2+10a+25}$	**3a.** $\dfrac{15}{c^2-12c+36}+\dfrac{3c}{c-6}$
b. $\dfrac{4-c}{c^2-8c+16}+\dfrac{2}{c-4}$	**b.** $\dfrac{x-2}{x-1}-\dfrac{3-3x}{x^2-2x+1}$	**b.** $\dfrac{a^2-4a}{a^2+8a+16}+\dfrac{a-4}{a+4}$
c. $\dfrac{2}{a+2}+\dfrac{4}{(a+2)^2}$	**c.** $\dfrac{8x}{(x+4)^2}-\dfrac{4}{x+4}$	**c.** $\dfrac{c+4}{(c-4)^2}-\dfrac{c+4}{c-4}$
4. $\dfrac{5}{3x-6}+\dfrac{3}{4x-8}$	**4.** $\dfrac{2a+3b}{2a+2b}+\dfrac{a}{3a+3b}$	**4.** $\dfrac{q+2b}{4a-4b}-\dfrac{b}{3a-3b}$
5. $\dfrac{2}{2x-8}+\dfrac{3}{4x-2}$	**5.** $\dfrac{x-y}{3x+3y}+\dfrac{x+y}{2x-2y}$	**5.** $\dfrac{b-2x}{4b+2x}-\dfrac{2b-x}{2b+4x}$
6a. $\dfrac{5}{3x+15}+\dfrac{4}{x^2-25}$	**6a.** $\dfrac{2c}{3c^2-3}+\dfrac{2}{5c+5}$	**6a.** $\dfrac{c+5d}{c^2-d^2}-\dfrac{2d}{c^2-cd}$
b. $\dfrac{a-4}{2a-10}+\dfrac{a}{a^2-10a+25}$	**b.** $\dfrac{4}{b^2-4b+4}-\dfrac{2}{b^2-4}$	**b.** $\dfrac{4a}{3a^2-3b^2}-\dfrac{a-b}{a^2+2ab+b^2}$

A

B

C

6c. $\dfrac{a}{4a+4}+\dfrac{2a}{a^2+3a+2}$

6c. $\dfrac{2}{x^2-9}+\dfrac{4}{x^2+7x+12}$

6c. $\dfrac{x}{x^2+5x+4}-\dfrac{1}{x^2+2x+1}$

d. $\dfrac{9}{2c^2+4c-16}-\dfrac{3}{2c^2-8}$

d. $\dfrac{5}{2x^2-12x+18}+\dfrac{2}{3x^2+6x-45}$

d. $\dfrac{2x}{5x^2-5x-30}+\dfrac{3x}{4x^2+20x+24}$

e. $\dfrac{2}{x^2-4}-\dfrac{3}{x^2-4x+4}+\dfrac{4}{x^2+x-2}$

e. $\dfrac{3}{x^2-y^2}+\dfrac{2}{x^2+2xy+y^2}-\dfrac{1}{x^2-2xy+y^2}$

e. $\dfrac{6}{b^2-10b+25}-\dfrac{2}{b^2-2b-15}+\dfrac{3}{b^2-9b+20}$

EXERCISE 64

Fractions—Changing Signs

I. Aim: To change signs of fractions.

II. Procedure

1. Change signs of fractions as follows:
   a) The signs of all terms of the numerator may be changed if the signs of all terms of the denominator are changed or vice-versa.
   b) The signs of all terms of either the numerator or denominator may be changed if the sign preceding the fraction is changed.

2. After the signs have been changed complete solution as directed.

III. Sample Solutions

Change to lowest terms:

1. $\dfrac{x-y}{y^2-x^2}=-\dfrac{x-y}{x^2-y^2}=-\dfrac{\cancel{x-y}^{\,1}}{(x+y)(\cancel{x-y})}=-\dfrac{1}{x+y}$

Answer, $-\dfrac{1}{x+y}$

Multiply as indicated:

2. $\dfrac{x^2-8x+15}{x^2-10x+25}\cdot\dfrac{10+3x-x^2}{15-2x-x^2}$

$=\dfrac{x^2-8x+15}{x^2-10x+25}\cdot\dfrac{x^2-3x-10}{x^2+2x-15}$

$=\dfrac{(\cancel{x-5})(\cancel{x-3})}{(\cancel{x-5})(\cancel{x-5})}\cdot\dfrac{(\cancel{x-5})(x+2)}{(x+5)(\cancel{x-3})}=\dfrac{x+2}{x+5}$

Answer, $\dfrac{x+2}{x+5}$

Combine:

3. $\dfrac{3}{x+3}-\dfrac{2}{3-x}-\dfrac{4x}{x^2-9}$

$=\dfrac{3}{x+3}+\dfrac{2}{x-3}-\dfrac{4x}{x^2-9}$

$=\dfrac{3}{x+3}+\dfrac{2}{x-3}-\dfrac{4x}{(x+3)(x-3)}$

l.c.d. $=(x+3)(x-3)$

$\dfrac{3x-9}{(x+3)(x-3)}+\dfrac{2x+6}{(x+3)(x-3)}-\dfrac{4x}{(x+3)(x-3)}$

$=\dfrac{3x-9+2x+6-4x}{(x+3)(x-3)}$

$=\dfrac{\cancel{x-3}^{\,1}}{(x+3)(\cancel{x-3})}=\dfrac{1}{x+3}$

Answer, $\dfrac{1}{x+3}$

Preliminary Examples

State whether each of the following statements is true or false:

SET 1

1. $\dfrac{+6}{+3} = \dfrac{-6}{-3}$

2. $\dfrac{+6}{+3} = \dfrac{-6}{+3}$

3. $\dfrac{+6}{-3} = \dfrac{-6}{+3}$

4. $\dfrac{+x^5}{+x^2} = \dfrac{-x^5}{+x^2}$

5. $\dfrac{-x^2}{+a} = \dfrac{+x^2}{-a}$

SET 2

1. $+\dfrac{+10}{+2} = -\dfrac{-10}{+2}$

2. $-\dfrac{+10}{+2} = -\dfrac{-10}{-2}$

3. $+\dfrac{-12}{+6} = -\dfrac{+12}{-6}$

4. $-\dfrac{+a^2}{-a} = +\dfrac{-a^2}{-a}$

5. $-\dfrac{-d^6}{-d^2} = -\dfrac{+d^6}{+d^2}$

SET 3

1. $\dfrac{3}{x-y} = \dfrac{-3}{y-x}$

2. $\dfrac{a-b}{b-a} = \dfrac{b-a}{a-b}$

3. $\dfrac{5}{b^2-a^2} = \dfrac{5}{a^2-b^2}$

4. $\dfrac{a+2}{a^2-3a+7} = \dfrac{2+a}{7-3a+a^2}$

5. $\dfrac{b-2}{b^2+3b-5} = \dfrac{2-b}{5-3b-b^2}$

SET 4

1. $+\dfrac{c-d}{d^2-c^2} = +\dfrac{d-c}{d^2-c^2}$

2. $-\dfrac{3a}{b-a} = +\dfrac{3a}{a-b}$

3. $+\dfrac{a}{a+b} = -\dfrac{a}{b+a}$

4. $-\dfrac{x-y}{x^2-y^2} = +\dfrac{y-x}{x^2-y^2}$

5. $+\dfrac{a-3}{a^2-9} = -\dfrac{a-3}{9-a^2}$

DIAGNOSTIC TEST

1. Change to lowest terms:

$$\dfrac{a-b}{b^2-a^2}$$

2. Multiply:

$$\dfrac{a^2-49}{a^2+4a+4} \cdot \dfrac{2-a-a^2}{49-a^2}$$

3. Combine:

$$\dfrac{7}{y+2} + \dfrac{5}{2-y} + \dfrac{y+18}{y^2-4}$$

Related Practice Examples

SET 1

Change to lowest terms:

1. $\dfrac{2a+b}{b+2a}$

2. $\dfrac{3x-y}{y-3x}$

3. $\dfrac{a+3}{9-a^2}$

4. $\dfrac{2a-2b}{b-a}$

5. $\dfrac{2x-8}{12-3x}$

6. $\dfrac{c^2-b^2}{b^2+2bc+c^2}$

7. $\dfrac{x+3}{6-x-x^2}$

8. $\dfrac{m-4}{8+2m-m^2}$

9. $\dfrac{2ab-a^2-b^2}{5a^2-5b^2}$

10. $\dfrac{3c^2-3d^2}{2cd-c^2-d^2}$

SET 2

Multiply

1. $\dfrac{9-a^2}{a-5} \cdot \dfrac{25-a^2}{a-3}$

2. $\dfrac{x^2-16}{x^2+2x+1} \cdot \dfrac{3+2x-x^2}{16-x^2}$

3. $\dfrac{d^2-36}{8-2d-d^2} \cdot \dfrac{d^2-4d+4}{12+4d-d^2}$

Divide:

4. $\dfrac{3}{x-y} \div \dfrac{6}{y-x}$

5. $\dfrac{b^2-64}{b^2-10b+25} \div \dfrac{64-b^2}{10b-b^2-25}$

6. $\dfrac{a^2-2ax+x^2}{4a+4x} \div \dfrac{a^2-x^2}{8a+8x}$

SET 3

Combine:

1. $\dfrac{2}{x-y} - \dfrac{1}{y-x}$

2. $\dfrac{4}{a-b} + \dfrac{2}{b-a}$

3. $\dfrac{3}{c^2-d^2} + \dfrac{5}{d-c}$

4. $\dfrac{6a}{2a-x} - \dfrac{3x}{x-2a}$

5. $\dfrac{a-2}{4-a^2} + \dfrac{2-a}{a^2-4}$

6. $\dfrac{x}{2x-8} + \dfrac{4x}{16-x^2}$

7. $\dfrac{8b}{3-b} + \dfrac{3b}{b+3}$

8. $\dfrac{2}{a+3} + \dfrac{4}{3-a} + \dfrac{3a+15}{a^2-9}$

9. $\dfrac{m+n}{m-n} - \dfrac{m-n}{m+n} + \dfrac{m^2}{n^2-m^2}$

10. $\dfrac{x}{64-x^2} + \dfrac{2}{3x-24} - \dfrac{3}{2x+16}$

EXERCISE 65
Mixed Expressions and Complex Fractions

I. Aim: To simplify mixed expressions involving multiplication or division and complex fractions.

II. Procedure

1. To simplify mixed expressions involving multiplication or division, change the expressions which are inclosed in parentheses to fractions by addition or subtraction. Then multiply or divide as directed.

2. To simplify complex fractions, add or subtract (as indicated) the fractions in the numerator. Do the same to the fractions in the denominator. Then divide the resulting answer in the numerator by the resulting answer in the denominator.
   Note: Every complex fraction can be changed to an example in division because every fraction is an indicated division.

III. Sample Solutions

Simplify, as indicated:

1. $\left(\dfrac{a}{b}+2\right)\left(\dfrac{a}{b}+3\right)$

$= \dfrac{a+2b}{b} \times \dfrac{a+3b}{b}$

$= \dfrac{(a+2b)(a+3b)}{b^2}$ or $\dfrac{a^2+5ab+6b^2}{b^2}$

Answer, $\dfrac{a^2+5ab+6b^2}{b^2}$

2. $\left(3-\dfrac{x}{y}\right) \div \left(9-\dfrac{x^2}{y^2}\right)$

$= \left(\dfrac{3y-x}{y}\right) \div \left(\dfrac{9y^2-x^2}{y^2}\right)$

$= \dfrac{\overset{1}{\cancel{3y-x}}}{\underset{1}{\cancel{y}}} \times \dfrac{\overset{y}{\cancel{y^2}}}{(3y+x)\cancel{(3y-x)}} = \dfrac{y}{3y+x}$

Answer, $\dfrac{y}{3y+x}$

3. $\dfrac{\dfrac{3}{4}}{\dfrac{15}{16}}$

$= \dfrac{3}{4} \div \dfrac{15}{16}$

$= \dfrac{\overset{1}{\cancel{3}}}{\underset{1}{\cancel{4}}} \times \dfrac{\overset{4}{\cancel{16}}}{\underset{5}{\cancel{15}}} = \dfrac{4}{5}$

Answer, $\dfrac{4}{5}$

4. $\dfrac{\dfrac{x^2-y^2}{a+b}}{\dfrac{x-y}{a^2-b^2}}$

$= \dfrac{x^2-y^2}{a+b} \div \dfrac{x-y}{a^2-b^2}$

$= \dfrac{(x+y)\cancel{(x-y)}}{\cancel{a+b}} \times \dfrac{(a+b)(a-b)}{\cancel{x-y}} = (x+y)(a-b)$

Answer, $(x+y)(a-b)$

5. $\dfrac{x+\dfrac{12}{x-7}}{x-3}$

$= \left(x+\dfrac{12}{x-7}\right) \div (x-3)$

$= \left(\dfrac{x^2-7x+12}{x-7}\right) \div (x-3)$

$= \dfrac{(x-3)(x-4)}{x-7} \times \dfrac{1}{x-3} = \dfrac{x-4}{x-7}$

Answer, $\dfrac{x-4}{x-7}$

6. $\dfrac{\dfrac{a}{b}-\dfrac{b}{a}}{\dfrac{a^2}{b}-b}$

$= \left(\dfrac{a}{b}-\dfrac{b}{a}\right) \div \left(\dfrac{a^2}{b}-b\right)$

$= \left(\dfrac{a^2-b^2}{ab}\right) \div \left(\dfrac{a^2-b^2}{b}\right)$

$= \dfrac{a^2-b^2}{ab} \times \dfrac{b}{a^2-b^2} = \dfrac{1}{a}$

Answer, $\dfrac{1}{a}$

DIAGNOSTIC TEST

Simplify:

1. $\left(\dfrac{c}{d}-1\right)\left(1+\dfrac{d}{c}\right)$

2. $\left(\dfrac{b^2}{4}-4x^2\right) \div \left(\dfrac{b}{2}+2x\right)$

3. $\dfrac{\dfrac{3}{8}}{\dfrac{9}{16}}$

4. $\dfrac{\dfrac{x^2-y^2}{x}}{\dfrac{x+y}{x^2}}$

5. $\dfrac{b+2}{b-\dfrac{b}{b+3}}$

6. $\dfrac{\dfrac{m-n}{m}+\dfrac{m-n}{n}}{\dfrac{m-n}{n}-\dfrac{m-n}{m}}$

Related Practice Examples

Simplify:

SET 1

1. $\left(2+\dfrac{3}{a}\right)\left(2-\dfrac{3}{a}\right)$

2. $\left(\dfrac{a}{x}+3\right)\left(\dfrac{a}{x}+2\right)$

3. $\left(1+\dfrac{x}{x+y}\right)\left(1-\dfrac{y^2}{x^2}\right)$

4. $\left(3+\dfrac{6}{x+1}\right)\left(2-\dfrac{1}{x+3}\right)$

5. $\left(x+6+\dfrac{9}{x}\right)\left(x-\dfrac{3x}{x+3}\right)$

SET 2

1. $\left(4+\dfrac{1}{x}\right) \div \left(4-\dfrac{1}{x}\right)$

2. $\left(1-\dfrac{b}{a}\right) \div \left(a-\dfrac{b^2}{a}\right)$

3. $\left(x-\dfrac{x^2}{y}\right) \div \left(1-\dfrac{x}{y}\right)$

4. $\left(\dfrac{a-b}{b}-\dfrac{a-b}{a}\right) \div \left(\dfrac{a}{b}-\dfrac{b}{a}\right)$

5. $\left(\dfrac{4}{x-2}+1\right) \div \left(\dfrac{3}{x^2-4}+1\right)$

| SET 3 | SET 4 | SET 5 | SET 6a | SET 6b |

SET 3

1. $\dfrac{\frac{1}{2}}{\frac{3}{4}}$

2. $\dfrac{\frac{5}{3}}{\frac{10}{9}}$

3. $\dfrac{2\frac{1}{2}}{1\frac{3}{4}}$

4. $\dfrac{4+\frac{1}{2}}{\frac{5}{8}}$

5. $\dfrac{3+\frac{3}{4}}{2-\frac{1}{2}}$

SET 4

1. $\dfrac{\dfrac{a}{x^2}}{\dfrac{a^2}{x}}$

2. $\dfrac{\dfrac{3b^2}{8c^3}}{\dfrac{7b}{16c^2}}$

3. $\dfrac{\dfrac{a}{a+b}}{\dfrac{b}{a+b}}$

4. $\dfrac{\dfrac{c^2-d^2}{c}}{\dfrac{c-d}{c^2}}$

5. $\dfrac{\dfrac{a^2-b^2}{c+d}}{\dfrac{a+b}{c^2-d^2}}$

SET 5

1. $\dfrac{1}{1-\dfrac{b}{a}}$

2. $\dfrac{x}{x-\dfrac{x}{2}}$

3. $\dfrac{a-3}{a-\dfrac{3}{a-2}}$

4. $\dfrac{\dfrac{a+2}{2a}}{a^2-4}$

5. $\dfrac{x-\dfrac{35}{x-2}}{x+5}$

SET 6a

1. $\dfrac{\dfrac{m^2}{2}-2}{\dfrac{m}{2}-1}$

2. $\dfrac{c-\dfrac{d^2}{c}}{1+\dfrac{d}{c}}$

3. $\dfrac{a^2-\dfrac{b^2}{9}}{a+\dfrac{b}{3}}$

4. $\dfrac{a-\dfrac{b^2}{a}}{\dfrac{a}{b}-\dfrac{b}{a}}$

5. $\dfrac{\dfrac{x}{y}-\dfrac{y}{x}}{\dfrac{x}{y}+\dfrac{y}{x}}$

SET 6b

1. $\dfrac{x+5+\dfrac{6}{x}}{x-\dfrac{9}{x}}$

2. $\dfrac{\dfrac{x}{x+y}}{1-\dfrac{y}{x+y}}$

3. $\dfrac{a+\dfrac{a}{a+2}}{a-\dfrac{a}{a+2}}$

4. $\dfrac{c-\dfrac{cd}{c+d}}{c+\dfrac{cd}{c-d}}$

5. $\dfrac{\dfrac{x-y}{x}+\dfrac{x-y}{y}}{\dfrac{x-y}{y}-\dfrac{x-y}{x}}$

REVIEW OF UNIT NINE

Change to lowest terms:

1. $\dfrac{18b^6x^2y}{28a^4b^3x^7}$

2. $\dfrac{y^2-36}{y^2-5y-6}$

Multiply:

3. $\dfrac{3c^2d^9}{7x^2y^6}\cdot\dfrac{8dy}{15c^2x}\cdot\dfrac{5x^3y^4}{2cd^6}$

4. $\dfrac{6m-18}{m^2-6m+9}\cdot\dfrac{m^2-9}{m^2-3m-18}$

Divide:

5. $\dfrac{(r-s)^2}{8r^2}\div\dfrac{r^2-s^2}{12s}$

Combine:

6. $\dfrac{b^2}{b+7}-\dfrac{49}{b+7}$

7. $\dfrac{1}{c}+\dfrac{1}{d}$

8. $\dfrac{5m+2n}{4m}-\dfrac{4m-7n}{8n}$

9. $\dfrac{2x}{x-6}+\dfrac{x-2}{x+4}$

10. $\dfrac{y-4}{y-3}-\dfrac{y-7}{y+8}+\dfrac{y+8}{y^2+5y-24}$

11. Reduce to lowest terms:

$$\frac{x^2-a^2}{a^2-2ax+x^2}$$

12. Divide:

$$\frac{6}{c-y}\div\frac{b-x}{y-c}$$

13. Combine:

$$\frac{3}{s+4}-\frac{5}{4-s}+\frac{24}{s^2-16}$$

14. Simplify:

$$\left(1+\frac{n}{m}\right)\div\left(1-\frac{n^2}{m^2}\right)$$

15. Simplify:

$$\frac{\dfrac{a-b}{b}-\dfrac{a-b}{a}}{\dfrac{a-b}{a}+\dfrac{a-b}{b}}$$

CUMULATIVE ALGEBRA REVIEW

1. Add: $5t^2-3t+6$; $9-4t^2$; t^2-t-12

2. From $9xy+4y^2$ take x^2-9xy.

3. Transform the formula $b^2=(h+a)(h-a)$ by removing parentheses.

4. Find the value of the expression n^3+3n^2-7n+3 when $n=-2$. Determine whether this value equals the remainder when n^3+3n^2-7n+3 is divided by $n+2$?

5. Solve and check: $n+n+2+n+4=51$

6. Solve and check: $8-(x-3)+(x+7)=3(x+12)$

7. Find the value of S when $\pi=3.14$, $D=24$, and $N=500$, using the formula $S=\dfrac{\pi DN}{12}$.

8. A rectangular garden is 15 feet longer than it is wide. What is its length and width if it takes 342 feet of fencing to enclose it?

9. Multiply by inspection:
a) $(\frac{7}{8}a^2-cd^3)(\frac{7}{8}a^2+cd^3)$ b) $(5m^3+9x^2y)^2$ c) $(3d-11y)(6d-7y)$ d) $6b(b-3)(b+8)$

10. Factor: a) $25n^2+100y^2$ b) $.16x^2-9y^2$ c) $r^2-18r-63$ d) $81s^2-72s+16$ e) $18b^2+61b-90$

11. Change to lowest terms: $\dfrac{10a^4b^3}{10a^4b^3-15a^2b^5}$

12. Multiply: $\dfrac{6b^3}{5d^2x^3}\cdot\dfrac{x^4y}{14b^2}\cdot\dfrac{35d^3}{9bx}$

13. Divide: $\dfrac{4n-20}{n^2-2n-15}\div\dfrac{n^2-9}{n^2+6n+9}$

14. Combine: $\dfrac{12}{c^2-8c+12}+\dfrac{c}{c-6}-\dfrac{c-5}{c-2}$

KEYED ACHIEVEMENT TEST

1. Express as a formula: The number of short tons (T) in a given number of pounds (p) is equal to the number of pounds divided by 2,000. ①

2. Using the formula $V=\pi r^2h$, find the value of h when $V=7{,}850$, $\pi=3.14$, and $r=10$. ⑫

3. Solve and check: $2(x+5)+2x=46$ ㊱

4. Subtract $2a^2-a+6$ from $9+a-a^2$ ㉖

5. Remove parentheses and, if possible, add like terms: $7y(3y-5)-(y+2)(y-6)$ ㉜

6. Divide $16s^3-32s^2+52s-20$ by $8s-4$. Check by multiplication. ㉟

7. Multiply by inspection: $(12x+5y)(12x+5y)$ ㊾

8. Multiply by inspection: $(3t-7)(9t+6)$ (53)

9. Factor: $49m^2+154mn+121n^2$ ㊿

10. Factor: $64a^2y^2-16a^2$ (55)

11. Change to lowest terms: $\dfrac{27b^9x^2y^6}{18a^5b^2x^2}$ (57)

12. Multiply: $\dfrac{9x^2+81}{x^2-9}\cdot\dfrac{6x-18}{x^4+18x^2+81}$ (58)

13. Divide: $\dfrac{27b^4c^3}{8d^5}\div 9b^2d^3$ (59)

14. Combine: $\dfrac{2x}{x-2}+\dfrac{2-3x}{x^2-x-2}-\dfrac{x+2}{x+1}$ (63)

INTRODUCTION TO UNIT TEN

Not all algebraic solutions of problems or applications involving formulas can be translated into simple equations. In many cases, the equations formulated are fractional and very often are expressed as proportions. A *fractional equation* is one which contains the unknown in one or more of the denominators. Equations with fractional coefficients are also included in this unit because the principles used in the solution are the same as those used in the solution of fractional equations.

A *proportion* is a statement that two ratios are equal. Since ratios generally are written in fraction form, a proportion may be treated as a fractional equation. There are four terms in a proportion. If any three are known, the fourth may be determined.

When solving a fractional equation, we shall find it necessary to get rid of the fractions which the equation contains so that we may transform the given equation to a simple equation. This is called "clearing the equation of fractions." To do this, we multiply both sides of the equation by the lowest common denominator of the given fractions, employing the principle that the products are equal when equals are multiplied by equals.

It should be noted that a term containing a fractional coefficient may be written as a fraction: $\frac{1}{3}n$ is the same as $\frac{n}{3}$. $\frac{5}{8}x$ is the same as $\frac{5x}{8}$.

ARITHMETIC PRACTICE

1. Find the lowest common denominator:

   a) $\frac{1}{2}$ and $\frac{1}{5}$ b) $\frac{1}{6}$ and $\frac{1}{18}$ c) $\frac{1}{8}$ and $\frac{1}{12}$ d) $\frac{1}{4}$, $\frac{1}{8}$, and $\frac{1}{16}$ e) $\frac{1}{8}$, $\frac{1}{10}$, and $\frac{1}{16}$

2. Multiply:

   a) $\frac{1}{6}\times24$ b) $\frac{5}{8}\times16$ c) $\frac{7}{12}\times60$ d) $\frac{13}{16}\times96$ e) $40\times\frac{9}{10}$ f) $72\times\frac{17}{24}$ g) $90\times\frac{13}{18}$ h) $105\times\frac{11}{15}$

3. Add:

   a) $6.7+2.5$ b) $.8+.32$ c) $6.4+.19$ d) $21+.45$ e) $.056+.2$ f) $.7+.3$ g) $1+.04$ h) $.94+3.5$

4. Subtract:

   a) $.9-.4$ b) $.004-.0003$ c) $.35-.3$ d) $.8-.59$ e) $4.9-.15$ f) $8-.6$ g) $7.5-.75$ h) $3.625-.125$

5. Multiply:

   a) $8\times.6$ b) $4\times.002$ c) $.01\times.3$ d) $.025\times.08$ e) $.03\times.003$ f) $3.14\times.04$ g) $.1\times.1$ h) $.15\times.06$

6. Divide:

   a) $4)\overline{9.2}$ .b) $.3)\overline{8.7}$ c) $.08)\overline{4}$ d) $.002)\overline{5}$ e) $1.5)\overline{6}$ f) $.6)\overline{72}$ g)$.03)\overline{.9}$ h) $1.04)\overline{26}$

7. Use short methods:

   a) $10\times.9$ b) $100\times.35$ c) $1,000\times8.93$ d) 100×25.07 e) $1,000\times.4$ f) $10\times.02$ g) $100\times.053$
   h) $1,000\times4.38$

UNIT TEN—FRACTIONAL EQUATIONS

EXERCISE 66

Proportion Type of Fractional Equations

I. Aim: To solve the proportion type of both fractional equations and equations with fractional coefficients.

II. Procedure

Solve by either of the following methods:

1. Solution 1: (See sample solutions 1, 2, 3 and 4)
   a) Find the lowest common denominator (l.c.d.)
   b) Multiply each and every term (whole number or fraction) on both sides of the equation by the l.c.d. to clear the equation of all fractions.
   c) Solve the resulting equation. For procedure see Exercise 36.
   d) Check by substituting the root in the given equation.

2. Solution 2: (See sample solutions 5, 6 and 7)
   a) To clear the equation of all fractions cross multiply by multiplying the numerator of the first fraction by the denominator of the second fraction and the numerator of the second fraction by the denominator of the first fraction.
   b) Write the first product equal to the second product.
   c) Solve the resulting equation.
   d) Check by substituting the root in the given equation.

III. Sample Solutions

SOLUTION 1

Check:

1. $\dfrac{x}{2} = 8$

$\dfrac{16}{2} = 8$

$\dfrac{x}{\cancel{2}} \cdot \cancel{2} = 8 \cdot 2$

$8 = 8$

$x = 16$

Answer, $x = 16$

Check:

2. $\dfrac{b}{4} = \dfrac{3}{2}$

$\dfrac{6}{4} = \dfrac{3}{2}$

$\dfrac{b}{\cancel{4}} \cdot \cancel{4} = \dfrac{3}{\cancel{2}} \cdot \cancel{4}^{2}$

$1\frac{1}{2} = 1\frac{1}{2}$

$b = 6$

Answer, $b = 6$

Check:

3. $\dfrac{2a-3}{6} = \dfrac{2a+3}{10}$

$\dfrac{12-3}{6} = \dfrac{12+3}{10}$

$\dfrac{2a-3}{\cancel{6}} \cdot \cancel{30}^{5} = \dfrac{2a+3}{\cancel{10}} \cdot \cancel{30}^{3}$

$\dfrac{9}{6} = \dfrac{15}{10}$

$10a - 15 = 6a + 9$

$1\frac{1}{2} = 1\frac{1}{2}$

$10a - 6a = 15 + 9$

$4a = 24$

$a = 6$

Answer, $a = 6$

Check:

4. $\dfrac{x+2}{x-2} = \dfrac{x+11}{x+1}$

$\dfrac{4+2}{4-2} = \dfrac{4+11}{4+1}$

$\dfrac{x+2}{\cancel{x-2}} \cdot (x-2)(x+1) = \dfrac{x+11}{\cancel{x+1}} \cdot (x-2)(x+1)$

$\dfrac{6}{2} = \dfrac{15}{5}$

$x^2 + 3x + 2 = x^2 + 9x - 22$

$3 = 3$

$x^2 - x^2 + 3x - 9x = -2 - 22$

$-6x = -24$

$x = 4$

Answer, $x = 4$

SOLUTION 2

Check:

5. $\dfrac{7}{2} = \dfrac{2x}{3}$ $\dfrac{7}{2} = \dfrac{10\frac{1}{2}}{3}$

$4x = 21$ $3\frac{1}{2} = 3\frac{1}{2}$

$x = 5\frac{1}{4}$

Answer, $x = 5\frac{1}{4}$

Check:

6. $\dfrac{4x+3}{3} = \dfrac{7x-1}{4}$ $\dfrac{12+3}{3} = \dfrac{21-1}{4}$

$16x + 12 = 21x - 3$ $\dfrac{15}{3} = \dfrac{20}{4}$

$16x - 21x = -12 - 3$ $5 = 5$

$-5x = -15$

$x = 3$

Answer, $x = 3$

7. $\dfrac{x+4}{x-1} = \dfrac{x-2}{x-4}$

$x^2 - 16 = x^2 - 3x + 2$

$x^2 - x^2 + 3x = 16 + 2$

$3x = 18$

$x = 6$

Answer, $x = 6$

Check:

$\dfrac{6+4}{6-1} = \dfrac{6-2}{6-4}$

$\dfrac{10}{5} = \dfrac{4}{2}$

$2 = 2$

DIAGNOSTIC TEST

Solve and check:

1. $\dfrac{x}{4} = 5$

2. $\dfrac{a}{16} = \dfrac{5}{4}$

3. $\dfrac{b}{2} = \dfrac{2}{3}$

4. $\dfrac{3}{10} = \dfrac{m}{15}$

5. $\dfrac{3x}{5} = 6$

6. $\dfrac{9}{2} = \dfrac{3y}{4}$

7. $\dfrac{x-5}{12} = \dfrac{5}{6}$

8. $2x = \dfrac{5x-6}{4}$

9. $\dfrac{5c-2}{3} = \dfrac{8-3c}{5}$

10. $\dfrac{3}{5} = \dfrac{1}{2x}$

11. $\dfrac{8}{3x} = \dfrac{4}{4x-5}$

12. $\dfrac{x-2}{x+4} = \dfrac{x+1}{x+10}$

Related Practice Examples

Solve and check.

SET 1

1. $\dfrac{a}{5} = 3$

2. $\dfrac{b}{7} = 8$

3. $\dfrac{x}{4} = 4$

4. $7 = \dfrac{a}{5}$

5. $6 = \dfrac{x}{4}$

6. $\dfrac{a}{6} = 12$

7. $\dfrac{1}{3}x = 2$

8. $\dfrac{1}{8}a = 10$

9. $8 = \dfrac{1}{3}x$

10. $5 = \dfrac{1}{4}b$

SET 2

1. $\dfrac{a}{2} = \dfrac{1}{2}$

2. $\dfrac{b}{6} = \dfrac{2}{3}$

3. $\dfrac{d}{4} = \dfrac{3}{2}$

4. $\dfrac{c}{15} = \dfrac{3}{5}$

5. $\dfrac{5}{6} = \dfrac{a}{30}$

6. $\dfrac{7}{3} = \dfrac{m}{21}$

7. $\dfrac{3}{7} = \dfrac{d}{28}$

8. $\dfrac{4}{25} = \dfrac{c}{5}$

9. $\dfrac{1}{8}a = \dfrac{3}{4}$

10. $\dfrac{4}{5} = \dfrac{1}{10}b$

SET 3

1. $\dfrac{b}{4} = \dfrac{2}{5}$

2. $\dfrac{x}{8} = \dfrac{10}{7}$

3. $\dfrac{x}{10} = \dfrac{4}{3}$

4. $\dfrac{2}{3} = \dfrac{b}{8}$

5. $\dfrac{a}{2} = \dfrac{1}{3}$

6. $\dfrac{1}{5} = \dfrac{a}{2}$

7. $\dfrac{9}{10} = \dfrac{b}{11}$

8. $\dfrac{4}{5} = \dfrac{m}{16}$

9. $\dfrac{1}{2}x = \dfrac{2}{3}$

10. $\dfrac{2}{5} = \dfrac{1}{7}a$

SET 4

1. $\dfrac{b}{4} = \dfrac{1}{6}$

2. $\dfrac{x}{10} = \dfrac{4}{15}$

3. $\dfrac{r}{8} = \dfrac{11}{6}$

4. $\dfrac{a}{25} = \dfrac{12}{10}$

5. $\dfrac{1}{8} = \dfrac{x}{12}$

6. $\dfrac{3}{16} = \dfrac{y}{6}$

7. $\dfrac{9}{10} = \dfrac{x}{14}$

8. $\dfrac{15}{8} = \dfrac{x}{10}$

9. $\dfrac{1}{12}x = \dfrac{5}{16}$

10. $\dfrac{20}{9} = \dfrac{1}{6}y$

SET 5

1. $\dfrac{2a}{3} = 4$

2. $\dfrac{3x}{4} = 6$

3. $\dfrac{3b}{10} = 9$

4. $\dfrac{2x}{5} = 4$

5. $6 = \dfrac{3d}{2}$

6. $3 = \dfrac{3a}{5}$

7. $\dfrac{5b}{8} = 8$

8. $14 = \dfrac{7y}{8}$

9. $\dfrac{3}{5}x = 6$

10. $5 = \dfrac{7}{8}y$

SET 6

1. $\dfrac{2b}{5} = \dfrac{4}{5}$

2. $\dfrac{2x}{15} = \dfrac{2}{5}$

3. $\dfrac{7m}{9} = \dfrac{14}{3}$

4. $\dfrac{15}{2} = \dfrac{5a}{12}$

5. $\dfrac{3b}{16} = \dfrac{3}{4}$

6. $\dfrac{5}{8} = \dfrac{3x}{4}$

7. $\dfrac{2c}{5} = \dfrac{2}{3}$

8. $\dfrac{5}{6} = \dfrac{2a}{5}$

9. $\dfrac{3x}{8} = \dfrac{1}{6}$

10. $\dfrac{9b}{10} = \dfrac{3}{4}$

SET 7

1. $\dfrac{a+2}{3} = 2$

2. $7 = \dfrac{y-2}{4}$

3. $\dfrac{a+4}{9} = \dfrac{5}{9}$

4. $\dfrac{x+1}{8} = \dfrac{1}{4}$

5. $\dfrac{1}{3} = \dfrac{x+1}{9}$

6. $\dfrac{b+2}{4} = \dfrac{2}{3}$

7. $\dfrac{x-2}{6} = \dfrac{3}{4}$

8. $\dfrac{5x-4}{3} = 2$

9. $\dfrac{4x+5}{6} = \dfrac{7}{2}$

10. $\dfrac{4}{5} = \dfrac{5x-9}{20}$

SET 8

1. $\dfrac{x+4}{5} = x$

2. $b = \dfrac{5b+3}{6}$

3. $\dfrac{x+2}{4} = \dfrac{x}{2}$

4. $\dfrac{a+8}{3} = \dfrac{a}{5}$

5. $\dfrac{b-2}{6} = \dfrac{b}{4}$

6. $\dfrac{x}{5} = \dfrac{x-3}{2}$

7. $\dfrac{3b+3}{4} = \dfrac{b}{2}$

8. $\dfrac{a}{8} = \dfrac{2a-5}{6}$

9. $\dfrac{3b+7}{5} = \dfrac{2b}{3}$

10. $\dfrac{5a-6}{5} = \dfrac{2a}{5}$

SET 9a

1. $\dfrac{x+2}{2} = \dfrac{x+6}{4}$

2. $\dfrac{c+3}{2} = \dfrac{c+5}{4}$

3. $\dfrac{x+6}{6} = \dfrac{x+2}{8}$

4. $\dfrac{x-5}{3} = \dfrac{x+3}{6}$

5. $\dfrac{y+6}{5} = \dfrac{y-2}{3}$

6. $\dfrac{x-5}{10} = \dfrac{x+4}{4}$

7. $\dfrac{b-2}{8} = \dfrac{b+4}{24}$

8. $\dfrac{x-5}{4} = \dfrac{x-2}{3}$

9. $\dfrac{x-3}{2} = \dfrac{x-4}{6}$

10. $\dfrac{5-x}{6} = \dfrac{2+x}{8}$

SET 9b

1. $\dfrac{3x+1}{5} = \dfrac{2x+5}{5}$

2. $\dfrac{4a+2}{3} = \dfrac{a+3}{2}$

3. $\dfrac{2y+3}{2} = \dfrac{3y+6}{4}$

4. $\dfrac{6x+7}{10} = \dfrac{2x+9}{6}$

5. $\dfrac{3x+7}{5} = \dfrac{2x-3}{3}$

6. $\dfrac{3b+34}{14} = \dfrac{b+44}{21}$

7. $\dfrac{2a-5}{15} = \dfrac{3a-20}{10}$

8. $\dfrac{4x-3}{5} = \dfrac{7x-9}{8}$

9. $\dfrac{6-a}{2} = \dfrac{2a+9}{4}$

10. $\dfrac{11-3x}{4} = \dfrac{6-x}{6}$

SET 10

1. $\dfrac{8}{a} = 4$

2. $2 = \dfrac{6}{b}$

3. $\dfrac{5}{x} = \dfrac{5}{6}$

4. $\dfrac{7}{10} = \dfrac{7}{y}$

5. $\dfrac{6}{b} = \dfrac{3}{4}$

6. $\dfrac{2}{5} = \dfrac{10}{x}$

7. $\dfrac{15}{2a} = 5$

8. $16 = \dfrac{8}{3a}$

9. $\dfrac{4}{5x} = \dfrac{1}{5}$

10. $\dfrac{8}{3x} = \dfrac{2}{5}$

SET 11a

1. $\dfrac{5}{x+1} = \dfrac{5}{8}$

2. $\dfrac{4}{a+5} = \dfrac{2}{3}$

3. $\dfrac{3}{x-4} = \dfrac{3}{5}$

4. $\dfrac{5}{8} = \dfrac{2}{b+3}$

5. $\dfrac{2}{y-2} = \dfrac{5}{9}$

6. $\dfrac{5}{6} = \dfrac{3}{a+3}$

7. $\dfrac{5}{x+2} = \dfrac{10}{x+3}$

8. $\dfrac{4}{m-3} = \dfrac{6}{m+3}$

9. $\dfrac{7}{x+4} = \dfrac{3}{x-2}$

10. $\dfrac{4}{x-1} = \dfrac{7}{x-5}$

SET 11b

1. $\dfrac{x}{x+2} = \dfrac{5}{7}$

2. $\dfrac{5}{4} = \dfrac{x}{x-2}$

3. $\dfrac{1}{2y+5} = \dfrac{1}{9}$

4. $\dfrac{3}{3a+2} = \dfrac{3}{8}$

5. $\dfrac{6}{2b-3} = \dfrac{6}{b}$

6. $\dfrac{x}{4x+3} = \dfrac{2}{5}$

7. $\dfrac{3}{2x} = \dfrac{7}{5x-2}$

8. $\dfrac{5}{2x-5} = \dfrac{10}{3x+5}$

9. $\dfrac{8}{5y+6} = \dfrac{4}{5y-2}$

10. $\dfrac{1}{4y-5} = \dfrac{4}{2y-7}$

SET 12

1. $\dfrac{x+5}{x-5} = \dfrac{x-1}{x-7}$

2. $\dfrac{x-3}{x+1} = \dfrac{x-6}{x-5}$

3. $\dfrac{a-2}{a-4} = \dfrac{a-7}{a+1}$

4. $\dfrac{b+1}{b+5} = \dfrac{b-4}{b-1}$

5. $\dfrac{x-2}{x-6} = \dfrac{x+2}{x-4}$

6. $\dfrac{a+4}{a-4} = \dfrac{a-4}{a+4}$

7. $\dfrac{m+3}{m-3} = \dfrac{m+15}{m}$

8. $\dfrac{2b}{b+2} = \dfrac{2b+8}{b+7}$

9. $\dfrac{x}{4-x} = \dfrac{9-2x}{2x-5}$

10. $\dfrac{2x-5}{3x-4} = \dfrac{2x-3}{3x-2}$

EXERCISE 67

Equations with Fractional Coefficients

I. Aim: To solve more difficult equations having fractional coefficients.

II. Procedure

1. Find the lowest common denominator (l.c.d.).

2. Multiply each and every term (whole number or fraction) on both sides of the equation by the l.c.d. to clear the equation of all fractions.
   Note—If a fraction is preceded by a plus sign, do not change any signs when writing the product. If a fraction is preceded by a minus sign, change all signs when writing the product. See sample solution 2.

3. Solve the resulting equation.

4 Check by substituting the root in the given equation.

III. Sample Solutions

Check:

1. $\dfrac{x}{2}+\dfrac{x}{3}=5$ $\dfrac{6}{2}+\dfrac{6}{3}=5$

$\dfrac{x}{2}\cdot\dfrac{3}{6}+\dfrac{x}{3}\cdot\dfrac{2}{6}=5\cdot6$ $3+2=5$

$3x+2x=30$ $5=5$

$5x=30$

$x=6$

Answer, $x=6$

Check:

2. $\dfrac{x+6}{2}-\dfrac{2x-3}{5}=\dfrac{3x+4}{4}$ $\dfrac{4+6}{2}-\dfrac{8-3}{5}=\dfrac{12+4}{4}$

$\dfrac{x+6}{2}\cdot\dfrac{10}{20}-\dfrac{2x-3}{5}\cdot\dfrac{4}{20}=\dfrac{3x+4}{4}\cdot\dfrac{5}{20}$ $\dfrac{10}{2}-\dfrac{5}{5}=\dfrac{16}{4}$

$10x+60-8x+12=15x+20$ $5-1=4$

$10x-8x-15x=-60-12+20$ $4=4$

$-13x=-52$

$x=4$

Answer, $x=4$

DIAGNOSTIC TEST

Solve and check:

1. $\dfrac{x}{3}+\dfrac{x}{4}=14$

2. $\dfrac{y}{2}=\dfrac{5}{6}-\dfrac{y}{3}$

3. $x+\dfrac{x}{2}+\dfrac{x}{3}+\dfrac{x}{4}+\dfrac{x}{6}=27$

4. $\dfrac{b-1}{3}+\dfrac{b+5}{5}=6$

5. $\dfrac{m+2}{2}-\dfrac{m-6}{8}=\dfrac{m+11}{4}$

6. $\dfrac{5x-1}{2}-\dfrac{3x+5}{5}=\dfrac{7x+13}{6}$

Related Practice Examples

SET 1

Solve and check:

1. $\dfrac{x}{3}+\dfrac{x}{2}=10$

2. $\dfrac{a}{4}-\dfrac{a}{8}=3$

3. $4=\dfrac{b}{6}+\dfrac{b}{3}$

4. $2=\dfrac{x}{3}-\dfrac{x}{5}$

5. $\dfrac{y}{8}+6=\dfrac{y}{4}$

6. $\dfrac{z}{10}=9-\dfrac{z}{5}$

SET 1 (*Continued*)

7. $x = \dfrac{x}{3} + 4$ 8. $6 = c - \dfrac{c}{3}$ 9. $\dfrac{x}{3} - 5 = 0$ 10. $0 = 9 - \dfrac{3x}{4}$

SET 2

1. $\dfrac{x}{10} + \dfrac{x}{5} = \dfrac{9}{10}$

2. $\dfrac{b}{6} + \dfrac{b}{3} = \dfrac{1}{2}$

3. $\dfrac{x}{3} - \dfrac{x}{4} = \dfrac{1}{12}$

4. $\dfrac{a}{8} - \dfrac{a}{12} = \dfrac{1}{8}$

5. $\dfrac{35}{48} = \dfrac{x}{16} + \dfrac{x}{12}$

6. $\dfrac{9}{40} = \dfrac{c}{8} - \dfrac{c}{10}$

7. $\dfrac{b}{8} + \dfrac{3}{4} = \dfrac{b}{5}$

8. $\dfrac{x}{3} - \dfrac{2}{3} = \dfrac{x}{4}$

9. $\dfrac{5y}{6} + \dfrac{2y}{3} = \dfrac{9}{2}$

10. $\dfrac{4x}{5} - \dfrac{3x}{8} = \dfrac{17}{4}$

SET 3

1. $\dfrac{1}{4} + \dfrac{1}{2} = x$

2. $x + \dfrac{x}{2} + \dfrac{x}{3} = 22$

3. $a - \dfrac{a}{2} + \dfrac{a}{4} = 6$

4. $y + \dfrac{y}{2} + \dfrac{y}{3} + \dfrac{y}{4} = 50$

5. $b - \dfrac{b}{3} + \dfrac{b}{5} = 26$

6. $x = 1 + \dfrac{x}{2} + \dfrac{x}{4} + \dfrac{x}{8} + \dfrac{x}{16}$

7. $\dfrac{x}{2} + \dfrac{2x}{3} + \dfrac{3x}{4} = 23$

8. $\dfrac{5x}{6} + \dfrac{x}{4} + \dfrac{2x}{3} = 42$

9. $\dfrac{5a}{8} + \dfrac{a}{3} - \dfrac{7a}{8} = 4$

10. $\dfrac{3x}{2} - \dfrac{5x}{16} - \dfrac{3x}{8} = 26$

SET 4

1. $\dfrac{x}{2} + \dfrac{x+2}{3} = 9$

2. $\dfrac{b+5}{6} + \dfrac{b+3}{5} = 4$

3. $\dfrac{y+5}{2} + \dfrac{y+1}{4} = 5$

4. $\dfrac{x-3}{6} + \dfrac{x+3}{3} = 5$

5. $\dfrac{c-2}{6} + \dfrac{c-4}{8} = \dfrac{3}{2}$

6. $\dfrac{x+3}{8} + \dfrac{x}{5} = 2$

7. $\dfrac{b+1}{5} + \dfrac{b+2}{2} = 4$

8. $\dfrac{a+1}{3} + \dfrac{a+3}{4} = \dfrac{a+3}{2}$

9. $\dfrac{x+2}{4} + \dfrac{x+4}{6} = \dfrac{x+1}{2}$

10. $\dfrac{x+9}{4} + \dfrac{x+1}{2} = \dfrac{x-11}{5}$

SET 5

1. $\dfrac{x}{2} - \dfrac{x+2}{5} = 2$

2. $\dfrac{c+7}{2} - \dfrac{c+3}{4} = 4$

3. $\dfrac{d+4}{3} - \dfrac{d-5}{6} = 4$

4. $\dfrac{x+8}{4} - \dfrac{x+5}{9} = 2$

5. $\dfrac{x+5}{4} - \dfrac{x+3}{8} = \dfrac{7}{4}$

6. $\dfrac{y-1}{12} - \dfrac{y+1}{16} = \dfrac{1}{24}$

7. $\dfrac{x-4}{2} - 2 = \dfrac{x-6}{4}$

8. $\dfrac{x-5}{2} - \dfrac{x-3}{4} = \dfrac{x-7}{10}$

9. $\dfrac{x+8}{3} - \dfrac{x-4}{5} = x$

10. $\dfrac{m+10}{4} - \dfrac{m-10}{6} = \dfrac{m+10}{2}$

SET 6

1. $\dfrac{x+2}{5}+\dfrac{3x}{2}=14$

2. $\dfrac{4y+3}{4}-\dfrac{5y}{6}=\dfrac{13}{12}$

3. $\dfrac{5a+3}{8}+\dfrac{3a+5}{2}=5$

4. $6=\dfrac{8x-1}{3}+\dfrac{2x+1}{5}$

5. $\dfrac{7x-2}{11}-\dfrac{2x-7}{3}=1$

6. $\dfrac{7a+5}{8}-2=\dfrac{3a+15}{10}$

7. $3=\dfrac{3x-4}{2}-\dfrac{4x-5}{3}$

8. $\dfrac{3x-5}{3}+\dfrac{5x+3}{6}=\dfrac{13}{3}$

9. $\dfrac{2y-5}{4}+\dfrac{3y+1}{2}=5\tfrac{1}{4}$

10. $\dfrac{2m+3}{3}+\dfrac{8m+3}{9}=2m$

11. $\dfrac{2x+3}{5}+\dfrac{2x+3}{6}=\dfrac{3x+4}{4}$

12. $\dfrac{4b-3}{6}-\dfrac{2b-5}{8}=\dfrac{7b}{16}$

13. $\dfrac{7m-6}{10}+\dfrac{4m+3}{5}=\dfrac{16m-13}{15}$

14. $6-\dfrac{4(x-3)}{3}=\dfrac{x-2}{2}$

15. $\dfrac{4-3x}{8}+2=\dfrac{x-5}{4}-x$

EXERCISE 68

Fractional Equations

I. Aim: To solve more difficult fractional equations.

II. Procedure

1. If possible, factor denominators before finding the l.c.d. See sample solutions 2 and 3.

2. If necessary, change signs of fractions. See sample solution 3.

3. To complete solution follow procedure outlined in exercise 67.

III. Sample Solutions

1. $\dfrac{3}{4}+\dfrac{2}{3x}=\dfrac{14}{6x}-\dfrac{1}{12}$

$\dfrac{3}{\cancel{4}}\cdot\cancel{12}x+\dfrac{2}{\cancel{3x}}\cdot\cancel{12x}=\dfrac{14}{\cancel{6x}}\cdot\cancel{12x}-\dfrac{1}{\cancel{12}}\cdot\cancel{12}x$

$9x+8=28-x$
$9x+x=28-8$
$10x=20$
$x=2$

Answer, $x=2$

Check:

$\dfrac{3}{4}+\dfrac{2}{6}=\dfrac{14}{12}-\dfrac{1}{12}$

$\dfrac{3}{4}+\dfrac{1}{3}=\dfrac{13}{12}$

$1\tfrac{1}{12}=1\tfrac{1}{12}$

2. $\dfrac{x}{x-3}=\dfrac{2x^2+x}{x^2-9}-\dfrac{x-2}{x+3}$

$\dfrac{x}{x-3}=\dfrac{2x^2+x}{(x+3)(x-3)}-\dfrac{x-2}{x+3}$

$\dfrac{x}{x-3}\cdot(x+3)(x-3)=\dfrac{2x^2+x}{(x+3)(x-3)}\cdot(x+3)(x-3)-\dfrac{x-2}{x+3}\cdot(x+3)(x-3)$

$x^2+3x=2x^2+x-x^2+5x-6$

$x^2+3x-2x^2-x+x^2-5x=-6$

$-3x=-6$

$x=2$

Answer, $x=2$

Check:

$\dfrac{2}{2-3}=\dfrac{8+2}{4-9}-\dfrac{2-2}{2+3}$

$\dfrac{2}{-1}=\dfrac{10}{-5}-\dfrac{0}{5}$

$-2=-2$

3. $\dfrac{2x}{x+1}-\dfrac{3}{1-x}=\dfrac{2x^2+1}{x^2-1}$

$\dfrac{2x}{x+1}-\dfrac{3}{1-x}=\dfrac{2x^2+1}{(x+1)(x-1)}$

$\dfrac{2x}{x+1}+\dfrac{3}{x-1}=\dfrac{2x^2+1}{(x+1)(x-1)}$

$\dfrac{2x}{x+1}\cdot(x+1)(x-1)+\dfrac{3}{x-1}\cdot(x+1)(x-1)=\dfrac{2x^2+1}{(x+1)(x-1)}\cdot(x+1)(x-1)$

$2x^2-2x+3x+3=2x^2+1$

$2x^2-2x+3x-2x^2=-3+1$

$x=-2$

Answer, $x=-2$

Check:

$\dfrac{-4}{-2+1}-\dfrac{3}{1+2}=\dfrac{8+1}{4-1}$

$\dfrac{-4}{-1}-\dfrac{3}{3}=\dfrac{9}{3}$

$4-1=3$

$3=3$

DIAGNOSTIC TEST

Solve and check:

1. $\dfrac{3}{x}+\dfrac{5}{3}=\dfrac{19}{3x}$

2. $\dfrac{4}{5}+\dfrac{7}{4x}=\dfrac{13}{2x}-\dfrac{3}{20}$

3. $\dfrac{2}{a-3}+\dfrac{3a+1}{a+3}=3$

4. $\dfrac{5}{x+4}+\dfrac{3}{x-1}=\dfrac{9x+4}{x^2+3x-4}$

5. $\dfrac{y}{y+2}=\dfrac{2y^2+6}{y^2-4}-\dfrac{y+1}{y-2}$

6. $\dfrac{2a-1}{2a+1}+\dfrac{1}{4a^2-1}=2-\dfrac{2a}{2a-1}$

7. $\dfrac{3}{5-x}+\dfrac{1}{3-x}=\dfrac{7x+3}{15-8x+x^2}$

8. $\dfrac{5}{r+4}-\dfrac{4}{4-r}=\dfrac{7r+8}{r^2-16}$

Related Practice Examples

Solve and check:

SET 1

1. $\dfrac{1}{3}+\dfrac{1}{6}=\dfrac{1}{x}$

2. $\dfrac{2}{b}+\dfrac{1}{2}=\dfrac{5}{2b}$

3. $\dfrac{4}{x}+\dfrac{15}{2x}=\dfrac{23}{4}$

4. $\dfrac{11}{2x}-\dfrac{2}{3x}=\dfrac{1}{6}$

5. $\dfrac{9}{4a}-\dfrac{1}{8}=1$

SET 2

1. $\dfrac{4}{x}+2=\dfrac{14}{x}-3$

2. $\dfrac{2}{3y}+\dfrac{1}{4}=\dfrac{11}{6y}-\dfrac{1}{3}$

3. $\dfrac{5}{2b}+\dfrac{1}{6}=\dfrac{3}{5b}+\dfrac{4}{5}$

4. $\dfrac{1}{2}-\dfrac{3}{2x}=\dfrac{4}{x}-\dfrac{5}{12}$

5. $1+\dfrac{1}{2x}+\dfrac{2}{3x}=\dfrac{13}{6x}$

SET 3

1. $\dfrac{15}{x}+\dfrac{9x-7}{x+2}=9$

2. $\dfrac{6a-12}{a+3}+\dfrac{5}{a-2}=6$

3. $\dfrac{3a-2}{a+1}=4-\dfrac{a+2}{a-1}$

4. $\dfrac{2s-4}{s-4}-2=\dfrac{20}{s+4}$

5. $\dfrac{3x-4}{x-2}-3=\dfrac{6}{x+2}$

SET 4

1. $\dfrac{4}{x+2}+\dfrac{2}{x-4}=\dfrac{30}{x^2-2x-8}$

2. $\dfrac{2}{y-3}-\dfrac{4}{y+3}=\dfrac{8}{y^2-9}$

3. $\dfrac{2}{c-5}-\dfrac{1}{c-2}=\dfrac{9}{c^2-7c+10}$

4. $\dfrac{4}{x+2}+\dfrac{3x-2}{x^2-4}=\dfrac{4}{x-2}$

5. $\dfrac{3}{d+3}+\dfrac{5}{d+4}=\dfrac{12d+19}{d^2+7d+12}$

SET 5

1. $\dfrac{2x}{x^2-1}+\dfrac{x+3}{x+1}=\dfrac{x+1}{x-1}$

2. $\dfrac{a+2}{a+1}-\dfrac{a}{a+2}=\dfrac{4a+1}{a^2+3a+2}$

3. $\dfrac{m+1}{m+3}+\dfrac{m-3}{m-2}=\dfrac{2m^2-15}{m^2+m-6}$

4. $\dfrac{6x^2+14}{4x^2-9}-\dfrac{2x+1}{2x-3}=\dfrac{x+1}{2x+3}$

5. $\dfrac{y+5}{y^2-4}-\dfrac{3}{2y-4}=\dfrac{1}{2y+4}$

SET 6

1. $\dfrac{2}{x+4}+\dfrac{1}{x+2}+\dfrac{x^2+3}{x^2+6x+8}=1$

2. $\dfrac{2d}{d-1}-\dfrac{3}{d^2-1}=4-\dfrac{2d-1}{d+1}$

3. $\dfrac{5x-7}{2x-3}+\dfrac{x+2}{2x+3}-\dfrac{6}{4x^2-9}=3$

4. $\dfrac{5t-2}{5t-3}=1+\dfrac{3}{5t+3}+\dfrac{2t}{25t^2-9}$

5. $2-\dfrac{3x-2}{3x-1}=\dfrac{2x}{3x+1}+\dfrac{3x^2+20}{9x^2-1}$

SET 7

1. $\dfrac{2}{4-x}+\dfrac{3}{4+x}=\dfrac{17}{16-x^2}$

2. $\dfrac{26}{1-n^2}=\dfrac{3}{1-n}-\dfrac{2}{1+n}$

3. $\dfrac{3}{2-r}-\dfrac{2}{2+r}=\dfrac{7}{4-r^2}$

4. $\dfrac{3}{3-x}+\dfrac{1}{2-x}=\dfrac{2+3x}{6-5x+x^2}$

5. $\dfrac{1+b}{5-b}-\dfrac{4}{5+b}=\dfrac{15+b^2}{25-b^2}$

SET 8

1. $\dfrac{7x+5}{x+2}+\dfrac{x+1}{2-x}=6$

2. $\dfrac{2a}{a+1}-\dfrac{a}{1-a}=3$

3. $\dfrac{3}{y+3}-\dfrac{5}{3-y}=\dfrac{9y+1}{y^2-9}$

4. $\dfrac{4x+1}{x^2-x-6}+\dfrac{2}{3-x}=\dfrac{5}{x+2}$

5. $\dfrac{2m^2-25}{m^2-3m+2}+\dfrac{m-3}{2-m}=\dfrac{m+2}{m-1}$

EXERCISE 69

Decimal Equations

I. Aim: To solve decimal equations.

II. Procedure

Solve by either of the following methods:

1. Solution 1:
   a) Transpose all unknown terms on one side of the equation and all known terms on the other side.
   b) Solve the resulting equation.
   c) Check by substituting the root in the given equation.

2. Solution 2:
   a) Multiply all terms in the equation by some multiple of 10 to clear the equation of decimals.
   b) Solve the resulting equation.
   c) Check by substituting the root in the given equation.

III. Sample Solutions

SOLUTION 1

1. $.8x = .32$
   $x = .4$
   Answer, $x = .4$

   Check:
   $.8(.4) = .32$
   $.32 = .32$

2. $b + .7 = 5.4$
   $b = 5.4 - .7$
   $b = 4.7$
   Answer, $b = 4.7$

   Check:
   $4.7 + .7 = 5.4$
   $5.4 = 5.4$

3. $2.6x - .6 = 54$
   $2.6x = 54 + .6$
   $2.6x = 54.6$
   $x = 21$
   Answer, $x = 21$

   Check:
   $2.6(21) - .6 = 54$
   $54.6 - .6 = 54$
   $54 = 54$

4. $x + .05x = 42$
   $1.05x = 42$
   $x = 40$
   Answer, $x = 40$

   Check:
   $40 + .05(40) = 42$
   $40 + 2 = 42$
   $42 = 42$

5. $.7x + .6 = .2x + 2.1$
   $.7x - .2x = 2.1 - .6$
   $.5x = 1.5$
   $x = 3$
   Answer, $x = 3$

   Check:
   $.7(3) + .6 = .2(3) + 2.1$
   $2.1 + .6 = .6 + 2.1$
   $2.7 = 2.7$

SOLUTION 2

1. $.8x = .32$
   $80x = 32$
   $x = \frac{32}{80}$
   $x = \frac{2}{5}$ or $.4$
   Answer, $x = \frac{2}{5}$ or $.4$

2. $b + .7 = 5.4$
   $10b + 7 = 54$
   $10b = 54 - 7$
   $10b = 47$
   $b = 4\frac{7}{10}$ or 4.7
   Answer, $b = 4.7$

3. $2.6x - .6 = 54$
   $26x - 6 = 540$
   $26x = 540 + 6$
   $26x = 546$
   $x = 21$
   Answer, $x = 21$

4. $x + .05x = 42$
   $100x + 5x = 4200$
   $105x = 4200$
   $x = 40$
   Answer, $x = 40$

5. $.7x + .6 = .2x + 2.1$
   $7x + 6 = 2x + 21$
   $7x - 2x = 21 - 6$
   $5x = 15$
   $x = 3$
   Answer, $x = 3$

SOLUTION 1

6. $.02(x-2)=1$
$.02x-.04=1$
$.02x=1+.04$
$.02x=1.04$
$x=52$
Answer, $x=52$

Check:
$.02(52-2)=1$
$.02(50)=1$
$1=1$

SOLUTION 2

6. $.02(x-2)=1$
$2(x-2)=100$
$2x-4=100$
$2x=100+4$
$2x=104$
$x=52$
Answer, $x=52$

DIAGNOSTIC TEST

Solve and check:

1. $.4x=.36$
2. $b+.3=1.2$
3. $1.5x-.4=4.1$
4. $a+.06a=21.2$
5. $x-.25x=.35x+24$
6. $.03(c-10)=.07(c-50)$

Related Practice Examples

Solve and check:

SET 1

1. $2x=.8$
2. $.3b=.6$
3. $.8m=5.68$
4. $.5s=20$
5. $.04x=100$
6. $.7y=2.1$
7. $6x=.12$
8. $.09a=7.2$
9. $1.04x=52$
10. $1.25b=625$

SET 2

1. $x+.5=3.6$
2. $c+2=4.7$
3. $d+3.54=5.8$
4. $x-.4=6.25$
5. $b-3=.27$
6. $x-.02=2.5$
7. $.8=b+.3$
8. $12=d-1.4$
9. $s-2=8.5$
10. $y+3.6=9$

SET 3

1. $.3x+.2=.8$
2. $.5c+.8=3.3$
3. $2.4y+.15=.87$
4. $3.2x-.3=6.1$
5. $.6h-.8=4$
6. $.2x-.7=.78$
7. $.04a+8=10.4$
8. $1.02x+4.8=55.8$
9. $2.5y-.5=24.5$
10. $.24+8y=.64$

SET 4

1. $.3x+1.2x=4.5$
2. $3.7y+2.1y=8.7$
3. $4.2s-3.6s=9.6$
4. $x+.04x=104$
5. $.92x-124=.3x$
6. $.8x-6=.2x$
7. $a+.05a=525$
8. $1.2y-.08=.8y$
9. $40-3.5x=.5x$
10. $2.6b-.8=.6b$

SET 5

1. $.6x+.3=.3x+.9$
2. $g+3.5=.7g-.1$
3. $.06r-.25=.03r+.35$
4. $x+.05x+.02x=321$
5. $2x+1.08x-30.6=.02x$
6. $.4x+.2x=.24+.3x$
7. $x+.4=.6x+2$
8. $1.8m+.5m-.48=.7m$
9. $.05b+1.8=.25b-.2$
10. $1.2x+.05x=.15x+5.5$

SET 6

1. $.04(x-5)=4$
2. $.3(a-2)=.2a$
3. $.02(m+.6)=.04m$
4. $.06(x-5)=.05(x-4)$
5. $.25(x+60)=6+x$
6. $.75(x+6)=21$
7. $.06c=.08(c-50)$
8. $.04x+.05(500-x)=23$
9. $.03x+.02(800-x)=19$
10. $.06x+.04(1500-x)=72$

EXERCISE 70

Number Problems

I. **Aim:** To solve number problems.

II. **Procedure**

1. See Exercise 40—procedure for solving number problems.

III. **Sample Solutions**

The sum of one fourth of a certain number and three eighths of the same number is 15. Find the number.

Solution:

Let $\quad x =$ the number

$*\quad \dfrac{1}{4}x + \dfrac{3}{8}x = 15$

$\dfrac{x}{\cancel{4}} \cdot \cancel{8}^{2} + \dfrac{3x}{\cancel{8}} \cdot \cancel{8} = 15 \cdot 8$

$2x + 3x = 120$

$5x = 120$

$x = 24$

Answer, $x = 24$

* The equation is determined by the following fact:

$\frac{1}{4}$ of the number plus $\frac{3}{8}$ of the number equals 15

Check:

$\frac{1}{4} \times 24 = \quad 6$

$\frac{3}{8} \times 24 = \quad 9$

$\overline{}$

sum $\quad 15$

Practice Problems

A. Representations.

(*Do not write in this book*)

Copy the table below and fill in the missing numbers:

Number	4	18	5	8	x	$4x$	$9x$	$x-12$	$6-x$	$2x+7$
$\frac{1}{2}$ of Number										
$\frac{3}{4}$ of Number										

B. Problems.

1. If one half of a certain number is added to one third of the same number, the sum is 5. Find the number.

2. What number increased by $\frac{5}{8}$ of itself equals 26?

3. One number is 24 more than another. If the larger is divided by the smaller, the quotient is 5. Find the numbers.

4. What number must be added to both the numerator and denominator of the fraction $\frac{5}{11}$ to make the answer equal to $\frac{2}{3}$?

5. What is the value of an estate if a man wills $\frac{1}{3}$ of it to his daughter, $\frac{1}{4}$ of it to his son, and the remainder, $10,000, to his wife?

EXERCISE 71
Age Problems

I. Aim: To solve age problems.

II. Procedure

1. See Exercises 40 and 41—procedure for solving age problems. In these problems the age of the older person may be represented by some letter and the other ages represented in terms of that letter.

III. Sample Solution

Helen is one third as old as her sister. In 6 years she will be one half as old. How old is Helen now?

Solution:

Let x = sister's present age in yr.

Then $\frac{1}{3}x$ or $\frac{x}{3}$ = Helen's present age in yr.

$x + 6$ = sister's age in yr. 6 yr. hence.

$\frac{x}{3} + 6$ = Helen's age in yr. 6 yr. hence.

$*\ \frac{x}{3} + 6 = \frac{1}{2}(x+6)$

$\frac{x}{\cancel{3}} \cdot \cancel{6}^{2} + 6 \cdot 6 = \frac{x+6}{\cancel{2}} \cdot \cancel{6}^{3}$

$2x + 36 = 3x + 18$

$36 - 18 = 3x - 2x$

$18 = x$

$x = 18$ yr. — sister's present age.

$\frac{x}{3} = 6$ yr. — Helen's present age.

Answer, Helen is 6 yr. old.

* The equation is determined by the following fact:

Helen's age 6 yr. hence equals one half of her sister's age at that time.

Check:

	Helen		Sister
	Present age		
6 yr. =		$\frac{1}{3} \times$	18 yr.
	6 yr. hence		
12 yr. =		$\frac{1}{2} \times$	24 yr.

Practice Problems

1. John is one half as old as his father. The sum of their ages is 63 years. How old is John?

2. Mary is one sixth as old as her mother. In 12 years she will only be one third as old. What are their ages now?

3. George is one fourth as old as his dad. Six years ago he was one tenth as old. Find George's present age.

4. Frank is one half as old as his dad. He is now 20 years old. In how many years will he be three fourths as old as his father?

5. Bill's age four years ago was two thirds of what his age will be one year from now. How old is he now?

EXERCISE 72
Ratio and Proportion

I. Aim: To solve ratio and proportion problems.

II. Procedure

    1. Make a proportion in which the unknown is represented by some letter or algebraic expression.

    2. Solve the resulting equation.

    3. Check the word problem—not the equation.

III. Sample Solution

    A motorist uses 18 gallons of gasoline in driving 270 miles. At that rate how many miles can he go on 24 gallons of gasoline?

Solution:

Let x = no. of miles motorist can go on 24 gallons

$$* \quad \frac{x}{24} = \frac{270}{18}$$

$$18x = 6480$$
$$x = 360 \text{ miles}$$

Answer, 360 miles

* The equation is determined by the following proportion:

Unknown distance is to 24 gallons as known distance is to 18 gallons.

Check:

$$\frac{15 \text{ mi. per gallon}}{18)270} \qquad \frac{15 \text{ mi. per gallon}}{24)360}$$

Practice Problems

A. Representations.

Find the ratio of

1. 6 to 3.	2. 4 to 8.	3. 9 to 6.	4. 2 to 7.	5. x to 5.
6. 4 to y.	7. x to y.	8. $4x$ to x.	9. $5-x$ to x.	10. $400-x$ to 400.

B. Problems.

  1. Stewart earns $97 in 4 days. How many days will it take him to earn $485?

  2. Peggy saves $18 in 8 weeks. How long will it take her to save $81 at the same rate?

  3. A picture is now $2\frac{1}{4}$ inches high and $3\frac{1}{4}$ inches wide. How high will the picture be, when enlarged, if the width is to be 13 inches?

  4. A tree casts a shadow of 28 feet, while a 6-foot post near by casts a shadow of 4 feet. What is the height of the tree?

  5. A flagpole casts a shadow 27 feet, while near by a boy, 5 feet tall, casts a shadow 3 feet. Find the height of the flagpole.

  6. A motorist uses 25 gallons of gasoline in traveling 350 miles. How much gasoline will he use in going 462 miles?

  7. A man pays $110 taxes on a property assessed at $3,800. What will be the taxes on a house assessed at $6,350 if the same rate is used?

  8. A salesman sold a total of $630 worth of merchandise in 3 days. If he maintains that average, what would his sales be for 16 days?

  9. Mr. Bailey and Mr. Bindrim, partners in a business, agree to divide their profits in the ratio 3:4. In one year they earned $3,500 profits. How much did each get?

 10. A motorist travels 152 miles in 4 hours. At that rate how long will it take him to travel 247 miles?

EXERCISE 73

Work Problems

I. Aim: To solve work problems.

II. Procedure

1. Represent the unknown term by some letter or algebraic expression. If necessary, represent the other unknown quantities in terms of that letter.

2. The equation is determined by the following obvious fact: The amount of work done by one person in a certain time plus the amount of work done by a second person in the same time is equal to the total amount of work done by both persons in that time. See equation in the sample solution below.

3. Solve the resulting equation.

4. Check the word problem—not the equation.

III. Sample Solution

John can mow a lawn in 20 minutes and Donald can do it in 30 minutes. How long does it take the two boys to mow the lawn together if they use two lawn mowers?

Solution:

Let $x =$ no. of minutes it takes both boys together.   Check:

Then $\dfrac{1}{x} =$ part of work done by both in 1 min.   John does $\dfrac{1}{20} \times 12 = \dfrac{3}{5}$ of all work.

$\dfrac{1}{20} =$ part of work done by John in 1 min.   Donald does $\dfrac{1}{30} \times 12 = \dfrac{2}{5}$ of all work.

$\dfrac{1}{30} =$ part of work done by Donald in 1 min.   Together they do $\dfrac{5}{5}$ or all the work.

$$\frac{1}{20} + \frac{1}{30} = \frac{1}{x}$$

$$\frac{1}{20} \cdot 60x + \frac{1}{30} \cdot 60x = \frac{1}{x} \cdot 60x$$

$$3x + 2x = 60$$

$$5x = 60$$

$$x = 12 \text{ minutes}$$

Answer, 12 minutes

Practice Problems

A. Representations.

(Do not write in this book)

Copy the table below and fill in the missing numbers:

1.	John can mow a lawn in	30 min.	48 min.	x min.	$2x$ min.
	Part of lawn he can mow in 1 min.				

Copy the table below and fill in the missing numbers. (*Do not write in this book.*)

2.	Two pipes can fill a tank in	3 hr.	7 hr.	x hr.	$3x$ hr.
	Part of tank pipes can fill in 1 hr.				

B. Problems.

SET 1

1. Pam can mow a lawn in 24 minutes, and Sharon can do it in 48 minutes. How long does it take them to mow the lawn together if they use two lawn mowers?

2. A farmer can plow a field in 12 hours, and a second farmer can plow it in 36 hours. If they work together, using two plows, how long will it take them to plow the field?

3. Joyce can paint a house in 8 days, but her mother can do it in 6 days. How long does it take both to paint the house if they work together?

4. Paul can address 75 envelopes in 60 minutes, but Ann can do the same number in 30 minutes. If they work together, how long will it take them to address 75 envelopes?

5. A water tank can be filled by one pipe in 3 hours and by a second pipe in 2 hours. How many hours will it take the two pipes together to fill the tank?

SET 2

1. Paul can clean his house in 6 hours but it takes 9 hours for his brother to do it. How long will it take them to clean the house if they work together?

2. It takes 45 minutes for Barbara to wash the family car. Her younger sister can do it in 1 hour. If they work together, how long will it take to wash the car?

3. It takes 1 hour 40 minutes for 1 sprinkler to water a lawn and 2 hours 30 minutes for a smaller sprinkler. How long will it take to water the lawn if both sprinklers operate at the same time?

4. It generally takes 20 minutes for Elaine to wash and dry the dishes and straighten up the kitchen after dinner. Her son, George, can do it in 25 minutes. If they work together, how long should it take?

5. A certain wading pool can be filled with water in 16 minutes by using a water hose. It takes 20 minutes to empty the wading pool. How long will it take the water to reach the top if the water is permitted to run in and out at the same time?

SET 3

1. Jo can mow the lawn twice as quickly as Polly. Together they can do it in 4 hours. How long will it take each girl to mow the lawn alone?

2. A farmer can plow a field in 9 hours, and a second farmer can do it in 18 hours. After the first farmer had plowed for 3 hours, the second joined in and together they completed the plowing of the field. How long did it take them?

3. Charles can type a certain number of form letters in a third of the time it takes Martin. If they do it together, they can complete the task in 12 hours. How long will it take Charles to do all the typing?

4. Ruth can paint a house in 8 days, but she and her sister can do the same job in 6 days. How many days will it take the sister to paint the house alone?

5. A tank can be filled by one pipe in 4 hours, and can be emptied by another pipe in 6 hours. If the two pipes are open, how long will it take to fill the tank?

EXERCISE 74
Mixture Problems

I. Aim: To solve mixture problems.

II. Procedure

1. There are two types of simple mixture problems; one in which the solution is weakened and another in which it is strengthened. Analyze the representations in the sample solutions for procedure.

2. Either fractional or decimal equivalents may be used for %.

3. Solve the resulting equation.

4. Check the word problem—not the equation.

III. Sample Solutions

1. How many ounces of water must be added to 16 ounces of a 25% nitric acid solution to make a 10% solution?

Solution:

Let x = no. of ounces of water to be added.
$\quad\quad$ 16 = total no. of ounces in given solution.
Then $16+x$ = total no. of ounces in new solution.
$\quad\quad$ 4 = no. of ounces of nitric acid (25% of 16).

$$\frac{1}{10}(16+x) \text{ or } \frac{16+x}{10} = 10\% \text{ of no. of ounces in new solution.}$$

$$* \frac{16+x}{10} = 4$$

$$16+x = 40$$
$$x = 40-16$$
$$x = 24 \text{ ounces of water to be added.} \quad \text{Answer, 24 ounces}$$

* The equation is determined by the following fact:

10% of the no. of ounces in the new solution equals 4 ounces of nitric acid.

Check:

$\quad$ 16 ounces in given solution
$\quad$ 24 ounces of water to be added
$\quad$ ——
$\quad$ 40 ounces in new solution
$\quad$ $\frac{4}{40}$ = 10% nitric acid solution.

2. How many quarts of alcohol must be added to 40 quarts of a 20% solution to make a $33\frac{1}{3}$% solution?

Solution:

Let x = no. of quarts of alcohol to be added.
$\quad\quad$ 8 = no. of quarts of alcohol in given solution (20% of 40).
$\quad\quad$ $8+x$ = no. of quarts of alcohol in new solution.
$\quad\quad$ 40 = total no. of quarts in given solution.
$\quad\quad$ $40+x$ = total no. of quarts in new solution.

$$\frac{1}{3}(40+x) \text{ or } \frac{40+x}{3} = 33\frac{1}{3}\% \text{ of no. of quarts in new solution.}$$

$$* \frac{40+x}{3} = 8+x$$

$$40+x = 24+3x$$
$$40-24 = 3x-x$$
$$16 = 2x$$
$$8 = x$$
$$x = 8 \text{ quarts of alcohol to be added.} \quad \text{Answer, 8 quarts}$$

* The equation is determined by the following fact:

$33\frac{1}{3}$% of the no. of quarts in the new solution equals the no. of quarts of alcohol in the new solution.

Check:

$\quad$ 40 qt. in given solution
$\quad$ + 8 qt. of alcohol to be added
$\quad$ ——
$\quad$ 48 qt. in the new solution

$\quad$ 8 qt. of alcohol in given solution
$\quad$ + 8 qt. of alcohol to be added
$\quad$ ——
$\quad$ 16 qt. of alcohol in new solution

$\quad$ $\frac{16}{48}$ = $33\frac{1}{3}$% solution

Practice Problems

A. Representations.

Fill in the missing numbers by representing the percentages by a number or algebraic expression. Use fractional equivalents in columns I and III and decimal equivalents in columns II and IV:

(Copy the table below. *Do not write in this book*)

	I	II	III	IV
	60 oz.	24 qt.	$5+x$ oz.	$24+x$ qt.
25%				
20%				
5%				
$33\frac{1}{3}\%$				

B. Problems—Type 1.

1. How many ounces of water must be added to 20 ounces of a 30% sulphuric acid solution to make a 15% solution?

2. How many ounces of water must be added to 28 ounces of a 25% hydrochloric acid solution to make a 5% solution?

3. A dairy has 400 quarts of milk containing 5% butter fat. How many quarts of milk containing no butter fat must be added to produce milk containing 4% butter fat?

4. If there are 2 pounds of salt in a 20-pound salt solution, how many pounds of water must be added to make an 8% salt solution?

5. A chemist has 6 quarts of a $33\frac{1}{3}\%$ acetic acid solution. How many quarts of water must be added to make a 20% solution?

Problems—Type 2.

1. How many quarts of alcohol must be added to 25 quarts of a 20% solution to make a 60% solution?

2. How many ounces of sulphuric acid must be added to 32 ounces of a 25% solution to make a 40% solution?

3. How many pounds of salt must be added to 20 pounds of a 10% salt solution to make it a $33\frac{1}{3}\%$ solution?

4. How many ounces of vinegar must be added to 40 ounces of a 10% solution to make it a 25% solution?

5. There are 10 quarts of a 20% anti-freeze solution in the radiator of a car. How many quarts of anti-freeze must be added to make a 50% anti-freeze solution?

EXERCISE 75

Business Problems

I. Aim: To solve business problems.

II. Procedure

1. Represent the unknown term by some letter or algebraic expression. If there are two or more unknowns, represent one unknown by some letter and the others in terms of that letter.

2. Change the % to either its decimal or fractional equivalent.

3. Translate the word statement into an equation.

4. Solve the resulting equation.

5. Check the word problem—not the equation.

III. Sample Solution

Mr. Jones invests $2,400, part at 6% and the rest at 4% annual interest. If his total annual income from both investments is $126, how much does he invest at each rate?

Solution:

Let x = amount invested at 6% in dollars.
Then $2,400 - x$ = amount invested at 4% in dollars.
$.06x$ = annual income from the 6% investment.
$.04(2,400 - x)$ = annual income from the 4% investment.
* $.06x + .04(2,400 - x) = 126$
$6x + 4(2,400 - x) = 12,600$
$6x + 9,600 - 4x = 12,600$
$6x - 4x = 12,600 - 9,600$
$2x = 3,000$
$x = \$1,500$ invested at 6%
$2,400 - x = \$900$ invested at 4%
Answer, $1,500 at 6% and $900 at 4%

* The equation is determined by the following fact:

Income from 6% investment plus income from 4% investment equal total income.

Check:

$1,500	$900
.06	.04
$90.00	$36.00
$1,500	$90
+ 900	+ 36
$2,400	$126

Practice Problems

A. Representations.

Copy the table below and fill in the missing numbers:

(Do not write in this book)

Amount invested	$1,000	$3,000	x	x	$3x$	$\frac{1}{2}x$	$100 - x$	$2,000 - x$
Rate of interest	6%	4%	5%	2%	5%	4%	2%	3%
Income								

B. Problems

1. Ms. Becker invests $2,700, part at 5% and the rest at 6% annual interest. How much does she invest at each rate if her total annual interest from both investments is $144?

2. A man invests $6,000, part at 6% and the rest at 2% annual interest. If he receives a total annual income of $272 from both investments, how much does he invest at each rate?

3. A 4% investment brings an annual return of $17 less than a 3% investment. Find the two amounts invested if the total amount invested is $4,650.

4. A woman invests $1,500 more at 4% than she does at 5%. If the total annual income from both investments is $231, how much does she invest at 5%?

5. Mrs. Brown invests a certain amount of money at 4% annual interest and twice as much at 5%. If her total annual income from both investments is $84, how much does she invest at each rate?

6. Mr. Smith invests $4,800, part at 3% and the rest at 6% annual interest. How much does he invest at 6% if his total annual income from both investments is $189?

7. A man invests $3,500, some of it at 6% and the rest at 4% annual interest. Find how much money he invests at each rate if he receives the same amount of interest on each investment.

8. A borrowed $1,200 from B and C. If he paid a total of $43 annual interest, paying B at the rate of 4% and C at the rate of 3%, how much money did he borrow from B?

9. Mr. Stewart invests $\frac{1}{4}$ of his savings at 6% annual interest, $\frac{2}{3}$ at 8%, and the rest at 10%. If the total annual income from these investments is $230, what is the total amount of his investments?

10. Mr. Jones receives an annual income of $78 from his investments. He has invested $\frac{1}{2}$ of his savings at 3% annual interest, $\frac{1}{3}$ at 6%, and the rest at 5%. Find how much money he has invested at each rate.

C. Miscellaneous Problems

1. At what price must a dealer sell a chair which costs $39 to make 35% profit on the selling price?

2. A dealer sold a radio for $91, making 30% profit on the cost. How much did it cost?

3. Find the selling price if the:

Rate of profit on selling price is	20%	45%	30%	15%	37½%
Cost is	$18	$275	$56	$68	$450

4. Find the cost if the:

Rate of profit on cost is	40%	25%	35%	10%	33⅓%
Selling price is	$7	$10	$81	$132	$48

5. Find the list price of a camera which sells for $21 when a 12½% discount is allowed.

6. A dealer wishes to make a profit of 25% on the selling price of a refrigerator after allowing a 4% discount. What price should he mark the refrigerator if it cost him $180?

7. Mr. Williams paid $140 for a rug at a 20% reduction sale. If the dealer's mark-up was 33⅓% of the cost, how much profit did the dealer make?

8. A manufacturer sold suits to a retail merchant, making 25% profit on the cost of each suit. If the retail merchant sold these suits for $52 each, making 30% of his cost, how much did each suit cost the manufacturer?

9. June receives $45 per week as salary and an additional 8% commission on the amount of her sales. How much must she sell each week to earn $75 total compensation?

10. Find the face of a note discounted for 1 month at 6% annual interest if the net proceeds are $2,388.

REVIEW OF UNIT TEN

Solve and check:

1. $\dfrac{a}{28}=\dfrac{5}{7}$

2. $\dfrac{x-3}{x+7}=\dfrac{x-2}{x+10}$

3. $x-\dfrac{x}{2}+\dfrac{x}{3}-\dfrac{x}{4}=21$

4. $\dfrac{2b+3}{5}-\dfrac{3b-2}{4}=\dfrac{b-12}{6}$

5. $\dfrac{5}{3y}+\dfrac{3}{4}=\dfrac{20}{6y}-\dfrac{1}{12}$

6. $\dfrac{12}{t+5}+\dfrac{5t-1}{t-2}=5$

7. $\dfrac{a+1}{a+2}-\dfrac{a}{a+5}=\dfrac{6a-1}{a^2+7a+10}$

8. $\dfrac{3x+2}{3x+4}+\dfrac{3x-3}{3x-4}=2+\dfrac{5x-4}{9x^2-16}$

9. $\dfrac{m+3}{m+7}+\dfrac{m-6}{7-m}=\dfrac{2m+7}{m^2-49}$

10. $.04x+.06(900-x)=46$

11. Joe is one seventh as old as his cousin. In 8 years he will be one third as old. What are their ages now?

12. If the scale length of $4\frac{1}{2}$ inches represents an actual distance of 72 miles, what distance does the scale length of 7 inches represent?

13. A man invested $6,500, part at 4% and the rest at 5% annual interest. If he receives $62 annual interest more on his 4% investment than on his 5% investment, how much did he invest at each rate?

14. A machine can fill 1,000 cases of beverage in 3 hours. A second machine requires 5 hours to prepare the same amount. How long will it take both machines together to fill an order of 5,000 cases?

15. How many oz. of water must be added to 30 oz. of a 60% alcohol solution to make a 40% solution?

CUMULATIVE ALGEBRA REVIEW

1. Express as a formula: The magnetic course ($M.C.$) equals the true course ($T.C.$) increased by the west variation ($W.V.$).

2. Find the value of D_w if $D_t=91$ and $D_p=33$, using the formula $D_t=D_w+D_p$

3. Combine: $7xy-3x^2+y^2-9xy-2y^2-x^2-2xy$

4. Subtract: m^2-n^2 from $m^2-2mn+n^2$

5. Multiply: $6a^2-3ab+b^2$ by $2a-3b$

6. Divide: c^5+x^5 by $c+x$

7. Remove parentheses and, if possible, add like terms: $3a-[4a-(2b-a)-b]+5b$

8. Solve and check: $40x+50(90-x)=4,200$

9. A dealer sold an automobile for $1,488, gaining 20% of its cost. How much did it cost?

Find products mentally: 10. $(3x^2y-4z)(3x^2y+4z)$ 11. $(12bc-x^3)^2$ Factor: 12. $4x^2+16$ 13. $3n^2-30n-72$

14. Change to lowest terms:
$$\dfrac{15a-40}{9a^2-64}$$

15. Multiply:
$$\dfrac{8r^2s^3}{3x^6y}\cdot\dfrac{18x^8}{25r^3s}$$

16. Divide:
$$\dfrac{3c-6d}{15cd}\div\dfrac{c^2-4d^2}{c^2+4cd+4d^2}$$

17. Combine:
$$\dfrac{b-2}{b-9}-\dfrac{b}{b+2}+\dfrac{22}{b^2-7b-18}$$

18. Solve and check: $\dfrac{x}{6}+\dfrac{x}{8}=28$

19. Solve and check: $\dfrac{a+3}{a-5}+\dfrac{a-7}{a+5}=\dfrac{2a^2+10}{a^2-25}$

20. How far from an airport can an airplane fly and yet return (radius of action) in 8 hours if its outgoing speed is 160 m.p.h. and its return speed is 240 m.p.h.?

KEYED ACHIEVEMENT TEST

1. Find the value of W if $H.P.=4$, using the formula $H.P.=\dfrac{W}{746}$. ⑫

2. Find the product mentally: $(3c-8d)(3c-8d)$ ㊾

3. Factor: $m^2-10m-56$ ㊷

4. Change to lowest terms: $\dfrac{6n-4}{9n^2-12n+4}$ ㊲

5. Divide: $\dfrac{7a-21b}{9}\div\dfrac{14}{3a-9b}$ ㊹

6. Combine: $\dfrac{3c}{c-8}+\dfrac{c+2}{c-4}$ ㊽

7. Solve and check: $\dfrac{x-6}{x+2}=\dfrac{x-7}{x-1}$ ㊻

8. Solve and check: $\dfrac{2y+5}{10}+\dfrac{3y+6}{12}=10$ ㊺

9. Solve and check: $\dfrac{n+21}{n+6}-\dfrac{n-4}{n-7}=\dfrac{3-2n}{n^2-n-42}$ ㊻⑧

10. An alloy of copper and zinc weighing 35 pounds is 40% zinc. How many pounds of copper must be added to make the alloy contain only 28% zinc? ㊼

INTRODUCTION TO UNIT ELEVEN

Since letters are used both to represent numbers that are considered known quantities and numbers which are unknown and for which a solution is required, an equation containing both kinds of letters is called a *literal equation*. The study of literal equations generalizes the principles used in the solution of simple and fractional numerical equations. It also serves as a preparation for the study of the transformation of formulas.

If x represents the unknown and a and b represent known quantities, the equation $x+a=b$ is the general form of the equation type $x+3=6$, $x-a=b$ represents type $x-3=6$, $ax=b$ represents type $3x=6$, and $\frac{x}{a}=b$ represents type $\frac{x}{3}=6$. Particular attention should be paid to types $ax=b$ and $a+x=b$. In the solution of $ax=b$, both sides are divided by a with the result $x=\frac{b}{a}$. However, in the solution of $a+x=b$, a is subtracted from each side with the result $x=b-a$.

The principles used in numerical equations are employed in the solution of literal equations. Where the unknown appears in two or more unlike terms, the process of factoring is required in the solution.

❍❍

ARITHMETIC MAINTENANCE DRILL

Do the following examples:

1. Add:
   4,864
   53,937
   1,526
   309
   75,283

2. Subtract:
   63,507
   9,872

3. Multiply:
   647
   869

4. Divide:
   725)506050

5. Add:
   $8\frac{2}{3}+5\frac{5}{16}+4\frac{1}{4}$

6. Subtract:
   $16\frac{3}{8}-10\frac{11}{32}$

7. Multiply:
   $13\frac{1}{3}\times2\frac{1}{4}$

8. Divide:
   $6\frac{3}{4}\div18$

9. Add:
   $\$.39+\$6.84+\$73.97+\$5.69$

10. Subtract:
    $9.7-.32$

11. Multiply:
    $.54\times.05$

12. Divide:
    $\$.10)\$18.$

13. Round off to nearest thousandth: 2.06251

14. Change .4 to a common fraction.

15. Divide by short method: $9.21\div1000$

16. Find 175% of 684.

17. What % of 72 is 18?

18. 4% of what number is 900?

19. Find the square root of 751,689.

20. Change 4 yards 9 inches to feet.

UNIT ELEVEN—LITERAL EQUATIONS

EXERCISE 76

Simple Literal Equations

I. Aim: To solve simple literal equations.

II. Procedure

1. Solve for the unknown letter in terms of the other given letters. Use the principles outlined in Exercise 36.

2. If any unknown term is inclosed within parentheses, remove parentheses in order to use that term in the solution of the equation. See sample solution 8.

3. If the unknown is in 2 or more terms which cannot be combined as a single term, factor to get the unknown term. See sample solutions 7 and 8.

4. Check by substituting the root in the given equation.

III. Sample Solutions

Solve for x or y:

1. $2bcx = 8bc^2$

$x = 4c$

Answer, $x = 4c$

Check:

$2bc \cdot 4c = 8bc^2$

$8bc^2 = 8bc^2$

2. $ax = 1$

$x = \dfrac{1}{a}$

Answer, $x = \dfrac{1}{a}$

Check:

$a \cdot \dfrac{1}{a} = 1$

$1 = 1$

3. $a + x = 1$

$x = 1 - a$

Answer, $x = 1 - a$

Check:

$a + 1 - a = 1$

$1 = 1$

4. $6by - bc = by + 9bc$

$6by - by = 9bc + bc$

$5by = 10bc$

$y = 2c$

Answer, $y = 2c$

Check:

$12bc - bc = 2bc + 9bc$

$11bc = 11bc$

5. $mx - r = 2r - 5s$

$mx = 2r + r - 5s$

$mx = 3r - 5s$

$x = \dfrac{3r - 5s}{m}$

Answer, $x = \dfrac{3r - 5s}{m}$

Check:

$\not{m} \cdot \dfrac{3r - 5s}{\not{m}} - r = 2r - 5s$

$3r - 5s - r = 2r - 5s$

$2r - 5s = 2r - 5s$

6. $6ac + 3ax = 3ab$

$3ax = 3ab - 6ac$

$x = \dfrac{3ab - 6ac}{3a}$

$x = \dfrac{3a(b - 2c)}{3a}$

$x = b - 2c$

Check:

$6ac + 3a(b - 2c) = 3ab$

$6ac + 3ab - 6ac = 3ab$

$3ab = 3ab$

Answer, $x = b - 2c$

7. $my + ny = m^2 + 2mn + n^2$

$y(m + n) = (m + n)^2$

$y = \dfrac{(m + n)^2}{m + n}$

$y = m + n$

Answer, $y = m + n$

Check:

$m(m + n) + n(m + n)$

$= m^2 + 2mn + n^2$

$m^2 + mn + mn + n^2$

$= m^2 + 2mn + n^2$

$m^2 + 2mn + n^2$

$= m^2 + 2mn + n^2$

8. $c(x - c) = h(x - h)$

$cx - c^2 = hx - h^2$

$cx - hx = c^2 - h^2$

$x(c - h) = (c + h)(c - h)$

$x = \dfrac{(c + h)(\not{c - h})}{\not{c - h}}$

$x = c + h$

Check:

$c(c + h - c) = h(c + h - h)$

$c(h) = h(c)$

$ch = ch$

Answer, $x = c + h$

194

DIAGNOSTIC TEST

Solve for x or y:

1. $3x = 12d$
2. $4acx = 8a^2cd$
3. $5x = a$
4. $bx = 1$
5. $ny = m$
6. $x - 5b = 0$
7. $2a - y = 0$

8. $y - 3 = a$
9. $2x + 3d = 7d$
10. $cx - 1 = 0$
11. $4n + 2x = 5m$
12. $bx + dm = a$
13. $6y + 18 = 12c$
14. $ax = ar - at$

15. $7cx - 2c = 3cx + 6c$
16. $cx - b = 2a + 3b$
17. $5(d + y) = 2(2d + 3y)$
18. $ax + bx = a^2 - b^2$
19. $by - b^2 = cy - c^2$
20. $a(x - a) = b(x - b)$

Related Practice Examples

Solve for x or y:

SET 1
1. $5x = 5a$
2. $8y = 16d$
3. $9x = 27m$
4. $14b = 2x$
5. $30a = 6y$

SET 2
1. $ax = am$
2. $3abx = 6abc$
3. $ay = a^2$
4. $4ax = 36a^3$
5. $15b^2c^2d = 5bc^2y$

SET 3
1. $3x = b$
2. $4y = n$
3. $5x = 2r$
4. $8y = 12m$
5. $3c = 6y$

SET 4
1. $ay = 1$
2. $cx = 4$
3. $mx = 3$
4. $8 = dx$
5. $1 = by$

SET 5
1. $ax = b$
2. $c = by$
3. $bx = ac$
4. $2mx = hk$
5. $7bd = acy$

SET 6
1. $y - 4a = 0$
2. $x - 7c = 0$
3. $x + d = 0$
4. $0 = y - 5m$
5. $0 = x + 2h$

SET 7
1. $4b - x = 0$
2. $5m - y = 0$
3. $7k - x = 0$
4. $0 = 9r - x$
5. $0 = 3s - y$

SET 8
1. $x - 5 = b$
2. $y + 3 = a$
3. $5b + x = 2a$
4. $7m - x = 5n$
5. $4a = x - 3b$

SET 9
1. $3x + a = 10a$
2. $5x - m = 14m$
3. $6x + 5a = 11a$
4. $4by + 2bc = 10bc$
5. $2bx - m = 3m$

SET 10
1. $bx - 1 = 0$
2. $mx + 5 = 0$
3. $ay - b = 0$
4. $d - cx = 0$
5. $4x - b = 0$

SET 11
1. $2x - b = a$
2. $4m + 3y = 5b$
3. $a - 3x = b$
4. $c + 5x = 2a$
5. $16 = 3y - 5s$

SET 12
1. $ax = bc + d$
2. $by - 4 = 5c$
3. $nx - 3a = b$
4. $rx + 2d = 7t$
5. $2mnx - 3b = 4a$

SET 13
1. $2x = 2a + 2b$
2. $3y + 12 = 6b$
3. $10m + 5x = 25$
4. $6y - 4 = 8d$
5. $4x - 10 = 6t$

SET 14
1. $bx = ab + bc$
2. $cx = ac - bc$
3. $dy - ad = cd$
4. $2rs = 2rx - 2rt$
5. $my - mn - ms = 0$

SET 15
1. $a + 5x = 5a + 3x$
2. $8x - 3c = 4x + 9c$
3. $4y + 5ab = 7ab + 2y$
4. $2ax + ab = ax + 2ab$
5. $6bx - a = bx - 6a$

SET 16
1. $ax - b = 3a - 2b$
2. $ax - d = b - c$
3. $b + 5d = 5x - 3b$
4. $6y + 3b = 4a - b$
5. $a^2b + ab = a^2y - 2ab$

SET 17
1. $3(x - 2b) = 24b$
2. $7b = 2b - (x - 6b)$
3. $3(y - a) = 4(y - 2a)$
4. $5ax = c + 12a - (c - ax)$
5. $4(x - r) = 2x + 10r$

SET 18a
1. $x(b + c) = (b + c)(b - c)$
2. $x(c - d) = c^2 - d^2$
3. $mx - nx = m^2 - n^2$
4. $bx + cx = b^2 + 2bc + c^2$
5. $ay - 3y = a^2 - 6a + 9$

SET 18b
1. $x(a + b) = (a + b)(a - b)$
2. $x(a + b) = (a - b)(a - c)$
3. $x(a + b) = ab$
4. $mx - nx = m + n$
5. $cx + dx = c^2 - 2cd + d^2$

SET 19
1. $ay - a^2 = by - b^2$
2. $cx - c^2 = dx - 2cd + d^2$
3. $b^2 - my = -m^2 + 2bm - by$
4. $rx - 2rs = r^2 - sx + s^2$
5. $a^2 - ax = 3bx - 5ab - 6b^2$

SET 20
1. $c(y - c) = d(y - d)$
2. $b(b - x) = ax + a^2$
3. $bx - bd = c(x - d)$
4. $hx - h^2 = k(x - 2h + k)$
5. $b(x - b) = c(x + 2c - 3b)$

EXERCISE 77

Fractional Literal Equations

I. Aim: To solve fractional literal equations.

II. Procedure

1. Clear the equations of all fractions. Use the principles outlined in Exercises 66, 67, and 68.

2. Then solve the resulting literal equation. Use the principles outlined in Exercise 76.

III. Sample Solutions

Solve for x or y:

Check:

1. $\dfrac{3}{a} = \dfrac{6}{x}$ $\dfrac{3}{a} = \dfrac{6}{2a}$

$3x = 6a$ $\dfrac{3}{a} = \dfrac{3}{a}$

$x = 2a$

Answer, $x = 2a$

Check:

2. $\dfrac{a}{y} = \dfrac{b}{c}$ $\dfrac{a}{\dfrac{ac}{b}} = \dfrac{b}{c}$

$by = ac$

$y = \dfrac{ac}{b}$ $\dfrac{b}{c} = \dfrac{b}{c}$

Answer, $y = \dfrac{ac}{b}$

Check:

3. $\dfrac{x+1}{x-1} = \dfrac{m+n}{m-n}$ $\dfrac{\dfrac{m}{n}+1}{\dfrac{m}{n}-1} = \dfrac{m+n}{m-n}$

$mx - nx + m - n = mx + nx - m - n$

$mx - nx - mx - nx = -m - m + n - n$ $\dfrac{m+n}{m-n} = \dfrac{m+n}{m-n}$

$-2nx = -2m$

$x = \dfrac{m}{n}$

Answer, $x = \dfrac{m}{n}$

Check:

4. $\dfrac{y-d}{cy} + \dfrac{c}{dy} = \dfrac{1}{d}$ $\dfrac{c+d-d}{c(c+d)} + \dfrac{c}{d(c+d)} = \dfrac{1}{d}$

$\dfrac{y-d}{cy} \cdot cdy + \dfrac{c}{dy} \cdot cdy = \dfrac{1}{d} \cdot cdy$ $\dfrac{c}{c(c+d)} + \dfrac{c}{d(c+d)} = \dfrac{1}{d}$

$dy - d^2 + c^2 = cy$ $\dfrac{1}{c+d} + \dfrac{c}{d(c+d)} = \dfrac{1}{d}$

$c^2 - d^2 = cy - dy$ $\dfrac{d}{d(c+d)} + \dfrac{c}{d(c+d)} = \dfrac{1}{d}$

$(c+d)(c-d) = y(c-d)$ $\dfrac{c+d}{d(c+d)} = \dfrac{1}{d}$

$c + d = y$

$y = c + d$ $\dfrac{1}{d} = \dfrac{1}{d}$

Answer, $y = c + d$

DIAGNOSTIC TEST

Solve for x or y:

1. $\dfrac{2}{b} = \dfrac{4}{x}$
2. $\dfrac{y}{3b} = \dfrac{a}{d}$
3. $\dfrac{c}{d} = \dfrac{x-d}{x-c}$
4. $\dfrac{1}{a} = \dfrac{1}{x} + \dfrac{1}{b}$

Related Practice Examples

Solve for x or y:

SET 1

1. $\dfrac{x}{a} = 1$
2. $\dfrac{a}{x} = 1$
3. $\dfrac{1}{x} = \dfrac{1}{a}$
4. $\dfrac{3y}{10n} = \dfrac{6m}{5n}$
5. $\dfrac{4x}{3a} = \dfrac{8d}{3a}$

SET 2

1. $\dfrac{1}{x} = a$
2. $\dfrac{m}{x} = 5c$
3. $\dfrac{2}{b} = \dfrac{3}{x}$
4. $\dfrac{c}{d} = \dfrac{b}{y}$
5. $\dfrac{cy}{d} = \dfrac{h}{k}$

SET 3a

1. $\dfrac{6b}{x-b} = 3$
2. $\dfrac{2s}{x-s} = \dfrac{1}{2}$
3. $\dfrac{x+c}{x-d} = 4$
4. $\dfrac{x-2}{2} = \dfrac{b}{a}$
5. $\dfrac{x-n}{x-m} = \dfrac{m}{n}$

SET 3b

1. $\dfrac{4}{x-2a} = \dfrac{2}{x-6a}$
2. $\dfrac{3d}{y+2} = \dfrac{2d}{y-2}$
3. $\dfrac{m}{x+b} + \dfrac{n}{x-b} = 0$
4. $\dfrac{y+1}{y-1} = \dfrac{h+k}{h-k}$
5. $\dfrac{2a+x}{2a-x} = \dfrac{2a-x}{2a+x}$

SET 4a

1. $\dfrac{x}{2} - \dfrac{a}{2} = a$
2. $\dfrac{1}{x} = \dfrac{1}{a} + \dfrac{1}{b}$
3. $\dfrac{x}{a} + \dfrac{x}{b} = 1$
4. $\dfrac{y}{a} + \dfrac{y}{b} + \dfrac{y}{c} = 1$
5. $\dfrac{x}{m} + \dfrac{x}{n} = m+n$

SET 4b

1. $\dfrac{x-b}{ax} = \dfrac{1}{b} - \dfrac{a}{bx}$
2. $\dfrac{a^2}{y} - a = \dfrac{b^2}{y} - b$
3. $\dfrac{2x}{3a} - \dfrac{3x+4a}{2a} = 3$
4. $\dfrac{49}{abx} + \dfrac{4x-16ab}{x} = \dfrac{7}{ab}$
5. $\dfrac{ab}{x} = a^2b^2 - ab + \dfrac{1}{x}$

REVIEW OF UNIT ELEVEN

Solve for x or y and check:

1. $12x = 48b$ 　　2. $3cy = 18c^3$ 　　3. $6y = m$ 　　4. $2rx = s$ 　　5. $t + x = n$

6. $y - 3b = a$ 　　7. $9d - x = 0$ 　　8. $mx - 1 = 0$ 　　9. $3y - 9 = 15a$ 　　10. $bx + 7c = 3a$

11. $6nx - 5n = 4nx + 3n$ 　　12. $4(y + 3b) = 8(5b - 3y)$ 　　13. $mx - m^2 = nx - n^2$ 　　14. $b(y - b) = c(y - c)$

15. $\dfrac{c}{x} = b$ 　　16. $\dfrac{m}{n} = \dfrac{r}{y}$ 　　17. $\dfrac{y}{a} + \dfrac{y}{b} = 1$ 　　18. $\dfrac{1}{m} = \dfrac{1}{n} + \dfrac{1}{x}$ 　　19. $\dfrac{y-a}{y-b} = \dfrac{b}{a}$ 　　20. $\dfrac{c^2}{x} + 3d = \dfrac{6cd - 9d^2}{x} + c$

CUMULATIVE ALGEBRA REVIEW

1. Express as a formula: Power (P) equals work (W) divided by time (t).

2. Find the value of V when $\pi = 3.14$, $d = 9$, and $h = 16$, using the formula $V = \frac{1}{4}\pi d^2 h$.

3. One meter equals 39.37 inches. How many inches are in 5 meters? 8 meters? Write a formula showing the number of inches (i) in m meters.

4. Using signed numbers, find the closing price of a stock on Wednesday if it opened at $28\frac{1}{2}$ points on Monday, and gained $1\frac{1}{2}$ points, then lost $\frac{5}{8}$ point on Tuesday and $1\frac{3}{4}$ points on Wednesday.

5. Find the Centigrade temperature when the Fahrenheit temperature is 23°. Formula $C = \frac{5}{9}(F - 32)$.

6. Combine: $12a^2 - 3ab - 2b^2 + 3ab - b^2 - 5a^2 + 4b^2$ 　　7. Subtract $9x - 3y + z$ from $6x + z$.

8. Multiply $6m^2 - 5m + 2$ by $3m - 1$. 　　9. Divide $10n^3 - 18n + 8$ by $5n^2 + 5n - 4$.

10. Transform the following formula by removing parentheses: $A = \frac{1}{4}\pi(D + d)(D - d)$.

11. Multiply by inspection: $(4a - 6)(4a + 9)$ 　12. Factor: $a^2 - 14a - 72$ 　13. Solve and check: $7x - 9 = 8x - 12$

14. How long will it take an airplane, flying at an average speed of 210 m.p.h., to overtake another airplane which took off from the same airport 4 hours earlier and was flying at an average speed of 140 m.p.h.?

15. Change to lowest terms: $\dfrac{8b - 6x}{16b^2 - 24bx + 9x^2}$ 　16. Multiply: $\dfrac{4x^2}{4x^2 - 100} \cdot \dfrac{3x + 15}{18x}$ 　17. Divide: $\dfrac{6a^3 y}{25cx^2} \div \dfrac{12a^4 x}{35cy}$

18. Combine: $\dfrac{c - 4}{3} + \dfrac{8 - c}{8} - \dfrac{2c + 5}{6}$ 　　19. Solve and check: $\dfrac{3x}{5} + \dfrac{x - 5}{20} = 29$

20. Solve and check:

$$\dfrac{y - 5}{y - 6} - \dfrac{y - 3}{y + 8} = \dfrac{5y - 2}{y^2 + 2y - 48}$$

21. Solve for x and check:

$$6ax - 4ab = ax + 6ab$$

22. Solve for y and check:

$$\dfrac{y}{r} - s = r - \dfrac{y}{s}$$

23. What mark must a pupil get in an algebra test to bring his average up to 80 if his other test marks are 72, 84, and 79?

24. A tank can be filled by one pipe in 4 hours and by a second pipe in 8 hours. It can be emptied by a third pipe in 6 hours. If the three pipes are open, how long will it take to fill the tank?

ooooooooooooooooooooooooooooooooooooooooooooooooooooooooooooooooooooooooooo

KEYED ACHIEVEMENT TEST

1. Express as a formula: The discount (d) equals the rate of discount (r) times the list price (l). ①

2. Find the value of t if $v = 339$, $V = 51$, and $g = 32$, using the formula $v = V + gt$. ⑫

3. Solve and check: $10a - (2a - 6) = 0$ ㊱ 　　4. Remove parentheses, then combine:

$$4 - (2 + x)(2 - x) + 3x(6 - x)$$ ㉜

5. Multiply: $\dfrac{m^2 - n^2}{m^2 - mn - 2n^2} \cdot \dfrac{m^2 - 3mn + 2n^2}{(m - n)^2}$ ㊺ 　　6. Combine: $\dfrac{3}{x} + \dfrac{5}{x - 2} - \dfrac{7}{x + 3}$ ㉒

Solve for x or y and check: 7. $\dfrac{5y - 4}{8} - \dfrac{y - 2}{5} = \dfrac{y + 8}{4}$ ㉗ 　8. $cx - cd = d(x - d)$ ㊆ 　9. $\dfrac{1}{r} = \dfrac{1}{s} + \dfrac{1}{x}$ ㊆

10. A man invested $5,000 more at 4% than at 3%. If his annual income from the two investments is $830, how much did he invest at each rate? ㊖

INTRODUCTION TO UNIT TWELVE

The formulas $d = rt$, $t = \dfrac{d}{r}$, and $r = \dfrac{d}{t}$ express the interdependence or relationship between distance (d), rate of speed (r), and time of travel (t). If a student knows only the formula $d = rt$, by employing the principles studied in Unit Eleven, he could easily derive the other forms. Proficiency in the skill of transforming a formula is time-saving. Instead of memorizing each form of a given formula, the student is required to remember only one form. This rearrangement of formulas is also known as "changing the subject of the formula."

The development of ability to evaluate formulas is one of the most practical aims in the study of algebra, especially for students of science and advanced mathematics. In this unit evaluation is extended to more difficult formulas.

ᴏⓄᴏᴏᴏ

ARITHMETIC MAINTENANCE DRILL

Do the following examples:

1. Add:
   39
   955
   34,276
   98
   5,787

2. Subtract:
   176,000
   82,909

3. Multiply:
   5,280
   75

4. Divide:
   $71,172 \div 108$

5. Add:
   $5\frac{9}{16} + 1\frac{3}{32} + 3\frac{3}{4}$

6. Subtract:
   $8\frac{3}{4} - 5\frac{5}{6}$

7. Multiply:
   $4\frac{1}{2} \times 6\frac{2}{3}$

8. Divide:
   $16\frac{1}{2} \div 3\frac{1}{7}$

9. Add:
   $1.06 + 0.932 + 0.987$

10. Subtract:
    $\$5 - \$2.08$

11. Multiply:
    $144 \times \$16.58$

12. Divide:
    $.5\overline{)43}$

13. Round off to nearest hundred thousand: 5,847,065

14. Change $\frac{11}{16}$ to a decimal fraction.

15. Multiply by short method: 100×8.2

16. Find $16\frac{2}{3}\%$ of $\$13.80$.

17. $\$3.50$ is what $\%$ of $\$14$?

18. $\frac{7}{12}$ of what number is 84?

19. Square $\frac{3}{4}$.

20. Change 8 hours 40 seconds to minutes.

UNIT TWELVE—REARRANGING AND EVALUATION OF FORMULAS

List of Formulas Used in Exercises 78, 79, and 80

1. $p = 4s$	18. $a = \dfrac{360}{n}$	25. $A = s^2$	34. $S = \dfrac{n}{2}(a+l)$
2. $A = lw$		26. $A = \pi r^2$	
3. $A = ab$		27. $V = s^3$	
4. $A = bh$	19. $A = \dfrac{ab}{2}$	28. $V = \pi r^2 h$	35. $\dfrac{V}{V'} = \dfrac{P'}{P}$
5. $V = Bh$			
6. $d = rt$	20. $V = \dfrac{Bh}{3}$	29. $S = \dfrac{a}{1-r}$	36. $\dfrac{W_1}{W_2} = \dfrac{L_2}{L_1}$
7. $c = \pi d$			
8. $i = prt$		30. $s = \dfrac{at^2}{2}$	37. $\dfrac{1}{f} = \dfrac{1}{d} + \dfrac{1}{D}$
9. $V = lwh$	21. $I = \dfrac{E}{R}$		
10. $c = 2\pi r$			
11. $A = p + i$	22. $d = \dfrac{m}{v}$	31. $F = \dfrac{mv^2}{gr}$	38. $\dfrac{PV}{T} = \dfrac{P'V'}{T'}$
12. $s = c + g$			
13. $l = c - s$	23. $v = \dfrac{s}{t}$	32. $F = \dfrac{9}{5}C + 32$	39. $I = \dfrac{nE}{R+nr}$
14. $p = 2l + 2w$			
15. $v = V + gt$		33. $A = \dfrac{h}{2}(b+b')$	40. $S = \dfrac{rl-a}{r-1}$
16. $A = p + prt$	24. $a = \dfrac{v}{t}$		
17. $l = a + (n-1)d$			

EXERCISE 78

Rearranging Formulas

I. Aim: To rearrange formulas.

II. Procedure

1. Copy formula.

2. Using the letter to be solved as the unknown term and the other letters of the formula as the known terms, follow the principles outlined in Exercises 76 and 77.

III. Sample Solutions

Use list of formulas above to get formula corresponding to number given:

1. Use formula No. 5 and solve for h.

$$V = Bh$$

$$\frac{V}{B} = h$$

$$h = \frac{V}{B}$$

Answer, $h = \dfrac{V}{B}$

2. Use formula No. 8 and solve for p.

$$i = prt$$

$$\frac{i}{rt} = p$$

$$p = \frac{i}{rt}$$

Answer, $p = \dfrac{i}{rt}$

(See list of formulas on page 200)

3. Use formula No. 16 and solve for r.

$$A = p + prt$$

$$A - p = prt$$

$$\frac{A - p}{pt} = r$$

$$r = \frac{A - p}{pt}$$

Answer, $r = \dfrac{A - p}{pt}$

4. Use formula No. 21 and solve for R.

$$I = \frac{E}{R}$$

$$IR = E$$

$$R = \frac{E}{I}$$

Answer, $R = \dfrac{E}{I}$

5. Use formula No. 34 and solve for n.

$$S = \frac{n}{2}(a + l)$$

$$S = \frac{n(a + l)}{2}$$

$$2S = n(a + l)$$

$$\frac{2S}{a + l} = n$$

$$n = \frac{2S}{a + l}$$

Answer, $n = \dfrac{2S}{a + l}$

6. Use formula No. 33 and solve for b.

$$A = \frac{h}{2}(b + b')$$

$$A = \frac{h(b + b')}{2}$$

$$2A = h(b + b')$$

$$2A = bh + b'h$$

$$2A - b'h = bh$$

$$\frac{2A - b'h}{h} = b$$

$$b = \frac{2A - b'h}{h}$$

Answer, $b = \dfrac{2A - b'h}{h}$

7. Use formula No. 36 and solve for L_2.

$$\frac{W_1}{W_2} = \frac{L_2}{L_1}$$

$$W_1 L_1 = W_2 L_2$$

$$\frac{W_1 L_1}{W_2} = L_2$$

$$L_2 = \frac{W_1 L_1}{W_2}$$

Answer, $L_2 = \dfrac{W_1 L_1}{W_2}$

8. Use formula No. 39 and solve for n.

$$I = \frac{nE}{R + nr}$$

$$IR + Inr = nE$$

$$IR = nE - Inr$$

$$IR = n(E - Ir)$$

$$\frac{IR}{E - Ir} = n$$

$$n = \frac{IR}{E - Ir}$$

Answer, $n = \dfrac{IR}{E - Ir}$

DIAGNOSTIC TEST

To rearrange the formulas in the following problems use the list of formulas on page 200. Take formula corresponding to number given in the first column and rearrange for letter given in the second column.

Formula No.	Solve For	Formula No.	Solve For	Formula No.	Solve For
1. 3	b	6. 23	t	10. 36	L_1
2. 9	w	7. 31	r	11. 39	E
3. 12	g	8. 33	h	12. 29	r
4. 14	l	9. 34	l	13. 40	r
5. 21	E				

Related Practice Examples

Use the list of formulas on page 200. Take the formula corresponding to number given in the first column and rearrange for letter given in the second column.

SET 1a		SET 1b		SET 2		SET 3	
Formula No.	Solve For	Formula No.	Solve For	Formula No.	Solve For	Formula No.	Solve For
1. 1	s	1. 2	l	1. 10	r	1. 13	c
2. 2	w	2. 3	a	2. 8	t	2. 11	i
3. 4	h	3. 4	b	3. 9	h	3. 15	V
4. 6	t	4. 5	B	4. 8	r	4. 13	s
5. 7	d	5. 6	r	5. 9	l	5. 17	a

SET 4		SET 5		SET 6		SET 7	
Formula No.	Solve For	Formula No.	Solve For	Formula No.	Solve For	Formula No.	Solve For
1. 14	w	1. 22	m	1. 18	n	1. 30	a
2. 15	t	2. 23	s	2. 21	R	2. 31	m
3. 16	t	3. 24	v	3. 22	v	3. 31	g
4. 16	r	4. 19	b	4. 23	t	4. 30	t^2
5. 17	d	5. 20	B	5. 24	t	5. 31	v^2

SET 8		SET 9		SET 10		SET 11	
Formula No.	Solve For	Formula No.	Solve For	Formula No.	Solve For	Formula No.	Solve For
1. 17	d	1. 17	n	1. 35	V	1. 21	E
2. 16	p	2. 33	b	2. 36	W_2	2. 29	a
3. 34	n	3. 34	a	3. 35	P	3. 39	E
4. 33	h	4. 33	b'	4. 38	P'	4. 40	a
5. 32	C	5. 34	l	5. 38	T'	5. 40	l

SET 12		SET 13	
Formula No.	Solve For	Formula No.	Solve For
1. 23	t	1. 37	d
2. 31	r	2. 37	f
3. 29	r	3. 37	D
4. 39	R	4. 39	n
5. 39	r	5 40	r

EXERCISE 79
Evaluation of Formulas

I. **Aim:** To evaluate formulas.

II. **Procedure**

1. Copy formula.

2. Substitute numbers for letters.

3. Perform the necessary operations.

4. Solve the resulting equation. If necessary, use the principles outlined in Exercises 66, 67, 68, and 69.

5. Check by substituting given numbers and answer in formula.

III. **Sample Solutions**

Use list of formulas on page 200 to get formula corresponding to number given:

1. Using formula No. 8, find the value of t if $i=24$, $p=200$, and $r=.04$.

$$i = prt$$
$$24 = 200 \times .04 \times t$$
$$24 = 8t$$
$$3 = t$$
$$t = 3$$

Answer, $t = 3$

Check:
$$24 = 200 \times .04 \times 3$$
$$24 = 24$$

2. Using formula No. 18, find the value of n if $a = 40$.

$$a = \frac{360}{n}$$
$$40 = \frac{360}{n}$$
$$40n = 360$$
$$n = 9$$

Answer, $n = 9$

Check:
$$40 = \frac{360}{9}$$
$$40 = 40$$

3. Using formula No. 32, find the value of C if $F = 176$.

$$F = \frac{9}{5}C + 32$$
$$176 = \frac{9}{5}C + 32$$
$$176 - 32 = \frac{9}{5}C$$
$$144 = \frac{9}{5}C$$
$$\frac{5}{\cancel{9}} \cdot \cancel{144}^{16} = \frac{\cancel{5}}{\cancel{9}} \cdot \frac{\cancel{9}}{\cancel{5}}C$$
$$80 = C$$
$$C = 80$$

Answer, $C = 80$

Check:
$$176 = \frac{9}{5} \cdot 80 + 32$$
$$176 = 144 + 32$$
$$176 = 176$$

4. Using formula No. 34, find the value of l if $S = 136$, $n = 8$, and $a = 3$.

$$S = \frac{n}{2}(a + l)$$
$$136 = \frac{8}{2}(3 + l)$$
$$136 = 4(3 + l)$$
$$136 = 12 + 4l$$
$$136 - 12 = 4l$$
$$124 = 4l$$
$$31 = l$$
$$l = 31$$

Answer, $l = 31$

Check:
$$136 = \frac{8}{2}(3 + 31)$$
$$136 = 4(34)$$
$$136 = 136$$

5. Using formula No. 37, find the value of d if $f=2$ and $D=6$.

$$\frac{1}{f}=\frac{1}{d}+\frac{1}{D}$$

$$\frac{1}{2}=\frac{1}{d}+\frac{1}{6}$$

Check:

$$\frac{1}{2}=\frac{1}{3}+\frac{1}{6}$$

$$\frac{1}{2}=\frac{1}{2}$$

$$\frac{1}{2}\cdot 6d=\frac{1}{d}\cdot 6d+\frac{1}{6}\cdot 6d$$

$$3d=6+d$$
$$3d-d=6$$
$$2d=6$$
$$d=3 \qquad \text{Answer, } d=3$$

6. Using formula No. 38, find the value of T' if $P=3$, $V=8$, $T=4$, $P'=5$, and $V'=12$.

$$\frac{PV}{T}=\frac{P'V'}{T'}$$

$$\frac{3\cdot 8}{4}=\frac{5\cdot 12}{T'}$$

$$\frac{24}{4}=\frac{60}{T'}$$

$$6=\frac{60}{T'}$$

$$6T'=60$$
$$T'=10 \qquad \text{Answer, } T'=10$$

Check:

$$\frac{3\cdot 8}{4}=\frac{5\cdot 12}{10}$$

$$\frac{24}{4}=\frac{60}{10}$$

$$6=6$$

7. Using formula No. 39, find r if $I=4$, $n=5$, $E=24$, and $R=10$.

$$I=\frac{nE}{R+nr}$$

$$4=\frac{5\cdot 24}{10+5r}$$

$$4=\frac{120}{10+5r}$$

$$40+20r=120$$

$$20r=120-40$$
$$20r=80$$
$$r=4 \qquad \text{Answer, } r=4$$

Check:

$$4=\frac{5\cdot 24}{10+5\cdot 4}$$

$$4=\frac{120}{10+20}$$

$$4=\frac{120}{30}$$

$$4=4$$

8. Using formula No. 40, find r if $S=93$, $a=3$, and $l=48$.

$$S=\frac{rl-a}{r-1}$$

$$93=\frac{48r-3}{r-1}$$

$$93r-93=48r-3$$

$$93r-48r=93-3$$
$$45r=90$$
$$r=2$$
Answer, $r=2$

Check:

$$93=\frac{2\cdot 48-3}{2-1}$$

$$93=\frac{96-3}{1}$$

$$93=93$$

DIAGNOSTIC TEST

Use list of formulas on page 200. Take formula corresponding to the number given in the first column. Find the value of the unknown letter, given in the second column, by substituting the numbers, given in the third column, for the other letters in the formula.

Formula No.	Evaluate	If		Formula No.	Evaluate	If
1. 3	A	$a=8$; $b=5$.		13. 34	S	$n=5$; $a=2$; $l=18$.
2. 2	w	$A=28$; $l=7$.		14. 40	S	$r=2$; $l=48$; $a=3$.
3. 6	r	$d=120$; $t=3$.		15. 39	E	$I=4$; $n=4$; $R=8$; $r=3$.
4. 9	w	$V=96$; $l=8$; $h=3$.		16. 33	h	$A=50$; $b=12$; $b'=8$.
5. 15	v	$V=10$; $g=32$; $t=4$.		17. 34	a	$S=24$; $n=4$; $l=9$.
6. 11	i	$A=150$; $p=110$.		18. 35	P'	$V=3$; $V'=4$; $P=8$.
7. 16	t	$A=58$; $p=50$; $r=.04$.		19. 38	T	$P=6$; $V=4$; $P'=16$;
8. 22	d	$m=18$; $v=3$.				$V'=2$; $T'=4$.
9. 23	s	$v=20$; $t=5$.		20. 16	p	$A=230$; $r=.03$; $t=5$.
10. 21	R	$I=2$; $E=110$.		21. 37	d	$f=4$; $D=12$.
11. 28	V	$\pi=\frac{22}{7}$; $r=14$; $h=5$.		22. 39	r	$I=4$; $n=4$; $E=40$; $R=16$.
12. 32	C	$F=68$.		23. 40	r	$S=80$; $l=54$; $a=2$.

Related Practice Examples

SET 1

Formula No.	Evaluate	If
1. 1	p	$s=5.$
2. 2	A	$l=8; w=6.$
3. 4	A	$b=5; h=2.$
4. 7	c	$\pi=\frac{22}{7}; d=21.$
5. 8	i	$p=30; r=.05; t=4.$

SET 2

Formula No.	Evaluate	If
1. 1	s	$p=32.$
2. 3	b	$A=30; a=6.$
3. 5	h	$V=54; B=9.$
4. 6	t	$d=72; r=36.$
5. 7	d	$\pi=3.14; c=9.42.$

SET 3

Formula No.	Evaluate	If
1. 2	l	$A=42; w=6.$
2. 3	a	$A=50; b=5.$
3. 4	b	$A=56; h=8.$
4. 5	B	$V=49; h=7.$
5. 6	r	$d=60; t=2.$

SET 4

Formula No.	Evaluate	If
1. 8	t	$i=8; p=40; r=.04.$
2. 10	r	$c=31.4; \pi=3.14.$
3. 9	l	$V=160; w=4; h=5.$
4. 8	p	$i=32; r=.10; t=4.$
5. 8	r	$i=36; p=60; t=10.$

SET 5

Formula No.	Evaluate	If
1. 11	A	$p=50; i=7.$
2. 12	s	$c=94; g=18.$
3. 13	l	$c=40; s=36.$
4. 14	p	$l=12; w=8.$
5. 16	A	$p=50; r=.06; t=8.$

SET 6

Formula No.	Evaluate	If
1. 11	p	$A=64; i=14.$
2. 12	c	$s=80; g=10.$
3. 13	c	$l=5; s=30.$
4. 13	s	$l=12; c=75.$
5. 15	V	$v=94; g=32; t=2.$

SET 7

Formula No.	Evaluate	If
1. 14	w	$p=20; l=6.$
2. 15	t	$v=116; V=20; g=32.$
3. 16	t	$A=44; p=40; r=.05.$
4. 14	l	$p=26; w=5.$
5. 16	r	$A=104; p=80; t=5.$

SET 8

Formula No.	Evaluate	If
1. 18	a	$n=9.$
2. 19	A	$a=8; b=4.$
3. 20	V	$B=9; h=7.$
4. 21	I	$E=110; R=5.$
5. 23	v	$s=60; t=5.$

SET 9

Formula No.	Evaluate	If
1. 21	E	$I=11; R=20.$
2. 22	m	$d=2; v=5.$
3. 23	s	$v=15; t=6.$
4. 24	v	$a=30; t=4.$
5. 19	b	$A=24; a=6.$

SET 10

Formula No.	Evaluate	If
1. 18	n	$a=60.$
2. 21	R	$I=10; E=220.$
3. 22	v	$d=2; m=16.$
4. 23	t	$v=25; s=100.$
5. 24	t	$a=32; v=128.$

SET 11

Formula No.	Evaluate	If
1. 25	A	$s=5.$
2. 26	A	$\pi=\frac{22}{7}; r=7.$
3. 27	V	$s=6.$
4. 28	V	$\pi=\frac{22}{7}; r=14; h=5.$
5. 28	V	$\pi=3.14; r=5; h=4.$

SET 12

Formula No.	Evaluate	If
1. 32	F	$C=100.$
2. 32	F	$C=40.$
3. 32	C	$F=86.$
4. 32	C	$F=140.$
5. 32	C	$F=50.$

SET 13

Formula No.	Evaluate	If
1. 17	l	$a=3$; $n=5$; $d=4$.
2. 33	A	$h=8$; $b=10$; $b'=4$.
3. 34	S	$n=7$; $a=2$; $l=8$.
4. 33	A	$h=4$; $b=9$; $b'=3$.
5. 34	S	$n=6$; $a=5$; $l=30$.

SET 14

Formula No.	Evaluate	If
1. 31	F	$m=100$; $v=20$; $g=32$; $r=10$.
2. 29	S	$a=4$; $r=\frac{1}{2}$.
3. 39	I	$n=5$; $E=20$; $R=5$; $r=4$.
4. 40	S	$r=2$; $l=64$; $a=2$.
5. 40	S	$r=3$; $l=81$; $a=3$.

SET 15

Formula No.	Evaluate	If
1. 31	m	$F=2$; $g=32$; $r=1$; $v=2$.
2. 29	a	$S=12$; $r=\frac{1}{3}$.
3. 39	E	$I=3$; $n=4$; $R=4$; $r=3$.
4. 40	a	$S=341$; $r=4$; $l=256$.
5. 40	l	$S=62$; $r=2$; $a=4$.

SET 16

Formula No.	Evaluate	If
1. 17	d	$l=17$; $a=5$; $n=7$.
2. 33	h	$A=64$; $b=9$; $b'=7$.
3. 34	n	$S=84$; $a=4$; $l=24$.
4. 33	h	$A=50$; $b=12$; $b'=8$.
5. 34	n	$S=135$; $a=3$; $l=27$.

SET 17

Formula No.	Evaluate	If
1. 17	n	$l=20$; $a=6$; $d=2$.
2. 33	b	$A=72$; $h=6$; $b'=10$.
3. 34	a	$S=110$; $n=10$; $l=20$.
4. 33	b'	$A=96$; $h=8$; $b=13$.
5. 34	l	$S=55$; $n=5$; $a=3$.

SET 18

Formula No.	Evaluate	If
1. 35	V	$V'=3$; $P'=4$; $P=6$.
2. 35	P	$V'=8$; $P'=15$; $V=5$.
3. 36	L_2	$W_1=5$; $L_1=18$; $W_2=9$.
4. 36	W_2	$W_1=3$; $L_1=32$; $L_2=12$.
5. 35	V'	$V=1$; $P=15$; $P'=5$.

SET 19

Formula No.	Evaluate	If
1. 38	V	$P=10$; $T=4$; $P'=15$; $V'=4$; $T'=12$.
2. 38	P	$V=6$; $T=2$; $P'=3$; $V'=15$; $T'=5$.
3. 38	T	$P=5$; $V=6$; $P'=20$; $V'=1$; $T'=5$.
4. 38	V'	$P=3$; $V=14$; $T=7$; $P'=4$; $T'=6$.
5. 38	T'	$P=9$; $V=6$; $T=3$; $P'=24$; $V'=3$.

SET 20

Formula No.	Evaluate	If
1. 16	p	$A=56$; $r=.04$; $t=3$.
2. 16	p	$A=108$; $r=.02$; $t=4$.
3. 16	p	$A=212$; $r=.06$; $t=1$.
4. 16	p	$A=92$; $r=.03$; $t=5$.
5. 16	p	$A=30$; $r=.05$; $t=4$.

SET 21

Formula No.	Evaluate	If
1. 37	f	$d=6$; $D=3$.
2. 37	f	$d=24$; $D=8$.
3. 37	d	$f=3$; $D=4$.
4. 37	D	$f=4$; $d=8$.
5. 37	d	$f=16$; $D=48$.

SET 22

Formula No.	Evaluate	If
1. 29	r	$S=8$; $a=4$.
2. 39	R	$I=4$; $n=5$; $E=16$; $r=3$.
3. 39	R	$I=2$; $n=8$; $E=12$; $r=4$.
4. 39	r	$I=5$; $n=3$; $E=20$; $R=6$.
5. 39	r	$I=2$; $n=4$; $R=8$; $R=4$.

SET 23

Formula No.	Evaluate	If
1. 39	n	$I=2$; $E=7$; $R=2$; $r=3$.
2. 39	n	$I=4$; $E=12$; $R=6$; $r=2$.
3. 40	r	$S=62$; $l=32$; $a=2$.
4. 40	r	$S=363$; $l=243$; $a=3$.
5. 40	r	$S=124$; $l=4$; $a=64$.

REVIEW OF UNIT TWELVE

1. Solve for n by rearranging formula $C=np$.
2. Rearrange formula $A=\pi ab$, solving for a.
3. Transform formula $P=\frac{F}{A}$, solving for F.
4. Using formula $r=\frac{p}{b}$, solve for b.
5. Transform formula $p=b+2e$, solving for e.
6. Solve for r', using formula $\frac{c}{c'}=\frac{r}{r'}$.
7. Rearrange formula $C=\frac{5}{9}(F-32)$, solving for F.
8. Solve for h by transforming formula $A=2\pi rh+2\pi r^2$.
9. Transform formula $\frac{1}{R}=\frac{1}{R_1}+\frac{1}{R_2}$, solving for R_2.
10. Solve for r by rearranging formula $S=\frac{rl-a}{r-1}$.

Find the value of:

11. s when $R=8$ and $c=9$, using the formula $R=\frac{s}{c}$.
12. C when $F=185$, using the formula $F=\frac{9}{5}C+32$.
13. t when $P=40$, $F=60$, and $d=10$, using the formula $P=\frac{Fd}{t}$.
14. R_4 when $R_1=800$, $R_2=480$, and $R_3=750$, using the formula $\frac{R_1}{R_2}=\frac{R_3}{R_4}$.
15. b' when $A=198$, $h=9$, and $b=25$, using the formula $A=\frac{h}{2}(b+b')$.
16. n when $l=96$, $a=12$, and $d=6$, using the formula $l=a+(n-1)d$.
17. D when $f=24$ and $d=72$, using the formula $\frac{1}{f}=\frac{1}{D}+\frac{1}{d}$.
18. l when $A=374$, $\pi=\frac{22}{7}$, and $r=7$, using the formula $A=\pi r^2+\pi rl$.
19. p when $A=384$, $r=.03$, and $t=20$, using the formula $A=p+prt$.
20. n when $I=3$, $E=12$, $R=10$, and $r=2$, using the formula $I=\frac{nE}{R+nr}$.

CUMULATIVE ALGEBRA REVIEW

1. The selling price equals the cost plus the operating expenses plus the profit. Write a formula expressing the profit (p) in terms of the selling price (s), cost (c), and operating expenses (e).
2. Subtract the sum of $2x^2-3x+8$ and x^2-9x-3 from $3x^2-4x-1$.
3. Is $x^4-x^3y+x^2y^2-xy^3+y^4$ the correct quotient when x^5-y^5 is divided by $x-y$? Check by numerical substitution using $x=2$ and $y=3$.
4. Combine: $a-3b-\frac{a^2}{a+3b}$
5. Simplify: $\frac{10^{19}\times 10^8}{3\cdot 10^{11}}$
6. Solve and check: $\frac{3t-1}{t+6}-2=\frac{t+2}{t-9}$
7. Transform the formula $S=\frac{a}{1-r}$, solving for r.
8. Solve and check: $(x-4)(x+2)-(x^2-2)=4$
9. Find the value of F if $W=360$, $h=5$, and $d=15$, using the formula $\frac{F}{W}=\frac{h}{d}$.
10. Divide a 15-foot board into two parts so that one part is $\frac{2}{3}$ as long as the other.

KEYED ACHIEVEMENT TEST

1. Divide $16x^4-625y^4$ by $2x+5y$. ㉟
2. Solve and check: $30y+40(70-y)=2550$ ㊱
3. Find product mentally: $(6ab^2-5y^3)(6ab^2+5y^3)$ ㊼
4. Factor: $3n^3-27n^2-156n$. (55)
5. Combine: $\frac{3c}{c-d}+\frac{2c^2}{c^2-d^2}-\frac{c}{c+d}$ (63)
6. Solve and check: $x-\frac{x}{2}+\frac{x}{4}-\frac{x}{8}=10$ (67)
7. Solve for x and check: $\frac{m}{x}=n$ (77)
8. Rearrange formula $S=\frac{\pi DN}{12}$, solving for N. (78)
9. Find the value of P if $H.P.=25$, $L=2.5$, $A=30$, and $N=125$, using the formula $H.P.=\frac{PLAN}{33000}$ (79)
10. How can you change \$7 in dimes and quarters, using an equal number of each kind of coin? ㊷

INTRODUCTION TO UNIT THIRTEEN

In formulas and equations having two literal quantities (letters), any change in one quantity will produce a change in the other.

In the equation $y = x + 6$, when x is 3, then $y = 3 + 6$ or $y = 9$; when $x = 5$, then $y = 5 + 6$ or $y = 11$. The value of y depends on the value we give x.

Both x and y are called *variables* because they may change in value. x is the *independent variable* because it may assume any value. y is the *dependent variable* because its values depend on the values of the independent variable, x. Some quantities do not change in value. They are called *constants*. Any arithmetic number is a constant.

When one quantity depends upon another for its value, the first quantity is said to be a *function* of the second quantity. In the formula $c = 3.14d$, c is a function of d.

A formula shows the relationship between quantities by means of symbols, letters, and numbers. Sometimes we are required to determine what effect a change in one quantity of a formula will have upon another.

What effect does a change in the length of the side of a square have upon the perimeter of the square? To determine this, let us construct a table of values by assuming values for s in the formula $p = 4s$ to obtain corresponding values for p.

s	2	4	5	6	8	10
p	8	16	20	24	32	40

From this table we see,

    Doubling the values of s (from 2 to 4) will double the value of p (from 8 to 16).

    Trebling the value of s (from 2 to 6) will treble the value of p (from 8 to 24).

    Halving the value of s (from 10 to 5) will halve the value of p (from 40 to 20)

A change in the value of s produces the same change in the value of p. Or, p *varies directly* as s.

What effect does a change in the rate of speed have upon the length of time it takes to travel 150 miles? To determine this, let us construct a table of values by assuming values for r in the formula $t = \dfrac{150}{r}$ to obtain corresponding values for t.

From this table we see,

r	10	15	25	30	50	75
t	15	10	6	5	3	2

    Doubling the value of r (from 15 to 30) will halve the value of t (from 10 to 5).

    Trebling the value of r (from 25 to 75) will make t equal one third its original value (from 6 to 2).

    Halving the value of r (from 50 to 25) will double the value of t (from 3 to 6).

A change in the value of r produces an inverse change in the value of t. Or, t *varies inversely* as r.

What effect does a change in the length of the side of a square have upon the area of the square? To determine this, let us construct a table of values by assuming values for s in the formula $A = s^2$ to obtain corresponding values for A.

s	1	2	3	4	6	12
A	1	4	9	16	36	144

From this table we see,

    Doubling (or 2 times) the value of s (from 1 to 2) makes A equal 4 times its original value (from 1 to 4).

    Trebling (or 3 times) the value of s (from 2 to 6) makes A equal 9 times its original value (from 4 to 36).

    Halving the value of s (from 4 to 2) makes A equal one fourth its original value (from 16 to 4).

    A change in the value of s produces the square of this change in the value of A. Or A *varies directly as the square* of s.

In this unit the principles of variation are used in evaluating formulas.

UNIT THIRTEEN—VARIATION

EXERCISE 80

Variation with Formulas

I. Aim: To use the principles of variation in evaluating formulas.

II. Procedure

1. Types of variation studied in these exercises:
   a) Direct Variation.
      In the formula $A = lw$, A varies directly as w if l is constant.
   b) Inverse Variation.

      In the formula $r = \dfrac{d}{t}$, r varies inversely as t if d is constant.

   c) Direct as the Square Variation.
      In the formula $A = \pi r^2$, A varies directly as the square of r.

2. To evaluate formulas using variation select either of the following methods:
   a) Solution 1.
      (1) Find the ratio of the 2 independent variables.
      (2) Select the type of variation necessary to relate the dependent variable to the independent variable. Find the correct ratio of the two dependent variables.
      (3) Multiply the known dependent variable by the ratio found in step 2 to get answer.
   b) Solution 2.
      Write a proportion in which the ratio of the 2 independent variables is related to the ratio of the 2 dependent variables following the principles outlined in the different types of variation.

III. Sample Solutions

1. If $A = 36$ when $w = 4$ in the formula $A = lw$, find A if $w = 12$ and l is constant.

   Solution 1

   (1) $\dfrac{12}{4} = 3$

   (2) A varies directly as w. Use ratio 3.
   (3) $\quad\;\; 36$
   $\quad\underline{\times \quad 3}$
   $\quad\;\, 108$
   Answer, 108

   Solution 2

   Let $x =$ area of 2nd rectangle

   * $\dfrac{x}{36} = \dfrac{12}{4}$ * Area of 2nd rectangle is to area of 1st rectangle as the width of 2nd rectangle is to the width of 1st rectangle.

   $\dfrac{x}{36} = 3$

   $x = 108$
   Answer, 108

2. If $r = 45$ when $t = 2$ in the formula $r = \dfrac{d}{t}$, find r if $t = 6$ and d is constant.

   Solution 1

   (1) $\dfrac{6}{2} = 3$

   (2) r varies inversely as t. Use ratio $\frac{1}{3}$.
   (3) $\frac{1}{3} \times 45 = 15$
   Answer, 15

   Solution 2

   Let $x =$ 2nd rate

   * $\dfrac{x}{45} = \dfrac{2}{6}$ * 2nd rate is to 1st rate as 1st time is to 2nd time.

   $6x = 90$
   $x = 15$ Answer, 15

3. If $A = 154$ when $r = 7$ in the formula $A = \pi r^2$, find A if $r = 28$.

Solution 1

(1) $\dfrac{28}{7} = 4$

(2) A varies directly as the square of r. Use ratio 16.

(3)
$$
\begin{array}{r}
154 \\
\times\ 16 \\
\hline
924 \\
154 \\
\hline
2464
\end{array}
$$

Answer, 2464

Solution 2

Let $x =$ area of 2nd circle.

* $\dfrac{x}{154} = \dfrac{(28)^2}{(7)^2}$

$\dfrac{x}{154} = \dfrac{28 \times 28}{7 \times 7}$

$\dfrac{x}{154} = 16$

$x = 2464$

* Area of 2nd circle is to area of 1st circle as the square of the radius of the 2nd circle is to the square of the radius of the 1st circle.

Preliminary Examples

Use the list of formulas on page 200. Take formula corresponding to the number given in the first column. Find whether the dependent variable varies: directly as, inversely as, or directly as the square of the independent variable. Obviously, in these exercises, the remaining terms in the formula are to be considered constant terms.

	Formula No.	Dependent Variable	Independent Variable	Constant Terms
1.	7	c	d	π
2.	2	A	l	w
3.	6	d	t	r
4.	18	a	n	360
5.	21	I	R	E
6.	28	V	r	π; h
7.	34	S	n	a; 1; 2
8.	30	s	t	a
9.	39	I	E	R; r; n
10.	35	V	P	V'; P'

DIAGNOSTIC TEST

Find the missing word in examples 1, 2, and 3.　(*Do not write in this book.*)

1. In the formula $A = bh$ if b is doubled and h is constant, then A is _____.

2. In the formula $a = \dfrac{360}{n}$ if n is halved, then a is _____.

3. In the formula $A = s^2$ if s is trebled, then A is _____.
In examples 4, 5 and 6 find the dependent variable using the independent variable.

4. In the formula $A = lw$, $A = 42$ when $l = 6$. Find the value of A when $l = 18$ and w is constant.

5. In the formula $I = \dfrac{E}{R}$, $I = 22$ when $R = 10$. Find the value of I when $R = 20$ and E is constant.

6. In the formula $s = \dfrac{at^2}{2}$, $s = 256$ when $t = 4$. Find the value of s when $t = 20$ and a is constant.

Related Practice Examples

Take formula from the list on page 200 corresponding to the number given.
Find the missing words in sets 1a, 1b, 2, and 3.

(*Do not write in this book.*)

SET 1a

1. In formula #1, if s is increased, then p is _____.
2. In formula #3, if a is doubled and b is constant, then A is _____.
3. In formula #6, if r is halved and t is constant, then d is _____.
4. In formula #9, if l is trebled and w and h are constant, then V is _____.
5. In formula #10, if r is doubled, then c is _____.

SET 1b

1. In formula #19, if b is decreased and a is constant, then A is _____.
2. In formula #21, if E is doubled and R is constant, then I is _____.
3. In formula #31, if m is trebled and g, r and v are constant then F is _____.
4. In formula #33, if h is halved and b and b' are constant, then A is _____.
5. In formula #36, if L_2 is doubled and W_2 and L_1 are constant, then W_1 is _____.

SET 2

1. In formula #18, if n is increased, then a is _____.
2. In formula #21, if R is decreased, and E is constant, then I is _____.
3. In formula #22, if v is doubled and m is constant, then d is _____.
4. In formula #31, if r is halved and g, v and m are constant, then F is _____.
5. In formula #35, if V' is trebled and V and P are constant then P' is _____.

SET 3

1. In formula #25, if s is increased, the A is _____.
2. In formula #26, if r is doubled, then A is _____.
3. In formula #28, if r is trebled and h is constant, then V is _____.
4. In formula #30, if t is halved and a is constant, then s is _____.
5. In formula #31, if v is doubled and m, g and r are constant then F is _____.

Use formula from the list on page 200 corresponding to number given. Find the dependent variable using the independent variable. Obviously, the remaining terms in the formula are to be considered constant terms.

SET 4a

	Formula No.	If	When	Evaluate Dependent Variable	When Independent Variable	Constant Terms
1.	1	$p=32$	$s=8$	p	$s=24$	4
2.	2	$A=24$	$w=3$	A	$w=12$	l
3.	3	$A=35$	$a=5$	A	$a=10$	b
4.	4	$A=54$	$b=6$	A	$b=18$	h
5.	5	$V=28$	$h=4$	V	$h=2$	B
6.	6	$d=150$	$r=30$	d	$r=45$	t
7.	7	$c=22$	$d=7$	c	$d=21$	π
8.	8	$i=12$	$t=2$	i	$t=10$	$p; r$
9.	9	$V=36$	$l=6$	V	$l=2$	$w; h$
10.	10	$c=12.56$	$r=2$	c	$r=12$	$\pi; 2$

Formula No.	If	When	Evaluate Dependent Variable	When Independent Variable	Constant Terms
			SET 4b		
1. 19	$A = 12$	$b = 4$	A	$b = 12$	a; 2
2. 20	$V = 50$	$h = 2$	V	$h = 14$	B; 3
3. 21	$I = 11$	$E = 55$	I	$E = 220$	R
4. 21	$I = 5$	$E = 110$	I	$E = 22$	R
5. 22	$d = 4$	$m = 8$	d	$m = 12$	v
6. 23	$v = 7$	$s = 35$	v	$s = 70$	t
7. 24	$a = 5$	$v = 40$	a	$v = 24$	t
8. 28	$V = 462$	$h = 3$	V	$h = 15$	π; r
9. 33	$A = 40$	$h = 4$	A	$h = 5$	b; b'; 2
10. 36	$W_1 = 25$	$L_2 = 2$	W_1	$l_2 = 6$	W_2; L_1
			SET 5		
1. 18	$a = 120$	$n = 3$	a	$n = 9$	360
2. 18	$a = 72$	$n = 5$	a	$n = 20$	360
3. 21	$I = 55$	$R = 2$	I	$R = 22$	E
4. 21	$I = 20$	$R = 11$	I	$R = 55$	E
5. 22	$d = 6$	$v = 4$	d	$v = 16$	m
6. 22	$d = 2$	$v = 6$	d	$v = 3$	m.
7. 23	$v = 240$	$t = 8$	v	$t = 2$	s
8. 24	$a = 3$	$t = 18$	a	$t = 3$	v
9. 31	$F = 3$	$r = 4$	F	$r = 3$	m; v; g
10. 35	$V = 8$	$P = 4$	V	$P = 2$	V': P'
			SET 6		
1. 25	$A = 9$	$s = 3$	A	$s = 15$	
2. 25	$A = 64$	$s = 8$	A	$s = 2$	
3. 26	$A = 154$	$r = 7$	A	$r = 21$	π
4. 26	$A = 12.56$	$r = 2$	A	$r = 10$	π
5. 28	$V = 1232$	$r = 14$	V	$r = 7$	π; h
6. 28	$V = 157$	$r = 5$	V	$r = 1$	π; h
7. 30	$s = 144$	$t = 3$	s	$t = 9$	a; 2
8. 30	$s = 16$	$t = 1$	s	$t = 10$	a; 2
9. 31	$F = 3$	$V = 4$	F	$v = 12$	m; g; r
10. 31	$F = 3$	$v = 6$	F	$v = 4$	m; g; r

REVIEW OF UNIT THIRTEEN

Find what effect a change in one quantity has upon a related quantity:

1. If the value of s is halved in the formula $p = 3s$, then the value of p is ——.
2. If the value of t is trebled in the formula $r = \frac{270}{t}$, then the value of r is ——.
3. If the value of s is doubled in the formula $A = 6s^2$, then the value of A is ——.
4. In the formula $F = Ma$ if the value of a is doubled and M remains constant, then the value of F is ——.
5. In the formula $P = I^2R$ if the value of I is halved and R remains constant, then the value of P is ——.

Find the required values, using the principles of variation:

6. In the formula $c = \pi d$, $c = 66$ when $d = 21$. Find the value of c when $d = 63$.
7. In the formula $i = prt$, $i = 48$ when $p = 320$. Find the value of i when $p = 1{,}600$ and r and t are constant.
8. In the formula $r = \frac{p}{b}$, $r = 0.2$ when $b = 80$. Find the value of r when $b = 20$ and p remains constant.
9. In the formula $P = \frac{W}{t}$, $P = 60$ when $W = 300$. Find the value of P when $W = 15$ and t remains constant.
10. In the formula $s = 16t^2$, $s = 400$ when $t = 5$. Find the value of s when $t = 20$.

CUMULATIVE ALGEBRA REVIEW

1. Express as a formula: The volume of a cube (V) is equal to the cube of the edge (e).
2. Transform the following formula by removing parentheses: $A = \frac{h}{2}(b + b')$.
3. Find the value of the expression $x^3 - 13x - 14$ when $x = 4$. Determine whether this value equals the remainder when $x^3 - 13x - 14$ is divided by $x - 4$.
4. Transform formula $S = \frac{n}{2}(a + l)$, solving for a.
5. a) Find the product mentally: $(6c^3 - \frac{1}{2}d^2)^2$
   b) Factor: $5x^5 - 80x$.
6. Combine: $\frac{3a - 2b}{8b} - \frac{a - 5b}{4a}$
7. Solve and check: $\frac{y - 6}{y - 7} = \frac{y + 9}{y + 3}$
8. Find the value of R if $R_1 = 4$, $R_2 = 2$, and $R_3 = 6$, using the formula $\frac{1}{R} = \frac{1}{R_1} + \frac{1}{R_2} + \frac{1}{R_3}$.
9. In the formula $d = \frac{m}{v}$, $d = 25$ when $v = 9$. Find the value of d when $v = 15$ and m remains constant.
10. A lamp was sold for \$11 after a 12% discount on the list price was allowed. What was the list price?

KEYED ACHIEVEMENT TEST

1. Solve and check: $3x - 2x(4 - x) = 2x^2 + 15$ ㊱
2. Subtract $2c^2 - 20$ from $3c^4 - 14$. ㉖
3. Divide: $\frac{b^2 - 16a^2}{8ab} \div \frac{b^2 - ab - 12a^2}{4b^2}$ (59)
4. Combine: $\frac{3b}{b - c} + \frac{2c^2}{b^2 - c^2} - \frac{4c}{b + c}$ (63)
5. Solve and check: $\frac{x - 2}{x} + \frac{x + 5}{x + 2} = 2$ (68)
6. Solve for y and check: $\frac{y - a}{b} = \frac{y - b}{a}$ (77)
7. Transform formula $E = Ir + IR$, solving for I. (78)
8. Find the value of h if $A = 785$, $\pi = 3.14$, and $d = 10$, using the formula $A = \pi dh + \frac{1}{2}\pi d^2$. (79)
9. a) In the formula $I = \frac{P}{E}$, $I = 2$ when $E = 55$. Find the value of I when $E = 220$ and P remains constant. (80)
   b) In the formula $D = \frac{CdAV^2}{2}$, $D = 60$ when $V = 100$. Find the value of D when $V = 300$, and C, d, and A remain constant. (80)
10. An airplane is sighted 72 miles from an airbase, flying at an estimated speed of 180 m.p.h. toward the airbase. If it takes an interceptor airplane 4 minutes to take off, flying at a speed of 300 m.p.h., how far from the base will it intercept the first airplane? ㊸

INTRODUCTION TO UNIT FOURTEEN

Pupils are already familiar with the bar, line, and circle graphs and the pictograph. A *graph* is a picture showing the relationship of two or more number facts. Since an equation or formula having two literal quantities expresses the relationship between the quantities, the graph of the equation or formula is the picture of this relationship.

A simple equation with one unknown is satisfied by only one value. The equation $x+6=8$ is satisfied only when $x=2$. However, an equation with two unknowns (or two variables) is satisfied by an infinite number of pairs of values. The equation $x+y=8$ is satisfied when $x=1$ and $y=7$, $x=2$ and $y=6$, $x=3\frac{1}{2}$ and $y=4\frac{1}{2}$, $x=5.3$ and $y=2.7$, $x=-1$ and $y=9$, etc. Other pairs of values satisfying the equation may be obtained by assuming some value for one variable and determining the corresponding value of the other variable. By drawing the graph of the equation it is possible to get a picture of the relationship of the variables.

Simple equations with two unknowns are sometimes called *linear equations* because the graphs of these equations are straight lines.

Frequently in problems dealing with two related quantities it is difficult to represent the quantities in terms of only one unknown. However, if two unknowns are used, two equations containing the unknowns must be formulated and must be solved together. Thus, a pair of values must be found which satisfies both equations, often called *simultaneous equations*. This may be done graphically by drawing the graphs of each equation and determining the *coordinates* (values of the two variables) of the point of intersection.

Sometimes the graphs of the two given equations are a pair of parallel lines. In this case there is no common point and these equations, called *inconsistent equations*, do not have a common solution. The inconsistent equations $x+y=9$ and $x+y=4$ illustrate why there is no common solution. It is impossible for the sum of the same two numbers to equal first nine and then four.

The graphs of two given equations may also be one and the same line. In this case the equations, called *dependent equations*, have many common solutions. The dependent equations $x-2y=9$ and $4x-8y=36$ illustrate why the identical line is produced. The second equation may be obtained by multiplying both sides of the first equation by 4. Thus, the two given equations are really the same equation.

Simultaneous linear equations may also be solved algebraically. Students generally find the algebraic methods easier than the graphic method. In the algebraic solutions one of the unknowns is eliminated so that a simple equation in only the other unknown remains. This elimination may be accomplished either by the processes of addition or subtraction or by the substitution of an equal expression for one of the unknowns.

Graphs of formulas are useful in industry and science. Although direct substitution in the formula produces more accurate results, the graph of the formula provides a method of getting answers without doing the actual computation. See page 217.

UNIT FOURTEEN—SYSTEMS OF EQUATIONS

EXERCISE 81

Graphing Equations

I. Aim: To draw a graph of a linear equation having two unknowns.

II. Procedure

1. Solve the given equation for y.
2. Make a table of values, heading one column "x," and the other column "y."
   a) Take a value (any number) for the variable x. Then, using the rearranged equation (step 1), find the corresponding value of "y."
   b) Write the assumed x-value and the corresponding y-value in the table. These values form the co-ordinates of a point on the graph.
   c) Take at least two other values for x and find their corresponding values for y. Write these values in the table.
3. Plot these points by locating their co-ordinates (x and y values). If the x-value (abscissa) is a positive number, count horizontally to the right of the y-axis. If it is a negative number, count to the left of the y-axis. If the y-value (ordinate) is a positive number, count vertically above the x-axis. If it is a negative number, count below the x-axis.
4. Draw a line through these three points.
5. To check, take any other point on the line and find its co-ordinates (x and y value). If the line is the graph of the given equation, then the co-ordinates of this point should satisfy the equation.
   Note: If an equation has only one unknown term, its graph is a line parallel to an axis.
   a) If the unknown is a y term, then the line will be parallel to the x-axis.
   b) If the unknown is an x term, then the line will be parallel to the y-axis.

III. Sample Solutions

1. $x + y = 5$
   $y = 5 - x$

x	y
1	4
3	2
5	0

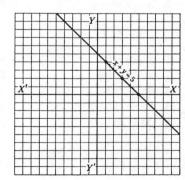

2. $2y = 8x$
   $y = 4x$

x	y
0	0
2	8
−1	−4

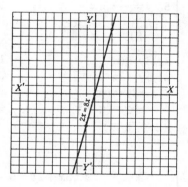

3. $2x - y = -3$
   $2x + 3 = y$
   $y = 2x + 3$

x	y
0	3
2	7
−4	−5

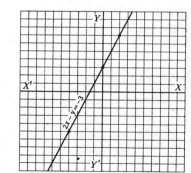

4. $3x + 4y = 8$
   $4y = 8 - 3x$
   $y = \dfrac{8 - 3x}{4}$

x	y
0	2
4	−1
−4	5

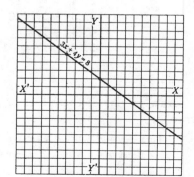

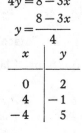

Preliminary Examples

On graph paper draw the axes and locate the following points:

Note—The first number is the x-value and the second number is the y-value of the point.

SET 1	SET 2	SET 3	SET 4	SET 5
1. $(3, 4)$	**1.** $(-2, 3)$	**1.** $(3, -2)$	**1.** $(-1, -1)$	**1.** $(0, 0)$
2. $(5, 2)$	**2.** $(-1, 4)$	**2.** $(6, -3)$	**2.** $(-5, -2)$	**2.** $(0, 5)$
3. $(8, 1)$	**3.** $(-5, 2)$	**3.** $(8, -5)$	**3.** $(-3, -4)$	**3.** $(1, 0)$
4. $(2, 7)$	**4.** $(-7, 1)$	**4.** $(2, -4)$	**4.** $(-6, -3)$	**4.** $(0, -3)$
5. $(4, 8)$	**5.** $(-4, 4)$	**5.** $(3, -7)$	**5.** $(-8, -6)$	**5.** $(-5, 0)$

DIAGNOSTIC TEST

Draw graphs of the following equations:

1. $y = x + 3$	**4.** $y = 2x$	**7.** $2x + y = 0$	**10.** $4x + 2y = 12$
2. $x + y = 4$	**5.** $2y = -8x$	**8.** $3x + y = 10$	**11.** $x = 6$
3. $x - y = 1$	**6.** $2y = x$	**9.** $5x - 2y = -2$	

Related Practice Examples

Draw graphs of the following equations:

SET 1	SET 2	SET 3	SET 4
1. $y = x + 1$	**1.** $x + y = 3$	**1.** $x - y = 2$	**1.** $y = x$
2. $y = x - 2$	**2.** $x + y = 7$	**2.** $x - y = 5$	**2.** $y = 3x$
3. $y = 2 + x$	**3.** $x + y = -4$	**3.** $x - y = -1$	**3.** $y = -x$
4. $y = 5 - x$	**4.** $y - 2 = x$	**4.** $4 - y = x$	**4.** $y = -4x$
5. $y = -2 - x$	**5.** $y - x = -5$	**5.** $3 - x = -y$	**5.** $-y = -2x$

SET 5	SET 6	SET 7	SET 8
1. $3y = 6x$	**1.** $3y = x$	**1.** $x + y = 0$	**1.** $2x + y = 5$
2. $4y = 7x$	**2.** $4y = x$	**2.** $x - 3y = 0$	**2.** $y + 3x = 3$
3. $-2y = 6x$	**3.** $-2y = x$	**3.** $4x + 2y = 0$	**3.** $4x = 15 - y$
4. $-6y = -24x$	**4.** $-5y = -x$	**4.** $8y + 2x = 0$	**4.** $10 = 3x + y$
5. $3y = -5x$	**5.** $-9y = 3x$	**5.** $3x - 2y = 0$	**5.** $2x - y = -4$

SET 9	SET 10	SET 11
1. $3x + 2y = 6$	**1.** $2x + 2y = 6$	**1.** $y = 2$
2. $4x + 3y = 12$	**2.** $6x + 3y = 9$	**2.** $x = 4$
3. $5x - 2y = 20$	**3.** $8x - 2y = 10$	**3.** $x = -3$
4. $4x - 5y = 6$	**4.** $9y - 12x = 15$	**4.** $y = -7$
5. $2x - 3y = -12$	**5.** $10x - 4y = 12$	**5.** $x = -1$

Miscellaneous Examples

Draw graphs of these sets of equations. Place each set of lines on a separate sheet. Then analyze the graphs:

1.	2.	3.	4.	5.
$x + y = 3$	$x + y = 6$	$x + y = 2$	$x + y = 4$	$x + y = 6$
$x + y = 4$	$x - y = 4$	$3x + 3y = 6$	$5x - 2y = -1$	$x + y = -2$
			$3x - 4y = 5$	$x - 3y = -10$
				$3x - y = 14$

APPLICATIONS — GRAPHS OF FORMULAS

Using graphs to determine values

In problems where the solution requires the use of a formula for which a graph is available, answers may be obtained directly from the graph. For example:

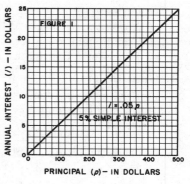

To find the annual interest at 5% on a principal of $340 by means of the graph in figure 1:

1. Find the point where the vertical line representing the principal of $340 crosses the line representing the formula.
2. Find the horizontal line that passes through this point.
3. Find the value represented by this line. It is $17 interest.

To find the principal that must be invested at 5% to earn $23 interest each year:

1. Find the point where the horizontal line representing $23 interest crosses the line representing the formula.
2. Find the vertical line that passes through this point.
3. Find the value represented by this line. It is $460 principal.

Practice Problems

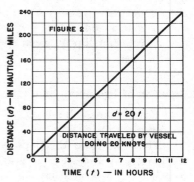

The graph in figure 2 shows the relationship between the time and distance traveled by a vessel doing 20 knots (nautical miles per hour).
Answer the following directly from the graph:

1. How far does a steamer travel in $3\frac{1}{2}$ hours at 20 knots?
2. At 20 knots how long will it take a submarine to go 170 nautical miles?
3. If a dirigible averages 20 knots, how far can it go in $4\frac{1}{4}$ hours?
4. How long will it take a cruiser doing 20 knots to go 210 nautical miles?
5. At 20 knots how far can a destroyer go in $6\frac{3}{4}$ hours?

Drawing graphs of formulas

To draw the graph of a formula having two literal quantities such as $i = .05p$ (see figure 1):

1. Make a table of values showing the relationship between the quantities. Substitute values for p in the formula $i = .05p$ to obtain corresponding values for i. Write the related values in tabular form.

p	$100	$200	$240	$300	$360	$400
i	$5	$10	$12	$15	$18	$20

2. On graph paper draw two guide lines (axes), the horizontal scale at the bottom representing one of the literal quantities and the vertical scale on the left representing the other literal quantity. Scales must be selected so that numbers in the table may be represented conveniently. Label each scale. In figure 1, each square on the horizontal scale represents a principal of $20 and each square on the vertical scale represents an annual interest of $1.

3. Locate and mark the points where the lines representing pairs of corresponding values cross each other. In figure 1, points representing $p = 100, $i = 5; $p = 200, $i = 10; $p = 400, $i = 20 were used.

4. Draw a line through these points. This line is the graph of the formula. The graph of the formula $i = .05p$ is a straight line. When the graphs are straight lines, it is necessary to locate only two points, although the use of three points is recommended. Not all graphs of formulas are straight lines. The graph of the formula $A = s^2$ is a curved line.

5. Write the formula and title.

Practice Problems

1. Draw the graphs of the formulas showing the relationship between:
   a) Perimeter and length of side of a square: $p = 4s$.
   b) Absolute—Centigrade temperature readings: $A = C + 273$.
   c) Complementary angles: $B = 90 - A$.   d) Radius and diameter of a circle: $r = \dfrac{d}{2}$.
   e) Fahrenheit-Centigrade temperature readings: $F = 1.8C + 32$.

2. Draw the graphs of the formulas showing the relationship between:
   a) Perimeter and length of side of a regular hexagon: $p = 6s$.
   b) Circumference and radius of a circle: $c = 6.28r$.   c) Feet and inches: $f = \dfrac{i}{12}$.
   d) Supplementary angles: $M = 180 - N$.   e) Annual interest at 2% and principal: $i = .02p$.

3. Develop the formula from the given facts, then draw the graph of the formula in each of the following:
   a) Money is invested at $3\frac{1}{2}$% interest. Draw a graph showing the relationship between the annual interest and principal.
   b) An airplane flies at an average ground speed of 300 m.p.h. Draw a graph showing the relationship between distance and flying time.
   c) The sum of $100 is borrowed at 6% interest. Draw a graph showing the relationship between the total interest and the time (in years) for which the money is borrowed.
   d) The wage scale for a certain type of work is $1.50 per hour. Draw a graph showing the relationship between wages earned and the number of hours of work (40 hours maximum).
   e) The speed in feet per second equals $\frac{22}{15}$ times the speed in miles per hour. Draw a graph showing the relationship between speeds expressed in feet per second and in miles per hour.

Solution of Problems by Graphs

   Graphs may be used to solve problems. Suppose we are required to find:
   How far from the depot and at what time a truck leaving at noon, traveling at an average speed of 40 m.p.h., will overtake another truck which left the same depot 2 hours earlier and was averaging 30 m.p.h.?
   Figure 3 shows the first truck is overtaken 240 miles from the depot and at 6 P.M. The graph of $d = 30t$ represents the path of the first truck and the graph of $d = 40t$ represents the path of the second truck.

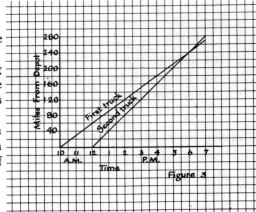

FIGURE 3

Practice Problems

   Use graphs to solve each of the following problems:

1. A freight train leaves a station at 4 P.M. traveling at the rate of 15 m.p.h. A passenger train leaves the same station 3 hours later headed for the same destination but goes at the rate of 45 m.p.h. At what time will the passenger train overtake the freight train?

2. A cruiser left port at 4 A.M. Four hours later a destroyer followed. How many hours will it take the destroyer, averaging 30 knots, to overtake the cruiser, averaging 18 knots?

3. Show by graph when the rate of 7 cents for printing each negative with free developing is cheaper than the rate of 5 cents for each print with a charge of 15 cents for developing.

4. One laundry charges $1.30 for the first 25 pieces and 5¢ for each additional piece. Another company charges $1.00 for the first 15 pieces and 4¢ for each additional piece. Show by graph when one rate is cheaper than the other.

5. Show by graph when a $25 weekly salary and 10% commission on sales is better than a $40 weekly salary and 6% commission.

EXERCISE 82

Solving by Graph

I. Aim: To solve graphically two linear equations having two unknowns.

Note to teacher—The sets of equations in Exercises 83 and 84 may also be solved graphically.

II. Procedure

1. Draw the graphs of the two equations on one set of axes.

2. Find the co-ordinates (x and y values) of the point where the two lines intersect. This is the common solution of the two equations.
Note—If the two lines are parallel, there is no common solution.

3. Check by substituting the x and y values (found in step 2) in the two given equations.

III. Sample Solutions

1. $x - y = 2$
$2x + 3y = 9$

$$x - y = 2$$
$$x - 2 = y$$
$$y = x - 2$$

$$2x + 3y = 9$$
$$3y = 9 - 2x$$
$$y = \frac{9 - 2x}{3}$$

x	y
0	−2
4	2
7	5

x	y
0	3
3	1
6	−1

2. $x + y = 0$
$3x - 2y = 10$

$$x + y = 0$$
$$y = -x$$

$$3x - 2y = 10$$
$$3x - 10 = 2y$$
$$\frac{3x - 10}{2} = y$$
$$y = \frac{3x - 10}{2}$$

x	y
0	0
3	−3
−4	4

x	y
0	−5
4	1
6	4

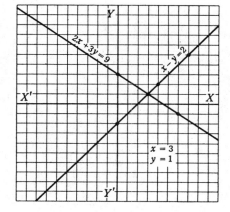

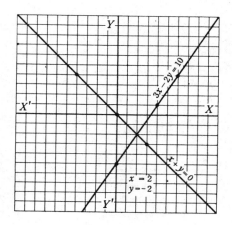

Check:

$3 - 1 = 2 \qquad 6 + 3 = 9$
$2 = 2 \qquad\qquad 9 = 9$
Answer, $x = 3$ and $y = 1$

Check:

$2 - 2 = 0 \qquad 6 + 4 = 10$
$0 = 0 \qquad\qquad 10 = 10$
Answer, $x = 2$ and $y = -2$

DIAGNOSTIC TEST

Solve the following sets of equations graphically:

1. $y = x + 1$
   $x + y = 5$

2. $y = -2x$
   $3x - y = 5$

3. $x - y = -7$
   $4x + 3y = 7$

4. $x - 6y = 2$
   $2x = 5y - 3$

5. $5x + 3y = 12$
   $x + 2y = 8$

6. $x + y = 0$
   $y = -3x$

Related Practice Examples

Solve the following pairs of equations graphically:

SET 1a

1. $y = x$
   $x + y = 4$
2. $y = 4x$
   $x + y = 5$
3. $x = 2y$
   $x - y = 2$
4. $x = 5y$
   $x - y = 4$
5. $y = 3x$
   $x + y = 8$

SET 1b

1. $y = x + 3$
   $x + y = 9$
2. $y = x - 1$
   $x + y = 11$
3. $x = y + 5$
   $2x + y = 13$
4. $x = y - 2$
   $3x - y = 8$
5. $y = x - 3$
   $2x + 3y = 16$

SET 1c

1. $x + y = 6$
   $x - y = 2$
2. $x + y = 5$
   $x - 2y = -4$
3. $2x - y = 0$
   $3y - 2x = 4$
4. $2x = 5 + y$
   $3x - 4y = 0$
5. $3x - 5y = 2$
   $4x - 6 = 5y$

SET 2a

1. $y = -x$
   $x - y = 2$
2. $y = -3x$
   $4x + y = 2$
3. $x = -4y$
   $2x + 3y = 10$
4. $x = 2$
   $2x - 3y = 13$
5. $3x = -5y$
   $x + 4y = -7$

SET 2b

1. $y = x - 4$
   $x + y = -2$
2. $x = y + 7$
   $y = 2x - 10$
3. $x + y = -1$
   $x - y = 3$
4. $x - y = 8$
   $2x + 3y = 6$
5. $3x + 4y = -6$
   $4x - 2y = 14$

SET 3a

1. $y = -2x$
   $x + y = 1$
2. $2y = -x$
   $x - y = -6$
3. $2x = -3y$
   $x + y = -2$
4. $x = -3$
   $x + 2y = 5$
5. $3x + y = 0$
   $2x + y = 2$

SET 3b

1. $y = 6 - x$
   $x - y = -10$
2. $x + y = 1$
   $x - y = -7$
3. $2x + y = -5$
   $x + 2y = 2$
4. $5x + y = -3$
   $2x = 3y - 8$
5. $4x - 3y = -11$
   $2x + 5y = 1$

SET 4a

1. $y = x$
   $x + y = -4$
2. $x = 3y$
   $2x - y = -5$
3. $3x = 2y$
   $x - 3y = 7$
4. $y = -5$
   $x - y = 2$
5. $4x - 2y = 0$
   $3x + 2y = -7$

SET 4b

1. $y = x + 1$
   $x + y = -5$
2. $x + y = -6$
   $x - y = 4$
3. $3x + y = -7$
   $x - 3y = 1$
4. $5x - 2y = -7$
   $5 = y - 3x$
5. $2x - 7y = 6$
   $5x - 8y = -4$

SET 5

1. $x = y - 1$
   $x + 4y = 4$
2. $x + y = 3$
   $2x - y = 6$
3. $x - 3y = 6$
   $3x - y = 2$
4. $3x - y = -12$
   $2x + 8 = y$
5. $4x - 5y = -4$
   $3x = 2y - 3$

SET 6

1. $y = x$
   $3x + y = 0$
2. $x + y = 0$
   $x - 2y = 0$
3. $y = -2x$
   $3y + x = 0$
4. $2x - 5y = 0$
   $3x = 2y$
5. $x - y = 0$
   $3y = 2x$

EXERCISE 83

Elimination by Addition or Subtraction

I. Aim: To solve two simultaneous linear equations having two unknowns by the addition or subtraction method of elimination.

II. Procedure

1. If the two equations have an unknown whose coefficients are of equal absolute value, then:

    a) If the coefficients have opposite signs, add the two equations, thus eliminating that unknown. See sample solution 1.
    b) If the coefficients have the same sign, subtract one equation from the other, thus eliminating that unknown. See sample solution 2.
    c) Solve the resulting equation for the remaining unknown.
    d) Substitute the value of this unknown in any equation containing the two unknowns to find the value of the other unknown.

2. a) If the two equations do not have an unknown whose coefficient in both is of equal absolute value, multiply, if necessary, either equation or both by such numbers as will make the coefficient of one of the unknowns of equal absolute value. See sample solutions 4, 5 and 6.
    b) Then follow procedure outlined in step 1.

3. Check by substituting both values in the two given equations.

III. Sample Solutions

1. $(1)\ x+y=8$ $(1)\ 5+y=8$ Check:
   $(2)\ \underline{x-y=2}$ $y=8-5$ $5+3=8$
   $\quad 2x\quad =10$ $y=3$ $8=8$
   $\qquad x=5$ $5-3=2$
   Answer, $x=5$ and $y=3$ $2=2$

2. $(1)\ 5m-3n=12$ $(1)\ 15-3n=12$ Check:
   $(2)\ \underline{2m-3n=\ 3}$ $-3n=12-15$ $15-3=12$
   $\quad 3m\quad =9$ $-3n=-3$ $12=12$
   $\qquad m=3$ $n=1$ $6-3=3$
   Answer, $m=3$ and $n=1$ $3=3$

3. $(1)\ 3x+\ y=10$ $(1)\ 3x-2=10$ Check:
   $(2)\ \underline{3x-2y=16}$ $3x=10+2$ $12-2=10$
   $\quad 3y=-6$ $3x=12$ $10=10$
   $\quad\ y=-2$ $x=4$ $12+4=16$
   Answer, $x=4$ and $y=-2$ $16=16$

4. $(1)\ 7x-2y=2$ $(2)\ 6+4y=30$ Check:
   $(2)\ \underline{3x+4y=30}$ $4y=30-6$ $14-12=2$
   $14x-4y=\ 4$ $4y=24$ $2=2$
   $\underline{3x+4y=30}$ $y=6$ $6+24=30$
   $17x\quad =34$ $30=30$
   $\qquad x=2$
   Answer, $x=2$ and $y=6$

5. $(1)\ 2x+\ 3y=6$ $(1)\ -6+3y=6$
   $(2)\ 3x+\ 4y=7$ $3y=6+6$
   $8x+12y=24$ $3y=12$
   $\underline{9x+12y=21}$ $y=4$
   $-x\quad =3$ Check:
   $\qquad x=-3$ $-6+12=6$
   Answer, $x=-3$ and $y=4$ $6=6$
   $-9+16=7$
   $7=7$

6. $(1)\ 8a-\ 6b=14$ $(1)\ 8-6b=14$
   $(2)\ -6a+\ 9b=-15$ $-6b=14-8$
   $24a-18b=42$ $-6b=6$
   $\underline{-12a+18b=-30}$ $b=-1$
   $12a\quad =12$ Check:
   $\qquad a=1$ $8+6=14$
   Answer, $a=1$ and $b=-1$ $14=14$
   $-6-9=-15$
   $-15=-15$

DIAGNOSTIC TEST

Solve and check:

1. $x+y=9$
   $x-y=3$

2. $a-3b=1$
   $2a+3b=20$

3. $5m+n=15$
   $3m+n=11$

4. $2c-5d=7$
   $4c-5d=19$

5. $2x-3y=-4$
   $2x+5y=12$

6. $-5b-4x=23$
   $2b-4x=2$

7. $2x+6y=18$
   $4x-3y=6$

8. $4x+2y=12$
   $5x+3y=17$

9. $6x-4y=20$
   $8x-10y=36$

Related Practice Examples

Solve and check:

SET 1

1. $x+y=12$
   $x-y=2$

2. $x+y=5$
   $x-y=1$

3. $x-y=5$
   $x+y=11$

4. $m-n=4$
   $m+n=6$

5. $c+d=13$
   $c-d=5$

6. $x-y=-1$
   $x+y=9$

7. $a+b=8$
   $a-b=-4$

8. $u-v=-3$
   $u+v=5$

9. $r+s=10$
   $r-s=0$

10. $d-t=0$
    $d+t=6$

SET 2

1. $3x+y=10$
   $4x-y=4$

2. $6x+y=27$
   $2x-y=5$

3. $5b-c=33$
   $7b+c=51$

4. $x+2y=15$
   $x-2y=-9$

5. $4x-5y=-2$
   $2x+5y=14$

6. $a+3b=8$
   $6a-3b=27$

7. $5b-6d=-1$
   $3b+6d=9$

8. $12x-9y=12$
   $x+9y=79$

9. $6r-7s=0$
   $4r+7s=70$

10. $4m+3n=15$
    $4m-3n=9$

SET 3

1. $2x+y=10$
   $x+y=6$

2. $4x+y=14$
   $3x+y=11$

3. $2c+d=13$
   $5c+d=28$

4. $5x+3y=30$
   $3x+3y=18$

5. $4x+5y=41$
   $7x+5y=53$

6. $3a+2b=17$
   $9a+2b=35$

7. $7m+4n=80$
   $6m+4n=72$

8. $-8b+7c=4$
   $4b+7c=40$

9. $5x+8y=23$
   $-3x+8y=-1$

10. $2x+9y=47$
    $-5x+9y=40$

SET 4

1. $3x-y=5$
   $x-y=1$

2. $5b-c=17$
   $3b-c=9$

3. $2m-n=2$
   $7m-n=12$

4. $4a-2b=2$
   $3a-2b=-1$

5. $9x-5y=-22$
   $6x-5y=-28$

6. $5c-4d=0$
   $8c-4d=12$

7. $4x-7y=12$
   $8x-7y=24$

8. $-5m-8n=-65$
   $m-8n=-35$

9. $4y-6x=12$
   $-2y-6x=-24$

10. $-7r-10s=-96$
    $-9r-10s=-112$

SET 5

1. $x+5y=7$
   $x+3y=5$

2. $b-3c=-2$
   $b-4c=-4$

3. $3c+4d=26$
   $3c-5d=8$

4. $-2y-3z=-13$
   $-2y+6z=14$

5. $-5r+4s=0$
   $-5r+6s=10$

6. $-4m-\ n=-16$
   $-4m-5n=-32$

7. $x+3y=9$
   $-x+7y=21$

8. $-9b-4c=-71$
   $9b-2c=59$

9. $8a+6b=56$
   $-8a-4b=-48$

10. $-6n+9r=33$
    $6n-2r=16$

SET 6

1. $x-y=4$
   $x+y=0$

2. $4x+y=3$
   $x+y=0$

3. $5a-b=-13$
   $2a-b=-7$

4. $m+6n=19$
   $m-2n=-13$

5. $3x-2y=-5$
   $5x+2y=-19$

6. $8r+6s=-54$
   $3r-6s=-12$

7. $2s+3t=13$
   $4s+3t=5$

8. $8r-7d=69$
   $6r-7d=57$

9. $9x+10y=32$
   $-3x+10y=56$

10. $-5x-8y=26$
    $-7x+8y=-2$

	SET 7	SET 8	SET 9
1.	$2a - b = 8$ $a + 2b = 9$	$2x + 3y = 5$ $3x - 2y = 1$	$4x + 6y = 10$ $10x - 8y = 2$
2.	$4c + d = 15$ $c + 4d = 15$	$3x + 5y = 27$ $2x + 3y = 17$	$12x - 16y = 20$ $8x + 6y = 30$
3.	$3x + 8y = -6$ $6x + 4y = -12$	$5x - 3y = -2$ $3x - 4y = -10$	$10a + 4b = 28$ $6a + 18b = 48$
4.	$4x + 2y = 12$ $2x + 6y = -4$	$7a + 4b = 51$ $6a - 5b = 10$	$20m - 6n = 72$ $8m - 4n = 32$
5.	$5m + 3n = 39$ $m - n = 3$	$9m - 5n = 13$ $4m - 6n = 2$	$15s + 10t = 40$ $9s + 8t = 32$
6.	$2x - 9y = 40$ $6x - 3y = 24$	$4x - 3y = -7$ $3x + 7y = 4$	$8a + 6b = 4$ $6a - 10b = -26$
7.	$2a - 3b = 13$ $3a - b = 2$	$6x + 2y = 18$ $5x - 9y = 47$	$9b - 4d = 30$ $6b + 14d = -30$
8.	$5x - 2y = 3$ $2x - y = 0$	$11c - 4d = 74$ $9c - 7d = 68$	$4x - 12y = -20$ $6x + 15y = 102$
9.	$5x - 2y = -4$ $3x + 4y = 34$	$5r - 3s = 12$ $8r - 2s = 8$	$12x - 9y = 21$ $10x - 6y = 10$
10.	$-4a - 6b = 36$ $2a - 9b = 78$	$-4b + 6c = 2$ $3b - 7c = 6$	$21x + 12y = -99$ $14x - 8y = -18$

EXERCISE 84

Elimination by Substitution

I. **Aim**: To solve two simultaneous linear equations having two unknowns by the substitution method of elimination.

II. **Procedure**

1. Select the simpler equation and solve it for one unknown in terms of the second unknown.

2. Using the other given equation, replace the unknown, solved for in step 1, by the expression found equal to it.

3. Then solve the resulting equation to find the value of the second unknown.

4. To find the first unknown, substitute the value of the second unknown (found in step 3) in the rearranged equation of step 1.

5. Check by substituting both values in the two given equations.

III. **Sample Solutions**

1. (1) $y = 2x$ (1) $y = 2x$
   (2) $3x + 2y = 21$ $y = 6$

   _____

   (2) $3x + 2(2x) = 21$ Check:
        $3x + 4x = 21$ $6 = 6$
            $7x = 21$ $9 + 12 = 21$
              $x = 3$ $21 = 21$

   Answer, $x = 3$ and $y = 6$

2. (1) $y = x - 3$ (1) $y = x - 3$
   (2) $2x + 3y = 16$ $y = 5 - 3$
                          $y = 2$

   _____

   (2) $2x + 3(x - 3) = 16$ Check:
        $2x + 3x - 9 = 16$ $2 = 5 - 3$
           $2x + 3x = 16 + 9$ $2 = 2$
                $5x = 25$ $10 + 6 = 16$
                 $x = 5$ $16 = 16$

   Answer, $x = 5$ and $y = 2$

3. (1) $y = -3x$ (1) $y = -3x$
     (2) $5x - y = 8$ $y = -3$

     (2) $5x - (-3x) = 8$ Check:
        $5x + 3x = 8$ $-3 = -3$
           $8x = 8$ $5 + 3 = 8$
            $x = 1$ $8 = 8$
Answer, $x = 1$ and $y = -3$

4. (1) $x = y - 4$ (1) $x = y - 4$
     (2) $4y - 3x = 14$ $x = 2 - 4$
                         $x = -2$

     (2) $4y - 3(y - 4) = 14$ Check:
        $4y - 3y + 12 = 14$ $-2 = 2 - 4$
          $4y - 3y = 14 - 12$ $-2 = -2$
                 $y = 2$ $8 + 6 = 14$
Answer, $x = -2$ and $y = 2$ $14 = 14$

5. (1) $x + 2y = 10$ (3) $x = 10 - 2y$
     (2) $2x - y = 5$ $x = 10 - 6$
                         $x = 4$

     (1) $x + 2y = 10$
     (3) $x = 10 - 2y$
     (2) $2(10 - 2y) - y = 5$ Check:
         $20 - 4y - y = 5$ $4 + 6 = 10$
         $-4y - y = 5 - 20$ $10 = 10$
            $-5y = -15$ $8 - 3 = 5$
               $y = 3$ $5 = 5$
Answer, $x = 4$ and $y = 3$

6. (1) $3x + 2y = 0$ (3) $y = -\dfrac{3x}{2}$
     (2) $2x + 5y = -11$

     (1) $3x + 2y = 0$ $y = -\dfrac{6}{2}$
          $2y = -3x$
                          $y = -3$
     (3) $y = -\dfrac{3x}{2}$

     (2) $2x + 5\left(-\dfrac{3x}{2}\right) = -11$ Check:
                             $6 - 6 = 0$
        $2x - \dfrac{15x}{2} = -11$ $0 = 0$
                             $4 - 15 = -11$
        $4x - 15x = -22$ $-11 = -11$
           $-11x = -22$ Answer, $x = 2$
              $x = 2$ and $y = -3$

DIAGNOSTIC TEST

Solve and check:

1. $y = x$
    $x + y = 4$

2. $x = -3y$
    $2x + 7y = 1$

3. $y = x + 2$
    $2x + 3y = 21$

4. $x = y - 3$
    $4x + 2y = 24$

5. $y = 2x$
    $x - 3y = 10$

6. $y = -4x$
    $x - 2y = 27$

7. $x = y + 3$
    $4y - 2x = 2$

8. $y = 6 - x$
    $9x - 5y = 40$

9. $y = 3$
    $8x + 5y = 31$

10. $x + y = 6$
     $3x - 4y = 4$

11. $8x = 2y$
     $2x + 3y = 42$

12. $2x = 5y$
     $5x - 4y = 17$

13. $3x + 2y = -5$
     $7x - 3y = 19$

14. $4x = 5y$
     $4x - 3y = 8$

Related Practice Examples

Solve and check:

SET 1

1. $y = x$
    $x + y = 6$

2. $x = y$
    $3x + y = -8$

3. $y = 4x$
    $x + 2y = 36$

4. $x = 3y$
    $2x + 5y = 33$

5. $6x = y$
    $3x + 4y = -27$

SET 2

1. $y = -x$
    $3x + y = 4$

2. $y = -2x$
    $2x + 5y = -8$

3. $x = -4y$
    $3x + 2y = -30$

4. $y = -3x$
    $6x + 5y = 18$

5. $-5y = x$
    $2x + 7y = 12$

SET 3

1. $y = x + 3$
   $2x + 4y = 24$
2. $y = x + 1$
   $5x + 3y = 51$
3. $x = y + 4$
   $3x + 7y = -18$
4. $y = 6x + 3$
   $2x + 6y = -20$
5. $y = 3 + x$
   $3x + 8y = 46$

SET 4

1. $y = x - 2$
   $x + 5y = 20$
2. $y = x - 5$
   $2x + 4y = 10$
3. $x = y - 1$
   $3x + 2y = -13$
4. $y = 5 - x$
   $6x + 5y = -23$
5. $x = 3 - y$
   $4x + 7y = 18$

SET 5

1. $y = x$
   $4x - y = 6$
2. $y = 3x$
   $2x - 3y = -7$
3. $x = 2y$
   $7y - 4x = -3$
4. $y = 6x$
   $3x - 5y = 27$
5. $x = 4y$
   $5y - x = -2$

SET 6

1. $y = -x$
   $x - y = 2$
2. $x = -y$
   $y - x = 6$
3. $y = -3x$
   $2x - 3y = 22$
4. $y = -7x$
   $x - 5y = -72$
5. $y = -2x$
   $6x - 4y = -70$

SET 7

1. $y = x + 2$
   $2x - y = 1$
2. $y = 2x + 5$
   $x - 3y = -20$
3. $x = y + 3$
   $2y - x = -5$
4. $y = 6 + x$
   $4x - 5y = -28$
5. $y = 3x + 2$
   $9x - 7y = 22$

SET 8

1. $y = x - 1$
   $4x - y = 19$
2. $y = 3x - 2$
   $6x - 4y = -16$
3. $x = 4y - 5$
   $5y - x = 4$
4. $y = 8 - 3x$
   $4x - 5y = -2$
5. $x = 7 - 2y$
   $3y - 8x = 20$

SET 9

1. $x = 5$
   $2x + 3y = 19$
2. $y = 2$
   $3x - 5y = -1$
3. $x = -3$
   $4x + 7y = 2$
4. $y = -7$
   $3x + 6y = -27$
5. $x = 0$
   $8x - 3y = 6$

SET 10

1. $x + y = 5$
   $2x + 5y = 16$
2. $2x + y = 7$
   $4x - 2y = -6$
3. $x + 3y = 16$
   $7x + 4y = 10$
4. $x - y = 5$
   $3x - 2y = 14$
5. $4x - y = 0$
   $6x - 3y = 12$

SET 11

1. $2x = 4y$
   $4x + 2y = 10$
2. $4x = 2y$
   $5x - 3y = -3$
3. $9x = 3y$
   $6x + 5y = -42$
4. $12x = 4y$
   $3x - 2y = -9$
5. $5x = -10y$
   $8x - 4y = 40$

SET 12

1. $2x = 3y$
   $5x + y = 34$
2. $5y = 2x$
   $3x - 2y = 22$
3. $4y = 3x$
   $7y - 5x = -2$
4. $6y = 9x$
   $8x + 4y = 28$
5. $10x = -4y$
   $5x - 3y = 25$

SET 13

1. $2x + 3y = 7$
   $3x - 2y = 4$
2. $4x - 3y = 18$
   $5x - 4y = 23$
3. $6x + 5y = 13$
   $3x + 4y = 14$
4. $2x + 7y = -21$
   $7x - 2y = 6$
5. $5x - 3y = 19$
   $4x + 6y = 32$

SET 14

1. $2x = 5y$
   $2x + 3y = 32$
2. $4x = 6y$
   $7x - 6y = 9$
3. $2x + y = 0$
   $3x - y = 10$
4. $2x + 5y = 9$
   $3x - 5y = 1$
5. $4x - 3y = 11$
   $2x - 3y = 13$

Applications

1. Using formulas $A = p + i$ and $i = prt$, derive a formula for A in terms of p, r, and t.

2. Using formulas $c = 2\pi r$ and $r = \dfrac{d}{2}$, derive a formula for c in terms of π and d.

3. Derive a formula for P in terms of I and R, using the formulas $P = IE$ and $E = IR$.

4. Using the formulas $p = 4s$ and $A = s^2$, derive a formula for A in terms of p.

5. Derive a formula for A in terms of c, using the formulas $A = \pi r^2$ and $c = 2\pi r$.

6. Using the formulas $P = \dfrac{W}{t}$, $W = Fd$, and $v = \dfrac{d}{t}$, derive a formula for P in terms of F and v.

7. Derive a formula for S in terms of n, a, and d, using the formulas $l = a + (n-1)d$ and $S = \dfrac{n}{2}(a + l)$.

EXERCISE 85

Miscellaneous Examples Having Two Unknowns

I. Aim: To solve more difficult pairs of simultaneous linear equations having two unknowns by either method of elimination.

II. Procedure

1. a) If either or both equations contain similar terms, transpose and combine to get the two unknowns on the left member and the known term on the right member of the equation.
   b) Then follow procedure outlined in Exercises 83 and 84. See sample solution 1.

2. If either or both equations contain parentheses, remove parentheses, then follow step 1. See sample solution 2.

3. If either or both equations contain decimals, multiply the decimal equations by some multiple of 10 to clear the equations of decimals. See Exercise 69. Then follow either step 1 or step 2. See sample solution 3.

4. If either or both equations are fractional equations or have fractional coefficients, clear the equations of all fractions. See Exercises 66 to 68. Then follow either Step 1 or Step 2. See sample solution 4.

5. If the given equations are fractional equations of the reciprocal type, eliminate the unknowns by addition or subtraction before clearing the equations of fractions.
   Note: The above method may be used to find the values of both unknowns, or, if after one unknown is found by the above method, substitute its value in one of the equations to obtain the value of the other unknown. See sample solution 5.

6. If the given equations are literal equations, follow the same procedures of simplification and elimination as outlined for the numerical equations. If necessary, refer to Exercise 76 and 77. See sample solution 6.
   Note: If the first unknown has a complicated answer, the original two equations may be used again to get the value of the second unknown.

III. Sample Solutions

1.
$$(1) \quad 2x+3 = 7-y$$
$$(2) \quad 5x-2y = 4x-3$$

$$(1) \quad 2x+3 = 7-y$$
$$2x+y = 7-3$$
$$(3) \quad 2x+y = 4$$

$$(2) \quad 5x-2y = 4x-3$$
$$5x-4x-2y = -3$$
$$(4) \quad x-2y = -3$$

Check:
$$2+3 = 7-2$$
$$5 = 5$$

Answer, $x=1$ and $y=2$

$$(3) \quad 2x+y = 4$$
$$(4) \quad x-2y = -3$$

$$4x+2y = 8$$
$$x-2y = -3$$

$$5x = 5$$
$$x = 1$$

$$(3) \quad 2+y = 4$$
$$y = 4-2$$
$$y = 2$$

$$5-4 = 4-3$$
$$1 = 1$$

2.
$$(1) \quad 4(x-3) = 3(y+3)$$
$$(2) \quad 8-(2y+1) = 17-2x$$

$$(1) \quad 4(x-3) = 3(y+3)$$
$$4x-12 = 3y+9$$
$$4x-3y = 12+9$$
$$(3) \quad 4x-3y = 21$$

$$(2) \quad 8-(2y+1) = 17-2x$$
$$8-2y-1 = 17-2x$$
$$2x-2y = 17-8+1$$
$$(4) \quad 2x-2y = 10$$

$$(3) \quad 4x-3y = 21$$
$$(4) \quad 2x-2y = 10$$

$$4x-3y = 21$$
$$4x-4y = 20$$

$$y = 1$$

$$(3) \quad 4x-3 = 21$$
$$4x = 21+3$$
$$4x = 24$$
$$x = 6$$

Check:
$$4(6-3) = 3(1+3) \qquad 8-(2+1) = 17-12$$
$$4(3) = 3(4) \qquad 8-(3) = 5$$
$$12 = 12 \qquad 5 = 5$$

Answer, $x=6$ and $y=1$

3. (1) $\quad .04x + .02y = 5$
(2) $\quad .5(x-2) - .4y = 29$

(1) $\quad .04x + .02y = 5$
(3) $\qquad 4x + 2y = 500$

(2) $\quad .5(x-2) - .4y = 29$
$\qquad 5(x-2) - 4y = 290$
$\qquad 5x - 10 - 4y = 290$
$\qquad 5x - 4y = 290 + 10$
(4) $\qquad 5x - 4y = 300$

(3) $\quad 4x + 2y = 500$
(4) $\quad 5x - 4y = 300$

$\qquad 8x + 4y = 1000$
$\qquad 5x - 4y = \ \ 300$

$\qquad 13x \quad\ \ = 1300$
$\qquad x = 100$
(3) $\quad 400 + 2y = 500$
$\qquad 2y = 500 - 400$
$\qquad 2y = 100$
$\qquad y = 50$

Answer, $x = 100$ and $y = 50$

Check:
$.04(100) + .02(50) = 5$
$\qquad\qquad 4 + 1 = 5$
$\qquad\qquad\quad 5 = 5$

$.5(100 - 2) - .4(50) = 29$
$\qquad .5(98) - .4(50) = 29$
$\qquad\qquad 49 - 20 = 29$
$\qquad\qquad\quad\ 29 = 29$

4. (1) $\quad \dfrac{x}{5} + \dfrac{y}{2} = 4$

(2) $\quad \dfrac{x-1}{3} = \dfrac{y+2}{2}$

(1) $\quad \dfrac{x}{5} \cdot 10 + \dfrac{y}{2} \cdot 10 = 4 \cdot 10$

(3) $\qquad 2x + 5y = 40$

(2) $\qquad \dfrac{x-1}{3} = \dfrac{y+2}{2}$

$\qquad 2x - 2 = 3y + 6$
$\qquad 2x - 3y = 6 + 2$
(4) $\qquad 2x - 3y = 8$

(3) $\quad 2x + 5y = 40$
(4) $\quad 2x - 3y = \ \ 8$

$\qquad 8y = 32$
$\qquad y = 4$

(4) $\quad 2x - 12 = 8$
$\qquad 2x = 8 + 12$
$\qquad 2x = 20$
$\qquad x = 10$

Check:
$\dfrac{10}{5} + \dfrac{4}{2} = 4$
$\qquad 2 + 2 = 4$
$\qquad\quad 4 = 4$

$\dfrac{10-1}{3} = \dfrac{4+2}{2}$
$\qquad \dfrac{9}{3} = \dfrac{6}{2}$
$\qquad\ 3 = 3$

Answer, $x = 10$ and $y = 4$

5. (1) $\quad \dfrac{2}{x} + \dfrac{3}{y} = 2$

(2) $\quad \dfrac{8}{x} - \dfrac{6}{y} = 2$

$\qquad \dfrac{4}{x} + \dfrac{6}{y} = 4$

$\qquad \dfrac{8}{x} - \dfrac{6}{y} = 2$

$\qquad \dfrac{12}{x} \qquad = 6$

$\qquad 12 = 6x$
$\qquad 2 = x$
$\qquad x = 2$

(1) $\quad \dfrac{2}{2} + \dfrac{3}{y} = 2$

$\qquad 1 + \dfrac{3}{y} = 2$

$\qquad \dfrac{3}{y} = 2 - 1$

$\qquad \dfrac{3}{y} = 1$

$\qquad 3 = y$
$\qquad y = 3$

Check:
$\dfrac{2}{2} + \dfrac{3}{3} = 2$
$\qquad 1 + 1 = 2$
$\qquad\quad 2 = 2$

$\dfrac{8}{2} - \dfrac{6}{3} = 2$
$\qquad 4 - 2 = 2$
$\qquad\quad 2 = 2$

Answer, $x = 2$ and $y = 3$

6. (1) $\quad mx - ny = m^2 + n^2$
(2) $\qquad x - \ \ y = 2n$

$\qquad mx - ny = m^2 + n^2$
$\qquad nx - ny = 2n^2$

$\qquad mx - nx = m^2 - n^2$
$\qquad x(m-n) = (m+n)(m-n)$
$\qquad\qquad x = m + n$

(2) $\quad m + n - y = 2n$
$\qquad m + n - 2n = y$
$\qquad m - n = y$
$\qquad y = m - n$

Answer, $x = m + n$ and $y = m - n$

Check:
$m(m+n) - n(m-n) = m^2 + n^2$
$\qquad m^2 + mn - mn + n^2 = m^2 + n^2$
$\qquad\qquad m^2 + n^2 = m^2 + n^2$
$\qquad (m+n) - (m-n) = 2n$
$\qquad m + n - m + n = 2n$
$\qquad\qquad\qquad 2n = 2n$

DIAGNOSTIC TEST

Solve for x and y by either method of elimination and check:

1. $3x+7y=5$
   $6x+8y=7$

2. $6x+3y=19-2x$
   $9x-13=5y$

3. $4x+y=12$
   $2x-\frac{1}{2}y=2$

4. $7x-3y=16+(x-y)$
   $2(x-2)=4-(y+1)$

5. $x+y=1500$
   $.04x+.06y=74$

6. $\dfrac{x}{3}+\dfrac{y}{4}=4$

   $\dfrac{x}{y}=\dfrac{3}{4}$

7. $\dfrac{3}{x}+\dfrac{4}{y}=5$

   $\dfrac{6}{x}-\dfrac{8}{y}=2$

8. $rx-sy=r^2-s^2$
   $x+y=r+s$

Related Practice Examples

Solve for x and y by either method of elimination and check:

SET 1a

1. $2x+4y=4$
   $x-2y=0$
2. $6x-4y=-6$
   $3x+y=3$
3. $4x+7y=19$
   $6x-2y=-9$
4. $x-3y=3$
   $2x+9y=11$
5. $9x-2y=10$
   $3x+6y=-10$

SET 1b

1. $5x+7y=4$
   $9x+3y=4$
2. $x-3y=0$
   $4x-2y=5$
3. $3x-4y=3$
   $12x-2y=5$
4. $6x-4y=0$
   $5x+2y=4$
5. $7x+5y=15$
   $5x-9y=17$

SET 2a

1. $x=2y+1$
   $y=2x+1$
2. $5y=2x-4$
   $3x=8y+5$
3. $4x+8y=5y$
   $3x+1=-2y$
4. $6x=8-15y$
   $4x-4=-6y$
5. $3x+5y=2x$
   $x+3y=y$

SET 2b

1. $2x+3=7y$
   $4+3x+5y=15$
2. $x+3=2-y$
   $2x+1=3y-1$
3. $3x+2y=2x+2$
   $2x-6y=15+y$
4. $6x-3y=3x-y$
   $4x-5y=11+2x$
5. $2x+6y=13-2x$
   $9y+6=8x+15$

SET 3

1. $3x+2y=14$
   $x+\frac{1}{3}y=4$
2. $2x-5y=16$
   $\frac{2}{3}x+7y=-12$
3. $3x-y=19$
   $\frac{3}{4}x+4y=26$
4. $5x-\frac{1}{4}y=-18$
   $2x+y=6$
5. $3x+y=2$
   $2x-y=\frac{1}{2}$

SET 4

1. $2(x+4)=3(y+2)$
   $4(x-2)=5(y-2)$
2. $3-(x-5)=y+2$
   $2(x-y)=4-3y$
3. $8x-(2y+5)=x$
   $y-(3x-1)=4$
4. $(x-2)-(y-3)=8$
   $4(x+5)=y+3$
5. $3(x+2)=2(y+4)$
   $2x-3(y-10)=23$

SET 5a

1. $.6x+.2y=2.2$
   $.5x-.2y=1.1$
2. $.3x+.4y=2.4$
   $.5x-.3y=1.1$
3. $.12x+.02y=.78$
   $.03x+.04y=.3$
4. $.6x+y=7$
   $.2x+.5y=3$
5. $1.5x+.1y=6.2$
   $3x-.4y=11.2$

SET 5b

1. $x+y=1800$
   $.05x+.06y=96$
2. $x+y=700$
   $.15x+.25y=125$
3. $x-y=400$
   $.05x-.06y=4$
4. $.04(x-10)=.08(y-3)$
   $.5(x+4)=2y$
5. $.04(x-3)=.05(y+2)$
   $.2(x+2)=.1(6y+8)$

SET 6a

1. $x = 2y$

   $\dfrac{x}{3} + y = 10$

2. $\dfrac{x}{y} = \dfrac{2}{3}$

   $\dfrac{x+8}{3} = \dfrac{3y-2}{4}$

3. $\dfrac{x}{4} + \dfrac{y}{2} = 5$

   $\dfrac{x}{6} - \dfrac{y}{18} = 1$

4. $\dfrac{x}{2} - \dfrac{y}{3} = 1$

   $\dfrac{x}{4} - \dfrac{y}{9} = \dfrac{2}{3}$

5. $\dfrac{x}{10} = \dfrac{y}{5}$

   $\dfrac{x}{8} + \dfrac{y}{3} = \dfrac{7}{4}$

SET 6b

1. $\dfrac{3x-y}{5} = 2y - 1$

   $\dfrac{3x}{8} - \dfrac{y}{4} = \dfrac{1}{2}$

2. $\dfrac{x}{3} = \dfrac{y}{4}$

   $\dfrac{x-4}{4} - \dfrac{y-13}{3} = 1$

3. $\dfrac{x}{4} - 3 = \dfrac{y}{6}$

   $\dfrac{1}{2}x - y = -2$

4. $\dfrac{2x-4}{4} = \dfrac{3y-2}{2}$

   $\dfrac{4x-3}{2} - \dfrac{6-y}{3} = 2\tfrac{5}{6}$

5. $\dfrac{x+y}{2} = \dfrac{1}{2} + \dfrac{x-y}{3}$

   $\dfrac{1}{2}(x+2) - \dfrac{1}{3}(y+4) = 4$

SET 7a

1. $\dfrac{1}{x} + \dfrac{1}{y} = \dfrac{1}{2}$

   $\dfrac{1}{x} - \dfrac{1}{y} = \dfrac{1}{6}$

2. $\dfrac{1}{x} + \dfrac{1}{y} = \dfrac{3}{8}$

   $\dfrac{1}{x} - \dfrac{1}{y} = \dfrac{1}{8}$

3. $\dfrac{1}{x} + \dfrac{1}{y} = 5$

   $\dfrac{1}{x} - \dfrac{1}{y} = 1$

4. $\dfrac{4}{x} + \dfrac{6}{y} = 4$

   $\dfrac{6}{x} - \dfrac{6}{y} = 1$

5. $\dfrac{5}{x} + \dfrac{3}{y} = 26$

   $\dfrac{4}{x} + \dfrac{3}{y} = 22$

SET 7b

1. $\dfrac{2}{x} + \dfrac{3}{y} = 5$

   $\dfrac{4}{x} - \dfrac{1}{y} = 3$

2. $\dfrac{4}{x} + \dfrac{3}{y} = 7$

   $\dfrac{5}{x} - \dfrac{5}{y} = 0$

3. $\dfrac{5}{x} - \dfrac{9}{y} = \dfrac{1}{6}$

   $\dfrac{3}{x} - \dfrac{3}{y} = \dfrac{1}{2}$

4. $\dfrac{7}{x} + \dfrac{8}{y} = 2$

   $\dfrac{2}{x} + \dfrac{12}{y} = 20$

5. $\dfrac{3}{x} - y = 1$

   $\dfrac{1}{x} + 3y = 7$

SET 8a

1. $x + y = 3a$
   $x - y = a$
2. $2x + 3y = 12b$
   $3x - y = 7b$
3. $x + y = a$
   $x - y = b$
4. $x + y = 2a$
   $x - y = 2b$
5. $3x + 2y = 5a + b$
   $4x - 3y = a + 7b$

SET 8b

1. $ax + by = 5ab$
   $ax - by = 3ab$
2. $mx + ny = 4mn$
   $mx - ny = 0$
3. $cx + 2dy = 3cd$
   $3cx + dy = 4cd$
4. $bx + y = b^2 + c$
   $x + cy = b + c^2$
5. $ax - by = a^2 + b^2$
   $x + y = 2a$

SET 8c

1. $ax = by$
   $3ax - 2by = ab$
2. $ax + by = cd$
   $cx - dy = ab$
3. $\dfrac{y+d}{c} = \dfrac{x-c}{d}$

   $x - y = c + d$
4. $\dfrac{x}{3} + \dfrac{y}{2} = 2a$

   $2x - a = \dfrac{5y}{2}$
5. $\dfrac{x}{a} - \dfrac{y}{b} = 5$

   $\dfrac{x}{a} + \dfrac{y}{b} = 1$

EXERCISE 86
General Problems—Two Unknowns

I. Aim: To solve general problems in two unknowns.

II. Procedure

1. Represent one unknown by some letter and the second unknown by another letter.

2. Translate the word statement into two equations.

3. Solve the pair of simultaneous equations by either method of elimination.

4. Check the problem, not the equations.

III. Sample Solution

The sum of two numbers is 32 and their difference is 4. Find the numbers.

Solution:

Let x = one number
and y = other number

* (1) $x + y = 32$ (1) $18 + y = 32$ Check:
(2) $x - y = 4$ $y = 32 - 18$ 18 18

$y = 14$, other no. $+14$ -14

$2x = 36$

$x = 18$, one no. 32 4

Answer, 18 and 14

* The equations are determined by the following facts:

The sum of the two numbers = 32.

The difference of the two numbers = 4.

Practice Problems

A. Representations.

Represent the following statements, using numbers, letters, and symbols:

(Copy the table. *Do not write in this book*)

	First Number	6	15	x
	Second Number	4	8	y
1. The sum of the two numbers. 2. The difference between the two numbers. 3. Four more than the first number. 4. Three times the second number. 5. Five times the first number added to four times the second number.				

Solve and check the following problems. Use two equations with two unknowns.

B. Number problems.

1. The sum of two numbers is 45 and their difference is 7. Find the numbers.
2. The difference between two numbers is 24 and their sum is 48. Find the numbers.
3. The sum of two numbers is 22. Five times one number is equal to 6 times the second number. Find the numbers.
4. The difference between two numbers is 4. Twice the larger number is equal to three times the smaller number increased by two. Find the numbers.

5. Divide 24 into two numbers so that 4 less than six times the smaller number equals 5 more than three times the larger number. Find the numbers.

C. Miscellaneous problems.

1. John and Harry together weigh 210 pounds. The difference between three times John's weight and twice Harry's weight is 30 pounds. Find the weight of each boy.
2. The difference in ages of two boys is 5 years. The sum of their ages is 19 years. Find their ages.
3. There were 242 admission tickets sold. Three times the number of 50¢ tickets is 12 more than four times the number of 35¢ tickets. Find the number of 50¢ tickets.
4. The difference between the length and width of a rectangle is 7 inches. The perimeter of the rectangle is 50 inches. Find the length and width.
5. Joe has 28 coins. Some are nickels and some are dimes. The sum of the number of nickels and 3 times the number of dimes is 40. How many nickels and how many dimes does Joe have?

EXERCISE 87

Coin and Mixture Problems

I. Aim: To solve coin and mixture problems.

II. Procedure

1. Follow the procedure outlined in Exercise 86.

III. Sample Solution

John has 25 coins; some nickels and the rest dimes. The total value of all the coins is $1.80. Find the number of each kind of coin.

Solution:

Let x = no. of nickels
and y = no. of dimes
then $5x$ = value of nickels in cents
$10y$ = value of dimes in cents

* (1) $x + y = 25$ (1) $14 + y = 25$
  (2) $5x + 10y = 180$ $y = 25 - 14$
                              $y = 11$ dimes

$$10x + 10y = 250$$
$$5x + 10y = 180$$

$$5x = 70$$
$$x = 14 \text{ nickels}$$

Check:

14	14	11
+11	$.05	$.10
25	$.70	$1.10

$1.10
+ .70
———
$1.80

* The equations are determined by the following facts:

No. of nickels plus the no. of dimes = 25.
Value of nickels plus value of dimes = total value.

Answer, 14 nickels and 11 dimes

Practice Problems

A. Representations.

1. Copy the table and fill in the missing numbers. (*Do not write in this book*)

	Value of 1	No. of each	Total value		Value of 1	No. of each	Total value
1. $5 bills	$5	3	$15	6. Quarters		y	
2. Dimes		8		7. $2 bills		x	
3. 2¢ stamps		14		8. $10 bills		y	
4. Coffee—86¢ lb.		6 lb.		9. Tea—$1.90 lb.		x	
5. Nickels		x		10. Tea—$2 lb.		y	

2. Richard has 36 stamps, some 6¢ stamps and the rest 8¢ stamps. The value of all the stamps is $2.48. How many stamps of each kind does he have? Find the representations only.

(*Do not write in this book*)

B. Coin and stamp problems.

Kinds	Value of 1 stamp	No. of stamps	Total value
6¢ stamps			
8¢ stamps			

1. Mary has 18 coins, some quarters and the rest dimes. The total value of all the coins is $3.45. Find the number of each kind of coin.

2. George has $90 in $5 bills and $10 bills. He has 23 bills in all. How many $5 bills does he have?

3. Jack bought $8 worth of 6-cent and 8-cent stamps numbering 110 stamps in all. How many stamps of each kind did he buy?

4. Bob was given $9 to buy 6-cent and 8-cent stamps. He returned from the post office with 113 stamps and $1.46 in change. How many stamps of each kind did he buy?

5. When changing a $20 bill, Marilyn received 4 more $1 bills than three times the number of $5 bills. How many $1 bills did she receive?

C. Mixture problems.

1. A garden supply dealer mixes rye grass worth 40¢ a pound with blue grass worth $1.30 a pound. If he wishes to make a mixture of 50 pounds to sell at 67¢ a pound, how many pounds of each kind should he use?

2. A grocer mixes walnuts selling at 55¢ a pound and almonds selling at 70¢ a pound, making a mixture of 30 pounds to sell at 61¢. How many pounds of walnuts should he use?

3. How many pounds of candy at 80¢ a pound should be mixed with candy at $1.50 a pound to make 20 pounds of candy to sell at $1.01 a pound?

4. A grocer mixes tea worth $1.60 a pound with tea worth $2.20 a pound, making a blend to sell for $1.80 a pound. How many pounds of each kind should he use if he plans to blend 75 pounds?

5. How many pounds of dried prunes selling at 35¢ a pound should be mixed with dried apricots selling at 70¢ a pound to make a mixture of 100 pounds to sell at 42¢ per pound?

D. Miscellaneous problems.

1. Perennial rye grass cost twice as much per pound as domestic rye grass. If Ronald paid $9.10 for 10 pounds of perennial rye grass and 15 pounds of domestic rye grass, how much was he charged per pound for each kind of grass?

2. There were 2,500 persons watching a baseball game. The adults paid 75¢ for their admission tickets but the children paid only 25¢. If the total receipts amounted to $1,503, how many adults and how many children saw the game?

3. Chocolates cost 80¢ a pound more than hard candy. If Doris paid $5.90 for 4 pounds of chocolates and 2 pounds of hard candy, what did she pay per pound for the chocolates?

4. Seats in the reserved section at the school play cost 60¢ each and in the regular section 40¢ each. How many tickets of each kind were sold if the total receipts for 980 tickets amounted to $506?

5. A farmer sold 120 bushels of Delicious and Winesap apples. He charged $4 a bushel for the Delicious and $3 a bushel for the Winesaps. If he received $453, how many bushels of each did he sell?

EXERCISE 88

Investment Problems

I. **Aim:** To solve investment problems.

II. **Procedure**

1. Follow the procedure outlined in Exercise 86.

III. **Sample Solution**

A man invests $1,800; part at 4% annual interest and the rest at 6%. If he receives $84 annual interest, how much does he invest at each rate?

Solution:

Let $\qquad x =$ amount in dollars invested at 4%
and $\qquad y =$ amount in dollars invested at 6%
$\qquad .04x =$ annual income from 4% investment
$\qquad .06y =$ annual income from 6% investment

* (1) $\quad x + y = 1,800$
(2) $.04x + .06y = 84$

(1) $\quad x + y = 1,800$
(3) $\quad 4x + 6y = 8,400$

(2) $.04x + .06y = 84$
(3) $\quad 4x + 6y = 8,400$

$6x + 6y = 10,800$
$4x + 6y = 8,400$

$2x = 2,400$
$x = \$1,200$ at 4%
(1) $1,200 + y = 1,800$
$y = 1,800 - 1,200$
$y = \$600$ at 6%

Equations are determined by the following facts:
* Amount invested at 4% plus amount invested at 6% equal $1,800.

Income from 4% investment plus the income from the 6% investment equal $84.

Check:

$\$1,200$	$\$1,200$	$\$600$	$\$48$
$+ 600$	$\times .04$	$\times .06$	$+ 36$
$\$1,800$	$\$48.00$	$\$36.00$	$\$84$

Answer, $1,200 at 4% and $600 at 6%

Practice Problems

A. Representations.

A man invests his savings; part at 3% annual interest and the remainder at 5%. Using the above statement, find the following missing representations:

(Do not write in this book)

	Rate of Interest	Amount Invested	Income
1st investment 2nd investment	.03 .05	$2,000 $2,500	
1st investment 2nd investment	.03 .05	$1,800 $1,400	
1st investment 2nd investment	.03 .05	x y	

B. Problems.

1. A man invests $4,000; part at 6% annual interest and the rest at 8%. If he receives $270 annual interest, how much does he invest at each rate?

2. Mrs. Adams invests a part of her savings at 5% annual interest and the rest at 6%. If she receives an annual income of $196 from the total investment of $3,400, how much does she invest at 5%?

3. A 6% investment brings an annual return of $28 more than a 5% investment. The total amount invested is $1,200. Find the two amounts.

4. A woman invests a certain amount of money at 6% annual interest and $2,000 more than that amount at 8%. If the total annual income is $595, how much does she invest at 8%?

5. Mr. Jones invests $500 more at 5% annual interest than he does at 6%. If the income he receives from the 6% investment is $17 more than the income from the 5% investment, how much does he invest at each rate?

EXERCISE 89
Motion Problems

I. Aim: To solve motion problems.

II. Procedure

1. Follow the procedure outlined in Exercise 86. If necessary, use the motion formulas. See Exercise 43.

III. Sample Solution

An oarsman can row 24 miles downstream in 3 hours. However, the trip back over the same distance takes him 6 hours. Find the oarsman's rate of rowing in still water and the rate of the current.

Solution:

Let x = rate of rowing in still water in m.p.h.
and y = rate of current in m.p.h.

	Rate of boat	Time	Distance
Downstream	$x+y$	3	24
Upstream	$x-y$	6	24

* (1) $x+y=8$
   (2) $x-y=4$
         $\overline{\hphantom{xxxxxx}}$
     $2x\quad=12$
        $x=6$ m.p.h.—rate of rowing in still water
  (1) $6+y=8$
       $y=8-6$
       $y=2$ m.p.h.—rate of current

* The equations are determined by the following facts:

Rate of boat downstream equals distance divided by time $(24 \div 3) = 8$.

Rate of boat upstream equals distance divided by time $(24 \div 6) = 4$.

Check:

Rate of boat downsteam $= 6+2$ or 8 m.p.h.
Rate of boat upstream $= 6-2$ or 4 m.p.h.

Answer: Rate of rowing in still water is 6 m.p.h. and rate of current is 2 m.p.h.

$$\frac{3 \text{ hr.}}{8)\overline{24 \text{ miles}}} \qquad \frac{6 \text{ hr.}}{4)\overline{24 \text{ miles}}}$$

Practice Problems

A. Representations.

1. Find the missing numbers.

(*Do not write in this book*)

Rate of boat in still water	Rate of current	Rate of boat	
		Downstream	Upstream
10 m.p.h.	2 m.p.h.		
15 m.p.h.	4 m.p.h.		
x m.p.h.	3 m.p.h.		
12 m.p.h.	y m.p.h.		
x m.p.h.	y m.p.h.		

2. An oarsman can row 16 miles downstream in 2 hours. However, the trip back over the same distance takes him 4 hours. Find the oarsman's rate of rowing in still water and the rate of the current.
   (1) How is the rate of rowing in still water represented?
   (2) How is the rate of current represented?
   (3) Using the above statement find the following missing numbers:

(*Do not write in this book*)

	Rate	Time	Distance
Downstream			
Upstream			

B. Problems.

1. An oarswoman can row 24 miles downstream in 4 hours. The return trip over the same distance takes her 6 hours. Find the rate at which the oarswoman can row in still water and the rate of the current.

2. An airplane flies 360 miles with the wind in 2 hours. When flying against the wind, it takes 3 hours to fly the same distance. Find the rate of speed of the airplane in still air and the rate at which the wind is blowing.

3. A motorboat can go 120 miles downstream, in 4 hours, but the trip back takes $1\frac{1}{2}$ times as long. Find the rate of speed of the motorboat in still water and the rate of the current.

4. An airplane traveled 1800 miles in 3 hours, flying with the wind. On the return trip, however, flying against the wind, it took 4 hours to travel 2000 miles. Find the rate at which the wind was blowing and the rate of speed of the airplane in still air.

5. A girl walks from her home to the city in 4 hours, but she travels the same distance on her bicycle in one hour. If she rides 6 miles per hour faster than she walks, how fast does she ride on her bicycle?

EXERCISE 90

Digit Problems

I. **Aim:** To solve digit problems.

II. **Procedure**

    1. Follow the procedure outlined in Exercise 86.

      Note—In the number 32, 3 is the tens digit and 2 is the units digit. In representing the number however, 32 is thought of as being made up of 30 and 2. Here the value of the tens digit is 30 (10×3) not 3. See the representations in the sample solution.

III. **Sample Solution**

    The sum of the digits of a two-digit number is 9. The number is 6 times the units digit. Find the number.

    Solution:

Let x = tens digit
and y = units digit
then $10x + y =$ the number

* (1) $x + y = 9$ (1) $x + y = 9$
   (2) $10x + y = 6y$ (3) $10x - 5y = 0$

   (2) $10x + y = 6y$ $5x + 5y = 45$
        $10x + y - 6y = 0$ $10x - 5y = 0$
   (3) $10x - 5y = 0$

                 $15x = 45$
                   $x = 3$, tens digit
      (1) $3 + y = 9$
               $y = 9 - 3$
               $y = 6$, units digit
   Then $10x + y = 30 + 6 = 36$, the number

   Answer, 36

* The equations are determined by the following facts:

    The sum of the digits equals 9.

    The number is 6 times the units digit.

    Check:

       3
     $+6$ $36 = 6 \times 6$
     —
      9

Practice Problems

A. Representations.

   1. Find the missing numbers.

(Do not write in this book)

Tens Digit	Units Digit	Number
4	2	
5	7	
3	6	
t	u	
x	y	

2. The tens digit of a certain two-digit number is 6 more than the units digit. The number is 2 more than 8 times the sum of the two digits. Find the number.

Represent the following (using the above statement):

    (1) Units digit.
    (2) Tens digit.
    (3) The number.
    (4) Tens digit equals 6 more than the units digit.
    (5) The sum of the units and tens digits.
    (6) Eight times the sum of the two digits.
    (7) The number equals 2 more than 8 times the sum of the two digits.

B. Problems.

1. The sum of the digits of a two-digit number is 13. Twice the tens digit increased by two equals five times the units digit. Find the number.

2. A two-digit number is 6 times the units digit. If the sum of the digits is 9, what is the number?

3. The units digit of a certain two-digit number is 7 more than the tens digit. The number is 4 less than 3 times the sum of the two digits. Find the number.

4. The sum of the digits of a two-digit number is 12. If the digits are reversed, the new number is 18 less than the original number. What is the original number?

5. The sum of the digits of a two-digit number is 7. If the digits are reversed, the new number increased by 3 equals 4 times the original number. Find the original number.

REVIEW OF UNIT FOURTEEN

1. Draw graphs of the following equations: a) $y = x + 5$ b) $2x + y = 0$ c) $2x - 3y = 4$

2. Draw graphs of the following formulas: a) $p = 3s$ b) $i = .06p$ c) $c = \frac{22}{7}d$

3. Solve the following pairs of equations graphically:

  a) $y = 8 - x$ b) $y = -2x$ c) $2x + y = -7$ d) $x = 6$ e) $y = 3x$
      $x - y = 4$ $3x - 2y = -7$ $x - 3y = 7$ $4y - x = 2$ $5x + 2y = 0$

4. Solve by the addition or subtraction method of elimination and check:

  a) $3x - 2y = 9$ b) $5x + 9y = 9$ c) $8a - 3b = 12$ d) $3m + 5n = 31$ e) $4x - 6y = 0$
      $x + 2y = 11$ $5x + 7y = 17$ $4a - 6b = -12$ $2m - 3n = 8$ $6x + 8y = -34$

5. Solve by the substitution method of elimination and check:

  a) $y = 4x$ b) $y = x + 3$ c) $y = x - 5$ d) $x + y = 7$ e) $5x - 6y = 4$
      $5x + y = 18$ $3x + 2y = 21$ $4x - 3y = 17$ $6x - 2y = 18$ $4x + 7y = 15$

6. Solve for x and y by either method of elimination and check:

a) $x - 3(y + 4) = y$ b) $x + y = 2300$ e) $cx + dy = c^2 + d^2$
    $x - (3y + 4) = 10$ $.03x + .04y = 88$ c) $\dfrac{x}{3} + \dfrac{y}{6} = 7$ d) $\dfrac{2}{x} + \dfrac{3}{y} = 14$ $x + y = 2c$

                                             $\dfrac{2x + y}{7} = \dfrac{5x - 2y}{4}$ $\dfrac{3}{x} - \dfrac{2}{y} = 8$

7. An airplane flew 780 miles with the wind in 4 hours. The return trip over the same distance against the wind took 5 hours. Find the air speed (speed in still air) of the airplane and the rate at which the wind was blowing.

8. The sum of a two digit number is 10. If the digits are reversed, the new number decreased by 6 is one seventh of the original number. Find the number.

9. a) Using formulas $c = \pi d$ and $d = 2r$, derive a formula for c in terms of π and r.

    b) Derive a formula for P in terms of E and R, using the formulas $P = IE$ and $E = IR$.

10. a) Using formulas $A = \pi r^2$ and $r = \dfrac{d}{2}$, derive a formula for A in terms of π and d.

     b) Using formulas $s = vt$ and $v = \frac{1}{2}gt$, derive a formula for s in terms of g and t.

CUMULATIVE ALGEBRA REVIEW

1. The net proceeds are equal to the amount of sales minus the commission. Write a formula expressing the commission (c) in terms of the net proceeds (p) and the sales (s).

2. Transform the formula $A = 180 - B - C$ by inclosing the last two terms within parentheses preceded by a minus sign.

3. Divide: $\dfrac{10b^3}{9b^2 - 30b + 25} \div \dfrac{24b}{18b - 30}$
       4. Solve and check: $\dfrac{5}{4x} - \dfrac{3}{16} = \dfrac{9}{8x} - \dfrac{1}{8}$

5. Determine by substitution which of the following numbers: -2, 6, $-\frac{1}{2}$, 0, $\frac{3}{4}$ is the root of the equation $4x - (8 - x) = 21x$.

6. Find the value of F when $C = 80$, using the formula $C = \frac{5}{9}(F - 32)$.

7. Rewrite the formula $C = \dfrac{1}{\dfrac{1}{C_1} + \dfrac{1}{C_2}}$ with the right member in simplified form.

8. Using formulas $V = lwh$ and $B = lw$, derive a formula for V in terms of B and h.

9. Solve and check: $8(x - 4) = 2(5 - y)$

$$\frac{x + y}{3} = \frac{x - 2y}{12}$$

10. Tickets to a school football game cost 35 cents and 20 cents. How many tickets of each kind were sold if the total receipts for 752 tickets amounted to $212.95?

KEYED ACHIEVEMENT TEST

1. Reduce to lowest terms: $\dfrac{30b^2x^2 - 25bx^3}{40b^3x^2}$ ⑤⑦
     2. Combine: $\dfrac{5a + 4b}{3} - \dfrac{4a - b}{6}$ ⑥①

3. Find the value of T' when $V = 400$, $V' = 500$, and $T = 280$, using the formula $\dfrac{V}{V'} = \dfrac{T}{T'}$.   ⑦⑨

4. Solve and check: $\dfrac{d + 8}{d - 4} - \dfrac{d - 18}{d - 6} = \dfrac{48}{d^2 - 10d + 24}$ ⑥⑧
     5. Draw the graph of $3x + y = 7$ ⑧①

6. Solve graphically and check: $2x - y = 2$ ⑧②
$$x + 2y = 11$$
     7. Solve by addition or subtraction and check:
$$5x - 7y = 17 \quad ⑧③$$
$$3x + 8y = -2$$

8. Solve by substitution and check:
$$x - 5y = 4 \quad ⑧④$$
$$2x + y = -14$$
     9. Solve by either method of elimination and check:
$$\frac{x}{2} + \frac{y}{5} = 6 \quad ⑧⑤$$
$$\frac{x - 6}{4} + \frac{y - 7}{6} = 1$$

10. The sum of two numbers is 30. Four times the larger number decreased by 5 equals 7 more than eight times the smaller number. Find the numbers.   ⑧⑥

INTRODUCTION TO UNIT FIFTEEN

Our number system in arithmetic includes only rational numbers, that is, whole numbers, common fractions, and decimal fractions. It is extended in elementary algebra to include positive and negative numbers (see Unit Five), and the irrational number, a number which cannot be expressed as a whole number or fraction. In learning to operate with the irrational number in this unit, technical algebraic terms arise, the meanings of which are reviewed here.

A *factor* is any one of two or more numbers that are multiplied together.

An *exponent* shows how many times a number is used as a factor in multiplication.

The *power* of a number is the product obtained when a number is multiplied by itself one or more times.

The *square root* of a number is one of its two equal factors. Every number has two square roots numerically equal but opposite in sign. The square roots of 25 are $+5$ and -5 or briefly ± 5. The symbol $\pm$ indicates "plus or minus." The principal square root of a number is its positive square root.

The *cube root* of a number is one of its three equal factors. The cube root of 8 is 2. The cube root of -27 is -3.

The *fourth root* of a number is one of its four equal factors; the *fifth root* of a number is one of its five equal factors, etc.

The symbol $\sqrt{}$ is called the *radical sign*. A *radical* is an indicated root of a number. $\sqrt{5}$, $\sqrt[3]{8}$, and $\sqrt[5]{21}$ are radicals.

The number indicating the *root* or the *degree* or *order* of the radical is called the *index*. The index 3 in $\sqrt[3]{}$ indicates the cube root, and index 4 in $\sqrt[4]{}$ indicates the fourth root. The symbol $\sqrt{}$ without any written index indicates the square root.

Fractional exponents are also used to indicate roots. The exponent $\frac{1}{2}$ indicates the square root, exponent $\frac{1}{3}$ indicates the cube root, etc.

A *surd* is an indicated root of a positive whole number or fraction that cannot be found exactly. $\sqrt{6}$ is a surd.

The expression under the radical sign is called the *radicand*.

To *simplify a radical* means to make the radicand the smallest possible positive whole number containing no factors for which the indicated root can be found exactly. In the simplification of radicals we shall use the principle that the square root of a product is equal to the product of the square roots of the factors. $\sqrt{36} = \sqrt{4 \cdot 9} = \sqrt{4}\sqrt{9} = 2 \cdot 3 = 6$. However, the square root of a sum is not equal to the sum of the square roots.

Similar radicals are radicals of the same degree or order having the same radicand. $4\sqrt{5}$ and $2\sqrt{5}$ are similar radicals.

A *radical equation* is one which contains one or more radicals having the unknown in the radicand. The axiom, "the squares of equals are equal," is employed in the solution of the radical equation.

Skill in determining powers and roots of monomials and in simplifying and operating radicals is essential in the study of radical and quadratic equations and their applications.

UNIT FIFTEEN—POWERS AND ROOTS

EXERCISE 91

Powers of Monomials

I. Aim: To raise a monomial to a given power.

II. Procedure

1. Raise the numerical coefficient to the indicated power. Follow the rules of signs for multiplication.

2. Multiply each of the exponents of the given literal factors by the exponent of the power to which it is to be raised.

3. If the given term is a fraction, raise both the numerator and the denominator of the fraction to the indicated power.

III. Sample Solutions

Raise to indicated power:

1. $(4a^2xy^3)^2$ Answer, $16a^4x^2y^6$
2. $(-3xy^4)^2$ Answer, $9x^2y^8$
3. $(2bx^2)^3$ Answer, $8b^3x^6$
4. $(-5m^4)^3$ Answer, $-125m^{12}$
5. $(-3c^3d)^4$ Answer, $81c^{12}d^4$
6. $(2a^2b)^5$ Answer, $32a^{10}b^5$

7. $(\frac{2}{3}m^2y^3)^2$ Answer, $\frac{4}{9}m^4y^6$
8. $(.3b^3x)^2$ Answer, $.09b^6x^2$
9. $(c^2[x-y]^4)^2$ Answer, $c^4[x-y]^8$
10. $\left(\dfrac{d^2m}{5c^2x^5}\right)^2$ Answer, $\dfrac{d^4m^2}{25c^4x^{10}}$

DIAGNOSTIC TEST

Raise to indicated power:

1. $(3ab^3)^2$
2. $(-4x^2y^3)^2$
3. $(dm^4x)^3$
4. $(-5b^2x^5)^3$
5. $(-2a^3x)^4$
6. $(-3b^2c^4)^5$
7. $(\frac{1}{2}m^4n^5)^2$
8. $(-.3b^2)^3$
9. $(2a[x+y]^3)^2$
10. $\left(\dfrac{4cd^2}{-5b^3}\right)^2$

Related Practice Examples

Raise to indicated power:

SET 1	SET 2	SET 3	SET 4	SET 5
1. $(a)^2$	1. $(-b)^2$	1. $(x^2)^3$	1. $(-b)^3$	1. $(a^6)^4$
2. $(x^2)^2$	2. $(-c^2)^2$	2. $(a^4y)^3$	2. $(-c^5d^3)^3$	2. $(x^5y)^4$
3. $(c^5y^3)^2$	3. $(-x^3y^7)^2$	3. $(2b^3)^3$	3. $(-2a^2)^3$	3. $(2b^4)^4$
4. $(4x)^2$	4. $(-2a)^2$	4. $(3x^8)^3$	4. $(-5m^4)^3$	4. $(5c^2d^3)^4$
5. $(5ab^2)^2$	5. $(-5x^5)^2$	5. $(5cd^2)^3$	5. $(-6bx^3)^3$	5. $(3b^7x^5)^4$
6. $(8b^3)^2$	6. $(-3a^2b)^2$	6. $(4b^5x^4)^3$	6. $(-3r^2s^5)^3$	6. $(-bc^3)^4$
7. $(3a^3b^2)^2$	7. $(-7b^2x^4)^2$	7. $(6ax^2y^3)^3$	7. $(-8d^4xy^2)^3$	7. $(-2m)^4$
8. $(2x^2y^3)^2$	8. $(-6ab^2c^3)^2$	8. $(2m^5n^3x^2)^3$	8. $(-9ab^2c)^3$	8. $(-4axy^8)^4$
9. $(12x^3y^4)^2$	9. $(-10x^4yz^6)^2$	9. $(8bc^4d^7)^3$	9. $(-4m^5n^7y^8)^3$	9. $(-3bc^2d)^4$
10. $(6a^5x^4y^3)^2$	10. $(-9abcd^4)^2$	10. $(4a^4x^5y)^3$	10. $(-10c^2dx^3y)^3$	10. $(-5m^4xy^5z)^4$

SET 6	SET 7	SET 8	SET 9	SET 10
1. $(a^2)^5$	1. $(\frac{3}{4}x^5y)^2$	1. $(.2c)^2$	1. $(x[a+b])^2$	
2. $(xy^3)^5$	2. $(\frac{1}{3}m^4x^3)^2$	2. $(.6b^5x^2)^2$	2. $(c^3[x-y]^2)^2$	1. $\left(\dfrac{x}{b}\right)^2$
3. $(2c^4d^6)^5$	3. $(\frac{3}{8}ac^3d^2)^2$	3. $(-.5mn^4)^2$	3. $(3b[c+d]^4)^2$	
4. $(4xy^2z^3)^5$	4. $(\frac{7}{8}m^4xy^3)^2$	4. $(.3a^5y^6)^2$	4. $(-5x^2[x-y]^5)^2$	2. $\left(\dfrac{x^2}{3}\right)^2$
5. $(6b^4c^3d^7)^5$	5. $(\frac{1}{2}ab^4)^3$	5. $(-.1b^3c^4)^2$	5. $(2m^2[c+d]^4)^3$	
6. $(-x)^5$	6. $(\frac{2}{3}m^2n)^3$	6. $(.4c^2d)^3$	6. $(3b^4[a-b]^2)^3$	3. $\left(\dfrac{-4b^2}{5c}\right)^2$
7. $(-3b^3)^5$	7. $(\frac{1}{5}x^5y^3)^2$	7. $(-.9r^5s^4)^3$	7. $(4x^3[x+y]^3)^2$	
8. $(-2ay^5)^5$	8. $(\frac{3}{8}b^3x^2y^4)^2$	8. $(.2mx^2)^4$	8. $(-5a^2[c-4]^5)^2$	4. $\left(-\dfrac{3a^2b^4}{2x^2}\right)^2$
9. $(-4c^3dx^2)^5$	9. $(\frac{3}{8}a^3b^6x^2)^3$	9. $(.15d^5y^3)^2$	9. $(-7b^6[d+m]^3)^3$	
10. $(-5m^2x^4y)^5$	10. $(\frac{5}{6}c^7d^2x^5)^2$	10. $(-2.4a^2xz^3)^2$	10. $(6y^5[b+c]^6)^2$	5. $\left(-\dfrac{4r^2d^3}{3xy^4}\right)^3$

EXERCISE 92

Roots of Monomials

I. Aim: To find the root of a monomial.

II. Procedure

1. Find the root of its numerical coefficient by trial and error.

2. Find the root of its literal factors by dividing the exponent of each literal factor by the index of the root.

3. Prefix the product of the root of the numerical coefficient (step 1) and the root of the literal factors (step 2) by a $\pm$ sign if the required root is even and by the sign of the given monomial if it is odd.

4. If the given term is a fraction, find the indicated root of both the numerator and denominator of the fraction.

III. Sample Solutions

Find the square root of:

1. $25a^6x^2$ Answer, $\pm 5a^3x$

2. $.04m^4$ Answer, $\pm .2m^2$

3. $\frac{9}{16}c^2y^8$ Answer, $\pm\frac{3}{4}cy^4$

4. $a^2(m-n)^4$ Answer, $\pm a(m-n)^2$

5. $\dfrac{b^6}{81c^4}$ Answer, $\pm\dfrac{b^3}{9c^2}$

Find the cube root of:

6. $27a^6m^3$ Answer, $3a^2m$

7. $-8x^{12}y^9$ Answer, $-2x^4y^3$

8. Find the fourth root of $81b^4x^8$ Answer, $\pm 3bx^2$

9. Find the fifth root of $243c^{10}y^{15}$ Answer, $3c^2y^3$

DIAGNOSTIC TEST

1. Find the square root of $49m^6n^{10}$.
2. Find the cube root of $8a^{15}x^6$.
3. Find the cube root of $-64b^9y^3$.
4. Find the fourth root of $16d^4r^8$.
5. Find the fifth root of $-32a^{10}y^{15}$.

6. Find the square root of $.36c^8d^2$.
7. Find the square root of $\frac{1}{9}a^2x^{12}$.
8. Find the square root of $25b^4(c-d)^6$.
9. Find the square root of $\dfrac{36c^6d^{12}}{49x^2y^4}$.

Related Practice Examples

SET 1

Find the square root of:

1. x^2
2. $x^8 y^6 z^2$
3. $64x^6$
4. $49r^2 t^8$
5. $9x^4 y^{10}$
6. $16a^8 y^{12}$
7. $4a^2 b^4 c^6 d^8$
8. $36a^{12} y^{18}$
9. $144b^8 x^{14} y^{10}$
10. $100r^4 t^{16} x^{24}$

SET 2

Find the cube root of:

1. a^6
2. $c^3 x^9 y^{15}$
3. $8b^3 d^{12}$
4. $64m^6 n^{18} x^{24}$
5. $125a^9 x^3 y^{27}$

SET 3

Find the cube root of:

1. $-x^3$
2. $-a^9 b^3 c^{12}$
3. $-27y^6$
4. $-8m^9 x^{18} y^3$
5. $-64d^6 r^{15} t^{21}$

SET 4

Find the fourth root of:

1. d^8
2. $r^4 s^{16}$
3. $16m^{12}$
4. $81a^4 b^8 x^{24}$
5. $625x^{16} y^4 z^{20}$

SET 5

Find the fifth root of:

1. m^{10}
2. $b^5 x^{15}$
3. $32a^{10} y^{25} z^5$
4. $-b^{20} c^{10}$
5. $-243m^5 x^{30} y^{45}$

SET 6

Find the square root of:

1. $.25x^2$
2. $.09a^4 b^8$
3. $.64m^{10} n^6$
4. $.01c^6 d^2 x^{12}$
5. $1.69x^4 y^2 z^{16}$

SET 7

Find the square root of:

1. $\frac{1}{4} b^8$
2. $\frac{9}{25} x^4 y^2$
3. $\frac{36}{49} c^6 d^{10} y^4$
4. $\frac{81}{64} b^2 c^8 x^{12}$
5. $\frac{16}{121} x^8 y^4 z^{20}$

SET 8

Find the square root of:

1. $b^2(c+d)^2$
2. $a^4 x^2 (x-y)^4$
3. $49x^6 y^4 (x+y)^6$
4. $25b^8 (m-n)^4$
5. $16d^2 r^{10} (r+t)^8$

SET 9

Find the square root of:

1. $\dfrac{a^4}{16b^2}$
2. $\dfrac{4x^8 y^2}{81c^2 d^4}$
3. $\dfrac{25m^2 n^6}{64x^6 y^4}$
4. $\dfrac{100b^8 c^{12}}{9d^2 x^{10}}$
5. $\dfrac{144a^2 b^4 c^6}{49x^{16} v^{19} z^2}$

EXERCISE 93

Square Roots

I. Aim: To find the square root of a number.

II. Procedure

1. Separate the number into groups of two figures each, starting at the decimal point and forming the groups, first to the left and then to the right of the decimal point.
   Note: If there is an odd number of figures to the left of the decimal point, there will be one group containing a single number. However, if there is an odd number of figures to the right of the decimal point, add a zero so that each group contains two figures.

2. Find the largest square which can be subtracted from the first group at the left. Write it under the first group.

3. Write the square root of this largest square above the first group as the first figure of the square root.

4. Subtract the square number from the first group. Annex the next group to the remainder.

5. Form the trial divisor by multiplying the root already found by 2 and annexing a zero.
   Note: In the sample solutions the zero is not written but is used mentally.

6. Divide the remainder (step 4) by the trial divisor (step 5). Annex the quotient to the root already found; also add it to the trial divisor to form the complete divisor.

7. Multiply the complete divisor by the new figure of the root.

8. Subtract this product (step 7) from the remainder (step 4).

9. Continue this process until all the groups have been used or the desired number of decimal places has been obtained.

10. Since each figure of the root is placed directly above its corresponding group, the decimal point in the root is placed directly above the decimal point in the given number.

11. Check by squaring the root to obtain the given number.

III. Sample Solutions

1. Find the square root of 328,329.

$$
\begin{array}{r}
5\ \ 7\ \ 3 \\
\sqrt{32'83'29.} \\
25 \\
\hline
107)\ \ 783 \\
749 \\
\hline
1143)\ \ 3429 \\
3429 \\
\hline
\cdots\cdots
\end{array}
$$

Answer, 573

2. Find the square root of 935.2 correct to nearest hundredth.

$$
\begin{array}{r}
3\ \ 0.\ 5\ \ 8 \\
\sqrt{9'35.20'00'} \\
9 \\
\hline
605)\ \ 3520 \\
3025 \\
\hline
6108)\ \ 49500 \\
48864 \\
\hline
636
\end{array}
$$

Answer, 30.58

DIAGNOSTIC TEST

Find the square root of the following numbers. If there is a remainder find answer correct to nearest hundredth:

1. 209764   2. 256036   3. 5.29   4. 3   5. 768.4

Related Practice Examples

Find the square root of the following numbers. If there is a remainder, find answer correct to nearest hundredth:

SET 1	SET 2	SET 3	SET 4	SET 5
1. 576	**1.** 11025	**1.** 7.84	**1.** 2	**1.** .05
2. 7921	**2.** 94864	**2.** .0324	**2.** 8	**2.** 5.94
3. 21609	**3.** 817216	**3.** .0841	**3.** 15	**3.** 147.6
4. 889249	**4.** 368449	**4.** 54.76	**4.** 39	**4.** 3.5
5. 136161	**5.** 824464	**5.** .9409	**5.** 128	**5.** 207.59
6. 343396	**6.** 499849	**6.** 190.44	**6.** 346	**6.** 6.283
7. 5692996	**7.** 254016	**7.** 3.0276	**7.** 983	**7.** 25.9
8. 1580049	**8.** 4020025	**8.** 88.5481	**8.** 1000	**8.** .924
9. 72914521	**9.** 81036004	**9.** 7157.16	**9.** 2382	**9.** 94.617
10. 58491904	**10.** 64048009	**10.** 1070.5984	**10.** 4976	**10.** 503.419

EXERCISE 94
Roots of Monomials

I. Aim: To find the root of a monomial, indicated by the index of the radical.

II. Procedure

    1. Use the root indicated by the index of the given radical sign to mean the following:

        (a) The symbol $\sqrt{}$ indicates square root and means $\sqrt[2]{}$. The symbol $\sqrt{}$ or $+\sqrt{}$ indicates the positive square root. The symbol $-\sqrt{}$ indicates the negative square root. The symbol $\pm\sqrt{}$ indicates that both square roots are required. This use of symbolism is for all even roots: square root, fourth root, etc.

        (b) The symbol $\sqrt[3]{}$ with index 3 indicates the cube root; the symbol $\sqrt[4]{}$ with index 4 indicates the fourth root; $\sqrt[5]{}$, the fifth root; $\sqrt[6]{}$, the six root; etc.

    2. Follow the procedure outlined in Exercise 92.

III. Sample Solutions

    Find the indicated root:

1. $\sqrt{4a^2b^6}$	Answer, $2ab^3$	6. $\sqrt[3]{64c^3d^9}$	Answer, $4cd^3$
2. $-\sqrt{.64m^8}$	Answer, $-.8m^4$	7. $\sqrt[3]{-125m^6x^{12}}$	Answer, $-5m^2x^4$
3. $+\sqrt{\frac{16}{81}a^4x^2y^{10}}$	Answer, $+\frac{4}{9}a^2xy^5$	8. $\sqrt[4]{81b^{16}y^8}$	Answer, $3b^4y^2$
4. $\pm\sqrt{9b^2(r+s)^6}$	Answer, $\pm3b(r+s)^3$	9. $\sqrt[5]{-32c^{20}d^5}$	Answer, $-2c^4d$
5. $\sqrt{\frac{25m^4}{36c^2d^8}}$	Answer, $\frac{5m^2}{6cd^4}$		

DIAGNOSTIC TEST

    Find the indicated root:

1. (a) $\sqrt{16a^4b^6}$	2. $\sqrt[3]{27m^6y^9}$	5. $\sqrt[5]{243m^{10}x^5}$	8. $\sqrt{25a^2(b+c)^4}$
(b) $-\sqrt{81c^8x^2}$	3. $\sqrt[3]{-64c^3d^{12}}$	6. $\sqrt{.49r^2d^{10}}$	
(c) $\pm\sqrt{100d^6z^{16}}$	4. $\sqrt[4]{256x^8y^{12}}$	7. $\sqrt{\frac{4}{9}x^4y^6z^8}$	9. $\sqrt{\frac{64b^4c^2}{81m^8n^6}}$

Related Practice Examples

Find the indicated root:

SET 1(a)

1. $\sqrt{a^4x^2}$
2. $\sqrt{36b^6}$
3. $+\sqrt{9a^2c^8d^{16}}$
4. $+\sqrt{49x^{12}y^4}$
5. $\sqrt{144m^8n^{16}x^{20}}$

SET 1(c)

1. $\pm\sqrt{x^6y^{10}}$
2. $\pm\sqrt{144a^8b^4}$
3. $\pm\sqrt{49m^{12}x^2}$
4. $\pm\sqrt{81x^{10}y^6z^{14}}$
5. $\pm\sqrt{25c^2d^2x^{16}}$

SET 3

1. $\sqrt[3]{-a^6}$
2. $\sqrt[3]{-m^{15}t^9}$
3. $\sqrt[3]{-64c^3d^3}$
4. $\sqrt[3]{-27b^6c^{12}d^{18}}$
5. $\sqrt[3]{-8m^9x^{24}y^{27}}$

SET 5

1. $\sqrt[5]{b^5c^{20}}$
2. $\sqrt[5]{32m^{25}}$
3. $\sqrt[5]{-x^{10}}$
4. $\sqrt[5]{-32a^5b^{15}}$
5. $\sqrt[5]{-243c^{20}m^{10}x^5}$

SET 1(b)

1. $-\sqrt{m^8n^2}$
2. $-\sqrt{25x^4y^{10}}$
3. $-\sqrt{16b^{14}c^6}$
4. $-\sqrt{100n^4x^6y^{12}}$
5. $-\sqrt{64d^{10}r^2t^{18}}$

SET 2

1. $\sqrt[3]{d^{12}}$
2. $\sqrt[3]{b^3c^{18}}$
3. $\sqrt[3]{27a^6x^{15}}$
4. $\sqrt[3]{125d^9m^{21}}$
5. $\sqrt[3]{8r^3s^6t^9}$

SET 4

1. $\sqrt[4]{x^{12}}$
2. $\sqrt[4]{a^4b^{20}}$
3. $\sqrt[4]{625m^8n^{12}}$
4. $\sqrt[4]{16x^{16}y^4}$
5. $\sqrt[4]{81a^4b^{12}c^{24}}$

SET 6

1. $\sqrt{.04a^{14}}$
2. $\sqrt{.64b^2m^8}$
3. $\sqrt{.0009a^2m^6}$
4. $\sqrt{.81c^4d^{12}}$
5. $\sqrt{1.44b^2c^{10}d^2}$

SET 7

1. $\sqrt{\tfrac{1}{16}b^{16}}$
2. $\sqrt{\tfrac{4}{49}a^4c^8}$
3. $\sqrt{\tfrac{9}{64}n^6x^{18}}$
4. $\sqrt{\tfrac{25}{81}c^{12}d^2x^6}$
5. $\sqrt{\tfrac{121}{144}m^4n^2y^2}$

SET 8

1. $\sqrt{a^2(x+2)^2}$
2. $\sqrt{b^4c^6(b-c)^4}$
3. $\sqrt{4x^2(x+y)^6}$
4. $\sqrt{9b^2(4x-3y)^2}$
5. $\sqrt{25x^2y^4(m-2n)^8}$

SET 9

1. $\sqrt{\dfrac{x^4}{y^{20}}}$
2. $\sqrt{\dfrac{9b^2}{x^2y^4}}$
3. $\sqrt{\dfrac{25m^2n^6}{81a^{10}x^4}}$
4. $\sqrt{\dfrac{16r^4}{49d^8t^2}}$
5. $\sqrt{\dfrac{81a^2b^2c^8}{144x^2y^6}}$

Miscellaneous Examples

Simplify and combine:

1. $\sqrt{25}+\sqrt{4}$
2. $\sqrt{49}-\sqrt{9}$
3. $\sqrt{81}+\sqrt{64}$
4. $\sqrt{144}-\sqrt{36}$
5. $\sqrt{10+6}$
6. $\sqrt{48-12}$
7. $\sqrt{25\cdot4}$
8. $\sqrt{9\cdot16}$
9. $\sqrt{58+6}+\sqrt{16}$
10. $\sqrt{30-5}-\sqrt{5\cdot5}$
11. $2\sqrt{36}$
12. $5\sqrt{49}$
13. $8\sqrt{9}$
14. $4\sqrt{100}$
15. $-3\sqrt{81}$
16. $4\sqrt{64}+2\sqrt{25}$
17. $5\sqrt{9}+3\sqrt{16}$
18. $6\sqrt{49}+\sqrt{1}$
19. $3\sqrt{36}-2\sqrt{4}$
20. $8\sqrt{100}-5\sqrt{9}$
21. $\dfrac{2\sqrt{25}+3\sqrt{16}}{\sqrt{4}}$
22. $\dfrac{6\sqrt{36}-4\sqrt{25}}{2\sqrt{16}}$
23. $\dfrac{3\sqrt{49}-2\sqrt{9}}{\sqrt{25}}$
24. $\dfrac{9\sqrt{64}-5\sqrt{81}}{\sqrt{9}}$
25. $\dfrac{6\sqrt{100}+8\sqrt{144}}{2\sqrt{4}}$

EXERCISE 95
Roots of Monomials—Using Fractional Exponents

I. Aim: To find the root of a monomial, indicated by a fractional exponent.

II. Procedure

1. Follow the procedure outlined in Exercise 94.

2. Note that the fractional exponent $\frac{1}{2}$ means square root. Since $a^{\frac{1}{2}} \cdot a^{\frac{1}{2}} = a^{\frac{1}{2}+\frac{1}{2}} = a^1$, therefore $a^{\frac{1}{2}} = \sqrt{a}$. In a similar manner the fractional exponent $\frac{1}{3}$ may be shown to mean cube root $(a^{\frac{1}{3}} = \sqrt[3]{a})$, the fractional exponent $\frac{1}{4}$ to mean fourth root $(a^{\frac{1}{4}} = \sqrt[4]{a})$, etc.

III. Sample Solutions

Find the indicated root:

1. $(49m^2n^6)^{\frac{1}{2}}$ Answer, $7mn^3$ 3. $(64b^6)^{\frac{1}{3}}$ Answer, $4b^2$

2. $\left(\dfrac{4x^4}{81y^2}\right)^{\frac{1}{2}}$ Answer, $\dfrac{2x^2}{9y}$ 4. $(-125c^3y^9)^{\frac{1}{3}}$ Answer, $-5cy^3$

5. $(81a^4x^{12})^{\frac{1}{4}}$ Answer, $3ax^3$

DIAGNOSTIC TEST

Find the indicated root:

1. $(25)^{\frac{1}{2}}$ 3. $(16x^2y^6)^{\frac{1}{2}}$ 5. $(8)^{\frac{1}{3}}$ 7. $(-27y^{12})^{\frac{1}{3}}$

2. $(a^4b^2)^{\frac{1}{2}}$ 4. $\left(\dfrac{9c^8}{49d^4x^6}\right)^{\frac{1}{2}}$ 6. $(a^9x^3)^{\frac{1}{3}}$ 8. $(16x^8y^{12})^{\frac{1}{4}}$

Related Practice Examples

Find the indicated root:

SET 1	SET 2	SET 3	SET 4
1. $(4)^{\frac{1}{2}}$	1. $(x^2)^{\frac{1}{2}}$	1. $(36a^2)^{\frac{1}{2}}$	1. $\left(\dfrac{c^4}{36d^2}\right)^{\frac{1}{2}}$
2. $(36)^{\frac{1}{2}}$	2. $(y^6)^{\frac{1}{2}}$	2. $(9b^4)^{\frac{1}{2}}$	
3. $(64)^{\frac{1}{2}}$	3. $(x^4y^8)^{\frac{1}{2}}$	3. $(81y^{10})^{\frac{1}{2}}$	2. $\left(\dfrac{25x^8y^6}{c^4m^6}\right)^{\frac{1}{2}}$
4. $(100)^{\frac{1}{2}}$	4. $(a^6b^2)^{\frac{1}{2}}$	4. $(64c^{24})^{\frac{1}{2}}$	
5. $(25)^{\frac{1}{2}}$	5. $(c^{10}d^8)^{\frac{1}{2}}$	5. $(4x^2y^4)^{\frac{1}{2}}$	3. $\left(\dfrac{64a^{12}}{81b^4}\right)^{\frac{1}{2}}$
6. $(9)^{\frac{1}{2}}$	6. $(m^2n^2)^{\frac{1}{2}}$	6. $(25a^6b^2)^{\frac{1}{2}}$	
7. $(1)^{\frac{1}{2}}$	7. $(b^{12}x^6)^{\frac{1}{2}}$	7. $(144c^8d^{12})^{\frac{1}{2}}$	4. $\left(\dfrac{9c^2x^8}{100b^4y^6}\right)^{\frac{1}{2}}$
8. $(81)^{\frac{1}{2}}$	8. $(b^2c^{10}d^{14})^{\frac{1}{2}}$	8. $(49b^2c^{10})^{\frac{1}{2}}$	
9. $(144)^{\frac{1}{2}}$	9. $(x^4y^{18}z^8)^{\frac{1}{2}}$	9. $(121m^4r^2t^2)^{\frac{1}{2}}$	5. $\left(\dfrac{144a^2m^{10}}{49d^2r^{12}t^4}\right)^{\frac{1}{2}}$
10. $(49)^{\frac{1}{2}}$	10. $(m^2n^4x^6)^{\frac{1}{2}}$	10. $(100d^6r^8t^4)^{\frac{1}{2}}$	

SET 5	SET 6	SET 7	SET 8
1. $(1)^{\frac{1}{3}}$	1. $(x^6)^{\frac{1}{3}}$	1. $(8b^3)^{\frac{1}{3}}$	1. $(81)^{\frac{1}{4}}$
2. $(27)^{\frac{1}{3}}$	2. $(-a^3)^{\frac{1}{3}}$	2. $(64x^9)^{\frac{1}{3}}$	2. $(b^{12})^{\frac{1}{4}}$
3. $(-8)^{\frac{1}{3}}$	3. $(b^9m^3)^{\frac{1}{3}}$	3. $(125d^3t^6)^{\frac{1}{3}}$	3. $(x^4y^8)^{\frac{1}{4}}$
4. $(-125)^{\frac{1}{3}}$	4. $(x^{12}y^{21})^{\frac{1}{3}}$	4. $(-27x^6y^{15})^{\frac{1}{3}}$	4. $(256a^8)^{\frac{1}{4}}$
5. $(64)^{\frac{1}{3}}$	5. $(c^6d^{18})^{\frac{1}{3}}$	5. $(-64a^{24}b^{30})^{\frac{1}{3}}$	5. $(625m^{16}n^{20})^{\frac{1}{4}}$

EXERCISE 96

Simplification—Radicand Is a Whole Number

I. **Aim:** To simplify radicals of the second order (square root) when the radicand is a whole number.*

II. **Procedure**

1. Find two factors of the given radicand, one of which is the largest possible perfect square.

2. Find the square root of the perfect square factor and write it as the coefficient of the radical whose radicand is the other factor. See sample solutions 1 and 2.

3. If there is a coefficient in the given radical, multiply it by the square root found in step 2. See sample solutions 3, 4, and 5.

* Note: To simplify means to make the radicand the smallest possible positive whole number.

III. **Sample Solutions**

Simplify:

1. $\sqrt{75} = \sqrt{25 \cdot 3} = \sqrt{25}\sqrt{3} = 5\sqrt{3}$ Answer, $5\sqrt{3}$

2. $\sqrt{80} = \sqrt{16 \cdot 5} = \sqrt{16}\sqrt{5} = 4\sqrt{5}$ Answer, $4\sqrt{5}$

3. $2\sqrt{18} = 2\sqrt{9 \cdot 2} = 2\sqrt{9}\sqrt{2} = 2 \cdot 3\sqrt{2} = 6\sqrt{2}$ Answer, $6\sqrt{2}$

4. $-3\sqrt{32} = -3\sqrt{16 \cdot 2} = -3\sqrt{16}\sqrt{2} = -3 \cdot 4\sqrt{2} = -12\sqrt{2}$ Answer, $-12\sqrt{2}$

5. $\frac{1}{2}\sqrt{20} = \frac{1}{2}\sqrt{4 \cdot 5} = \frac{1}{2}\sqrt{4}\sqrt{5} = \frac{1}{2} \cdot 2\sqrt{5} = \sqrt{5}$ Answer, $\sqrt{5}$

DIAGNOSTIC TEST

Simplify:

     1. $\sqrt{8}$ 2. $\sqrt{48}$ 3. $2\sqrt{72}$ 4. $-5\sqrt{150}$ 5. $\frac{1}{3}\sqrt{45}$

Related Practice Examples

Simplify:

SET 1a	SET 1b	SET 2a	SET 2b	SET 3	SET 4	SET 5
1. $\sqrt{12}$	1. $\sqrt{45}$	1. $\sqrt{32}$	1. $\sqrt{108}$	1. $3\sqrt{8}$	1. $-\sqrt{44}$	1. $\frac{1}{3}\sqrt{18}$
2. $\sqrt{27}$	2. $\sqrt{125}$	2. $\sqrt{72}$	2. $\sqrt{216}$	2. $2\sqrt{60}$	2. $-5\sqrt{28}$	2. $\frac{1}{2}\sqrt{20}$
3. $\sqrt{50}$	3. $\sqrt{40}$	3. $\sqrt{200}$	3. $\sqrt{360}$	3. $4\sqrt{32}$	3. $-3\sqrt{63}$	3. $\frac{3}{4}\sqrt{80}$
4. $\sqrt{98}$	4. $\sqrt{63}$	4. $\sqrt{112}$	4. $\sqrt{176}$	4. $2\sqrt{150}$	4. $-8\sqrt{72}$	4. $\frac{2}{3}\sqrt{54}$
5. $\sqrt{20}$	5. $\sqrt{44}$	5. $\sqrt{180}$	5. $\sqrt{405}$	5. $5\sqrt{80}$	5. $-4\sqrt{80}$	5. $\frac{5}{6}\sqrt{108}$
6. $\sqrt{90}$	6. $\sqrt{56}$	6. $\sqrt{128}$	6. $\sqrt{320}$	6. $8\sqrt{18}$	6. $-6\sqrt{128}$	6. $-\frac{1}{4}\sqrt{48}$
7. $\sqrt{54}$	7. $\sqrt{147}$	7. $\sqrt{192}$	7. $\sqrt{300}$	7. $3\sqrt{48}$	7. $-7\sqrt{175}$	7. $-\frac{2}{3}\sqrt{162}$
8. $\sqrt{28}$	8. $\sqrt{76}$	8. $\sqrt{288}$	8. $\sqrt{208}$	8. $7\sqrt{99}$	8. $-9\sqrt{68}$	8. $-\frac{3}{8}\sqrt{40}$
9. $\sqrt{18}$	9. $\sqrt{175}$	9. $\sqrt{162}$	9. $\sqrt{432}$	9. $10\sqrt{96}$	9. $-10\sqrt{90}$	9. $-\frac{4}{5}\sqrt{75}$
10. $\sqrt{52}$	10. $\sqrt{117}$	10. $\sqrt{96}$	10. $\sqrt{243}$	10. $12\sqrt{108}$	10. $-12\sqrt{192}$	10. $-\frac{3}{4}\sqrt{32}$

EXERCISE 97

Simplification—Radicand Is an Algebraic Monomial

I. **Aim:** To simplify radicals of the second order (square root) when the radicand is an algebraic monomial.

II. **Procedure**

1. Follow the procedure outlined in Exercise 96.

   Note: Any even power of a literal factor is a perfect square term. Therefore, if the power is odd, take the next lower even power of each literal factor as the largest possible perfect square.

III. **Sample Solutions**

Simplify:

1. $\sqrt{x^4yz^2} = \sqrt{x^4z^2 \cdot y} = \sqrt{x^4z^2}\sqrt{y} = x^2z\sqrt{y}$ Answer, $x^2z\sqrt{y}$

2. $\sqrt{5a^3b^7} = \sqrt{a^2b^6 \cdot 5ab} = \sqrt{a^2b^6}\sqrt{5ab} = ab^3\sqrt{5ab}$ Answer, $ab^3\sqrt{5ab}$

3. $\sqrt{9c^5d} = \sqrt{9c^4 \cdot cd} = \sqrt{9c^4}\sqrt{cd} = 3c^2\sqrt{cd}$ Answer, $3c^2\sqrt{cd}$

4. $\sqrt{150b^7c^2} = \sqrt{25b^6c^2 \cdot 6b} = 5b^3c\sqrt{6b}$ Answer, $5b^3c\sqrt{6b}$

5. $2xy\sqrt{32x^3y^5} = 2xy\sqrt{16x^2y^4 \cdot 2xy} = 2xy\sqrt{16x^2y^4}\sqrt{2xy}$
   $= 2xy \cdot 4xy^2\sqrt{2xy} = 8x^2y^3\sqrt{2xy}$ Answer, $8x^2y^3\sqrt{2xy}$

6. $\dfrac{3}{5m}\sqrt{50m^2n^3} = \dfrac{3}{5m}\sqrt{25m^2n^2 \cdot 2n} = \dfrac{3}{5m} \cdot 5mn\sqrt{2n} = 3n\sqrt{2n}$ Answer, $3n\sqrt{2n}$

DIAGNOSTIC TEST

Simplify:

1. $\sqrt{a^2b}$ 3. $\sqrt{25x^2y^5}$ 5. $3a\sqrt{12a^4b^3}$ 7. $\dfrac{3}{4x}\sqrt{128ax^5}$

2. $\sqrt{x^3}$ 4. $\sqrt{18b^7}$ 6. $-x^2y\sqrt{48x^3y^9}$

Related Practice Examples

Simplify:

SET 1	SET 2	SET 3	SET 4
1. $\sqrt{x^2y}$	1. $\sqrt{a^3}$	1. $\sqrt{a^2y^8}$	1. $\sqrt{27a^4}$
2. $\sqrt{cd^2}$	2. $\sqrt{c^5}$	2. $\sqrt{9m}$	2. $\sqrt{32m^3}$
3. $\sqrt{m^4n}$	3. $\sqrt{d^9}$	3. $\sqrt{36xy^2}$	3. $\sqrt{75b^2x^3}$
4. $\sqrt{dr^8}$	4. $\sqrt{x^3y^7}$	4. $\sqrt{49c^6d^3}$	4. $\sqrt{40x^5y^7}$
5. $\sqrt{a^4dy^2}$	5. $\sqrt{m^5n^{11}}$	5. $\sqrt{100a^5x^7}$	5. $\sqrt{63a^6x^4}$
6. $\sqrt{5x^2}$	6. $\sqrt{7s^3}$	6. $\sqrt{4x^3y^4}$	6. $\sqrt{72mn^5}$
7. $\sqrt{3b^2c^4}$	7. $\sqrt{19r^7}$	7. $\sqrt{16m^9n^5}$	7. $\sqrt{45r^7d^3}$
8. $\sqrt{7mn^2}$	8. $\sqrt{23ac^3}$	8. $\sqrt{25ax^2y^3}$	8. $\sqrt{80a^2x^3y^9}$
9. $\sqrt{13c^4d}$	9. $\sqrt{5b^9x}$	9. $\sqrt{81d^7rt^2}$	9. $\sqrt{96bc^2d^5}$
10. $\sqrt{11x^2yz^6}$	10. $\sqrt{41x^5y^7}$	10. $\sqrt{64r^6s^8t^3}$	10. $\sqrt{128x^8y^9z^{10}}$

SET 5
1. $a\sqrt{a^4b^3}$
2. $bx^2\sqrt{a^5b^2x^6}$
3. $2\sqrt{100a}$
4. $4x\sqrt{50x^2}$
5. $2x^2y\sqrt{28x^2y^7}$

SET 6
1. $-\sqrt{54x^2y^3}$
2. $-c\sqrt{b^5c^3}$
3. $-3a\sqrt{20a^7}$
4. $-2c^2d\sqrt{45cd^4}$
5. $-7xy\sqrt{72x^3y^9}$

SET 7
1. $\dfrac{1}{3x}\sqrt{27x^5}$
2. $\dfrac{3}{2m}\sqrt{112a^2m^5}$
3. $\dfrac{5}{2x}\sqrt{80x^3y}$
4. $-\dfrac{3}{8b}\sqrt{96ab^7}$
5. $\dfrac{3a}{4b}\sqrt{32a^3b^4}$
6. $\dfrac{5x}{9y}\sqrt{162x^2y^2}$

EXERCISE 98

Simplification—Radicand Is a Fraction

I. Aim: To simplify radicals of the second order (square root) when the radicand is a fraction.*

II. Procedure

1. Multiply both numerator and denominator of the fraction by the smallest possible number which will make the denominator a perfect square.

2. Find two factors of the new fraction, one of which is the largest possible perfect square. This square is a fraction with the new denominator as its denominator.

3. Then follow the procedure outlined in Exercises 96 and 97.

4. If the radicand is a mixed number, change it to an improper fraction and follow steps 1 to 3.

   * Note: To simplify means to make the radicand the smallest possible positive whole number.

III. Sample Solutions

Simplify:

1. $\sqrt{\frac{2}{9}} = \sqrt{\frac{1}{9} \cdot 2} = \sqrt{\frac{1}{9}}\sqrt{2} = \frac{1}{3}\sqrt{2}$ Answer, $\frac{1}{3}\sqrt{2}$

2. $\sqrt{\frac{3}{5}} = \sqrt{\frac{3}{5} \cdot \frac{5}{5}} = \sqrt{\frac{15}{25}} = \sqrt{\frac{1}{25} \cdot 15} = \frac{1}{5}\sqrt{15}$ Answer, $\frac{1}{5}\sqrt{15}$

3. $\sqrt{\frac{7}{8}} = \sqrt{\frac{7}{8} \cdot \frac{2}{2}} = \sqrt{\frac{14}{16}} = \sqrt{\frac{1}{16} \cdot 14} = \frac{1}{4}\sqrt{14}$ Answer, $\frac{1}{4}\sqrt{14}$

4. $\sqrt{\dfrac{a}{x}} = \sqrt{\dfrac{a}{x} \cdot \dfrac{x}{x}} = \sqrt{\dfrac{ax}{x^2}} = \sqrt{\dfrac{1}{x^2} \cdot ax} = \dfrac{1}{x}\sqrt{ax}$ Answer, $\dfrac{1}{x}\sqrt{ax}$

5. $\sqrt{\dfrac{2a^4b^3}{3x^3}} = \sqrt{\dfrac{2a^4b^3}{3x^3} \cdot \dfrac{3x}{3x}} = \sqrt{\dfrac{6a^4b^3x}{9x^4}} = \sqrt{\dfrac{a^4b^2}{9x^4} \cdot 6bx} = \dfrac{a^2b}{3x^2}\sqrt{6bx}$ Answer, $\dfrac{a^2b}{3x^2}\sqrt{6bx}$

6. $\dfrac{2x}{c}\sqrt{\dfrac{5c^5}{4x}} = \dfrac{2x}{c}\sqrt{\dfrac{5c^5}{4x} \cdot \dfrac{x}{x}} = \dfrac{2x}{c}\sqrt{\dfrac{5c^5x}{4x^2}} = \dfrac{2x}{c}\sqrt{\dfrac{c^4}{4x^2} \cdot 5cx} = \dfrac{2x}{c} \cdot \dfrac{c^2}{2x}\sqrt{5cx} = c\sqrt{5cx}$ Answer, $c\sqrt{5cx}$

DIAGNOSTIC TEST

Simplify:

1. $\sqrt{\frac{5}{9}}$
2. $\sqrt{\frac{2}{3}}$
3. $\sqrt{\frac{5}{8}}$
4. $\sqrt{\frac{4}{5}}$
5. $\sqrt{1\frac{2}{7}}$

6. $\sqrt{3\frac{1}{2}}$
7. $\sqrt{\dfrac{b}{a^2}}$
8. $\sqrt{\dfrac{x^2}{y}}$

9. $\sqrt{\dfrac{2ab^2}{c^2d}}$
10. $\sqrt{\dfrac{x}{2}}$

11. $\sqrt{\dfrac{2x}{3y}}$
12. $5d\sqrt{\dfrac{5c}{6d^3}}$

13. $-\sqrt{\dfrac{3b^7}{8a^3x^5}}$
14. $\dfrac{5bx}{c^2}\sqrt{\dfrac{3c^4}{5bx^2}}$

Related Practice Examples

Simplify:

SET 1	SET 2a	SET 2b	SET 3	SET 4	SET 5	SET 6
1. $\sqrt{\frac{3}{4}}$	1. $\sqrt{\frac{1}{2}}$	1. $\sqrt{\frac{2}{7}}$	1. $\sqrt{\frac{3}{8}}$	1. $\sqrt{\frac{4}{3}}$	1. $\sqrt{\frac{24}{25}}$	1. $\sqrt{2\frac{1}{4}}$
2. $\sqrt{\frac{7}{9}}$	2. $\sqrt{\frac{1}{3}}$	2. $\sqrt{\frac{1}{6}}$	2. $\sqrt{\frac{5}{12}}$	2. $\sqrt{\frac{9}{10}}$	2. $\sqrt{\frac{8}{5}}$	2. $\sqrt{1\frac{3}{4}}$
3. $\sqrt{\frac{3}{64}}$	3. $\sqrt{\frac{2}{5}}$	3. $\sqrt{\frac{7}{10}}$	3. $\sqrt{\frac{7}{20}}$	3. $\sqrt{\frac{25}{32}}$	3. $\sqrt{\frac{18}{7}}$	3. $\sqrt{2\frac{1}{2}}$
4. $\sqrt{\frac{5}{16}}$	4. $\sqrt{\frac{3}{10}}$	4. $\sqrt{\frac{1}{5}}$	4. $\sqrt{\frac{19}{32}}$	4. $\sqrt{\frac{9}{15}}$	4. $\sqrt{\frac{28}{15}}$	4. $\sqrt{3\frac{1}{3}}$
5. $\sqrt{\frac{11}{36}}$	5. $\sqrt{\frac{5}{6}}$	5. $\sqrt{\frac{7}{15}}$	5. $\sqrt{\frac{13}{24}}$	5. $\sqrt{\frac{16}{7}}$	5. $\sqrt{\frac{27}{2}}$	5. $\sqrt{1\frac{7}{8}}$

SET 7	SET 8
1. $\sqrt{\dfrac{c}{x^2}}$	1. $\sqrt{\dfrac{a}{b}}$
2. $\sqrt{\dfrac{d}{m^2}}$	2. $\sqrt{\dfrac{m^4}{n}}$
3. $\sqrt{\dfrac{b}{a^4}}$	3. $\sqrt{\dfrac{x^2}{y^3}}$
4. $\sqrt{\dfrac{3x}{y^6}}$	4. $\sqrt{\dfrac{r}{s^3}}$
5. $\sqrt{\dfrac{2b}{c^2d^4}}$	5. $\sqrt{\dfrac{3c}{ab^5}}$

SET 9	SET 10	SET 11	SET 12	SET 13	SET 14
1. $\sqrt{\dfrac{a}{xy^2}}$	1. $\sqrt{\dfrac{a}{4}}$	1. $\sqrt{\dfrac{3a}{4b}}$	1. $2\sqrt{\dfrac{4}{9y}}$	1. $-\sqrt{\dfrac{b^4}{4c^3}}$	1. $\dfrac{2}{3}\sqrt{\dfrac{x}{2y^2}}$
2. $\sqrt{\dfrac{d^2}{r^4t}}$	2. $\sqrt{\dfrac{b}{3}}$	2. $\sqrt{\dfrac{13m}{16n}}$	2. $x\sqrt{\dfrac{5d}{8x^2}}$	2. $-3\sqrt{\dfrac{7xy^2}{12b}}$	2. $\dfrac{1}{2}\sqrt{\dfrac{4m^2n}{5}}$
3. $\sqrt{\dfrac{bc}{m^3n^4}}$	3. $\sqrt{\dfrac{x}{5}}$	3. $\sqrt{\dfrac{7a^2}{8cd}}$	3. $4m\sqrt{\dfrac{2a^2}{3m^2n}}$	3. $-2a\sqrt{\dfrac{5c^5}{6a^2b}}$	3. $-\dfrac{3}{4}\sqrt{\dfrac{8cd^3}{9xy}}$
4. $\sqrt{\dfrac{3x}{b^5c^2}}$	4. $\sqrt{\dfrac{m^2}{2}}$	4. $\sqrt{\dfrac{5a^2y}{12bx^2}}$	4. $6rt^2\sqrt{\dfrac{3c^3}{5r^7t^3}}$	4. $-mx\sqrt{\dfrac{3r^3x}{2m^4t^2}}$	4. $\dfrac{a}{b}\sqrt{\dfrac{2b^2c}{3ad^2}}$
5. $\sqrt{\dfrac{4a^2b}{x^8y^7}}$	5. $\sqrt{\dfrac{ab^2}{8}}$	5. $\sqrt{\dfrac{2c^4d^3}{5x^3y}}$	5. $2ax\sqrt{\dfrac{7x^5y^2}{18a^4b^2}}$	5. $-4b^2c\sqrt{\dfrac{4b^8d}{5c^3x^5}}$	5. $\dfrac{2ax}{5b^2}\sqrt{\dfrac{25b^3x^2}{2a^4y}}$

EXERCISE 99

Simplification—Radicals of the Third Order

I. Aim: To simplify radicals of the third order (cube root).

II. Procedure

1. Find two factors of the given radicand, one of which is the largest possible perfect cube.
   Note—If the radicand is a fraction, first multiply both the numerator and denominator by the smallest possible number which will make the denominator a perfect cube.

2. Find the cube root of the perfect cube factor and write it as the coefficient of the radical whose radicand is the other factor.

3. If there is a coefficient in the given radical, multiply it by the cube root found in step 2.

   Note: To simplify radicals of any order:
   a) Find 2 factors of the given radicand, one of which is the largest possible power whose degree is equal to the order of the radical.
   b) Find the root of that factor and write it as the coefficient of the radical whose radicand is the other factor.
   c) If there is a coefficient in the given radical, multiply it by the root found in step b.

III. Sample Solutions

Simplify:

1. $\sqrt[3]{32} = \sqrt[3]{8 \cdot 4} = \sqrt[3]{8} \cdot \sqrt[3]{4} = 2\sqrt[3]{4}$ Answer, $2\sqrt[3]{4}$

2. $\sqrt[3]{m^3 n^7 x^5} = \sqrt[3]{m^3 n^6 x^3 \cdot nx^2} = \sqrt[3]{m^3 n^6 x^3}\sqrt[3]{nx^2} = mn^2 x\sqrt[3]{nx^2}$ Answer, $mn^2 x\sqrt[3]{nx^2}$

3. $\sqrt[3]{-81d^4 x^{11}} = \sqrt[3]{-27d^3 x^9 \cdot 3dx^2} = -3dx^3\sqrt[3]{3dx^2}$ Answer, $-3dx^3\sqrt[3]{3dx^2}$

4. $\sqrt[3]{\dfrac{9a^3 b^5}{4x^2}} = \sqrt[3]{\dfrac{9a^3 b^5}{4x^2} \cdot \dfrac{2x}{2x}} = \sqrt[3]{\dfrac{18a^3 b^5 x}{8x^3}} = \sqrt[3]{\dfrac{a^3 b^3}{8x^3} \cdot 18b^2 x} = \dfrac{ab}{2x}\sqrt[3]{18b^2 x}$ Answer, $\dfrac{ab}{2x}\sqrt[3]{18b^2 x}$

DIAGNOSTIC TEST

Simplify:

1. $\sqrt[3]{16}$
2. $\sqrt[3]{-54}$
3. $\sqrt[3]{a^3 b^6 c^7}$
4. $\sqrt[3]{8a^3 x^2}$

5. $\sqrt[3]{-250a^4 b^6 x^2}$
6. $\sqrt[3]{\dfrac{2}{9}}$
7. $\sqrt[3]{\dfrac{b}{a^2}}$

8. $\sqrt[3]{\dfrac{3ac^3}{4x}}$
9. $\sqrt[3]{-\dfrac{2a^3}{3bc^4}}$

10. $-2\sqrt[3]{-\dfrac{5x^3}{16}}$
11. $\dfrac{5a}{3x}\sqrt[3]{\dfrac{27x^4}{25a^2}}$

Simplify:

SET 1	SET 2	SET 3	SET 4
1. $\sqrt[3]{24}$	1. $\sqrt[3]{-32}$	1. $\sqrt[3]{x^4}$	1. $\sqrt[3]{27a}$
2. $\sqrt[3]{54}$	2. $\sqrt[3]{-250}$	2. $\sqrt[3]{b^6 c^2}$	2. $\sqrt[3]{16b^5}$
3. $\sqrt[3]{128}$	3. $\sqrt[3]{-72}$	3. $\sqrt[3]{mn^2 r^3}$	3. $\sqrt[3]{128x^3 y^2}$
4. $\sqrt[3]{81}$	4. $\sqrt[3]{-108}$	4. $\sqrt[3]{x^9 yz^5}$	4. $\sqrt[3]{54c^4 d^7}$
5. $4\sqrt[3]{500}$	5. $2\sqrt[3]{-192}$	5. $\sqrt[3]{a^4 b^5 c^8}$	5. $\sqrt[3]{48b^3 c^2 y^8}$

SET 5	SET 6	SET 7	
1. $\sqrt[3]{-x^3 y^2 z^4}$	1. $\sqrt[3]{\dfrac{3}{8}}$	1. $\sqrt[3]{\dfrac{m}{x}}$	4. $\sqrt[3]{\dfrac{r}{c^3 d^4}}$
2. $\sqrt[3]{-24a^4 c}$	2. $\sqrt[3]{\dfrac{9}{16}}$		
3. $\sqrt[3]{-250b^5 x^3}$	3. $\sqrt[3]{\dfrac{5}{3}}$	2. $\sqrt[3]{\dfrac{c^3}{d^2}}$	5. $\sqrt[3]{\dfrac{5rt^6}{x^7 y^5}}$
4. $\sqrt[3]{-56m^7 n^8}$	4. $\sqrt[3]{\dfrac{4}{5}}$		
5. $\sqrt[3]{-81ab^2 c^9}$	5. $\sqrt[3]{\dfrac{7}{36}}$	3. $\sqrt[3]{\dfrac{2x}{ab^2}}$	

SET 8	SET 9	SET 10	SET 11
1. $\sqrt[3]{\dfrac{a^4 b^3}{2}}$	1. $\sqrt[3]{\dfrac{-b^2}{27}}$	1. $2\sqrt[3]{\dfrac{a^2 c^3}{64}}$	1. $\dfrac{5}{16}\sqrt[3]{\dfrac{8}{25}}$
2. $\sqrt[3]{\dfrac{3c}{5x^2}}$	2. $\sqrt[3]{\dfrac{-x^4 y^3}{4c^2}}$	2. $a\sqrt[3]{\dfrac{2m^5 n}{3s^3}}$	2. $\dfrac{3b}{a}\sqrt[3]{\dfrac{4a^4}{b}}$
3. $\sqrt[3]{\dfrac{7mn^5}{16b^2 c^4}}$	3. $\sqrt[3]{-\dfrac{2c^6}{9m^2 n^4}}$	3. $-x^2\sqrt[3]{\dfrac{4ab^6}{5x^5}}$	3. $\dfrac{2cd}{3x}\sqrt[3]{\dfrac{27x^4}{2c^2 d}}$
4. $\sqrt[3]{\dfrac{5d^6 x}{27r^2 s}}$	4. $\sqrt[3]{\dfrac{8r^2 t}{5x^3 y^4}}$	4. $-\sqrt[3]{-\dfrac{3a^5}{4}}$	4. $\dfrac{5x}{4r}\sqrt[3]{-\dfrac{64r^2 s^3}{25x^2 y}}$
5. $\sqrt[3]{\dfrac{8n^3 s^4}{25m^5 x^3}}$	5. $\sqrt[3]{\dfrac{9a^3 b^5}{16c^4 d^6}}$	5. $-4c\sqrt[3]{-\dfrac{7b^2}{16c}}$	5. $-\dfrac{2bd}{5m}\sqrt[3]{\dfrac{125m^6 n}{4bd^4}}$

EXERCISE 100

Addition and Subtraction of Radicals

I. Aim: To add and subtract radicals.

II. Procedure

    1. Simplify all radicals.

    2. Combine similar radicals by adding algebraically the coefficients of the radicals having the same radicand.

III. Sample Solutions

Simplify and combine:

1. $3\sqrt{6} - 7\sqrt{6} + 2\sqrt{6}$

    $= -2\sqrt{6}$

Answer, $-2\sqrt{6}$

2. $5\sqrt{3} - 4\sqrt{7} - 3\sqrt{3} + \sqrt{7}$

    $= 2\sqrt{3} - 3\sqrt{7}$

Answer, $2\sqrt{3} - 3\sqrt{7}$

3. $4\sqrt{27} - 2\sqrt{48} + \sqrt{147}$

    $= 4\sqrt{9 \cdot 3} - 2\sqrt{16 \cdot 3} + \sqrt{49 \cdot 3}$

    $= 4 \cdot 3\sqrt{3} - 2 \cdot 4\sqrt{3} + 7\sqrt{3}$

    $= 12\sqrt{3} - 8\sqrt{3} + 7\sqrt{3}$

    $= 11\sqrt{3}$

Answer, $11\sqrt{3}$

4. $10\sqrt{\frac{1}{5}} + 4\sqrt{18} + 3\sqrt{45} - 8\sqrt{\frac{1}{2}}$

    $= 10\sqrt{\frac{5}{25}} + 4\sqrt{9 \cdot 2} + 3\sqrt{9 \cdot 5} - 8\sqrt{\frac{2}{4}}$

    $= 10\sqrt{\frac{1}{25} \cdot 5} + 4 \cdot 3\sqrt{2} + 3 \cdot 3\sqrt{5} - 8\sqrt{\frac{1}{4} \cdot 2}$

    $= 10 \cdot \frac{1}{5}\sqrt{5} + 12\sqrt{2} + 9\sqrt{5} - 8 \cdot \frac{1}{2}\sqrt{2}$

    $= 2\sqrt{5} + 12\sqrt{2} + 9\sqrt{5} - 4\sqrt{2}$

    $= 11\sqrt{5} + 8\sqrt{2}$

Answer, $11\sqrt{5} + 8\sqrt{2}$

5. $x\sqrt{xy^3} + 3xy\sqrt{xy} - 2y\sqrt{x^3 y}$

    $= x\sqrt{y^2 \cdot xy} + 3xy\sqrt{xy} - 2y\sqrt{x^2 \cdot xy}$

    $= xy\sqrt{xy} + 3xy\sqrt{xy} - 2xy\sqrt{xy}$

    $= 2xy\sqrt{xy}$

Answer, $2xy\sqrt{xy}$

DIAGNOSTIC TEST

Simplify and combine:

1. $2\sqrt{3} + 4\sqrt{3} - \sqrt{3}$

2. $\sqrt{96} - \sqrt{54} - \sqrt{24}$

3. $3\sqrt{75} - 2\sqrt{48} + \sqrt{12}$

4. $\sqrt{\frac{2}{3}} - \sqrt{\frac{1}{6}} + \sqrt{\frac{3}{2}}$

5. $4\sqrt{\frac{1}{2}} + 2\sqrt{18} - 6\sqrt{\frac{2}{9}}$

6. $5\sqrt{x} - 3\sqrt{x} + a\sqrt{x}$

7. $a\sqrt{2b} + \sqrt{32a^2 b} - \dfrac{2}{b}\sqrt{8a^2 b^3}$

8. $6\sqrt{5} + 3\sqrt{2} - 4\sqrt{5} + \sqrt{2}$

9. $12\sqrt{\frac{1}{3}} - \sqrt{80} - \sqrt{27} + \sqrt{125}$

10. $\sqrt[3]{16} + 2\sqrt[3]{128} - \sqrt[3]{54}$

Related Practice Examples

Simplify and combine:

SET 1

1. $8\sqrt{5}+3\sqrt{5}+\sqrt{5}$
2. $3\sqrt{7}-4\sqrt{7}+2\sqrt{7}$
3. $3\sqrt{6}-8\sqrt{6}-5\sqrt{6}$
4. $\frac{1}{2}\sqrt{2}+\frac{1}{3}\sqrt{2}-\frac{1}{6}\sqrt{2}$
5. $2\sqrt{3}-\frac{2}{3}\sqrt{3}+\frac{1}{5}\sqrt{3}$

SET 2

1. $\sqrt{48}+\sqrt{12}+\sqrt{27}$
2. $\sqrt{98}-\sqrt{8}+\sqrt{32}$
3. $\sqrt{63}-\sqrt{28}-\sqrt{7}$
4. $\sqrt{80}+\sqrt{45}-\sqrt{20}$
5. $\sqrt{50}-\sqrt{72}+\sqrt{18}$

SET 3

1. $2\sqrt{8}+4\sqrt{50}+3\sqrt{18}$
2. $6\sqrt{54}-3\sqrt{24}-2\sqrt{6}$
3. $\sqrt{125}+2\sqrt{80}-3\sqrt{20}$
4. $2\sqrt{40}-\sqrt{90}+5\sqrt{160}$
5. $3\sqrt{99}-2\sqrt{44}-6\sqrt{11}$
6. $-\sqrt{75}-2\sqrt{48}-5\sqrt{12}$
7. $8\sqrt{150}+4\sqrt{96}-3\sqrt{600}$
8. $2\sqrt{162}-\sqrt{72}+6\sqrt{128}$
9. $\frac{1}{3}\sqrt{147}+\frac{2}{3}\sqrt{27}-\sqrt{108}$
10. $\frac{1}{2}\sqrt{180}+\frac{1}{3}\sqrt{45}-\frac{2}{5}\sqrt{20}$

SET 4

1. $\sqrt{\frac{1}{5}}+\sqrt{\frac{5}{4}}+\sqrt{\frac{4}{5}}$
2. $\sqrt{\frac{2}{25}}+\sqrt{\frac{1}{2}}-\sqrt{\frac{9}{2}}$
3. $\sqrt{\frac{1}{3}}-\sqrt{\frac{3}{4}}+\sqrt{\frac{4}{3}}$
4. $10\sqrt{\frac{2}{5}}-\sqrt{\frac{9}{10}}-\sqrt{\frac{1}{10}}$
5. $\sqrt{1\frac{1}{8}}+4\sqrt{\frac{1}{8}}+\sqrt{\frac{8}{9}}$

SET 5

1. $\sqrt{18}+4\sqrt{\frac{1}{2}}+3\sqrt{32}$
2. $5\sqrt{\frac{1}{5}}+7\sqrt{5}-2\sqrt{20}$
3. $6\sqrt{3}-2\sqrt{75}+4\sqrt{\frac{3}{16}}$
4. $\sqrt{24}-12\sqrt{\frac{1}{6}}+6\sqrt{\frac{2}{3}}$
5. $10\sqrt{\frac{2}{5}}-\frac{1}{3}\sqrt{\frac{5}{2}}-\sqrt{40}$

SET 6

1. $2\sqrt{a}+7\sqrt{a}-3\sqrt{a}$
2. $3x\sqrt{b}-2x\sqrt{b}+4x\sqrt{b}$
3. $2a\sqrt{xy}+a\sqrt{xy}+4b\sqrt{xy}-2b\sqrt{xy}$
4. $5\sqrt{mn}-3\sqrt{mn}+b\sqrt{mn}$
5. $2x\sqrt{ab}-2y\sqrt{ab}+4x\sqrt{ab}$

SET 7

1. $\sqrt{100x}-\sqrt{9x}+\sqrt{25x}$
2. $\sqrt{x^3y}+\sqrt{4x^3y}+2x\sqrt{xy}$
3. $a\sqrt{ab^3}+ab\sqrt{ab}+b\sqrt{a^3b}$
4. $3\sqrt{9xy^4}-y\sqrt{16xy^2}+2y^2\sqrt{25x}$
5. $4\sqrt{c^3d^3}+3cd\sqrt{4cd}-2c\sqrt{9cd^3}$

SET 8

1. $3\sqrt{2}+4\sqrt{2}+7\sqrt{3}-4\sqrt{3}$
2. $6\sqrt{a}+5\sqrt{a}-3\sqrt{b}+4\sqrt{b}$
3. $2b\sqrt{3c}+b\sqrt{5c}+b\sqrt{3c}-2b\sqrt{5c}$
4. $3a\sqrt{5}-2a\sqrt{5}+5a\sqrt{7}-6a\sqrt{7}$
5. $4m\sqrt{2n}-2n\sqrt{5m}-2m\sqrt{2n}-n\sqrt{5m}$

SET 9

1. $\sqrt{50}+\sqrt{98}-\sqrt{75}+\sqrt{27}$
2. $\sqrt{72}-\sqrt{80}-\sqrt{45}+\sqrt{\frac{1}{2}}$
3. $2\sqrt{63}+5\sqrt{54}-\sqrt{28}-3\sqrt{24}$
4. $8\sqrt{12}-10\sqrt{\frac{1}{3}}-\sqrt{108}+\sqrt{125}$
5. $4\sqrt{\frac{3}{8}}+\frac{1}{4}\sqrt{48}+2\sqrt{96}-8\sqrt{\frac{3}{4}}$

SET 10

1. $\sqrt[3]{81}+\sqrt[3]{24}+\sqrt[3]{192}$
2. $\sqrt[3]{625}+\sqrt[3]{135}-\sqrt[3]{40}$
3. $\sqrt[3]{128}+2\sqrt[3]{250}-3\sqrt[3]{16}$
4. $8\sqrt[3]{\frac{1}{4}}+\sqrt[3]{54}+\sqrt[3]{\frac{2}{8}}+\sqrt[3]{48}$
5. $\sqrt[3]{32}-2\sqrt[3]{81}-4\sqrt[3]{\frac{1}{2}}+\sqrt[3]{24}$

EXERCISE 101

Multiplication of Radicals—Monomial by a Monomial

I. Aim: To multiply a monomial radical by a monomial radical of the same order.*

II. Procedure

1. Multiply the coefficients of the given radicals to obtain the coefficient of the product, and multiply the radicands of the given radicals to obtain the radicand of the product.

2. If possible, simplify the resulting radical.

   * Note: The two radicals *must* be of the same order to be multiplied by the above rule. The radicands, however, do not necessarily have to be the same.

III. Sample Solutions

Multiply and simplify:

1. $4 \cdot 5\sqrt{2} = 20\sqrt{2}$ Answer, $20\sqrt{2}$
2. $\sqrt{6} \cdot \sqrt{8} = \sqrt{48} = \sqrt{16 \cdot 3} = 4\sqrt{3}$ Answer, $4\sqrt{3}$
3. $7\sqrt{3} \cdot 5\sqrt{2} = 35\sqrt{6}$ Answer, $35\sqrt{6}$
4. $2\sqrt{3} \cdot 2\sqrt{3} = 4\sqrt{9} = 4 \cdot 3 = 12$ Answer, 12
5. $\sqrt{6a^3} \cdot \sqrt{4x} = \sqrt{24a^3x} = \sqrt{4a^2 \cdot 6ax} = 2a\sqrt{6ax}$ Answer, $2a\sqrt{6ax}$
6. $\sqrt{\frac{4}{3}} \cdot \sqrt{\frac{3}{10}} = \sqrt{\frac{2}{5}} = \sqrt{\frac{10}{25}} = \sqrt{\frac{1}{25} \cdot 10} = \frac{1}{5}\sqrt{10}$ Answer, $\frac{1}{5}\sqrt{10}$
7. $\sqrt[3]{9} \cdot \sqrt[3]{6} = \sqrt[3]{54} = \sqrt[3]{27 \cdot 2} = 3\sqrt[3]{2}$ Answer, $3\sqrt[3]{2}$
8. $(-5\sqrt{2})^2 = 25\sqrt{4} = 25 \cdot 2 = 50$ Answer, 50

DIAGNOSTIC TEST

Multiply the following monomials and simplify the products:

1. $4 \cdot 3\sqrt{5}$
2. $\sqrt{2} \cdot \sqrt{3}$
3. $\sqrt{3} \cdot \sqrt{15}$
4. $\sqrt{7} \cdot \sqrt{7}$
5. $2\sqrt{3} \cdot 5\sqrt{7}$
6. $2\sqrt{5} \cdot 4\sqrt{15}$
7. $3\sqrt{5} \cdot 3\sqrt{5}$
8. $5\sqrt{2} \cdot \sqrt{8}$
9. $\frac{1}{2}\sqrt{3} \cdot 6\sqrt{12}$
10. $(-3\sqrt{3})(-4\sqrt{6})$
11. $\sqrt{a} \cdot \sqrt{x}$
12. $\sqrt{6a} \cdot \sqrt{12a}$
13. $\sqrt{8x^3} \cdot \sqrt{5y^2}$
14. $(2\sqrt{5bx^2})(-x\sqrt{10ab})$
15. $\sqrt{\frac{3}{8}} \cdot \sqrt{\frac{2}{3}}$
16. $\sqrt[3]{4} \cdot \sqrt[3]{6}$
17. $(2\sqrt{2})^2$
18. $(-6\sqrt{3})^2$

Related Practice Examples

Multiply and simplify:

SET 1	SET 2	SET 3	SET 4
1. $2 \cdot 4\sqrt{3}$	1. $\sqrt{5} \cdot \sqrt{2}$	1. $\sqrt{2} \cdot \sqrt{6}$	1. $\sqrt{3} \cdot \sqrt{3}$
2. $5 \cdot 2\sqrt{6}$	2. $\sqrt{3} \cdot \sqrt{7}$	2. $\sqrt{8} \cdot \sqrt{3}$	2. $\sqrt{5} \cdot \sqrt{5}$
3. $8 \cdot 3\sqrt{5}$	3. $\sqrt{2} \cdot \sqrt{3}$	3. $\sqrt{12} \cdot \sqrt{6}$	3. $\sqrt{8} \cdot \sqrt{8}$
4. $2\sqrt{2} \cdot 6$	4. $\sqrt{11} \cdot \sqrt{5}$	4. $\sqrt{5} \cdot \sqrt{15}$	4. $\sqrt{2} \cdot \sqrt{8}$
5. $7\sqrt{6} \cdot 3$	5. $\sqrt{6} \cdot \sqrt{7}$	5. $\sqrt{6} \cdot \sqrt{8}$	5. $\sqrt{3} \cdot \sqrt{27}$

	SET 5	SET 6	SET 7	SET 8
1.	$2\sqrt{3}\cdot3\sqrt{2}$	$3\sqrt{6}\cdot2\sqrt{8}$	$2\sqrt{2}\cdot2\sqrt{2}$	$4\sqrt{3}\cdot\sqrt{7}$
2.	$3\sqrt{5}\cdot4\sqrt{3}$	$2\sqrt{14}\cdot4\sqrt{2}$	$5\sqrt{6}\cdot5\sqrt{6}$	$5\sqrt{10}\cdot\sqrt{4}$
3.	$2\sqrt{7}\cdot2\sqrt{6}$	$2\sqrt{24}\cdot7\sqrt{3}$	$2\sqrt{18}\cdot6\sqrt{2}$	$\sqrt{2}\cdot3\sqrt{2}$
4.	$5\sqrt{5}\cdot3\sqrt{14}$	$4\sqrt{2}\cdot4\sqrt{27}$	$8\sqrt{2}\cdot2\sqrt{32}$	$\sqrt{12}\cdot6\sqrt{3}$
5.	$6\sqrt{13}\cdot2\sqrt{3}$	$5\sqrt{8}\cdot3\sqrt{10}$	$6\sqrt{5}\cdot3\sqrt{20}$	$2\sqrt{18}\cdot\sqrt{5}$

	SET 9	SET 10	SET 11	SET 12
1.	$\frac{1}{3}\sqrt{3}\cdot\sqrt{3}$	$(-\sqrt{5})(-\sqrt{8})$	$\sqrt{x}\cdot\sqrt{y}$	$\sqrt{5b}\cdot\sqrt{5b}$
2.	$\frac{1}{2}\sqrt{2}\cdot4\sqrt{10}$	$(-2\sqrt{12})(4\sqrt{5})$	$\sqrt{c}\cdot\sqrt{d}$	$\sqrt{2a}\cdot\sqrt{6a}$
3.	$\sqrt{15}\cdot\frac{1}{5}\sqrt{5}$	$(6\sqrt{3})(-\sqrt{18})$	$(-\sqrt{m})(-\sqrt{2n})$	$\sqrt{8bc}\cdot\sqrt{4bc}$
4.	$\frac{2}{3}\sqrt{6}\cdot\frac{1}{2}\sqrt{6}$	$(-3\sqrt{2})(-2\sqrt{2})$	$\sqrt{2x}\cdot\sqrt{3y}$	$\sqrt{6ax}\cdot\sqrt{9ax}$
5.	$\frac{1}{4}\sqrt{20}\cdot\frac{4}{5}\sqrt{5}$	$(-\frac{1}{2}\sqrt{6})(4\sqrt{3})$	$(-\sqrt{5a})(\sqrt{2b})$	$(-3\sqrt{3mn})(-\sqrt{3mn})$

	SET 13	SET 14	SET 15
1.	$\sqrt{ax}\cdot\sqrt{a}$	$2\sqrt{b}\cdot3\sqrt{ab^3}$	$\sqrt{\frac{1}{2}}\cdot\sqrt{6}$
2.	$\sqrt{a^3b}\cdot\sqrt{bc^3}$	$a\sqrt{2x}\cdot x\sqrt{6x}$	$\sqrt{\frac{4}{5}}\cdot\sqrt{\frac{1}{4}}$
3.	$(\sqrt{2c^3})(-\sqrt{5cd})$	$2m\sqrt{7mn}\cdot3\sqrt{7m}$	$\sqrt{\frac{3}{4}}\cdot\sqrt{\frac{1}{2}}$
4.	$\sqrt{6m^4}\cdot\sqrt{3mn^2}$	$3y\sqrt{6x^3y}\cdot2x\sqrt{8xy^4}$	$\sqrt{\frac{2}{3}}\cdot\sqrt{\frac{2}{3}}$
5.	$\sqrt{2a^2c}\cdot\sqrt{2c^2x}$	$(-5a\sqrt{2a^4b})(-4b\sqrt{12a^3b^4})$	$(-2\sqrt{\frac{1}{2}})(3\sqrt{\frac{3}{2}})$

	SET 16	SET 17	SET 18
1.	$\sqrt[3]{4}\cdot\sqrt[3]{4}$	$(\sqrt{5})^2$	$(-\sqrt{3})^2$
2.	$\sqrt[3]{9}\cdot\sqrt[3]{6}$	$(\sqrt{8})^2$	$(-4\sqrt{5})^2$
3.	$\sqrt[3]{2}\cdot\sqrt[3]{12}$	$(3\sqrt{3})^2$	$(-2\sqrt{2})^2$
4.	$\sqrt[3]{a^2}\cdot\sqrt[3]{ab}$	$(4\sqrt{6})^2$	$(-3\sqrt{x})^2$
5.	$\sqrt[3]{2c^3}\cdot\sqrt[3]{16x^2}$	$(x\sqrt{2a})^2$	$(-2a\sqrt{3b})^2$

EXERCISE 102

Multiplication of Radicals—Binomial by a Monomial

I. Aim: To multiply a binomial radical by a monomial radical of the same order.

II. Procedure

Multiply each term of the binomial radical by the monomial radical using the procedure outlined in Exercise 101.

III. Sample Solutions

Multiply and simplify:

1. $2(3-5\sqrt{3})=6-10\sqrt{3}$ Answer, $6-10\sqrt{3}$

2. $\sqrt{2}(\sqrt{5}+\sqrt{6})=\sqrt{10}+\sqrt{12}=\sqrt{10}+\sqrt{4\cdot3}=\sqrt{10}+2\sqrt{3}$ Answer, $\sqrt{10}+2\sqrt{3}$

3. $2\sqrt{3}(4\sqrt{3}-3\sqrt{7})=8\sqrt{9}-6\sqrt{21}=8\cdot3-6\sqrt{21}=24-6\sqrt{21}$ Answer, $24-6\sqrt{21}$

DIAGNOSTIC TEST

Multiply and simplify:

1. $5(3\sqrt{5}-6)$ 3. $\sqrt{6}(\sqrt{2}+4)$ 5. $\frac{1}{2}\sqrt{2}(\sqrt{2}+\frac{2}{3}\sqrt{12})$

2. $3(2\sqrt{3}-3\sqrt{2})$ 4. $-\sqrt{3}(\sqrt{18}-2\sqrt{12})$ 6. $-\sqrt{2}(\sqrt{8}-5\sqrt{6})$

Related Practice Examples

Multiply and simplify:

SET 1	SET 2	SET 3
1. $2(4\sqrt{2}+1)$	1. $3(\sqrt{5}-2\sqrt{2})$	1. $\sqrt{2}(\sqrt{3}+3)$
2. $4(3\sqrt{6}-2)$	2. $4(3\sqrt{7}+\sqrt{6})$	2. $\sqrt{6}(\sqrt{2}+5)$
3. $3(3+5\sqrt{3})$	3. $9(4\sqrt{3}-2\sqrt{10})$	3. $\sqrt{5}(\sqrt{5}-2)$
4. $8(2-3\sqrt{5})$	4. $8(5\sqrt{13}+4\sqrt{11})$	4. $\sqrt{3}(\sqrt{27}+4)$
5. $6(1-6\sqrt{8})$	5. $2(3\sqrt{12}-5\sqrt{8})$	5. $\sqrt{8}(2\sqrt{3}-5)$

SET 4	SET 5	SET 6
1. $\sqrt{3}(\sqrt{6}+\sqrt{3})$	1. $3\sqrt{2}(\sqrt{3}-5\sqrt{8})$	1. $-2(5\sqrt{3}-4\sqrt{7})$
2. $\sqrt{6}(\sqrt{2}-\sqrt{12})$	2. $5\sqrt{5}(3\sqrt{5}+2\sqrt{6})$	2. $-\sqrt{2}(-\sqrt{8}+2\sqrt{2})$
3. $\sqrt{2}(3\sqrt{2}+\sqrt{18})$	3. $\frac{1}{2}\sqrt{2}(\sqrt{6}+\frac{1}{2}\sqrt{2})$	3. $-\sqrt{6}(3\sqrt{2}+5\sqrt{8})$
4. $\sqrt{12}(2\sqrt{5}-4\sqrt{2})$	4. $\frac{1}{3}\sqrt{3}(\sqrt{3}-\frac{1}{3}\sqrt{6})$	4. $-3\sqrt{3}(3\sqrt{2}-5\sqrt{6})$
5. $\sqrt{10}(4\sqrt{6}-5\sqrt{8})$	5. $\frac{1}{5}\sqrt{5}(\frac{1}{5}\sqrt{5}+5\sqrt{2})$	5. $-\frac{1}{2}\sqrt{2}(4\sqrt{18}-\frac{1}{2}\sqrt{2})$

EXERCISE 103

Multiplication of Radicals—Binomial by a Binomial

I. Aim: To multiply a binomial radical by a binomial radical of the same order.

II. Procedure

1. Follow the rules for the multiplication of polynomials. See Exercise 31. The procedure for special products can also be used. See Unit Eight.

2. Simplify wherever possible.

III. Sample Solutions

1.
$$3\sqrt{6}+2$$
$$3\sqrt{6}-2$$
$$\overline{54+6\sqrt{6}}$$
$$-4-6\sqrt{6}$$
$$\overline{50}$$
Answer, 50

2.
$$5\sqrt{2}-\sqrt{3}$$
$$5\sqrt{2}+\sqrt{3}$$
$$\overline{50-5\sqrt{6}}$$
$$-3+5\sqrt{6}$$
$$\overline{47}$$
Answer, 47

3.
$$6\sqrt{3}+3\sqrt{8}$$
$$6\sqrt{3}+3\sqrt{8}$$
$$\overline{108+18\sqrt{24}}$$
$$+72+18\sqrt{24}$$
$$\overline{180+36\sqrt{24}}$$
$$=180+36\sqrt{4\cdot6}$$
$$=180+72\sqrt{6}$$
Answer, $180+72\sqrt{6}$

4.
$$(3\sqrt{5}-2\sqrt{6})^2=45-12\sqrt{30}+24$$
$$=69-12\sqrt{30}$$
Answer, $69-12\sqrt{30}$

DIAGNOSTIC TEST

Multiply and simplify:

1. $2\sqrt{5}+3$
   $2\sqrt{5}-3$

2. $3\sqrt{2}+5$
   $3\sqrt{2}+5$

3. $4\sqrt{3}-6$
   $2\sqrt{3}+7$

4. $3\sqrt{2}-\sqrt{6}$
   $3\sqrt{2}+\sqrt{6}$

5. $2\sqrt{8}-3\sqrt{3}$
   $2\sqrt{8}-3\sqrt{3}$

6. $4\sqrt{6}-3\sqrt{5}$
   $2\sqrt{6}-5\sqrt{5}$

7. $(\frac{1}{2}\sqrt{2}+\sqrt{3})(\frac{1}{2}\sqrt{2}-\sqrt{3})$

8. $(3-2\sqrt{5})^2$

Related Practice Examples

Multiply and simplify:

SET 1	SET 2	SET 3	SET 4	SET 5	SET 6
1. $\sqrt{2}+4$ $\quad\sqrt{2}-4$	1. $\sqrt{2}+2$ $\quad\sqrt{2}+2$	1. $\sqrt{3}+4$ $\quad\sqrt{3}+2$	1. $\sqrt{3}+\sqrt{2}$ $\quad\sqrt{3}-\sqrt{2}$	1. $\sqrt{5}+\sqrt{3}$ $\quad\sqrt{5}+\sqrt{3}$	1. $2\sqrt{8}+\sqrt{5}$ $\quad\sqrt{8}+3\sqrt{5}$
2. $2\sqrt{3}-3$ $\quad2\sqrt{3}+3$	2. $3\sqrt{3}+5$ $\quad3\sqrt{3}+5$	2. $5+\sqrt{5}$ $\quad3-\sqrt{5}$	2. $\sqrt{8}-\sqrt{5}$ $\quad\sqrt{8}+\sqrt{5}$	2. $\sqrt{2}-\sqrt{12}$ $\quad\sqrt{2}-\sqrt{12}$	2. $3\sqrt{6}-2\sqrt{3}$ $\quad2\sqrt{6}-4\sqrt{3}$
3. $5\sqrt{6}+2$ $\quad5\sqrt{6}-2$	3. $4\sqrt{2}-1$ $\quad4\sqrt{2}-1$	3. $3\sqrt{2}-4$ $\quad2\sqrt{2}+7$	3. $2\sqrt{3}+\sqrt{2}$ $\quad2\sqrt{3}-\sqrt{2}$	3. $3\sqrt{8}+\sqrt{6}$ $\quad3\sqrt{8}+\sqrt{6}$	3. $5\sqrt{2}+6\sqrt{6}$ $\quad3\sqrt{2}-2\sqrt{6}$
4. $6-3\sqrt{8}$ $\quad6+3\sqrt{8}$	4. $5+2\sqrt{6}$ $\quad5+2\sqrt{6}$	4. $4\sqrt{6}+3$ $\quad\sqrt{6}-5$	4. $5\sqrt{6}-2\sqrt{3}$ $\quad5\sqrt{6}+2\sqrt{3}$	4. $5\sqrt{10}-2\sqrt{18}$ $\quad5\sqrt{10}-2\sqrt{18}$	4. $2\sqrt{12}+5\sqrt{8}$ $\quad4\sqrt{12}-2\sqrt{8}$
5. $7+2\sqrt{5}$ $\quad7-2\sqrt{5}$	5. $3-5\sqrt{8}$ $\quad3-5\sqrt{8}$	5. $2\sqrt{8}-3$ $\quad3\sqrt{8}-4$	5. $\frac{1}{2}\sqrt{2}-6\sqrt{5}$ $\quad\frac{1}{2}\sqrt{2}+6\sqrt{5}$	5. $4\sqrt{7}+3\sqrt{8}$ $\quad4\sqrt{7}+3\sqrt{8}$	5. $6\sqrt{5}-3\sqrt{10}$ $\quad4\sqrt{5}+\sqrt{10}$

SET 7

1. $(\sqrt{5}+1)(\sqrt{5}-1)$
2. $(2\sqrt{6}-\sqrt{2})(2\sqrt{6}+\sqrt{2})$
3. $(4+5\sqrt{8})(4-5\sqrt{8})$
4. $(6-\frac{1}{2}\sqrt{2})(6+\frac{1}{2}\sqrt{2})$
5. $(\frac{1}{3}\sqrt{3}-2\sqrt{8})(\frac{1}{3}\sqrt{3}+2\sqrt{8})$

SET 8

1. $(\sqrt{8}+2)^2$
2. $(2\sqrt{3}-1)^2$
3. $(\sqrt{2}+\sqrt{3})^2$
4. $(5\sqrt{6}-6\sqrt{5})^2$
5. $(4\sqrt{6}+3\sqrt{3})^2$

EXERCISE 104

Division of Radicals

I. Aim: To divide a monomial radical or polynomial radical by a monomial radical of the same order.

II. Procedure

  1. Monomial radical by a monomial radical.
    a) Divide the coefficient of the numerator (dividend) by the coefficient of the denominator (divisor) to obtain the coefficient of the answer (quotient).
    b) Divide the radicand of the numerator (dividend) by the radicand of the denominator (divisor) to obtain the radicand of the answer (quotient).
    c) Simplify wherever possible.

  2. Polynomial radical by a monomial radical.
    Divide each term of the polynomial radical by the monomial radical denominator (divisor) using the procedure outlined above.

III. Sample Solutions

    Divide and simplify:

1. $\dfrac{\sqrt{10}}{\sqrt{5}} = \sqrt{2}$

    Answer, $\sqrt{2}$

3. $\dfrac{\sqrt{2}}{\sqrt{6}} = \sqrt{\tfrac{1}{3}} = \tfrac{1}{3}\sqrt{3}$

    Answer, $\tfrac{1}{3}\sqrt{3}$

5. $\dfrac{2}{3\sqrt{2}} = \tfrac{2}{3}\sqrt{\tfrac{1}{2}} = \tfrac{2}{3} \cdot \tfrac{1}{2}\sqrt{2} = \tfrac{1}{3}\sqrt{2}$

    Answer, $\tfrac{1}{3}\sqrt{2}$

2. $\dfrac{\sqrt{225}}{\sqrt{3}} = \sqrt{75} = 5\sqrt{3}$

    Answer, $5\sqrt{3}$

4. $\dfrac{32\sqrt{a^3b^2}}{4\sqrt{ab}} = 8\sqrt{a^2b} = 8a\sqrt{b}$

    Answer, $8a\sqrt{b}$

6. $\dfrac{\sqrt{24}+2\sqrt{60}-\sqrt{3}}{\sqrt{3}}$

    $= \sqrt{8}+2\sqrt{20}-1$

    $= 2\sqrt{2}+4\sqrt{5}-1$

    Answer, $2\sqrt{2}+4\sqrt{5}-1$

DIAGNOSTIC TEST

Divide and simplify:

1. $\dfrac{\sqrt{6}}{\sqrt{2}}$

2. $\dfrac{\sqrt{27}}{\sqrt{3}}$

3. $\dfrac{\sqrt{60}}{\sqrt{5}}$

4. $\dfrac{12\sqrt{98}}{4\sqrt{2}}$

5. $\dfrac{\sqrt{5}}{\sqrt{2}}$

6. $\dfrac{\sqrt{3}}{\sqrt{24}}$

7. $\dfrac{\sqrt{32a^4}}{\sqrt{2a}}$

8. $\dfrac{10\sqrt{16x^3y^2}}{2\sqrt{2xy}}$

9. $\dfrac{6}{\sqrt{3}}$

10. $\dfrac{\sqrt[3]{80}}{\sqrt[3]{5}}$

11. $\dfrac{4\sqrt{12}-2\sqrt{6}+6\sqrt{96}}{2\sqrt{3}}$

12. $\dfrac{\sqrt{8a^5b^5}+\sqrt{18a^3b^3}-\sqrt{24ab}}{\sqrt{2ab}}$

Related Practice Examples

Divide and simplify:

SET 1	SET 2	SET 3	SET 4	SET 5
1. $\dfrac{\sqrt{12}}{\sqrt{6}}$	1. $\dfrac{\sqrt{8}}{\sqrt{2}}$	1. $\dfrac{\sqrt{24}}{\sqrt{3}}$	1. $\dfrac{6\sqrt{8}}{3\sqrt{8}}$	1. $\dfrac{\sqrt{3}}{\sqrt{2}}$
2. $\dfrac{\sqrt{15}}{\sqrt{5}}$	2. $\dfrac{\sqrt{75}}{\sqrt{3}}$	2. $\dfrac{\sqrt{90}}{\sqrt{2}}$	2. $\dfrac{8\sqrt{20}}{2\sqrt{5}}$	2. $\dfrac{\sqrt{4}}{\sqrt{3}}$
3. $\dfrac{\sqrt{30}}{\sqrt{6}}$	3. $\dfrac{\sqrt{96}}{\sqrt{6}}$	3. $\dfrac{\sqrt{108}}{\sqrt{6}}$	3. $\dfrac{12\sqrt{12}}{4\sqrt{4}}$	3. $\dfrac{\sqrt{7}}{\sqrt{2}}$
4. $\dfrac{\sqrt{39}}{\sqrt{3}}$	4. $\dfrac{\sqrt{128}}{\sqrt{2}}$	4. $\dfrac{\sqrt{140}}{\sqrt{7}}$	4. $\dfrac{15\sqrt{96}}{5\sqrt{2}}$	4. $\dfrac{\sqrt{8}}{\sqrt{5}}$
5. $\dfrac{\sqrt{56}}{\sqrt{8}}$	5. $\dfrac{\sqrt{147}}{\sqrt{3}}$	5. $\dfrac{\sqrt{120}}{\sqrt{5}}$	5. $\dfrac{9\sqrt{125}}{9\sqrt{5}}$	5. $\dfrac{\sqrt{10}}{\sqrt{6}}$

SET 6	SET 7	SET 8	SET 9a	SET 9b
1. $\dfrac{\sqrt{1}}{\sqrt{2}}$	1. $\dfrac{\sqrt{ax}}{\sqrt{a}}$	1. $\dfrac{4\sqrt{a^2b}}{2\sqrt{ab}}$	1. $\dfrac{1}{\sqrt{2}}$	1. $\dfrac{2}{3\sqrt{2}}$
2. $\dfrac{\sqrt{5}}{\sqrt{8}}$	2. $\dfrac{\sqrt{x^3y^4}}{\sqrt{xy}}$	2. $\dfrac{12\sqrt{b^5c^2}}{3\sqrt{b^3c}}$	2. $\dfrac{4}{\sqrt{6}}$	2. $\dfrac{5}{2\sqrt{5}}$
3. $\dfrac{\sqrt{8}}{\sqrt{12}}$	3. $\dfrac{\sqrt{32b^3}}{\sqrt{8b}}$	3. $\dfrac{16\sqrt{8m^8}}{4\sqrt{4m^3}}$	3. $\dfrac{6}{\sqrt{8}}$	3. $\dfrac{1}{4\sqrt{2}}$
4. $\dfrac{\sqrt{10}}{\sqrt{18}}$	4. $\dfrac{\sqrt{60m^3n}}{\sqrt{5m}}$	4. $\dfrac{30\sqrt{27x^5y^3}}{6\sqrt{3xy^3}}$	4. $\dfrac{5}{\sqrt{5}}$	4. $\dfrac{a}{\sqrt{a}}$
5. $\dfrac{\sqrt{8}}{\sqrt{20}}$	5. $\dfrac{\sqrt{x^2y}}{\sqrt{xy^2}}$	5. $\dfrac{42\sqrt{40r^3t^2}}{3\sqrt{5rt}}$	5. $\dfrac{2}{\sqrt{3}}$	5. $\dfrac{2x^2}{3\sqrt{2x}}$

SET 10	SET 11	SET 12
1. $\dfrac{\sqrt[3]{24}}{\sqrt[3]{3}}$	1. $\dfrac{\sqrt{18}+\sqrt{50}}{\sqrt{2}}$	1. $\dfrac{\sqrt{a^3}+\sqrt{a^2}}{\sqrt{a}}$
2. $\dfrac{\sqrt[3]{108}}{\sqrt[3]{4}}$	2. $\dfrac{\sqrt{48}-\sqrt{24}}{\sqrt{3}}$	2. $\dfrac{\sqrt{a^3x^2}-\sqrt{a^2x^3}}{\sqrt{ax}}$
3. $\dfrac{\sqrt[3]{12}}{\sqrt[3]{2}}$	3. $\dfrac{\sqrt{80}+\sqrt{90}-\sqrt{15}}{\sqrt{5}}$	3. $\dfrac{\sqrt{x^3y^3}+\sqrt{x^2y^2}-\sqrt{xy}}{\sqrt{xy}}$
4. $\dfrac{\sqrt[3]{48}}{\sqrt[3]{3}}$	4. $\dfrac{6\sqrt{12}-4\sqrt{27}+2\sqrt{108}}{2\sqrt{3}}$	4. $\dfrac{\sqrt{4a^4b}-\sqrt{2a^6b}+\sqrt{8a^2b^2}}{\sqrt{2a^2b}}$
5. $\dfrac{\sqrt[3]{1000}}{\sqrt[3]{4}}$	5. $\dfrac{9\sqrt{30}+6\sqrt{150}-3\sqrt{2}}{3\sqrt{2}}$	5. $\dfrac{\sqrt{12m^2x^2}-\sqrt{24m^2x}-\sqrt{30mx^2}}{\sqrt{3mx}}$

EXERCISE 105
Radical Equations

I. Aim: To solve radical equations.

II. Procedure

1. If necessary, transpose terms so that the radical is on one member of the equation and all the other terms are on the other member.

2. Raise both members of the equation to that power which will remove the radical from the equation.

3. Then solve the resulting equation.

4. Check by substituting the root in the given equation.

III. Sample Solutions

Solve and check:

1. $\sqrt{3x} = 6$ Check:

$3x = 36$ $\sqrt{36} = 6$

$x = 12$ $6 = 6$

Answer, $x = 12$

2. $\sqrt{5x} - 3 = 12$ Check:

$\sqrt{5x} = 12 + 3$ $\sqrt{225} - 3 = 12$

$\sqrt{5x} = 15$ $15 - 3 = 12$

$5x = 225$ $12 = 12$

$x = 45$

Answer, $x = 45$

3. $2\sqrt{4x - 3} = 10$ Check:

$\sqrt{4x - 3} = 5$ $2\sqrt{28 - 3} = 10$

$4x - 3 = 25$ $2\sqrt{25} = 10$

$4x = 25 + 3$ $2 \cdot 5 = 10$

$4x = 28$ $10 = 10$

$x = 7$

Answer, $x = 7$

4. $\sqrt{x^2 + 9} = x + 1$ Check:

$x^2 + 9 = x^2 + 2x + 1$ $\sqrt{16 + 9} = 4 + 1$

$9 - 1 = x^2 - x^2 + 2x$ $\sqrt{25} = 5$

$8 = 2x$ $5 = 5$

$4 = x$

$x = 4$

Answer, $x = 4$

5. $\sqrt{\dfrac{2x}{5}} = 4$ Check:

$\dfrac{2x}{5} = 16$ $\sqrt{\frac{80}{5}} = 4$

$2x = 80$ $\sqrt{16} = 4$

$x = 40$ $4 = 4$

Answer, $x = 40$

6. $3\sqrt{x} = 2$ Check:

$\sqrt{x} = \frac{2}{3}$ $3\sqrt{\frac{4}{9}} = 2$

$x = \frac{4}{9}$ $3 \cdot \frac{2}{3} = 2$

$2 = 2$

Answer, $x = \frac{4}{9}$

DIAGNOSTIC TEST

Solve and check:

1. $\sqrt{x} = 3$

2. $\sqrt{2x} = 4$

3. $3\sqrt{x} = 6$

4. $\sqrt{x} + 1 = 5$

5. $\sqrt{3x} - 2 = 4$

6. $2\sqrt{2x} + 3 = 11$

7. $\sqrt{x + 2} = 3$

8. $4\sqrt{2x - 1} = 12$

9. $\sqrt{x^2 + 8} = x + 2$

10. $8 - \sqrt{2x} = 2$

11. $\sqrt{\dfrac{x}{2}} = 5$

12. $\sqrt{\dfrac{2x}{3}} = 6$

13. $2\sqrt{2x} = 5$

14. $3\sqrt{3x - 2} = 4$

Related Practice Examples

Solve and check:

SET 1
1. $\sqrt{x} = 2$
2. $\sqrt{x} = 5$
3. $\sqrt{y} = 4$
4. $\sqrt{x} = 1$
5. $6 = \sqrt{x}$

SET 2
1. $\sqrt{3x} = 6$
2. $\sqrt{5x} = 5$
3. $\sqrt{4x} = 8$
4. $\sqrt{6y} = 12$
5. $6 = \sqrt{2x}$

SET 3
1. $4\sqrt{x} = 8$
2. $2\sqrt{x} = 10$
3. $3\sqrt{2x} = 12$
4. $5\sqrt{3y} = 60$
5. $40 = 2\sqrt{5x}$

SET 4
1. $\sqrt{x} + 4 = 6$
2. $\sqrt{x} + 7 = 12$
3. $\sqrt{2y} + 11 = 15$
4. $12 + \sqrt{4x} = 20$
5. $15 = \sqrt{3x} + 9$

SET 5
1. $\sqrt{x} - 2 = 3$
2. $\sqrt{2x} - 5 = 7$
3. $\sqrt{5y} - 8 = 2$
4. $6 = \sqrt{3x} - 3$
5. $1 = \sqrt{4x} - 7$

SET 6
1. $3\sqrt{x} + 4 = 10$
2. $4\sqrt{3y} + 9 = 21$
3. $6\sqrt{2x} - 3 = 45$
4. $2\sqrt{5x} - 5 = 25$
5. $26 = 3\sqrt{2x} + 8$

SET 7
1. $\sqrt{x+1} = 4$
2. $\sqrt{x-3} = 8$
3. $\sqrt{2x+3} = 5$
4. $\sqrt{5y-4} = 9$
5. $3 = \sqrt{7y-5}$

SET 8
1. $2\sqrt{x+3} = 10$
2. $6\sqrt{y-4} = 18$
3. $3\sqrt{2x+5} = 9$
4. $4\sqrt{3x-2} = 16$
5. $8 = 8\sqrt{5x-4}$

SET 9
1. $\sqrt{x^2+3} = x+1$
2. $\sqrt{x^2-35} = x-5$
3. $\sqrt{x^2+27} = x+3$
4. $\sqrt{x^2+16} = x+8$
5. $x-4 = \sqrt{x^2-32}$

SET 10
1. $9 - \sqrt{x} = 2$
2. $12 - \sqrt{2x} = 4$
3. $3 = 15 - \sqrt{3x}$
4. $25 - 2\sqrt{5x} = 5$
5. $50 - 3\sqrt{8x} = 2$

SET 11
1. $\sqrt{\dfrac{x}{3}} = 1$
2. $\sqrt{\dfrac{x}{2}} = 3$
3. $\sqrt{\dfrac{y}{5}} = 2$
4. $\sqrt{\dfrac{x}{3}} = 5$
5. $2 = \sqrt{\dfrac{x}{4}}$

SET 12
1. $\sqrt{\dfrac{2x}{3}} = 4$
2. $\sqrt{\dfrac{3x}{5}} = 6$
3. $\sqrt{\dfrac{5x}{6}} = 5$
4. $\sqrt{\dfrac{5x}{2}} = 10$
5. $3 = \sqrt{\dfrac{3x}{4}}$

SET 13
1. $2\sqrt{x} = 3$
2. $5\sqrt{y} = 4$
3. $3\sqrt{2x} = 2$
4. $4\sqrt{5x} = 6$
5. $3 = 6\sqrt{3x}$

SET 14
1. $3\sqrt{2x-1} = 1$
2. $4\sqrt{5x-4} = 2$
3. $2\sqrt{3y-5} = 3$
4. $6\sqrt{4x-2} = 4$
5. $4 = 5\sqrt{2x-1}$

REVIEW OF UNIT FIFTEEN

1. Raise to indicated powers: a) $(8b^3c^4d)^2$ b) $(-3m^2n)^3$ c) $(-4x^4y^3)^4$ d) $(-\frac{7}{8}ay^6)^2$

2. Find the square root of $81a^6x^8y^2$ 3. Find the cube root of $-125b^9c^{12}$

4. Find the fourth root of m^4n^{12} 5. Find the square root of 725,904

6. Find the indicated roots: a) $\sqrt{144r^{16}x^4y^2}$ b) $\sqrt[3]{8s^{15}t^9}$ c) $\sqrt{.25b^2x^6}$ d) $\sqrt[4]{16y^{16}}$

7. Simplify and combine: a) $\sqrt{81}+\sqrt{36}$ b) $5\sqrt{16}+2\sqrt{100}$ c) $6\sqrt{49}-2\sqrt{9}$ d) $\sqrt{16+9}+\sqrt{64}$

8. Find the indicated roots: a) $(c^8d^6)^{\frac{1}{2}}$ b) $(49x^{10}y^4z^2)^{\frac{1}{2}}$ c) $(-64r^6y^{12})^{\frac{1}{3}}$ d) $(16a^8c^4)^{\frac{1}{4}}$

9. Simplify: a) $\sqrt{68}$ b) $3\sqrt{216}$ c) $\sqrt{32a^5x^4y}$ d) $2c\sqrt{7c^3d^9}$ e) $\sqrt{\frac{3}{8}}$ f) $\sqrt{\frac{4a}{5b^3}}$ g) $\sqrt[3]{128x^5y^9}$

10. Simplify and combine: a) $3\sqrt{48}+2\sqrt{108}-\sqrt{75}$ b) $5\sqrt{96}+4\sqrt{\frac{5}{8}}-18\sqrt{\frac{2}{3}}+\sqrt{90}$

11. Multiply: a) $3\sqrt{2}\cdot\sqrt{18}$ b) $(-2\sqrt{3})^2$ c) $5\sqrt{6}(\sqrt{2}-4\sqrt{12})$ d) $(2\sqrt{5}-3\sqrt{6})^2$

12. Divide: a) $\frac{\sqrt{48}}{\sqrt{6}}$ b) $\frac{\sqrt{7}}{\sqrt{5}}$ c) $\frac{14\sqrt{75}}{7\sqrt{3}}$ d) $\frac{3\sqrt{18}+12\sqrt{80}-6\sqrt{2}}{3\sqrt{2}}$

13. Solve and check: a) $6\sqrt{x}=12$ b) $\sqrt{x+3}=7$ c) $\sqrt{2x}-4=6$ d) $\sqrt{\frac{x}{5}}=4$

14. Rearrange formula $t=\pi\sqrt{\frac{l}{g}}$, solving for l.   15. Transform formula $I=\sqrt{\frac{P}{R}}$, solving for R.

CUMULATIVE ALGEBRA REVIEW

1. Draw the graph of the formula $i=.04p$.   2. How much less is $2c^2-8cd-5d^2$ than $6c^2-3cd+7d^2$?

3. Find the factor which multiplied by $5x^2-x+3$ will equal $20x^3-39x^2+19x-21$.

4. Combine: $\frac{6xy}{3x-y}+\frac{9xy}{x-3y}$ 5. Solve and check: $\frac{x}{4}+\frac{y}{6}=125$ 6. Simplify and combine: $3\sqrt{192}-6\sqrt{\frac{4}{3}}+\sqrt{147}$

$.15x+.2y=120$

7. Find the value of A if $a=6$, $b=8$, and $c=10$ using the formulas $S=\frac{a+b+c}{2}$ and $A=\sqrt{s(s-a)(s-b)(s-c)}$

8. Transform formula $r=\sqrt{\frac{A}{\pi}}$, solving for A.   9. Solve and check: $\frac{x-2}{x-4}+\frac{8}{x+1}=1$

10. A man invests $1,200 less at 3% annual interest than he does at 2%. If the annual income from the 3% investment is $18 more than that from the 2% investment, how much does he invest at each rate?

KEYED ACHIEVEMENT TEST

1. Combine:

$\frac{5}{cd}-\frac{6}{c-d}+\frac{2}{c+d}$ ⓖ62

2. Solve and check:

$\frac{2x-5}{6}+\frac{x+3}{8}=\frac{x+4}{4}$ ⓖ67

3. Solve for x and check:

$\frac{x}{b}-\frac{x}{c}=1$ ⓖ77

4. Draw the graph of $2x-3y=5$ ⓖ81   5. Solve and check: $(x+5)-(y-3)=-1$ ⓖ85

$3(y+3)=2(8-x)$

6. Find the value of R_2 when $I=5$, $E=110$, and $R_1=9$, using the formula $I=\frac{E}{R_1+R_2}$. ⓖ79

7. In the formula $A=\frac{1}{4}\pi d^2$, $A=154$ when $d=14$. Find the value of A when $d=56$. ⓖ80

8. Raise to the indicated power: $(-5a^7x^4y)^3$ ⓖ91   9. Find the square root of 407,044. ⓖ93

10. Find the indicated roots: a) $\sqrt{64c^8x^2}$ ⓖ94 b) $(-27b^6x^3)^{\frac{1}{3}}$ ⓖ95 c) Square root of $144a^{12}y^6$ ⓖ92

11. Simplify: a) $\sqrt{176}$ ⓖ96 b) $\sqrt{72x^5y^2}$ ⓖ97 c) $\sqrt{\frac{5}{6}}$ ⓖ98 d) $\sqrt[3]{-27s^6t^3}$ ⓖ99

12. Simplify and combine: $6\sqrt{98}-4\sqrt{\frac{3}{2}}+3\sqrt{162}+2\sqrt{54}$ ⓖ100   13. Multiply: $(4+\frac{1}{3}\sqrt{3})(4-\frac{1}{3}\sqrt{3})$ ⓖ103

14. Divide: $\frac{12\sqrt{48}-9\sqrt{24}}{3\sqrt{6}}$ ⓖ104   15. Solve and check: $\sqrt{x^2+45}=x+3$ ⓖ105

INTRODUCTION TO UNIT SIXTEEN

Many scientific and mathematical formulas contain literal quantities raised to the second power. Also, equations formulated from facts given in problems frequently contain the unknown raised to the second power. To solve for these quantities it will be necessary to understand the principles used in the solution of the quadratic equation.

A *quadratic equation* or *equation of the second degree* is an equation which, after its terms have been collected and simplified, contains the second power (but no higher power) of the unknown. If the equation has both the first power and the second power of the unknown, it is called a *complete quadratic equation*. $x^2 - 9x + 18 = 0$ and $4x^2 - 5x = 0$ are complete quadratic equations. If the equation contains the second power but not the first power of the unknown, it is called an *incomplete quadratic equation*. $9x^2 - 16 = 0$ and $x^2 = 64$ are incomplete quadratic equations.

Incomplete quadratic equations may be solved by a special method based on the axiom "square roots of equals are equal." Some complete and incomplete quadratic equations may be solved by factoring, using the fact that if the product of two factors is zero, at least one of the factors is zero. However, all quadratic equations may be solved by the method of completing the square and by the general quadratic formula. This formula is derived by solving the general quadratic equation $ax^2 + bx + c = 0$ for x in terms of a, b, and c, using the method of completing the square. In the quadratic formula a represents the numerical coefficient of x^2, b the numerical coefficient of x, and c the constant term.

Every quadratic equation has two roots.

ARITHMETIC MAINTENANCE DRILL

Do the following examples:

1. Add:
$62 + 357 + 1,096 + 43$

2. Subtract:
$930,575 - 26,819$

3. Multiply:
$4,692 \times 983$

4. Divide:
$3,600 \overline{)86,400}$

5. Add:
$2\frac{7}{8} + 9\frac{17}{32} + 1\frac{1}{2}$

6. Subtract:
$5\frac{3}{5} - 4\frac{7}{10}$

7. Multiply:
$12\frac{2}{3} \times 6$

8. Divide:
$5\frac{5}{8} \div 1\frac{3}{4}$

9. Add: $47.29
$6.58
$155.91
$18.07
$2.36

10. Subtract:
$5,280.17
$2,950.34

11. Multiply:
$.035 \times .02$

12. Divide:
$.06 \overline{).3}$

13. Round off to nearest hundredth: 6.1847

14. Change $\frac{18}{25}$ to a decimal fraction

15. Multiply by short method: $1,000 \times 9.89$

16. Find 24% of $849.50

17. What % of 650 is 260?

18. 56% of what number is 420?

19. Find the square root of 49,561,600

20. What part of a mile is 1,320 yards?

UNIT SIXTEEN—QUADRATIC EQUATIONS

EXERCISE 106

Solving Incomplete Quadratic Equations—A

I. Aim: To solve incomplete quadratic equations of the $x^2 = 4$ type where the term containing the first degree of the unknown is missing.

II. Procedure

1. If necessary, transpose all terms involving the square of the unknown to one member of the equation and all other terms to the other member.
   a) If the equation is fractional, clear the equation of all fractions, then transpose.
   b) If the equation involves parentheses, remove parentheses, then transpose.

2. Combine similar terms.

3. Divide both members by the coefficient of the square of the unknown.

4. Take the square root of both members. Write a $\pm$ sign before the square root of the known quantity.

5. If necessary, simplify the roots.

6. Check each root by substituting it in the original equation.

III. Sample Solutions

1. $x^2 = 81$

$x = \pm 9$

Answer, $x = \pm 9$

Check:

$(+9)^2 = 81 \qquad (-9)^2 = 81$

$81 = 81 \qquad\quad 81 = 81$

2. $3x^2 = 96$

$x^2 = 32$

$x = \pm\sqrt{32}$

$x = \pm 4\sqrt{2}$

Answer, $x = \pm 4\sqrt{2}$

Check:

$3(4\sqrt{2})^2 = 96 \qquad 3(-4\sqrt{2})^2 = 96$

$3(32) = 96 \qquad\qquad 3(32) = 96$

$96 = 96 \qquad\qquad\quad 96 = 96$

3. $x^2 - 17 = 0$

$x^2 = 17$

$x = \pm\sqrt{17}$

Answer, $x = \pm\sqrt{17}$

Check:

$(\sqrt{17})^2 - 17 = 0$

$17 - 17 = 0$

$0 = 0$

$(-\sqrt{17})^2 - 17 = 0$

$17 - 17 = 0$

$0 = 0$

4. $4x^2 - 27 = x^2$

$4x^2 - x^2 = 27$

$3x^2 = 27$

$x^2 = 9$

$x = \pm 3$

Answer, $x = \pm 3$

Check:

$4(3)^2 - 27 = (3)^2$

$4(9) - 27 = 9$

$36 - 27 = 9$

$9 = 9$

$4(-3)^2 - 27 = (-3)^2$

$4(9) - 27 = 9$

$36 - 27 = 9$

$9 = 9$

5. $\dfrac{x+2}{3} = \dfrac{4}{x-2}$

$x^2 - 4 = 12$

$x^2 = 12 + 4$

$x^2 = 16$

$x = \pm 4$

Answer, $x = \pm 4$

Check:

$\dfrac{4+2}{3} = \dfrac{4}{4-2} \qquad \dfrac{-4+2}{3} = \dfrac{4}{-4-2}$

$\dfrac{6}{3} = \dfrac{4}{2} \qquad\qquad \dfrac{-2}{3} = \dfrac{4}{-6}$

$2 = 2 \qquad\qquad\quad -\dfrac{2}{3} = -\dfrac{2}{3}$

6. $(x-6)(x+6) = 28$

$x^2 - 36 = 28$

$x^2 = 28 + 36$

$x^2 = 64$

$x = \pm 8$

Answer, $x = \pm 8$

Check:

$(8-6)(8+6) = 28$

$(2)(14) = 28$

$28 = 28$

$(-8-6)(-8+6) = 28$

$(-14)(-2) = 28$

$28 = 28$

DIAGNOSTIC TEST

Solve and check:

1. $x^2 = 9$
2. $x^2 = 48$
3. $x^2 = 15$
4. $6x^2 = 96$

5. $4x^2 = 100$
6. $2x^2 = 40$
7. $5x^2 = 35$
8. $x^2 - 25 = 0$

9. $x^2 - 24 = 0$
10. $x^2 - 23 = 0$
11. $3x^2 + 2x^2 = 20$
12. $2x^2 + x^2 = 24$

13. $9x^2 - 5x^2 = 28$
14. $2x^2 + 9 = 81 - 4x^2$
15. $\dfrac{4-x}{3} = \dfrac{4}{4+x}$
16. $(x+1)(x-1) = 15$

Related Practice Examples

Solve and check:

SET 1

1. $x^2 = 4$
2. $x^2 = 49$
3. $x^2 = 25$
4. $x^2 = 64$
5. $144 = x^2$

SET 2

1. $x^2 = 32$
2. $x^2 = 75$
3. $x^2 = 20$
4. $x^2 = 54$
5. $80 = x^2$

SET 3

1. $x^2 = 3$
2. $x^2 = 10$
3. $x^2 = 14$
4. $x^2 = 38$
5. $41 = x^2$

SET 4

1. $3x^2 = 12$
2. $7x^2 = 63$
3. $6x^2 = 150$
4. $5x^2 = 180$
5. $405 = 5x^2$

SET 5

1. $4x^2 = 36$
2. $9x^2 = 144$
3. $16x^2 = 64$
4. $25x^2 = 400$
5. $441 = 49x^2$

SET 6

1. $2x^2 = 24$
2. $3x^2 = 135$
3. $7x^2 = 188$
4. $9x^2 = 360$
5. $320 = 10x^2$

SET 7

1. $5x^2 = 10$
2. $7x^2 = 42$
3. $8x^2 = 88$
4. $9x^2 = 90$
5. $20 = 4x^2$

SET 8

1. $x^2 - 1 = 0$
2. $x^2 - 36 = 0$
3. $x^2 - 81 = 0$
4. $x^2 - 100 = 0$
5. $0 = x^2 - 9$

SET 9

1. $x^2 - 27 = 0$
2. $x^2 - 80 = 0$
3. $x^2 - 72 = 0$
4. $x^2 - 96 = 0$
5. $0 = x^2 - 18$

SET 10

1. $x^2 - 2 = 0$
2. $x^2 - 21 = 0$
3. $x^2 - 34 = 0$
4. $x^2 - 42 = 0$
5. $0 = x^2 - 19$

SET 11

1. $x^2 + x^2 = 18$
2. $4x^2 + 3x^2 = 175$
3. $8x^2 - 3x^2 = 320$
4. $4x^2 - x^2 = 243$
5. $288 = 2x^2 + 6x^2$

SET 12

1. $5x^2 + x^2 = 48$
2. $2x^2 + 7x^2 = 180$
3. $5x^2 - x^2 = 200$
4. $8x^2 - 5x^2 = 96$
5. $224 = 10x^2 - 2x^2$

SET 13

1. $x^2 + 3x^2 = 20$
2. $4x^2 + 5x^2 = 63$
3. $9x^2 - 2x^2 = 77$
4. $6x^2 - 4x^2 = 46$
5. $248 = 2x^2 + 6x^2$

SET 14

1. $5x^2 - 128 = 3x^2$
2. $3x^2 = 220 - 2x^2$
3. $4x^2 - 62 = 98 - 6x^2$
4. $13x^2 - 22 = 5x^2 + 26$
5. $3x^2 - 10 = x^2 + 214$

SET 15

1. $\dfrac{x}{2} = \dfrac{2}{x}$
2. $\dfrac{5}{x} = \dfrac{x}{8}$
3. $\dfrac{x+3}{2} = \dfrac{8}{x-3}$
4. $\dfrac{x-1}{4} = \dfrac{12}{x+1}$
5. $\dfrac{6-x}{4} = \dfrac{5}{6+x}$

SET 16

1. $(x+3)(x-3) = 18$
2. $(x-5)(x+5) = 39$
3. $(x+5)(x-4) = x$
4. $(x-4)(x+7) = 3x$
5. $(x-3)(x+2) + x = 0$

EXERCISE 107
Solving Incomplete Quadratic Equations—B

I. Aim: To solve incomplete quadratic equations of the type $x^2 = \frac{2}{5}$ where the term containing the first degree of the unknown is missing. Literal quadratic equations are also included.

II. Procedure

Follow the procedure outlined in exercise 106.

III. Sample Solutions

1. $x^2 = \frac{9}{16}$

   $x = \pm \frac{3}{4}$

   Answer, $x = \pm \frac{3}{4}$

   Check:

   $(\frac{3}{4})^2 = \frac{9}{16}$ $(-\frac{3}{4})^2 = \frac{9}{16}$

   $\frac{9}{16} = \frac{9}{16}$ $\frac{9}{16} = \frac{9}{16}$

2. $25x^2 - 4 = 0$

   $25x^2 = 4$

   $x^2 = \frac{4}{25}$

   $x = \pm \frac{2}{5}$

   Answer, $x = \pm \frac{2}{5}$

   Check:

   $25(\frac{2}{5})^2 - 4 = 0$

   $25(\frac{4}{25}) - 4 = 0$

   $4 - 4 = 0$

   $0 = 0$

   $25(-\frac{2}{5})^2 - 4 = 0$

   $25(\frac{4}{25}) - 4 = 0$

   $4 - 4 = 0$

   $0 = 0$

3. $6x^2 = 1$

   $x^2 = \frac{1}{6}$

   $x = \pm \sqrt{\frac{1}{6}}$

   $x = \pm \frac{1}{6}\sqrt{6}$

   Answer, $x = \pm \frac{1}{6}\sqrt{6}$

   Check:

   $6(\frac{1}{6}\sqrt{6})^2 = 1$ $6(-\frac{1}{6}\sqrt{6})^2 = 1$

   $6(\frac{1}{6}) = 1$ $6(\frac{1}{6}) = 1$

   $1 = 1$ $1 = 1$

4. $\dfrac{4x^2 - 5}{3} = \dfrac{2x^2 - 3}{2}$

   $8x^2 - 10 = 6x^2 - 9$

   $8x^2 - 6x^2 = 10 - 9$

   $2x^2 = 1$

   $x^2 = \frac{1}{2}$

   $x = \pm \sqrt{\frac{1}{2}}$

   $x = \pm \frac{1}{2}\sqrt{2}$

   Answer, $x = \pm \frac{1}{2}\sqrt{2}$

   Check:

   $\dfrac{4(\frac{1}{2}\sqrt{2})^2 - 5}{3} = \dfrac{2(\frac{1}{2}\sqrt{2})^2 - 3}{2}$

   $\dfrac{4(\frac{1}{2}) - 5}{3} = \dfrac{2(\frac{1}{2}) - 3}{2}$

   $\dfrac{2 - 5}{3} = \dfrac{1 - 3}{2}$

   $\dfrac{-3}{3} = \dfrac{-2}{2}$

   $-1 = -1$

   $\dfrac{4(-\frac{1}{2}\sqrt{2})^2 - 5}{3} = \dfrac{2(-\frac{1}{2}\sqrt{2})^2 - 3}{2}$

   $\dfrac{4(\frac{1}{2}) - 5}{3} = \dfrac{2(\frac{1}{2}) - 3}{3}$

   $\dfrac{2 - 5}{3} = \dfrac{1 - 3}{2}$

   $\dfrac{-3}{3} = \dfrac{-2}{2}$

   $-1 = -1$

5. $9x^2 - b^2 = 0$

   $9x^2 = b^2$

   $x^2 = \dfrac{b^2}{9}$

   $x = \pm \dfrac{b}{3}$

   Answer, $x = \pm \dfrac{b}{3}$

   Check:

   $9\left(\dfrac{b}{3}\right)^2 - b^2 = 0$

   $9\left(\dfrac{b^2}{9}\right) - b^2 = 0$

   $b^2 - b^2 = 0$

   $0 = 0$

   $9\left(-\dfrac{b}{3}\right)^2 - b^2 = 0$

   $9\left(\dfrac{b^2}{9}\right) - b^2 = 0$

   $b^2 - b^2 = 0$

   $0 = 0$

6. $ax^2 - 3b = 0$

   $ax^2 = 3b$

   $x^2 = \dfrac{3b}{a}$

   $x = \pm \sqrt{\dfrac{3b}{a}}$

   $x = \pm \dfrac{1}{a}\sqrt{3ab}$

   Answer, $x = \pm \dfrac{1}{a}\sqrt{3ab}$

   Check:

   $a\left(\dfrac{1}{a}\sqrt{3ab}\right)^2 - 3b = 0$

   $a\left(\dfrac{3b}{a}\right) - 3b = 0$

   $3b - 3b = 0$

   $0 = 0$

   $a\left(-\dfrac{1}{a}\sqrt{3ab}\right)^2 - 3b = 0$

   $a\left(\dfrac{3b}{a}\right) - 3b = 0$

   $3b - 3b = 0$

   $0 = 0$

DIAGNOSTIC TEST

Solve for x and check:

1. $x^2 = \frac{4}{25}$
2. $9x^2 = 64$
3. $16x^2 - 49 = 0$
4. $x^2 = \frac{7}{8}$

5. $16x^2 = 3$
6. $5x^2 - 2 = 0$
7. $7x^2 + 3 = 3x^2 + 8$
8. $\frac{5x+2}{8} = \frac{4}{5x-2}$

9. $x^2 = \frac{a^2}{4}$
10. $25x^2 = 81b^2$
11. $9x^2 - 49a^2d^2 = 0$
12. $x^2 - d = 0$

13. $x^2 = \frac{c}{a}$
14. $3mx^2 = b^3$
15. $cx^2 - 4d = 0$

Related Practice Examples

Solve for x and check:

SET 1

1. $x^2 = \frac{1}{4}$
2. $x^2 = \frac{4}{49}$
3. $x^2 = \frac{25}{144}$
4. $x^2 = \frac{81}{64}$
5. $\frac{4}{9} = x^2$

SET 2

1. $16x^2 = 9$
2. $25x^2 = 4$
3. $9x^2 = 49$
4. $100x^2 = 81$
5. $144 = 121x^2$

SET 3

1. $9x^2 - 4 = 0$
2. $36x^2 - 25 = 0$
3. $64x^2 - 81 = 0$
4. $144x^2 - 121 = 0$
5. $0 = 81x^2 - 49$

SET 4

1. $x^2 = \frac{1}{2}$
2. $x^2 = \frac{3}{4}$
3. $x^2 = \frac{5}{8}$
4. $x^2 = \frac{2}{5}$
5. $\frac{9}{10} = x^2$

SET 5

1. $3x^2 = 1$
2. $4x^2 = 5$
3. $6x^2 = 3$
4. $8x^2 = 9$
5. $12 = 5x^2$

SET 6

1. $2x^2 - 1 = 0$
2. $9x^2 - 2 = 0$
3. $8x^2 - 7 = 0$
4. $6x^2 - 5 = 0$
5. $0 = 4x^2 - 6$

SET 7

1. $6x^2 - 1 = 3 - 3x^2$
2. $4x^2 + 5 = x^2 + 6$
3. $5x^2 + 3x^2 = 5$
4. $90x^2 - 49 = 9x^2$
5. $6x^2 - 8 = 4x^2 - 3$

SET 8

1. $\frac{3x+4}{3} = \frac{3}{3x-4}$
2. $\frac{2x^2-3}{2} = \frac{x^2-3}{3}$
3. $\frac{4+x}{2x} = \frac{x}{4-x}$
4. $\frac{x^2-3x}{3} = \frac{4x^2-5x-8}{5}$
5. $\frac{2-3x}{3x} - \frac{2x}{2+3x} = 0$

SET 9

1. $x^2 = \frac{b^2}{9}$
2. $x^2 = \frac{m^6}{16}$
3. $x^2 = \frac{c^2d^4}{81}$
4. $x^2 = \frac{25d^2}{49}$
5. $\frac{4a^2c^2}{25} = x^2$

SET 10

1. $4x^2 = a^2$
2. $36x^2 = c^4$
3. $100x^2 = m^6n^2$
4. $81x^2 = 16b^4$
5. $64m^2 = 9x^2$

SET 11

1. $16x^2 - c^2 = 0$
2. $4x^2 - a^4m^2 = 0$
3. $49x^2 - 9b^2 = 0$
4. $144x^2 - 25d^2r^6 = 0$
5. $0 = 36x^2 - 81n^2t^4$

SET 12

1. $x^2 - a = 0$
2. $0 = x^2 - r$
3. $x^2 - 5b = 0$
4. $x^2 - 4c = 0$
5. $x^2 - 2a^2b = 0$

SET 13

1. $x^2 = \frac{b}{c}$
2. $x^2 = \frac{9}{b}$
3. $x^2 = \frac{r^2}{5t}$
4. $x^2 = \frac{a^3b}{m}$
5. $\frac{3d^5}{2r^3} = x^2$

SET 14

1. $ax^2 = c$
2. $b^3x^2 = d^2$
3. $c^2dx^2 = a^2b$
4. $2mx^2 = a^3$
5. $5c^3x^2 = 4r^3s^5$

SET 15

1. $bx^2 - a = 0$
2. $5x^2 - a^2m = 0$
3. $4mx^2 - n^3 = 0$
4. $6rx^2 - 2b^3 = 0$
5. $8bx^2 - 3ac = 0$

EXERCISE 108

Solution by Factoring

I. Aim: To solve quadratic equations by factoring.

II. Procedure

1. If necessary, transpose so that all terms are on the left member of the equation.
   a) If the equation is fractional, clear the equation of all fractions, then transpose.
   b) If the equation involves parentheses, remove parentheses, then transpose.
2. Combine similar terms.
3. Factor the left member completely.
4. Write each factor equal to zero.
5. Solve each of the resulting equations.
6. Check each root by substituting it in the given equation.

III. Sample Solutions

1. $x^2 - 5x = 0$

$x(x-5) = 0$

(1) $x = 0$

If $x - 5 = 0$

(2) $x = 5$

Answer, $x = 0$ and $x = 5$

Check:

$0 - 0 = 0$

$0 = 0$

$25 - 25 = 0$

$0 = 0$

2. $6x^2 + 5x = 0$

$x(6x + 5) = 0$

(1) $x = 0$

If $6x + 5 = 0$

$6x = -5$

(2) $x = -\frac{5}{6}$

Answer, $x = 0$ and $x = -\frac{5}{6}$

Check:

$0 + 0 = 0$

$0 = 0$

$6(-\frac{5}{6})^2 + 5(-\frac{5}{6}) = 0$

$6(\frac{25}{36}) + 5(-\frac{5}{6}) = 0$

$\frac{25}{6} - \frac{25}{6} = 0$

$0 = 0$

3. $5x^2 - 2x = 3x^2 - 5x$

$5x^2 - 3x^2 - 2x + 5x = 0$

$2x^2 + 3x = 0$

$x(2x + 3) = 0$

(1) $x = 0$

If $2x + 3 = 0$

$2x = -3$

(2) $x = -\frac{3}{2}$ or $-1\frac{1}{2}$

Answer, $x = 0$ and $x = -1\frac{1}{2}$

Check:

$0 - 0 = 0 - 0$

$0 = 0$

$5(-\frac{3}{2})^2 - 2(-\frac{3}{2}) = 3(-\frac{3}{2})^2 - 5(-\frac{3}{2})$

$5(\frac{9}{4}) - 2(-\frac{3}{2}) = 3(\frac{9}{4}) - 5(-\frac{3}{2})$

$\frac{45}{4} + 3 = \frac{27}{4} + \frac{15}{2}$

$14\frac{1}{4} = 14\frac{1}{4}$

4. $x^2 - 4 = 0$

$(x+2)(x-2) = 0$

If $x + 2 = 0$

(1) $x = -2$

If $x - 2 = 0$

(2) $x = 2$

Answer, $x = \pm 2$

Check:

$4 - 4 = 0$

$0 = 0$

$4 - 4 = 0$

$0 = 0$

5. $9x^2 = 16$

$9x^2 - 16 = 0$

$(3x+4)(3x-4) = 0$

If $3x + 4 = 0$

$3x = -4$

(1) $x = -\frac{4}{3}$ or $-1\frac{1}{3}$

If $3x - 4 = 0$

$3x = 4$

(2) $x = \frac{4}{3}$ or $1\frac{1}{3}$

Answer, $x = \pm 1\frac{1}{3}$

Check:

$9(1\frac{1}{3})^2 = 16$

$9(\frac{16}{9}) = 16$

$16 = 16$

$9(-1\frac{1}{3})^2 = 16$

$9(\frac{16}{9}) = 16$

$16 = 16$

6. $x^2 - 3x - 18 = 0$

$(x-6)(x+3) = 0$

If $x - 6 = 0$

(1) $x = 6$

If $x + 3 = 0$

(2) $x = -3$

Answer, $x = 6$ and $x = -3$

Check:

$36 - 18 - 18 = 0$

$0 = 0$

$9 + 9 - 18 = 0$

$0 = 0$

7. $x(x+3) = 28$

$x^2 + 3x = 28$

$x^2 + 3x - 28 = 0$

$(x+7)(x-4) = 0$

If $x + 7 = 0$

(1) $x = -7$

If $x - 4 = 0$

(2) $x = 4$

Answer, $x = -7$ and $x = 4$

Check:

$-7(-7+3) = 28$

$-7(-4) = 28$

$28 = 28$

$4(4+3) = 28$

$4(7) = 28$

$28 = 28$

8. $\dfrac{6}{x} + x = 7 - \dfrac{4}{x}$

$\dfrac{6}{\cancel{x}} \cdot \cancel{x} + x \cdot x = 7 \cdot x - \dfrac{4}{\cancel{x}} \cdot \cancel{x}$

$6 + x^2 = 7x - 4$

$x^2 - 7x + 6 + 4 = 0$

$x^2 - 7x + 10 = 0$

$(x-5)(x-2) = 0$

If $x - 5 = 0$

(1) $x = 5$

If $x - 2 = 0$

(2) $x = 2$

Answer, $x = 5$ and $x = 2$

Check:

$\frac{6}{5} + 5 = 7 - \frac{4}{5}$

$6\frac{1}{5} = 6\frac{1}{5}$

$\frac{6}{2} + 2 = 7 - \frac{4}{2}$

$3 + 2 = 7 - 2$

$5 = 5$

DIAGNOSTIC TEST

Solve by factoring and check:

1. $x^2 - 7x = 0$
2. $x^2 + 2x = 0$
3. $3x^2 - 2x = 0$
4. $4x^2 + x = 0$
5. $x^2 = 5x$

6. $3x^2 - 3x = x^2 + 4x$
7. $x^2 - 1 = 0$
8. $x^2 = 9$
9. $4x^2 - 25 = 0$
10. $81x^2 = 49$

11. $18x^2 - 5 = 2x^2 + 20$
12. $x^2 - 5x + 6 = 0$
13. $x^2 + 6x + 9 = 0$
14. $x^2 + 7x = 18$
15. $3x^2 + 6x = 2x^2 - 8$

16. $x(x + 5) = -4$
17. $\dfrac{x}{3} - 1 = \dfrac{6}{x}$
18. $2x^2 + 7x + 6 = 0$

Related Practice Examples

Solve by factoring and check:

SET 1

1. $x^2 - 6x = 0$
2. $x^2 - 3x = 0$
3. $x^2 - 2x = 0$
4. $x^2 - 9x = 0$
5. $0 = x^2 - x$

SET 2

1. $x^2 + 5x = 0$
2. $x^2 + x = 0$
3. $x^2 + 3x = 0$
4. $x^2 + 10x = 0$
5. $0 = x^2 + 7x$

SET 3

1. $2x^2 - 5x = 0$
2. $3x^2 - 7x = 0$
3. $4x^2 - 3x = 0$
4. $8x^2 - 4x = 0$
5. $0 = 3x^2 - 9x$

SET 4

1. $5x^2 + 3x = 0$
2. $9x^2 + 6x = 0$
3. $2x^2 + 8x = 0$
4. $4x^2 + 6x = 0$
5. $0 = 7x^2 + 10x$

SET 5

1. $x^2 = 2x$
2. $x^2 = x$
3. $3x^2 = 15x$
4. $x^2 = -3x$
5. $x^2 = -9x$

SET 6

1. $2x^2 + 3x = x^2 - 6x$
2. $5x^2 - 8x = 4x^2 + x$
3. $4x^2 - x = 2x^2 + 3x$
4. $8x^2 + 7x = 6x - 4x^2$
5. $3x^2 - x = 3x - 2x^2$

SET 7

1. $x^2 - 9 = 0$
2. $x^2 - 64 = 0$
3. $x^2 - 144 = 0$
4. $x^2 - 25 = 0$
5. $0 = x^2 - 81$

SET 8

1. $x^2 = 4$
2. $x^2 = 1$
3. $x^2 = 36$
4. $x^2 = 100$
5. $49 = x^2$

SET 9

1. $9x^2 - 16 = 0$
2. $36x^2 - 25 = 0$
3. $81x^2 - 100 = 0$
4. $64x^2 - 49 = 0$
5. $0 = 25x^2 - 4$

SET 10

1. $4x^2 = 1$
2. $25x^2 = 49$
3. $64x^2 = 81$
4. $144x^2 = 25$
5. $16 = 49x^2$

SET 11

1. $11x^2 - 3 = 2x^2 + 1$
2. $7x^2 + 5 = 30 + 3x^2$
3. $38x^2 - 2 = 7 - 11x^2$
4. $75x^2 - 72 = 9 - 25x^2$
5. $98x^2 + 4 = 5 - 46x^2$

SET 12

1. $x^2 - 7x + 10 = 0$
2. $x^2 + 6x + 8 = 0$
3. $x^2 - 4x - 12 = 0$
4. $x^2 + x - 12 = 0$
5. $0 = x^2 - 10x + 16$

SET 13

1. $x^2 - 4x + 4 = 0$
2. $x^2 - 10x + 25 = 0$
3. $x^2 + 2x + 1 = 0$
4. $x^2 + 8x + 16 = 0$
5. $0 = x^2 - 14x + 49$

SET 14

1. $x^2 - 3x = 28$
2. $x^2 - 6x = -5$
3. $x^2 + 15 = 8x$
4. $14 = x^2 + 5x$
5. $10x = 24 - x^2$

SET 15

1. $4x^2 - x = 3x^2 + 2$
2. $x^2 - 3x = 4x - 12$
3. $2x = x^2 + 13x + 16$
4. $x^2 + 16x + 10 = 46$
5. $42 - x^2 = 3x - 2x$

SET 16

1. $x(x + 4) = 12$
2. $x(x - 4) = -3$
3. $x(x - 3) = 2(10 - x)$
4. $x(x + 4) = 12(3 - x)$
5. $x(x - 5) = 5(x - 5)$

SET 17

1. $x = \dfrac{10}{x - 3}$
2. $\dfrac{x}{2} - 2 = \dfrac{6}{x}$
3. $\dfrac{2}{x} + 4 = x - \dfrac{3}{x}$
4. $\dfrac{4}{x + 5} = \dfrac{x}{x + 3}$
5. $\dfrac{1}{x + 3} = \dfrac{3 - x}{7 + x}$

SET 18

1. $3x^2 + 5x + 2 = 0$
2. $8x^2 - 22x - 21 = 0$
3. $2x^2 - 3x = 20$
4. $15x^2 - 20x = 11x - 10$
5. $9x^2 - 3 = 5x - 3x^2$

EXERCISE 109
Solution by Completing the Square

I. Aim: To solve quadratic equations by completing the square.

II. Procedure

1. If necessary, transpose all terms involving the unknown to the left member of the equation and the constant term to the right member.

2. If necessary, divide each term in the equation by the coefficient of the x^2 term. The equation will then be in the form $x^2 + bx = c$.

3. Find one half of the coefficient of x. Square it. Then add the answer to both members of the equation.

4. Factor the perfect trinomial square on the left member. Simplify the right member.

5. Find the square root of both members. Prefix a $\pm$ sign to the square root of the right member.

6. Write the square root of the left member (step 5) equal to the positive $(+)$ square root of the right member (step 5). Solve the resulting equation to find one root of the quadratic equation.

7. Write the square root of the left member (step 5) equal to the negative $(-)$ square root of the right member (step 5). Solve the resulting equation to find the second root of the quadratic equation.

8. Check each root by substituting it in the given equation.

III. Sample Solutions

1.
$$x^2 + 6x = 16$$
$$x^2 + 6x + 9 = 16 + 9$$
$$(x+3)^2 = 25$$
$$x + 3 = \pm 5$$
When $x + 3 = +5$
$$x = 5 - 3$$
(1) $\quad x = 2$
When $x + 3 = -5$
$$x = -5 - 3$$
(2) $\quad x = -8$
Answer, $x = 2$ and $x = -8$

Check:
$$4 + 12 = 16$$
$$16 = 16$$
$$64 - 48 = 16$$
$$16 = 16$$

2.
$$x^2 - 7x + 12 = 0$$
$$x^2 - 7x = -12$$
$$x^2 - 7x + (\tfrac{7}{2})^2 = -12 + (\tfrac{7}{2})^2$$
$$x^2 - 7x + \tfrac{49}{4} = -12 + \tfrac{49}{4}$$
$$(x - \tfrac{7}{2})^2 = \tfrac{1}{4}$$
$$x - \tfrac{7}{2} = \pm \tfrac{1}{2}$$
When $x - \tfrac{7}{2} = +\tfrac{1}{2}$
$$x = +\tfrac{1}{2} + \tfrac{7}{2} = \tfrac{8}{2}$$
(1) $\quad x = 4$
When $x - \tfrac{7}{2} = -\tfrac{1}{2}$
$$x = -\tfrac{1}{2} + \tfrac{7}{2} = \tfrac{6}{2}$$
(2) $\quad x = 3$
Answer, $x = 4$ and $x = 3$

Check:
$$16 - 28 + 12 = 0$$
$$0 = 0$$
$$9 - 21 + 12 = 0$$
$$0 = 0$$

3.
$$x^2 - 2x + \tfrac{7}{16} = 0$$
$$x^2 - 2x = -\tfrac{7}{16}$$
$$x^2 - 2x + 1 = -\tfrac{7}{16} + 1$$
$$(x-1)^2 = \tfrac{9}{16}$$
$$x - 1 = \pm \tfrac{3}{4}$$
When $x - 1 = +\tfrac{3}{4}$
$$x = 1 + \tfrac{3}{4}$$
(1) $\quad x = 1\tfrac{3}{4}$
When $x - 1 = -\tfrac{3}{4}$
$$x = 1 - \tfrac{3}{4}$$
(2) $\quad x = \tfrac{1}{4}$
Answer, $x = 1\tfrac{3}{4}$ and $x = \tfrac{1}{4}$

Check:
$$\tfrac{49}{16} - \tfrac{7}{2} + \tfrac{7}{16} = 0$$
$$3\tfrac{1}{2} - 3\tfrac{1}{2} = 0$$
$$0 = 0$$
$$\tfrac{1}{16} - \tfrac{1}{2} + \tfrac{7}{16} = 0$$
$$\tfrac{1}{2} - \tfrac{1}{2} = 0$$
$$0 = 0$$

4.
$$3x^2 - 7x - 6 = 0$$
$$3x^2 - 7x = 6$$
$$x^2 - \tfrac{7}{3}x = 2$$
$$x^2 - \tfrac{7}{3}x + (\tfrac{7}{6})^2 = 2 + (\tfrac{7}{6})^2$$
$$x^2 - \tfrac{7}{3}x + \tfrac{49}{36} = 2 + \tfrac{49}{36}$$
$$(x - \tfrac{7}{6})^2 = \tfrac{121}{36}$$
$$x - \tfrac{7}{6} = \pm \tfrac{11}{6}$$
When $x - \tfrac{7}{6} = +\tfrac{11}{6}$
$$x = \tfrac{11}{6} + \tfrac{7}{6} = \tfrac{18}{6}$$
(1) $\quad x = 3$
When $x - \tfrac{7}{6} = -\tfrac{11}{6}$
$$x = -\tfrac{11}{6} + \tfrac{7}{6} = -\tfrac{4}{6}$$
(2) $\quad x = -\tfrac{2}{3}$
Answer, $x = 3$ and $x = -\tfrac{2}{3}$

Check:
$$27 - 21 - 6 = 0$$
$$0 = 0$$
$$3(-\tfrac{2}{3})^2 - 7(-\tfrac{2}{3}) - 6 = 0$$
$$3(\tfrac{4}{9}) - 7(-\tfrac{2}{3}) - 6 = 0$$
$$\tfrac{4}{3} + \tfrac{14}{3} - 6 = 0$$
$$6 - 6 = 0$$
$$0 = 0$$

DIAGNOSTIC TEST

Solve by completing the square and check:

1. $x^2 + 4x = 12$
2. $x^2 + 8x = -12$
3. $x^2 + 2x - 24 = 0$

4. $x^2 - 10x = 39$
5. $x^2 - 16x = -48$
6. $x^2 - 8x - 20 = 0$

7. $x^2 + 3x = 10$
8. $x^2 - 5x = 24$
9. $x^2 - x = \frac{3}{4}$

10. $x^2 + \frac{3}{2}x = 1$
11. $4x^2 - x = 6$
12. $x^2 + 2bx - 8b^2 = 0$

13. $mx^2 + nx + k = 0$

Related Practice Examples

Solve by completing the square and check:

SET 1

1. $x^2 + 2x = 8$
2. $x^2 + 8x = 20$
3. $x^2 + 6x = 7$
4. $x^2 + 10x = 24$
5. $x^2 + 12x = 28$

SET 2

1. $x^2 + 8x = -15$
2. $x^2 + 6x = -5$
3. $x^2 + 10x = -24$
4. $x^2 + 18x = -56$
5. $x^2 + 12x = -27$

SET 3

1. $x^2 + 6x + 8 = 0$
2. $x^2 + 10x + 9 = 0$
3. $x^2 + 2x - 15 = 0$
4. $x^2 + 4x - 32 = 0$
5. $x^2 + 20x + 36 = 0$

SET 4

1. $x^2 - 2x = 8$
2. $x^2 - 10x = 11$
3. $x^2 - 6x = 27$
4. $x^2 - 8x = 84$
5. $x^2 - 16x = 80$

SET 5

1. $x^2 - 6x = -5$
2. $x^2 - 12x = -20$
3. $x^2 - 8x = -12$
4. $x^2 - 18x = -45$
5. $x^2 - 22x = -72$

SET 6

1. $x^2 - 4x - 32 = 0$
2. $x^2 - 10x - 75 = 0$
3. $x^2 - 12x + 27 = 0$
4. $x^2 - 26x + 48 = 0$
5. $x^2 - 22x - 75 = 0$

SET 7

1. $x^2 + 3x = 18$
2. $x^2 + x = 20$
3. $x^2 + 7x = 8$
4. $x^2 + 5x = 14$
5. $x^2 + 9x - 36 = 0$

SET 8

1. $x^2 - 5x = 36$
2. $x^2 - x = 2$
3. $x^2 - 11x = 42$
4. $x^2 - 3x = 70$
5. $x^2 - 7x - 18 = 0$

SET 9

1. $x^2 - x = -\dfrac{2}{9}$
2. $x^2 + 2x + \dfrac{3}{4} = 0$
3. $x^2 - x + \dfrac{3}{16} = 0$
4. $x^2 - 2x - \dfrac{5}{4} = 0$
5. $x^2 + 3x + \dfrac{20}{9} = 0$

SET 10

1. $x^2 - \dfrac{8}{3}x = 1$
2. $x^2 + \dfrac{x}{2} - 3 = 0$
3. $x^2 - \dfrac{x}{4} = \dfrac{3}{4}$
4. $x^2 - \dfrac{7}{2}x = -\dfrac{3}{2}$
5. $x^2 + \dfrac{11}{3}x + 2 = 0$

SET 11

1. $2x^2 - 7x = 4$
2. $3x^2 - 4x = -1$
3. $4x^2 - 13x - 12 = 0$
4. $16x^2 - 16x + 3 = 0$
5. $6x^2 + x - 12 = 0$

SET 12

1. $x^2 - 8ax = -15a^2$
2. $x^2 + 4bx + 3b^2 = 0$
3. $x^2 - 2cx = 8c^2$
4. $x^2 + 3ax - 18a^2 = 0$
5. $x^2 - 5mx - 36m^2 = 0$

SET 13

1. $2x^2 + 2bx = 4b^2$
2. $x^2 + \dfrac{b}{2}x = 3b^2$
3. $3x^2 + 2mx = 21m^2$
4. $2x^2 + 3bx - 2b^2 = 0$
5. $rx^2 + sx + t = 0$

EXERCISE 110 — Solution by Formula

Solution by Formula

I. Aim: To solve quadratic equations by formula.

II. Procedure

The general quadratic equation $ax^2+bx+c=0$ is solved by the method of completing the square (see Exercise 109), finding x in terms of a, b, and c. The resulting expression is the required formula.

$$ax^2+bx+c=0$$

$$ax^2+bx=-c$$

$$x^2+\frac{b}{a}x=-\frac{c}{a}$$

$$x^2+\frac{b}{a}x+\left(\frac{b}{2a}\right)^2=\left(\frac{b}{2a}\right)^2-\frac{c}{a}$$

$$x^2+\frac{b}{a}x+\frac{b^2}{4a^2}=\frac{b^2}{4a^2}-\frac{c}{a}$$

$$\left(x+\frac{b}{2a}\right)^2=\frac{b^2-4ac}{4a^2}$$

$$x+\frac{b}{2a}=\pm\frac{\sqrt{b^2-4ac}}{2a}$$

$$x=\frac{-b}{2a}\pm\frac{\sqrt{b^2-4ac}}{2a}$$

$$x=\frac{-b\pm\sqrt{b^2-4ac}}{2a}$$

1. If necessary, transpose so that all terms are on one member of the equation. Then combine similar terms.
   a) If the equation is fractional, clear the equation of all fractions, then transpose and combine.
   b) If the equation contains parentheses, remove parentheses, then transpose and combine.

2. Compare the given equation to the general quadratic equation $ax^2+bx+c=0$ and do the following:
   a) Find the numerical coefficient of x^2 and represent it as a.
   b) Find the numerical coefficient of x and represent it as b.
   c) Find the constant term and represent it as c.

   Note: Since $5x^2-4=0$ may be thought of as $5x^2+0x-4=0$ and $2x^2-3x=0$ as $3x^2-3x+0=0$, the b or c value of the missing term must be regarded as zero (0) in any incomplete quadratic equation.

3. Substitute the values for a, b and c in the formula: $x=\dfrac{-b\pm\sqrt{b^2-4ac}}{2a}$

4. Perform all necessary operations to get two values for x.

5. If necessary, simplify the roots.

6. Check each root by substituting it in the given equation.

III. Sample Solutions

1. $x^2+4x+3=0$

   $a=1$
   $b=4$
   $c=3$

   $$x=\frac{-b\pm\sqrt{b^2-4ac}}{2a}$$

   $$x=\frac{-4\pm\sqrt{16-12}}{2}$$

   $$x=\frac{-4\pm\sqrt{4}}{2}$$

   $$x=\frac{-4\pm2}{2}$$

   $$x=\frac{-4+2}{2}=\frac{-2}{2}$$

   (1) $x=-1$

   $$x=\frac{-4-2}{2}=\frac{-6}{2}$$

   (2) $x=-3$

   Answer, $x=-1$ and $x=-3$

   Check:

   $1-4+3=0$

   $0=0$

   $9-12+3=0$

   $0=0$

3. $3x^2 - 5x = 0$

$a = 3$

$b = -5$ $\quad x = \dfrac{-b \pm \sqrt{b^2 - 4ac}}{2a}$

$c = 0$ $\quad x = \dfrac{5 \pm \sqrt{25 - 0}}{6}$

$x = \dfrac{5 \pm \sqrt{25}}{6}$

$x = \dfrac{5 \pm 5}{6}$

$x = \dfrac{5 + 5}{6} = \dfrac{10}{6}$

(1) $x = 1\frac{2}{3}$

$x = \dfrac{5 - 5}{6} = \dfrac{0}{6}$

(2) $x = 0$

Check:

$0 - 0 = 0$

$3(1\frac{2}{3})^2 - 5(1\frac{2}{3}) = 0$

$3\left(\dfrac{25}{9}\right) - \dfrac{25}{3} = 0$

$\dfrac{25}{3} - \dfrac{25}{3} = 0$

$0 = 0$

Answer, $x = 1\frac{2}{3}$ and $x = 0$

4. $x^2 - 7 = 0$

$a = 1$

$b = 0$ $\quad x = \dfrac{-b \pm \sqrt{b^2 - 4ac}}{2a}$

$c = -7$ $\quad x = \dfrac{0 \pm \sqrt{0 + 28}}{2}$

$x = \dfrac{\pm \sqrt{28}}{2}$

$x = \dfrac{\pm 2\sqrt{7}}{2}$

$x = \pm \sqrt{7}$

Answer, $x = \pm \sqrt{7}$

Check:

$(\sqrt{7})^2 - 7 = 0$

$7 - 7 = 0$

$0 = 0$

$(-\sqrt{7})^2 - 7 = 0$

$7 - 7 = 0$

$0 = 0$

5. $2x^2 - 4x = 1$

$2x^2 - 4x - 1 = 0$

$a = 2$ $\quad x = \dfrac{-b \pm \sqrt{b^2 - 4ac}}{2a}$

$b = -4$

$c = -1$ $\quad x = \dfrac{4 \pm \sqrt{16 + 8}}{4}$

$x = \dfrac{4 \pm \sqrt{24}}{4}$

$x = \dfrac{4 \pm 2\sqrt{6}}{4}$

$x = \dfrac{2(2 \pm \sqrt{6})}{4}$

$x = \dfrac{2 \pm \sqrt{6}}{2}$

Answer, $x = \dfrac{2 \pm \sqrt{6}}{2}$

Check:

$2\left(\dfrac{2 + \sqrt{6}}{2}\right)^2 - 4\left(\dfrac{2 + \sqrt{6}}{2}\right) = 1$

$5 + 2\sqrt{6} - 4 - 2\sqrt{6} = 1$

$1 = 1$

$2\left(\dfrac{2 - \sqrt{6}}{2}\right)^2 - 4\left(\dfrac{2 - \sqrt{6}}{2}\right) = 1$

$5 - 2\sqrt{6} - 4 + 2\sqrt{6} = 1$

$1 = 1$

Note: To find irrational roots correct to the nearest hundredth, replace radical by decimal equivalent and perform the necessary operations.

The roots of sample solution 5 are used below.

$x = \dfrac{2 + \sqrt{6}}{2} = \dfrac{2 + 2.449}{2} = \dfrac{4.449}{2} = 2.22$

$x = \dfrac{2 - \sqrt{6}}{2} = \dfrac{2 - 2.449}{2} = \dfrac{-.449}{2} = -.22$

DIAGNOSTIC TEST

Solve by formula and check:

1. $x^2 + 7x + 12 = 0$
2. $x^2 - 8x + 12 = 0$
3. $x^2 + 2x - 15 = 0$
4. $x^2 - 4x - 32 = 0$
5. $x^2 - 4x + 4 = 0$
6. $3x^2 - 8x + 4 = 0$
7. $x^2 + 2x = 8$
8. $x^2 + 3x = 0$

9. $9x^2 - 4 = 0$
10. $x(x + 2) + 2(x - 2) = 1$
11. $x^2 - 2 = 0$
12. $2x^2 - 16 = 0$
13. $4x^2 - 3 = 0$
14. $x^2 - 3x - 2 = 0$
15. $x^2 + x - 11 = 0$
16. $3x^2 + 4x - 1 = 0$

17. $x^2 - 2x + 2 = 0$
18. $\dfrac{x}{6} - \dfrac{1}{3} = \dfrac{20}{x}$

Find roots correct to nearest hundredth:

19. $3x^2 - 6x + 2 = 0$
20. $x^2 + .2x - .08 = 0$

Solve by formula and check:

SET 1
1. $x^2 + 6x + 5 = 0$
2. $x^2 + 7x + 10 = 0$
3. $x^2 + 11x + 24 = 0$
4. $x^2 + 9x + 20 = 0$
5. $x^2 + 12x + 35 = 0$

SET 2
1. $x^2 - 9x + 8 = 0$
2. $x^2 - 8x + 15 = 0$
3. $x^2 - 12x + 20 = 0$
4. $x^2 - 6x + 8 = 0$
5. $x^2 - 12x + 27 = 0$

SET 3
1. $x^2 + 2x - 3 = 0$
2. $x^2 + 4x - 12 = 0$
3. $x^2 + 10x - 24 = 0$
4. $x^2 + 3x - 40 = 0$
5. $x^2 + 5x - 14 = 0$

SET 4
1. $x^2 - 3x - 4 = 0$
2. $x^2 - 4x - 12 = 0$
3. $x^2 - 12x - 28 = 0$
4. $x^2 - 9x - 36 = 0$
5. $x^2 - 3x - 40 = 0$

SET 5
1. $x^2 - 6x + 9 = 0$
2. $x^2 - 14x + 49 = 0$
3. $x^2 + 2x + 1 = 0$
4. $x^2 + 10x + 25 = 0$
5. $x^2 - 8x + 16 = 0$

SET 6a
1. $3x^2 - 9x + 6 = 0$
2. $2x^2 + 3x - 20 = 0$
3. $3x^2 + 5x + 2 = 0$
4. $2x^2 + 2x - 12 = 0$
5. $5x^2 - 13x + 6 = 0$

SET 6b
1. $2x^2 - x - 6 = 0$
2. $4x^2 + 4x - 8 = 0$
3. $2x^2 - 9x - 5 = 0$
4. $3x^2 - 10x + 3 = 0$
5. $6x^2 - 17x + 12 = 0$

SET 7
1. $x^2 - x = 6$
2. $x^2 + 8x = -12$
3. $x^2 - 7x = 18$
4. $6x^2 - 13x = 5$
5. $3x^2 + 6x = 24$

SET 8
1. $x^2 - 4x = 0$
2. $2x^2 - 7x = 0$
3. $x^2 + 2x = 0$
4. $6x^2 + 5x = 0$
5. $x^2 - x = 0$

SET 9
1. $x^2 - 9 = 0$
2. $x^2 - 36 = 0$
3. $4x^2 - 1 = 0$
4. $9x^2 - 25 = 0$
5. $16x^2 - 9 = 0$

SET 10
1. $2x^2 - 3x + 6 = x^2 + 2x$
2. $x(x - 10) + 24 = 0$
3. $x^2 - 3(x + 7) = x$
4. $(x + 3)^2 = 9(x + 1)$
5. $(x + 2)^2 = 2(5x - 2)$

SET 11
1. $x^2 - 6 = 0$
2. $x^2 - 13 = 0$
3. $2x^2 - 14 = 0$
4. $5x^2 - 15 = 0$
5. $4x^2 - 40 = 0$

SET 12
1. $x^2 - 12 = 0$
2. $x^2 - 32 = 0$
3. $2x^2 - 36 = 0$
4. $3x^2 - 60 = 0$
5. $2x^2 - 48 = 0$

SET 13
1. $4x^2 - 5 = 0$
2. $2x^2 - 1 = 0$
3. $5x^2 - 9 = 0$
4. $3x^2 - 2 = 0$
5. $8x^2 - 3 = 0$

SET 14
1. $x^2 + 3x - 1 = 0$
2. $x^2 + 5x - 2 = 0$
3. $x^2 + 7x + 2 = 0$
4. $2x^2 + 9x + 3 = 0$
5. $4x^2 + x - 1 = 0$

SET 15
1. $x^2 + 7x + 1 = 0$
2. $x^2 + x - 31 = 0$
3. $x^2 + 11x + 1 = 0$
4. $2x^2 + 7x - 13 = 0$
5. $5x^2 + 5x - 1 = 0$

SET 16
1. $x^2 + 3x - 9 = 0$
2. $x^2 + 4x + 1 = 0$
3. $2x^2 + 8x + 3 = 0$
4. $4x^2 + 2x - 3 = 0$
5. $3x^2 - 6x + 1 = 0$

SET 17
1. $x^2 - 2x + 3 = 0$
2. $x^2 + 5x + 7 = 0$
3. $3x^2 - 4x + 3 = 0$
4. $2x^2 + 3x + 5 = 0$
5. $4x^2 - 2x + 7 = 0$

SET 18
1. $\dfrac{x^2}{2} + \dfrac{3x}{4} = 11$
2. $\dfrac{x}{4} + \dfrac{1}{2} = \dfrac{2}{x}$
3. $\dfrac{2}{x-1} = \dfrac{x}{10}$
4. $\dfrac{6}{x+3} = \dfrac{x+2}{5}$
5. $\dfrac{x}{2x-1} = \dfrac{2x+3}{15}$

Find roots correct to nearest hundredth:

SET 19
1. $x^2 - 5x + 3 = 0$
2. $x^2 + 2x - 5 = 0$
3. $x^2 - 6x - 1 = 0$
4. $2x^2 + 5x + 1 = 0$
5. $3x^2 + 4x - 3 = 0$

SET 20
1. $x^2 - 1.7x - .6 = 0$
2. $x^2 - .35x + .015 = 0$
3. $x^2 + .36x + .0288 = 0$
4. $.16x^2 + 1.6x - 12 = 0$
5. $.2x^2 - 1.75x + 1.2 = 0$

EXERCISE 111

Rearranging and Evaluating Formulas

I. Aim: To rearrange and evaluate formulas.

II. Procedure

   1. To rearrange formulas, follow the principles outlined in Exercise 78 and Exercises 106 to 110.

   2. To evaluate formulas, follow the principles outlined in Exercise 79 and Exercises 106 to 110.

III. Sample Solutions

   1. Rearrange the formula $A = \pi r^2$ and solve for r.

$$A = \pi r^2$$
$$\frac{A}{\pi} = r^2$$
$$\sqrt{\frac{A}{\pi}} = r$$
$$r = \sqrt{\frac{A}{\pi}}$$

Answer, $r = \sqrt{\dfrac{A}{\pi}}$

   2. Find the value of I in the formula $W = I^2 R$ if $W = 100$ and $R = 25$.

$$W = I^2 R$$
$$100 = I^2 \times 25$$
$$100 = 25I^2$$
$$4 = I^2$$
$$2 = I$$
$$I = 2$$

Answer, $I = 2$

DIAGNOSTIC TEST

Take formula from list on page 276.

   1. Rearrange formula #3 and solve for I.

   2. Find the value of t in formula #7 if $s = 144$, and $g = 32$.

Related Practice Examples

SET 1

Take formula from list on page 276. Solve for letter in question by rearranging formula:

   1. Solve formula #1 for s.
   2. Solve formula #2 for s.
   3. Solve formula #4 for r.
   4. Solve formula #5 for r.
   5. Solve formula #6 for r.

   6. Solve formula #7 for t.
   7. Solve formula #8 for V.
   8. Solve formula #9 for v.
   9. Solve formula #10 for a.
   10. Solve formula #10 for b.

SET 2

Take formula from list below. Find the value of the letter in question.

	Formula #	Evaluate	A if:	B if:
1.	1	s	$A=36.$	$A=121.$
2.	2	s	$A=150.$	$A=384.$
3.	3	I	$W=72; R=8.$	$W=147; R=3.$
4.	4	r	$\pi=3.14; A=50.24.$	$\pi=22/7; A=154.$
5.	5	r	$\pi=3.14; A=113.04.$	$\pi=22/7; A=1232.$
6.	6	r	$V=62.8; \pi=3.14; h=5.$	$V=1408; \pi=22/7; h=7.$
7.	7	t	$s=400; g=32.$	$s=576; g=32.$
8.	8	V	$K=1024; m=8.$	$K=486; m=12.$
9.	9	v	$F=3; m=8; g=32; r=3.$	$F=10; m=16; g=32; r=5.$
10.	10	b	$h=25; a=20.$	$h=13; a=5.$

List of Formulas

1. $A=s^2$
2. $A=6s^2$
3. $W=I^2R$
4. $A=\pi r^2$
5. $A=4\pi r^2$
6. $V=\pi r^2 h$
7. $s=\frac{1}{2}gt^2$
8. $K=\frac{1}{2}mV^2$
9. $F=\frac{mv^2}{gr}$
10. $h^2=a^2+b^2$

Applications

1. The formula $s=16t^2$ may be used either to find the distance (s) in feet that an object falls in a given number of seconds (t) or the time the object requires to fall a given distance.
   a) How many feet does an object fall in 3 seconds? 5 seconds? 11 seconds?
   b) How many seconds does it take an object to fall 256 feet? 1,296 feet? 3,600 feet?

2. The dimensions of a well-proportioned rectangle may be determined by the formula $\frac{w}{l}=\frac{l}{w+l}$, with l representing the length and w the width of the rectangle. Using this formula, find to the nearest hundredth:
   a) The length of a rectangle when the width is 6 inches.
   b) The width of a rectangle when the length is 15 feet.
   c) The length and width of a rectangle when the perimeter is 8 feet.

3. The formula $V=\frac{1}{4}\pi d^2 h$ expresses the relation between the volume, diameter, and height of a cylinder.
   a) Find the volume of a cylinder if the diameter is 21 inches and the height is 15 inches.
   b) What must the diameter of a tank be to hold 1,155 gallons if the height is 4 feet? A cubic foot holds about $7\frac{1}{2}$ gallons.

4. The height (s) of an object in feet at the end of t seconds, when thrown upward with a velocity (v) in feet per second, may be determined by the formula $s=vt-16t^2$.
   a) Find the height of an object at the end of 5 seconds when thrown upward at the rate of 120 feet per second.
   b) How many seconds will it take an object to reach a height of 126 feet if it is thrown upward at the rate of 90 feet per second? As the object falls, when is it again at 126 feet?

5. The lift of an airplane may be determined by the formula $L=C\frac{d}{2}AV^2$ where L is the lift in pounds, C is the coefficient of lift, d is the air density, A is the wing area in square feet, and V is the velocity or air speed in feet per second.
   a) Find the lift of an airplane flying at an air speed of 180 miles per hour where the air density is .0024. Its wing area is 300 square feet and its coefficient of lift is .47.
   b) Find the velocity required to sustain a 1,600 pound airplane (lift) with a wing area of 320 square feet if the air density is .002 and the coefficient of lift is .50.

EXERCISE 112

Word Problems

I. Aim: To solve word problems which involve quadratic equations.

II. Procedure

1. Follow the principles outlined in Unit Seven to obtain an equation.

2. Solve the resulting equation. Use the principles outlined in Exercises 106 to 110.

III. Sample Solutions

The length of a rectangle is 3 inches more than the width. The area is 40 sq. inches. Find the length and width of the rectangle.

Solution:

Let x = width of rectangle in inches.
$x+3$ = length of rectangle in inches.

$$* \qquad x(x+3) = 40$$
$$x^2 + 3x = 40$$
$$x^2 + 3x - 40 = 0$$
$$(x+8)(x-5) = 0$$
If $\qquad x + 8 = 0$
$$x = -8**$$
If $\qquad x - 5 = 0$
$$x = 5 \text{ in.—width}$$
$$x + 3 = 8 \text{ in.—length}$$

Answer, length is 8 in. and width is 5 in.

* The equation is determined by the following fact:

Area of a rectangle equals the length times the width.

** Note: Negative root is meaningless in this problem.

Check:

8 in., length	8 in., length
−5 in., width	×5 in., width
3 in.	40 sq. in.

Solve the following problems and check the answers:

Practice Problems

a) **Number Problems.**

1. The sum of two numbers is 14 and their product is 48. Find the numbers.

2. One number is 2 more than a second number. If the product of the two numbers is 35, find the numbers.

3. If the square of a number is increased by three times the number, the result is 28. Find the number.

4. Four times the square of a number decreased by 6 equals 7 times the number increased by 9. Find the number.

5. The sum of two numbers is 8 and the sum of the squares of the numbers is 40. Find the numbers.

b) **Geometry Problems.**

1. The length of a rectangle is 4 inches more than the width. The area is 45 square inches. Find the length and width of the rectangle.

2. The width of a rectangle is 3 inches less than the length. The area is 70 square inches. Find the length and width of the rectangle.

3. The perimeter of a rectangle is 22 feet and its area is 24 square feet. Find the length and width of the rectangle.

4. If two parallel sides of a square are each increased by 6 inches and the other two parallel sides are each decreased by 1 inch, a rectangle is formed having twice the area of the square. How long is each side of the square?

5. The perimeter of a rectangle is 26 feet. If the length is increased by 4 feet and the width is increased by 3 feet, the area of the new rectangle is 96 square feet. Find the length and width of the original rectangle.

REVIEW OF UNIT SIXTEEN

1. Solve and check: a) $6x^2 = 24$ b) $x^2 - 56 = 0$ c) $9x^2 = 6$ d) $4x^2 - 19 = 2x^2 - 5$ e) $(x+2)(x-2) = 32$

2. Solve by factoring and check: a) $x^2 + 4x - 12 = 0$ b) $x^2 - 100 = 0$ c) $\dfrac{x}{x-4} + \dfrac{2x}{x-6} = 10$

3. Solve by completing the square and check: a) $x^2 + 8x = 33$ b) $x^2 - 7x - 18 = 0$ c) $14x^2 - 17x + 5 = 0$

4. Solve by formula and check: a) $x^2 - 14x + 24 = 0$ b) $x^2 + 3x - 5 = 0$ c) $4x^2 - (x+3)(x+5) = 20$

5. Transform formula $A = .7854d^2$, solving for d.   6. Rearrange formula $L = \dfrac{CdAV^2}{2}$, solving for V.

7. Find the value of E if $R = 80$ and $P = 500$, using the formula $R = \dfrac{E^2}{P}$.

8. Using the formula $K = \frac{1}{2}mV^2$, find the value of V when $K = 2,700$ and $m = 6$.

9. Find the value of r if $A = 1,496$, $\pi = \frac{22}{7}$, and $l = 20$, using the formula $A = \pi r^2 + \pi rl$.

10. Use formula $d = 16t^2$ to determine how long it takes a freely falling body to fall 784 feet.

CUMULATIVE ALGEBRA REVIEW

1. The net price is equal to the list price less the discount. Write a formula expressing the discount (d) in terms of the list price (l) and the net price (n).   2. From the sum of $3a - 7c$ and $4a - 6b - c$ take $3b - 5d$.

3. a) Find the product by inspection: $(5m - 4n)(7m - n)$ b) Factor: $7a^2 - 63a + 56$

4. Divide: $\dfrac{16a^2 - 80a}{5} \div a^2 - 25$ 5. Combine: $\dfrac{4}{c+9} - \dfrac{3}{9-c} - \dfrac{6c}{c^2 - 81}$

6. Rearrange formula $S = \dfrac{n}{2}(a+l)$, solving for l.   7. Solve and check:
$$9x(2x - 1) = 20$$

8. Find the value of s when $A = 726$, using the formula $A = 6s^2$.

9. The length of a rectangle is 1 inch more than the width. If the length is increased by 9 inches and the width is decreased by 4 inches, the area of the rectangle remains the same. Find the length and width of the original rectangle.

10. Solve and check: 11. Solve and check: 12. Simplify and combine:
$$\dfrac{x+4}{9} + \dfrac{3x-1}{2} - \dfrac{2x+5}{3} = 3$$

$$9(x+y) = 2(x-3)$$
$$2x - (y+5) = 4$$

$$5\sqrt{24} - 2\sqrt{128} + 6\sqrt{162} - 12\sqrt{\tfrac{2}{3}}$$

13. In the formula $P = \dfrac{E^2}{R}$, $P = 12$ when $E = 18$. Find the value of P when $E = 54$ and R remains constant.

14. Using formulas $R = \dfrac{s}{c}$ and $A = sc$, derive a formula for R in terms of A and c.

15. What is the radius of action of an airplane (how far can it fly from the base and yet return) in 7 hours if its outgoing speed is 135 m.p.h. and its return speed is 180 m.p.h.?

KEYED ACHIEVEMENT TEST

1. Combine: $\dfrac{6}{a^2 - b^2} - \dfrac{3}{a^2 - ab}$ ⓖ③   2. Solve and check: $\dfrac{3x-2}{x} = \dfrac{3x+3}{x+2}$ ⓖⓖ

3. Simplify and combine:
$$\sqrt{125} - 2\sqrt{27} + \sqrt{48} - 10\sqrt{\tfrac{1}{5}} \quad ⑩⓪⓪$$

4. Solve and check: $x + y = 6,000$ ⑧⑤
.05x + .06y = 230

5. Solve and check: $8x^2 = 96$ ⑩⓪⑥   6. Solve by factoring and check: $x(x - 9) = -8$ ⑩⓪⑧

7. Solve by completing the square: $2x^2 - x - 10 = 0$ ⑩⓪⑨   8. Solve by formula: $\dfrac{x}{2} - \dfrac{3}{4} = \dfrac{x+1}{x}$ ⑪①⓪

9. Find the value of I if $H = 194,400$, $R = 100$, and $t = 3,600$, using the formula $H = 0.24I^2Rt$. ⑪①①

10. The area of a rectangle is 168 square inches and its perimeter is 52 inches. Find its length and width. ⑪①②

INTRODUCTION TO UNIT SEVENTEEN

Since it is impossible to measure all distances and heights directly, engineers, surveyors, astronomers, and navigators find it necessary to employ indirect measurement. In this unit we shall study several methods of measuring indirectly. The Pythagorean Theorem and the essentials of numerical trigonometry will be treated as applications of the algebraic processes and principles studied in the preceding units.

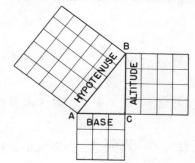

Trigonometry means triangle measure. We shall see that the sides and angles of a triangle are so related that when certain parts of a triangle are known, the other parts can be determined indirectly.

The Pythagorean Theorem expresses the relationship between the sides of a right triangle. The side opposite the right angle is called the *hypotenuse*. The other two sides are called the *altitude* and the *base*. The Pythagorean Theorem states that the square of the hypotenuse is equal to the sum of the squares of the other two sides. If any two sides of a right triangle are known, the third side may be found by the use of one of the following formulas: $c^2 = a^2 + b^2$, $c = \sqrt{a^2 + b^2}$; $a = \sqrt{c^2 - b^2}$; $b = \sqrt{c^2 - a^2}$.

In a right triangle the acute angles are complementary. Thus in right triangle ABC, $A = 90° - B$ and $B = 90° - A$.

In trigonometry, ratios of the sides of the right triangle and their relation to the acute angles are used to determine the unknown parts of the triangle.

The ratio of the side opposite an acute angle in a right triangle to the adjacent side is called the *tangent* of the angle (abbreviated *tan*). Thus in right triangle ABC, $\tan A = \dfrac{a}{b}$ and $\tan B = \dfrac{b}{a}$.

The ratio of the side opposite an acute angle in a right triangle to the hypotenuse is called the *sine* of the angle (abbreviated *sin*). Thus, $\sin A = \dfrac{a}{c}$ and $\sin B = \dfrac{b}{c}$.

The ratio of the adjacent side of an acute angle in a right triangle to the hypotenuse is called the *cosine* of the angle (abbreviated *cos*). Thus, $\cos A = \dfrac{b}{c}$ and $\cos B = \dfrac{a}{c}$.

The tangent ratio for a given acute angle is the same for right triangles of all sizes. This is also true of the sine and cosine ratios. In triangle ABC, $\tan 37° = \dfrac{\text{side } BC}{\text{side } AC} = \dfrac{15}{20}$ or .75, and in triangle ADE,

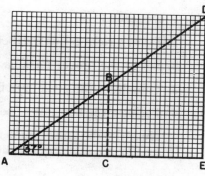

$\tan 37° = \dfrac{\text{side } DE}{\text{side } AE} = \dfrac{30}{40}$ or .75. In triangle ABC, $\sin 37° = \dfrac{\text{side } BC}{\text{side } AB} = \dfrac{15}{25}$

or .6, and in triangle ADE, $\sin 37° = \dfrac{\text{side } DE}{\text{side } AD} = \dfrac{30}{50} = .6$. In triangle ABC,

$\cos 37° = \dfrac{\text{side } AC}{\text{side } AB} = \dfrac{20}{25} = .8$, and in triangle ADE, $\cos 37° = \dfrac{\text{side } AE}{\text{side } AD} = \dfrac{40}{50}$

or .8. These ratios depend upon the size of the acute angles and not upon the size of the triangle. The table on page 293 gives the trigonometric values of these ratios for angles ranging from 0° to 90°.

Angles are measured both vertically and horizontally. An angle measured vertically between the horizontal line and the observer's line of sight to an object is called the *angle of elevation* when the object is above the observer and the *angle of depression* when the object is below the observer.

UNIT SEVENTEEN—NUMERICAL TRIGONOMETRY

The following is a list of formulas used in the study of numerical trigonometry. Refer to the right triangle ABC for meaning of letters used in the formulas.

Formulas

(1) $A = 90° - B$

(6) $\tan A = \dfrac{a}{b}$

(9) $\sin B = \dfrac{b}{c}$

(2) $B = 90° - A$

(7) $\tan B = \dfrac{b}{a}$

(10) $\cos A = \dfrac{b}{c}$

(3) $c = \sqrt{a^2 + b^2}$

(8) $\sin A = \dfrac{a}{c}$

(11) $\cos B = \dfrac{a}{c}$

(4) $a = \sqrt{c^2 - b^2}$

(5) $b = \sqrt{c^2 - a^2}$

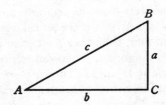

$A =$ angle A.
$B =$ angle B.
$C =$ angle $C = 90°$.
$a =$ side opposite $\angle A$—altitude.
$b =$ side opposite $\angle B$—base.
$c =$ side opposite $\angle C$—hypotenuse.

EXERCISE 113

Complementary Angles and Pythagorean Theorem

I. Aim: To find the complementary angle of a given angle in a right triangle; and to solve examples and word problems by the Pythagorean Theorem.

II. Procedure

1. Draw a right triangle, label it (see sample triangle in list of formulas) and place given numbers on it.

2. Select the proper formula.

3. Substitute the given numbers in the formula.

4. Perform the necessary operations.

   Note: In the angle problems, use the equivalent $1° = 60'$. See sample solution 2 for procedure in finding an angle containing degrees and minutes.

III. Sample Solutions

1. Find angle A if angle $B = 62°$.
   $$A = 90° - B$$
   $$A = 90° - 62°$$
   $$A = 28°$$

   Answer, $A = 28°$

2. Find angle B if angle $A = 28°40'$.

   $$B = 90° - A \qquad 90° = 89°60'$$
   $$B = 90° - 28°40' \qquad \underline{28°40'}$$
   $$B = 61°20' \qquad \overline{61°20'}$$

   Answer, $B = 61°20'$

280

3. In the right triangle ABC, find side c if side $a = 36$ in. and side $b = 15$ in.

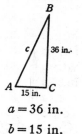

$$c = \sqrt{a^2 + b^2}$$
$$c = \sqrt{1296 + 225}$$
$$c = \sqrt{1521}$$
$$c = 39 \text{ inches}$$

$$\begin{array}{r} 1296 \\ +\ 225 \\ \hline 1521 \end{array}$$

$$\begin{array}{r} 3\quad 9 \\ \sqrt{15'21.} \\ 9 \\ \hline 69)\ 621 \\ 621 \\ \hline \end{array}$$

$a = 36$ in.

$b = 15$ in.

$c = ?$

Answer, $c = 39$ inches.

4. In the right triangle ABC, find side b if side $c = 40$ ft. and side $a = 24$ ft.

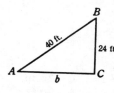

$$b = \sqrt{c^2 - a^2}$$
$$b = \sqrt{1600 - 576}$$
$$b = \sqrt{1024}$$
$$b = 32 \text{ ft.}$$

$$\begin{array}{r} 1600 \\ -\ 576 \\ \hline 1024 \end{array}$$

$$\begin{array}{r} 3\quad 2 \\ \sqrt{10'24.} \\ 9 \\ \hline 62)\ 124 \\ 124 \\ \hline \end{array}$$

$a = 24$ ft.

$b = ?$

$c = 40$ ft.

Answer, $b = 32$ ft.

DIAGNOSTIC TEST

Solve the following problems, using the appropriate formula.

In the right triangle ABC,
1. Find angle A if angle $B = 39°$.
2. Find angle B if angle $A = 53°27'$.
3. Find side c if side $a = 8$ feet and side $b = 15$ feet.
4. Find side a if side $c = 29$ in. and side $b = 20$ in.
5. Find side b if side $c = 159$ feet and side $a = 84$ feet.
6. How high up on a wall does a 25-foot ladder reach if the foot of the ladder is 7 feet from the wall?

Related Practice Examples

Solve the following problems, using the appropriate formula:
In the right triangle ABC,

SET 1		SET 2	
Find A if	**Find B if**	**Find A if**	**Find B if**
1. $B = 47°$	**6.** $A = 65°$	**1.** $B = 27°30'$	**6.** $A = 47°\ 8'$
2. $B = 25°$	**7.** $A = 21°$	**2.** $B = 68°30'$	**7.** $A = 84°20'$
3. $B = 83°$	**8.** $A = 6°$	**3.** $B = 34°15'$	**8.** $A = 73°39'$
4. $B = 16°$	**9.** $A = 45°$	**4.** $B = 59°45'$	**9.** $A = 31°25'$
5. $B = 74°$	**10.** $A = 32°$	**5.** $B = 15°58'$	**10.** $A = 60°50'$

SET 3a

Find c if

1. $a = 12$ ft.; $b = 35$ ft.
2. $a = 84$ in.; $b = 13$ in.
3. $a = 16$ ft.; $b = 30$ ft.
4. $a = 77$ ft.; $b = 36$ ft.
5. $a = 21$ in.; $b = 72$ in.
6. $a = 24$ yd.; $b = 70$ yd.
7. $b = 45$ in.; $a = 28$ in.
8. $a = 84$ ft.; $b = 135$ ft.
9. $b = 144$ ft.; $a = 60$ ft.
10. $a = 195$ ft.; $b = 216$ ft.

SET 4a

Find a if

1. $c = 65$ ft.; $b = 16$ ft.
2. $c = 41$ in.; $b = 40$ in.
3. $c = 50$ yd.; $b = 14$ yd.
4. $c = 65$ ft.; $b = 63$ ft.
5. $c = 97$ yd.; $b = 65$ yd.
6. $c = 89$ ft.; $b = 80$ ft.
7. $b = 84$ yd.; $c = 159$ yd.
8. $c = 200$ ft.; $b = 56$ ft.
9. $b = 45$ ft.; $c = 339$ ft.
10. $c = 255$ ft.; $b = 108$ ft.

SET 5a

Find b if

1. $c = 52$ in.; $a = 20$ in.
2. $c = 73$ ft.; $a = 48$ ft.
3. $c = 78$ yd.; $a = 30$ yd.
4. $c = 87$ in.; $a = 63$ in.
5. $c = 195$ ft.; $a = 48$ ft.
6. $c = 146$ yd.; $a = 96$ yd.
7. $a = 26$ ft.; $c = 170$ ft.
8. $c = 122$ ft.; $a = 120$ ft.
9. $a = 240$ yd.; $c = 267$ yd.
10. $c = 325$ ft.; $a = 165$ ft.

Find answers correct to nearest hundredth:

SET 3b

Find c if

1. $a = 12$ ft.; $b = 10$ ft.
2. $a = 23$ in.; $b = 16$ in.
3. $b = 50$ ft.; $a = 50$ ft.
4. $b = 64$ yd.; $a = 53$ yd.
5. $a = 100$ ft.; $b = 125$ ft.

SET 4b

Find a if

1. $c = 15$ in.; $b = 10$ in.
2. $c = 26$ ft.; $b = 14$ ft.
3. $b = 59$ yd.; $c = 81$ yd.
4. $b = 34$ ft.; $c = 40$ ft.
5. $c = 75$ ft.; $b = 65$ ft.

SET 5b

Find b if

1. $c = 18$ in.; $a = 16$ in.
2. $c = 31$ ft.; $a = 20$ ft.
3. $a = 48$ yd.; $c = 65$ yd.
4. $a = 60$ ft.; $c = 78$ ft.
5. $c = 84$ in.; $a = 69$ in.

SET 6

1. Find the hypotenuse of a right triangle if the altitude is 10 inches and the base is 24 inches.

2. Find the diagonal of a rectangle if the altitude is 56 inches and the base is 33 inches.

3. An empty lot is 100 feet long and 50 feet wide. Find the distance a boy walks if he crosses the lot diagonally from one corner to another.

4. How high up on a wall does a 13-foot ladder reach if the foot of the ladder is 5 feet from the wall?

5. Under baseball regulations, the distance between bases is 90 feet. What is the straight-line distance from second base to home plate?

6. A boat leaves a port, sailing 10 miles due east and then 16 miles due north. How far away from the port is the boat?

7. A swimming pool is 80 feet long and 30 feet wide. How many feet does a boy save by swimming diagonally across the pool instead of swimming the length and then the width of the pool?

8. Two telegraph poles, 32 feet and 39 feet high respectively, are 80 feet apart. How long is the wire from the top of one pole to the top of the second pole?

9. How much wire must be used to hold a 16-foot pole if the wire is attached to the pole, one foot below the top, and to the ground 8 feet from the foot of the pole?

10. A boy lets out 100 feet of string in flying a kite. The distance from a point on the ground directly under the kite to where the boy stands is 60 feet. If the boy holds the string 4 feet from the ground, how high is the kite?

EXERCISE 114

Tangent Ratio

I. Aim: To solve examples and word problems by the tangent ratio.

II. Procedure

1. To find the trigonometric value of the tangent of a given angle.
   a) If the angle is in degrees,
      (1) Look in the degree column of the table of trigonometric values for the given number of degrees. (See page 293.)
      (2) Then find the corresponding value in the tangent column.
   b) If the angle is in degrees and minutes (see sample solution 2),
      (1) Look in the degree column for the given number of degrees.
      (2) Then find the corresponding value in the tangent column.
      (3) Also find the trigonometric value of the next higher degree.
      (4) Find the difference between the above two trigonometric values (steps 2 and 3).
      (5) Find what part of 60 minutes is the given number of minutes.
      (6) Multiply this fraction (step 5) by the difference between the two trigonometric values (step 4).
      (7) Add this answer to the trigonometric value of the given number of degrees (step 2) to get final answer.

2. To find the angle when the trigonometric value of the tangent of the angle is given.
   a) If the given value is in the table,
      (1) Look for the given value in the column headed "tangent."
      (2) Find the corresponding angle in the degree column.
   b) If the given value is not in the table (see sample solution 4),
      (1) Find in the tangent column the two trigonometric values between which the given value is located,
      (2) Find the corresponding degrees of the two trigonometric values.
      (3) Find the difference between the two trigonometric values.
      (4) Subtract the smaller of the two trigonometric values from the given value.
      (5) Make a fraction in which answer in step 4 is the numerator and the answer in step 3 is the denominator.
      (6) Multiply this fraction by 60 to find the number of minutes.
      (7) Then write the number of degrees corresponding to the smaller tangent value (see step 2), and the number of minutes found in step 6 as the angle in question.

3. To solve examples and word problems.
   Follow the procedure outlined in exercise 113.

III. Sample Solutions

1. Find the value of tan 53°.
   $$\tan 53° = 1.3270$$
   Answer, 1.3270

2. Find the value of tan 31°45′.

tan 32°	= .6249	tan 31°	= .6009
tan 31°	= .6009	¾ × .0240	= .0180
difference	.0240	tan 31°45′	= .6189

$$\frac{45}{60} = \frac{3}{4} \times .0240 = .0180$$

Answer, .6189

3. Find angle B if tan $B = .8693$.

$$\tan 41° = .8693$$

Answer, $B = 41°$

4. Find angle A if tan $A = 4.8146$.

tan 79°	= 5.1446	tan A	= 4.8146
tan 78°	= 4.7046	tan 78°	= 4.7046
difference	.4400	difference	.1100

$$\frac{.1100}{.4400} = \frac{1}{4} \times 60' = 15'$$

Answer, $A = 78°15'$

5. Find side a if $A = 64°$ and $b = 125$ ft.

$A = 64°$

$a = ?$

$b = 125$ ft.

$$\tan A = \frac{a}{b}$$

$$\tan 64° = \frac{a}{125}$$

$$2.0503 = \frac{a}{125}$$

$$256.2875 \text{ ft.} = a$$

$$a = 256.2875 \text{ ft.}$$

Answer, $a = 256.2875$ ft.

```
      2.0503
    × 125
    102515
    41006
   20503
  256.2875
```

6. Find side a if $B = 22°$ and $b = 80.8$ ft.

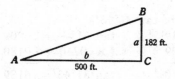

$B = 22°$

$a = ?$

$b = 80.8$ ft.

Solution 1

$$\tan B = \frac{b}{a}$$

$$\tan 22° = \frac{80.8}{a}$$

$$.404 = \frac{80.8}{a}$$

$$.404a = 80.8$$

$$a = 200 \text{ ft.}$$

Answer, 200 ft.

Solution 2

$A = 90° - B$

$A = 90° - 22°$

$A = 68°$

$$\tan A = \frac{a}{b}$$

$$\tan 68° = \frac{a}{80.8}$$

$$2.4751 = \frac{a}{80.8}$$

$$199.98808 = a$$

$$a = 200 \text{ ft.}$$

7. Find angle A if $a = 182$ ft. and $b = 500$ ft.

$A = ?$

$a = 182$ ft.

$b = 500$ ft.

$$\tan A = \frac{a}{b}$$

$$\tan A = \frac{182}{500}$$

$$\tan A = .3640$$

$$A = 20°$$

Answer, $A = 20°$

```
        .3640
 500)182.0000
     1500
     3200
     3000
      2000
      2000
```

DIAGNOSTIC TEST

Solve the following problems, using the table of trigonometric values on page 293:

1. Find the value of tan 32°.
2. Find the value of tan 64°30′.
3. Find angle A if tan $A = .4245$.
4. Find angle B if tan $B = 1.5852$.

In the right triangle ABC,

5. Find side a if angle $A = 20°$ and side $b = 50$ feet.
6. Find side b if angle $B = 53°$ and side $a = 200$ feet.
7. Find side b if angle $A = 29°$ and side $a = 25$ inches.
8. Find side a if angle $B = 68°$ and side $b = 150$ yards.
9. Find angle A if side $a = 132.7$ feet and side $b = 100$ feet.
10. Find angle B if side $a = 500$ feet and side $b = 404.9$ feet.
11. A lighthouse is 200 feet high. The angle of elevation of its top as viewed from a ship at sea is 15°. How far from the base of the lighthouse is the ship?

Related Practice Examples

Solve the following problems using the table of trigonometric values on page 293:

SET 1

Find the value of

1. tan 42°
2. tan 30°
3. tan 17°
4. tan 55°
5. tan 84°
6. tan 8°
7. tan 45°
8. tan 27°
9. tan 64°
10. tan 73°

SET 2

Find the value of

1. tan 27°30′
2. tan 67°30′
3. tan 51°15′
4. tan 9°15′
5. tan 82°45′
6. tan 34°45′
7. tan 42°20′
8. tan 12°10′
9. tan 85°50′
10. tan 61°25′

SET 3

Find angle A if

1. tan $A = 1.3764$
2. tan $A = .9004$
3. tan $A = .2867$
4. tan $A = 1.2799$
5. tan $A = 4.0108$
6. tan $A = .1405$
7. tan $A = 8.1443$
8. tan $A = .7265$
9. tan $A = 3.2709$
10. tan $A = 1.0000$

SET 4

Find angle B if

1. tan $B = .8542$
2. tan $B = .2962$
3. tan $B = 1.6323$
4. tan $B = .2555$
5. tan $B = 3.1260$
6. tan $B = .9408$
7. tan $B = 2.5726$
8. tan $B = .6049$
9. tan $B = 1.2649$
10. tan $B = 1.0540$

In the right triangle ABC,

SET 5

Find side a if

1. $A = 45°$; $b = 25$ ft.
2. $A = 61°$; $b = 50$ ft.
3. $A = 49°$; $b = 100$ ft.
4. $A = 20°$; $b = 75$ ft.
5. $A = 35°$; $b = 200$ ft.
6. $A = 66°$; $b = 150$ yd.
7. $A = 57°$; $b = 1000$ ft.
8. $A = 74°$; $b = 18$ in.
9. $A = 12°30′$; $b = 20$ in.
10. $A = 58°45′$; $b = 500$ yd.

SET 6

Find side b if

1. $B = 25°$; $a = 10$ mi.
2. $B = 60°$; $a = 30$ in.
3. $B = 31°$; $a = 25$ ft.
4. $B = 75°$; $a = 150$ ft.
5. $B = 5°$; $a = 40$ yd.
6. $B = 81°$; $a = 75$ ft.
7. $B = 47°$; $a = 50$ yd.
8. $B = 16°$; $a = 32$ ft.
9. $B = 23°30′$; $a = 80$ yd.
10. $B = 62°15′$; $a = 400$ ft.

SET 7

Find side b if

1. $A = 35°$; $a = 50$ in.
2. $A = 18°$; $a = 200$ yd.
3. $A = 74°$; $a = 75$ ft.
4. $A = 43°$; $a = 14$ in.
5. $A = 29°$; $a = 100$ ft.
6. $A = 56°$; $a = 10$ mi.
7. $A = 23°$; $a = 320$ ft.
8. $A = 82°$; $a = 270$ ft.
9. $A = 41°20′$; $a = 60$ in.
10. $A = 69°45′$; $a = 1000$ yd.

In the right triangle ABC,

SET 8	SET·9	SET 10
Find side a if	Find the angle A if	Find angle B if

SET 8	SET 9	SET 10
1. $B=39°$; $b=30$ ft.	1. $a=3.64$ ft.; $b=10$ ft.	1. $a=30$ in.; $b=7.479$ in.
2. $B=48°$; $b=100$ yd.	2. $a=82.012$ ft.; $b=40$ ft.	2. $a=350$ ft.; $b=141.4$ ft.
3. $B=14°$; $b=40$ in.	3. $a=373.21$ yd.; $b=100$ yd.	3. $a=500$ yd.; $b=902$ yd.
4. $B=22°$; $b=75$ ft.	4. $a=9.72$ in.; $b=50$ in.	4. $a=750$ ft.; $b=3008.1$ ft.
5. $B=81°$; $b=160$ ft.	5. $a=124.98$ ft.; $b=200$ ft.	5. $a=450$ yd.; $b=405.18$ yd.
6. $B=67°$; $b=20$ mi.	6. $a=404.9$ yd.; $b=500$ yd.	6. $a=340$ ft.; $b=340$ ft.
7. $B=52°$; $b=65$ ft.	7. $a=1327$ ft.; $b=1000$ ft.	7. $a=1500$ ft.; $b=974.1$ ft.
8. $B=4°$; $b=90$ in.	8. $a=144.97$ mi.; $b=140$ mi.	8. $a=2000$ ft.; $b=2856.2$ ft.
9. $B=18°20'$; $b=300$ ft.	9. $a=18.387$ mi.; $b=30$ mi.	9. $a=200$ ft.; $b=189.82$ ft.
10. $B=56°10'$; $b=750$ yd.	10. $a=1231.15$ ft.; $b=250$ ft.	10. $a=1000$ yd.; $b=2081.7$ yd.

SET 11

1. At a point 175 feet from the foot of a building the angle of elevation of the top is 60°. How high is the building?

2. Find the height of a flagpole if, at a point 200 feet from the foot of the pole, the angle of elevation of the top is 52°.

3. A lighthouse is 120 feet high. The angle of elevation of its top as viewed from a ship at sea is 36°30′. How far from the base of the lighthouse is the ship?

4. A chimney casts a shadow 62 feet when the angle of the sun is 41°45′. How high is the chimney?

5. The base of a rectangle is 23 inches. The diagonal makes an angle of 35° with the base. Find the altitude of the rectangle.

6. A building is 80 feet high. The angle of depression of a car in the street as viewed from the top of the building is 67°. How far is the car from the base of the building?

7. As viewed from a cliff, the angle of depression of a boat at sea is 29°. If the cliff is 180 feet above the river, how far is the boat from the foot of the cliff?

8. An airplane has an altitude of 1,200 feet when it is directly above point C. If the navigator of the airplane at that point finds that the angle of depression of a distant airport is 19°15′, how far is point C from the airport?

9. A road rises 24 feet in a level distance of 240 feet. Find the angle of elevation of the road.

10. What is the angle of elevation of the sun when a post, 8 feet high, casts a shadow 5 feet?

EXERCISE 115
Sine Ratio

I. Aim: To solve examples and word problems by the sine ratio.

II. Procedure

Follow the general principles outlined in exercise 114. However, use the trigonometric values of the sine column instead of those of the tangent column.

III. Sample Solutions

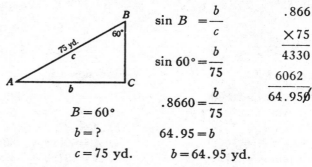

1. Find side a if $A = 74°$ and $c = 50$ ft.

$$\sin A = \frac{a}{c}$$

$$\sin 74° = \frac{a}{50}$$

$$.9613 = \frac{a}{50}$$

$$48.065 = a$$

$A = 74°$

$a = ?$

$c = 50$ ft.

$$\begin{array}{r} .9613 \\ \times 50 \\ \hline 48.0650 \end{array}$$

$a = 48.065$ ft.

Answer, $a = 48.065$ ft.

2. Find side b if $B = 60°$ and $c = 75$ yd.

$$\sin B = \frac{b}{c}$$

$$\sin 60° = \frac{b}{75}$$

$$.8660 = \frac{b}{75}$$

$$64.95 = b$$

$B = 60°$

$b = ?$

$c = 75$ yd.

$$\begin{array}{r} .866 \\ \times 75 \\ \hline 4330 \\ 6062 \\ \hline 64.950 \end{array}$$

$b = 64.95$ yd.

Answer, $b = 64.95$ yd.

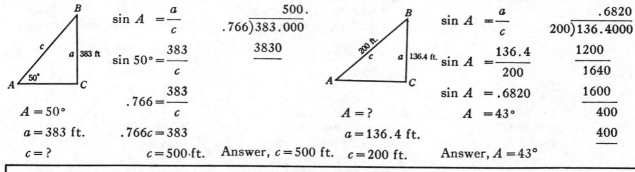

3. Find c if $A = 50°$ and $a = 383$ ft.

$$\sin A = \frac{a}{c}$$

$$\sin 50° = \frac{383}{c}$$

$$.766 = \frac{383}{c}$$

$$.766c = 383$$

$A = 50°$

$a = 383$ ft.

$c = ?$

$$\begin{array}{r} 500. \\ .766)\overline{383.000} \\ 3830 \\ \hline \end{array}$$

$c = 500$ ft. Answer, $c = 500$ ft.

4. Find angle A if $a = 136.4$ ft. and $c = 200$ ft.

$$\sin A = \frac{a}{c}$$

$$\sin A = \frac{136.4}{200}$$

$$\sin A = .6820$$

$$A = 43°$$

$A = ?$

$a = 136.4$ ft.

$c = 200$ ft.

$$\begin{array}{r} .6820 \\ 200)\overline{136.4000} \\ 1200 \\ \hline 1640 \\ 1600 \\ \hline 400 \\ 400 \\ \hline \end{array}$$

Answer, $A = 43°$

DIAGNOSTIC TEST

Solve the following problems using the table of trigonometric values on page 293:

1. Find the value of sin 43°.
2. Find the value of sin 74°15′.
3. Find angle B if $\sin B = .8572$.
4. Find angle A if $\sin A = .3665$.

In the right triangle ABC,
5. Find side a if angle $A = 32°$ and side $c = 20$ ft.
6. Find side b if angle $B = 69°$ and side $c = 75$ ft.
7. Find side b if angle $A = 47°$ and side $c = 130$ yd.
8. Find side a if angle $B = 16°$ and side $c = 10$ mi.
9. Find side c if angle $A = 20°$ and side $a = 342$ yd.
10. Find side c if angle $B = 66°$ and side $b = 1827$ ft.
11. Find angle A if side $a = 424$ ft. and side $c = 500$ ft.
12. Find angle B if side $b = 45$ yd. and side $c = 200$ yd.
13. How high is a kite if the string makes an angle of 48° with the ground and 200 feet of string is let out?

Related Practice Examples

Solve the following problems using the table of trigonometric values on page 293:

SET 1	SET 2	SET 3
Find the value of	Find the value of	Find angle B if

1. sin 60°	6. sin 41°	1. sin 42°30′	6. sin 71°10′	1. sin B = .9511	6. sin B = .7660
2. sin 36°	7. sin 30°	2. sin 18°30′	7. sin 53°20′	2. sin B = .6018	7. sin B = .9272
3. sin 74°	8. sin 24°	3. sin 22°45′	8. sin 32°50′	3. sin B = .8480	8. sin B = .1908
4. sin 5°	9. sin 57°	4. sin 65°15′	9. sin 14°12′	4. sin B = .4067	9. sin B = .4848
5. sin 52°	10. sin 86°	5. sin 37°40′	10. sin 47°36′	5. sin B = .0698	10. sin B = .9986

In the right triangle ABC,

SET 4	SET 5	SET 6
Find angle A if	Find side a if	Find side b if
1. sin A = .1822	1. A = 30°; c = 20 ft.	1. B = 20°; c = 50 yd.
2. sin A = .9170	2. A = 18°; c = 50 ft.	2. B = 56°; c = 30 ft.
3. sin A = .7518	3. A = 43°; c = 100 ft.	3. B = 13°; c = 20 mi.
4. sin A = .3638	4. A = 60°; c = 80 yd.	4. B = 35°; c = 75 ft.
5. sin A = .9524	5. A = 83°; c = 32 mi.	5. B = 81°; c = 400 ft.
6. sin A = .9824	6. A = 66°; c = 500 yd.	6. B = 50°; c = 340 yd.
7. sin A = .2868	7. A = 5°; c = 25 ft.	7. B = 11°; c = 1000 yd.
8. sin A = .0756	8. A = 24°; c = 1000 ft.	8. B = 74°; c = 60 mi.
9. sin A = .9979	9. A = 33°30′; c = 100 yd.	9. B = 53°30′; c = 100 ft.
10. sin A = .5892	10. A = 58°15′; c = 45 mi.	10. B = 86°24′; c = 200 yd.

SET 7	SET 8	SET 9
Find side b if	Find side a if	Find side c if
1. A = 72°; c = 30 ft.	1. B = 77°; c = 10 in.	1. A = 13°; a = 450 ft.
2. A = 27°; c = 50 yd.	2. B = 36°; c = 30 ft.	2. A = 30°; a = 100 ft.
3. A = 45°; c = 75 ft.	3. B = 47°; c = 55 ft.	3. A = 56°; a = 829 yd.
4. A = 15°; c = 300 ft.	4. B = 21°; c = 1000 ft.	4. A = 31°; a = 103 ft.
5. A = 32°; c = 500 yd.	5. B = 68°; c = 200 yd.	5. A = 58°; a = 424 ft.
6. A = 66°; c = 100 mi.	6. B = 5°; c = 175 ft.	6. A = 24°; a = 50 mi.
7. A = 54°; c = 83 ft.	7. B = 54°; c = 150 mi.	7. A = 67°; a = 150 ft.
8. A = 39°; c = 750 yd.	8. B = 16°; c = 500 ft.	8. A = 86°; a = 200 yd.
9. A = 14°30 ; c = 500 ft.	9. B = 63°30′; c = 600 ft.	9. A = 30°30′; a = 100 ft.
10. A = 41°15′; c = 250 yd.	10. B = 23°12′; c = 2000 ft.	10. A = 41°30′; a = 500 yd.

SET 10	SET 11	SET 12
Find side c if	Find angle A if	Find angle B if
1. B = 43°; b = 341 ft.	1. a = 20 ft.; c = 40 ft.	1. b = 32 ft.; c = 64 ft.
2. B = 60°; b = 866 yd.	2. a = 90 yd.; c = 400 yd.	2. b = 433 yd.; c = 500 yd.
3. B = 52°; b = 394 yd.	3. a = 103 ft.; c = 200 ft.	3. b = 829 ft.; c = 1000 ft.
4. B = 27°; b = 227 ft.	4. a = 454 yd.; c = 1000 yd.	4. b = 1023 yd.; c = 1500 yd.
5. B = 18°; b = 618 yd.	5. a = 171 ft.; c = 500 ft.	5. b = 41.2 ft.; c = 80 ft.
6. B = 57°; b = 100 ft.	6. a = 1272 ft.; c = 1500 ft.	6. b = 39.4 ft.; c = 50 ft.
7. B = 84°; b = 400 yd.	7. a = 34.1 ft ; c = 50 ft.	7. b = 61.8 mi.; c = 200 mi.
8. B = 12°; b = 225 ft.	8. a = 89.1 ft.; c = 1000 ft.	8. b = 53.46 ft.; c = 60 ft.
9. B = 29°30′; b = 900 yd.	9. a = 25 in.; c = 30 in.	9. b = 8 in.; c = 10 in.
10. B = 66°18′; b = 1000 ft.	10. a = 12 mi.; c = 28 mi.	10. b = 11 mi.; c = 16 mi.

SET 13

1. A 40-foot ladder makes an angle of 78° with the ground. How far up the side of the building does it reach?
2. How high is a kite if 180 feet of string is let out and the string makes an angle of 47° with the ground?
3. From the top of a cliff 200 feet high, the angle of depression of a boat is 54°. Find the distance from the boat to the top of the cliff.
4. The angle of elevation of a bridge approach is 5°. How high above the street level is an automobile after it is driven .3 of a mile up the approach roadway?
5. A 400-foot ramp rises a vertical distance of 60 feet at its peak. Find the angle of elevation of the ramp.

EXERCISE 116

Cosine Ratio

I. Aim: To solve examples and word problems by the cosine ratio.

II. Procedure

1. Follow the general principles outlined in exercise 114 but with the following exceptions:
   a) Use the trigonometric values of the cosine column instead of those of the tangent column.
   b) When interpolating:
      (1) In finding the trigonometric value of the cosine of an angle given in degrees and minutes (see sample solution 1), subtract the cosine value of the minutes from the cosine value of the degrees to get the answer. This replaces step 7 under 1 b) of procedure in Exercise 114.
      (2) In finding the angle if the given cosine value is not in the table (see sample solution 2), subtract the given value from the larger trigonometric value. This replaces step 4 under 2 b) of procedure in Exercise 114.

III. Sample Solutions

1. Find the value of cos 4°30′

cos 4° = .9976	cos 4° = .9976
cos 5° = .9962	½ × .0014 = .0007
difference .0014	cos 4°30′ = .9969

   $$\frac{30}{60} = \frac{1}{2} \times .0014 = .0007$$

   Answer, .9969

2. Find angle A if cos A = .6665

cos 48° = .6691	cos 48° = .6691
cos 49° = .6561	cos A = .6665
difference .0130	difference .0026

   $$\frac{.0026}{.0130} = \frac{1}{5} \times 60' = 12'$$

   Answer, $A = 48°12′$

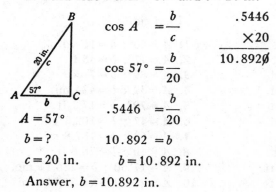

3. Find side b if $A = 57°$ and $c = 20$ in.

   $A = 57°$
   $b = ?$
   $c = 20$ in.

   $$\cos A = \frac{b}{c}$$
   $$\cos 57° = \frac{b}{20}$$
   $$.5446 = \frac{b}{20}$$
   $$10.892 = b$$
   $$b = 10.892 \text{ in.}$$

   $$\begin{array}{r} .5446 \\ \times 20 \\ \hline 10.8920 \end{array}$$

   Answer, $b = 10.892$ in.

4. Find side a if $B = 7°$ and $c = 40$ yd.

   $B = 7°$
   $a = ?$
   $c = 40$ yd.

   $$\cos B = \frac{a}{c}$$
   $$\cos 7° = \frac{a}{40}$$
   $$.9925 = \frac{a}{40}$$
   $$39.7 = a$$
   $$a = 39.7 \text{ yd.}$$

   $$\begin{array}{r} .9925 \\ \times 40 \\ \hline 39.7000 \end{array}$$

   Answer, $a = 39.7$ yd.

DIAGNOSTIC TEST

Solve the following problems using the table of trigonometric values on page 293:

1. Find the value of cos 26°.
2. Find the value of cos 34°45′.
3. Find angle A if cos $A = .5736$.
4. Find angle B if cos $B = .7518$.

In the right triangle ABC,

5. Find side b if angle $A = 55°$ and side $c = 60$ ft.
6. Find side a if angle $B = 17°$ and side $c = 25$ yd.
7. Find side c if angle $A = 36°$ and side $b = 161.8$ ft.
8. Find side c if angle $B = 77°$ and side $a = 450$ mi.
9. Find angle A if side $b = 227$ ft. and $c = 500$ ft.
10. Find angle B if side $a = 70$ yd. and $c = 4000$ yd.
11. The angle of elevation of a ramp is 6°. How long is the ramp if its horizontal distance is 300 ft.?

Related Practice Examples

Solve the following problems using the table of trigonometric values on page 293:

SET 1
Find the value of

1. cos 72°	6. cos 47°
2. cos 14°	7. cos 22°
3. cos 86°	8. cos 64°
4. cos 31°	9. cos 50°
5. cos 5°	10. cos 29°

SET 2
Find the value of

1. cos 24°30′	6. cos 42°40′
2. cos 63°30′	7. cos 56°12′
3. cos 34°15′	8. cos 17°48′
4. cos 75°45′	9. cos 69°50′
5. cos 6°20′	10. cos 38°24′

SET 3
Find angle A if

1. cos $A = .7771$	6. cos $A = .3256$
2. cos $A = .2419$	7. cos $A = .0872$
3. cos $A = .5878$	8. cos $A = .7314$
4. cos $A = .9205$	9. cos $A = .6691$
5. cos $A = .9976$	10. cos $A = .4384$

SET 4
Find angle B if

1. cos $B = .7132$	6. cos $B = .8962$
2. cos $B = .3543$	7. cos $B = .9977$
3. cos $B = .1779$	8. cos $B = .4514$
4. cos $B = .8526$	9. cos $B = .9603$
5. cos $B = .1103$	10. cos $B = .5962$

In the right triangle ABC,

SET 5
Find side b if

1. $A = 65°$; $c = 30$ ft.
2. $A = 28°$; $c = 80$ yd.
3. $A = 72°$; $c = 100$ ft.
4. $A = 49°$; $c = 16$ in.
5. $A = 33°$; $c = 200$ yd.
6. $A = 16°$; $c = 35$ mi.
7. $A = 58°$; $c = 500$ yd.
8. $A = 82°$; $c = 150$ ft.
9. $A = 38°30′$; $c = 300$ ft.
10. $A = 51°36′$; $c = 75$ yd.

SET 6
Find side a if

1. $B = 40°$; $c = 50$ ft.
2. $B = 35°$; $c = 25$ ft.
3. $B = 67°$; $c = 75$ yd.
4. $B = 81°$; $c = 100$ yd.
5. $B = 4°$; $c = 250$ yd.
6. $B = 23°$; $c = 425$ mi.
7. $B = 72°$; $c = 175$ ft.
8. $B = 54°$; $c = 1000$ yd.
9. $B = 46°15′$; $c = 200$ ft.
10. $B = 25°40′$; $c = 120$ ft.

SET 7
Find side c if

1. $A = 60°$; $b = 16$ yd.
2. $A = 77°$; $b = 45$ ft.
3. $A = 89°$; $b = 7$ yd.
4. $A = 32°$; $b = 424$ mi.
5. $A = 70°$; $b = 17.1$ ft.
6. $A = 47°$; $b = 102.3$ yd.
7. $A = 62°$; $b = 187.8$ mi.
8. $A = 40°$; $b = 76.6$ ft.
9. $A = 17°30′$; $b = 286.11$ mo.
10. $A = 23°12′$; $b = 36.764$ mi.

SET 8

Find side c if

1. $B = 7°$; $a = 397$ ft.
2. $B = 59°$; $a = 515$ ft.
3. $B = 47°$; $a = 341$ ft.
4. $B = 70°$; $a = 51.3$ mi.
5. $B = 63°$; $a = 113.5$ yd.
6. $B = 24°$; $a = 182.7$ ft.
7. $B = 84°$; $a = 2.09$ mi.
8. $B = 36°$; $a = 24.27$ yd.
9. $B = 56°30'$; $a = 27.595$ mi.
10. $B = 29°30'$; $a = 87.03$ ft.

SET 9

Find angle A if

1. $b = 18$ in.; $c = 36$ in.
2. $b = 90$ ft.; $c = 400$ ft.
3. $b = 227$ yd.; $c = 500$ yd.
4. $b = 829$ ft.; $c = 1000$ ft.
5. $b = 1149$ yd.; $c = 1500$ yd.
6. $b = 684$ yd.; $c = 2000$ yd.
7. $b = 412$ mi.; $c = 800$ mi.
8. $b = 43.3$ mi.; $c = 50$ mi.
9. $b = 8$ in.; $c = 10$ in.
10. $b = 5$ ft.; $c = 13$ ft.

SET 10

Find angle B if

1. $a = 341$ ft.; $c = 500$ ft.
2. $a = 309$ yd.; $c = 1000$ yd.
3. $a = 189.1$ mi.; $c = 200$ mi.
4. $a = 248$ yd.; $c = 496$ yd.
5. $a = 197$ mi.; $c = 250$ mi.
6. $a = 51.3$ ft.; $c = 150$ ft.
7. $a = 40.45$ mi.; $c = 50$ mi.
8. $a = 47.541$ yd.; $c = 65$ yd.
9. $a = 18$ in.; $c = 30$ in.
10. $a = 36$ ft.; $c = 39$ ft.

SET 11

1. The base of a right triangle is 20 inches and the angle opposite the altitude is 43°. Find the hypotenuse.
2. Find the distance from a point on the ground directly under a kite to where the boy who is flying it stands. 250 feet of string has been let out and the string makes an angle of 53° with the ground.
3. A boat sails 75 miles on a course E 32° N. Find how far east it has sailed.
4. The angle of elevation of a ramp is 7°. How long is the ramp if its horizontal distance is 220 feet?
5. A 30-foot ladder leans against a wall and its foot is 8 feet from the wall. What is the angle formed by the ladder and the wall if the angle between the ladder and the ground is first determined?

TABLE OF SQUARES AND SQUARE ROOTS

Number	Square	Square Root	Number	Square	Square Root	Number	Square	Square Root	Number	Square	Square Root	Number	Square	Square Root
1	1	1.000	31	961	5.568	61	3,721	7.810	91	8,281	9.539	121	14,641	11.000
2	4	1.414	32	1,024	5.657	62	3,844	7.874	92	8,464	9.592	122	14,884	11.045
3	9	1.732	33	1,089	5.745	63	3,969	7.937	93	8,649	9.644	123	15,129	11.091
4	16	2.000	34	1,156	5.831	64	4,096	8.000	94	8,836	9.695	124	15,376	11.136
5	25	2.236	35	1,225	5.916	65	4,225	8.062	95	9,025	9.747	125	15,625	11.180
6	36	2.449	36	1,296	6.000	66	4,356	8.124	96	9,216	9.798	126	15,876	11.225
7	49	2.646	37	1,369	6.083	67	4,489	8.185	97	9,409	9.849	127	16,129	11.269
8	64	2.828	38	1,444	6.164	68	4,624	8.246	98	9,604	9.899	128	16,384	11.314
9	81	3.000	39	1,521	6.245	69	4,761	8.307	99	9,801	9.950	129	16,641	11.358
10	100	3.162	40	1,600	6.325	70	4,900	8.367	100	10,000	10.000	130	16,900	11.402
11	121	3.317	41	1,681	6.403	71	5,041	8.426	101	10,201	10.050	131	17,161	11.446
12	144	3.464	42	1,764	6.481	72	5,184	8.485	102	10,404	10.100	132	17,424	11.489
13	169	3.606	43	1,849	6.557	73	5,329	8.544	103	10,609	10.149	133	17,689	11.533
14	196	3.742	44	1,936	6.633	74	5,476	8.602	104	10,816	10.198	134	17,956	11.576
15	225	3.873	45	2,025	6.708	75	5,625	8.660	105	11,025	10.247	135	18,225	11.619
16	256	4.000	46	2,116	6.782	76	5,776	8.718	106	11,236	10.296	136	18,496	11.662
17	289	4.123	47	2,209	6.856	77	5,929	8.775	107	11,449	10.344	137	18,769	11.705
18	324	4.243	48	2,304	6.928	78	6,084	8.832	108	11,664	10.392	138	19,044	11.747
19	361	4.359	49	2,401	7.000	79	6,241	8.888	109	11,881	10.440	139	19,321	11.790
20	400	4.472	50	2,500	7.071	80	6,400	8.944	110	12,100	10.488	140	19,600	11.832
21	441	4.583	51	2,601	7.141	81	6,561	9.000	111	12,321	10.536	141	19,881	11.874
22	484	4.690	52	2,704	7.211	82	6,724	9.055	112	12,544	10.583	142	20,164	11.916
23	529	4.796	53	2,809	7.280	83	6,889	9.110	113	12,769	10.630	143	20,449	11.958
24	576	4.899	54	2,916	7.348	84	7,056	9.165	114	12,996	10.677	144	20,736	12.000
25	625	5.000	55	3,025	7.416	85	7,225	9.220	115	13,225	10.724	145	21,025	12.042
26	676	5.099	56	3,136	7.483	86	7,396	9.274	116	13,456	10.770	146	21,316	12.083
27	729	5.196	57	3,249	7.550	87	7,569	9.327	117	13,689	10.817	147	21,609	12.124
28	784	5.292	58	3,364	7.616	88	7,744	9.381	118	13,924	10.863	148	21,904	12.166
29	841	5.385	59	3,481	7.681	89	7,921	9.434	119	14,161	10.909	149	22,201	12.207
30	900	5.477	60	3,600	7.746	90	8,100	9.487	120	14,400	10.954	150	22,500	12.247

REVIEW OF UNIT SEVENTEEN

In the right triangle ABC, (See page 279)

1. a) Find angle A if angle $B=48°$ b) Find angle B if angle $A=73°\ 15'$

Using the table of trigonometric values on page 293 when necessary, find:

2. The value of a) tan 57° b) sin 15° c) cos 81° d) tan 9° 45′ e) cos 26° 30′ f) sin 70° 20′.
3. Angle A if $\tan A=.5543$ b) Angle B if $\sin B=.7986$ c) Angle A if $\cos A=.7193$.
4. a) Angle B if $\tan A=4.0108$ b) Angle A if $\sin B=.1908$ c) Angle A if $\cos B=.0872$.
5. Side c if side $a=48$ ft. and side $b=55$ ft.
6. Side b if side $a=33$ yd. and side $c=65$ yd.
7. Side a if side $c=53$ mi. and side $b=28$ mi.
8. Side a if angle $A=40°$ and side $b=100$ ft.
9. Side b if angle $A=62°$ and side $a=50$ yd.
10. Angle B if side $a=91$ mi. and side $b=250$ mi.
11. Side b if angle $B=19°$ and side $c=200$ ft.
12. Side c if angle $A=54°$ and side $a=30$ mi.
13. Angle A if side $a=63$ ft. and side $c=126$ ft.
14. Side b if angle $A=73°$ and side $c=400$ yd.
15. An airplane, flying 180 miles from airport M due east to airport N, drifts off its course in a straight line and is 75 miles due north of airport N. What distance did the airplane actually fly?
16. The light from a searchlight is observed on a cloud at a horizontal distance of 1,600 feet. If the angle of elevation is 70°, what is the height of the cloud?

CUMULATIVE ALGEBRA REVIEW

1. Express as a formula: The area of the surface of a sphere (S) is equal to four times *Pi* times the square of the radius (r).
2. Divide $8y^3-1$ by $2y+1$.
3. Solve and check: $(a-6)(a-1)=a(a-5)$
4. Solve and check: $18x^2-39x=7$
5. Combine: $\frac{b^2}{4a^2}-\frac{c}{2a}$
6. Solve and check: $\frac{2x+8}{2x+3}+\frac{4x+5}{x+2}=5$
7. Solve and check: $5x-6y=14$, $4x-7y=20$
8. Using formulas $\tan A=\frac{\sin A}{\cos A}$, $\sin A=\frac{a}{c}$, and $\cos A=\frac{b}{c}$, express $\tan A$ in terms of a and b.
9. Find the value of r if $V=8{,}910$, $\pi=\frac{22}{7}$ and $h=35$, using the formula $V=\pi r^2 h$.
10. From the "crow's nest" of a ship, 100 feet above the water, a lifeboat is observed at an angle of depression of 4°. What is the horizontal distance from the ship to the lifeboat?

KEYED ACHIEVEMENT TEST

1. Solve and check: $25n+50(18-n)=800$ ㊱
2. Multiply: $\frac{8m^3-8m}{m^2+6m+5}\cdot\frac{m^2+4m-5}{(m-1)^2}$ (58)
3. Combine: $\frac{2x}{x+y}-\frac{3y}{x-y}+\frac{3y^2}{x^2-y^2}$ (63)
4. Solve and check: $\frac{3x+1}{10}-\frac{x-6}{4}=2$ (67)
5. What is the selling price of a table if it cost \$27 and the profit is 40% of the selling price? ⑬ (75)
6. Transform formula $T=\frac{R}{S_1}+\frac{R}{S_2}$, solving for R. (78)
7. Solve graphically: $4x=8y$, $3x-2y=4$ (82)
8. Find the value r when $S=200$, $l=135$, and $a=5$, using the formula $S=\frac{rl-a}{r-1}$. (79)
9. Solve and check: $\frac{2x+7}{3}=\frac{7y-1}{4}$, $\frac{2x-y}{10}-\frac{x-4y}{12}=\frac{7}{6}$ (85)
10. Simplify and combine: $\sqrt{56}-2\sqrt{160}+12\sqrt{\frac{5}{8}}-4\sqrt{\frac{7}{2}}$ (100)
11. Solve by formula and check: $8x^2-6x-9=0$ (110)
12. A rectangle is 30 inches long and 16 inches wide. What is the length of the diagonal? (113)

In right triangle ABC, find: 13. Side a if side $b=100$ yd. and angle $A=53°$ (114)

14. Side b if side $c=40$ mi. and angle $B=31°$. (115)
15. Side c if side $b=1{,}000$ ft. and angle $A=60°$. (116)

TABLE OF SINES, COSINES, AND TANGENTS

Angle	Sine	Cosine	Tangent	Angle	Sine	Cosine	Tangent
0°	.0000	1.0000	.0000	46°	.7193	.6947	1.0355
1°	.0175	.9998	.0175	47°	.7314	.6820	1.0724
2°	.0349	.9994	.0349	48°	.7431	.6691	1.1106
3°	.0523	.9986	.0524	49°	.7547	.6561	1.1504
4°	.0698	.9976	.0699	50°	.7660	.6428	1.1918
5°	.0872	.9962	.0875	51°	.7771	.6293	1.2349
6°	.1045	.9945	.1051	52°	.7880	.6157	1.2799
7°	.1219	.9925	.1228	53°	.7986	.6018	1.3270
8°	.1392	.9903	.1405	54°	.8090	.5878	1.3764
9°	.1564	.9877	.1584	55°	.8192	.5736	1.4281
10°	.1736	.9848	.1763	56°	.8290	.5592	1.4826
11°	.1908	.9816	.1944	57°	.8387	.5446	1.5399
12°	.2079	.9781	.2126	58°	.8480	.5299	1.6003
13°	.2250	.9744	.2309	59°	.8572	.5150	1.6643
14°	.2419	.9703	.2493	60°	.8660	.5000	1.7321
15°	.2588	.9659	.2679	61°	.8746	.4848	1.8040
16°	.2756	.9613	.2867	62°	.8829	.4695	1.8807
17°	.2924	.9563	.3057	63°	.8910	.4540	1.9626
18°	.3090	.9511	.3249	64°	.8988	.4384	2.0503
19°	.3256	.9455	.3443	65°	.9063	.4226	2.1445
20°	.3420	.9397	.3640	66°	.9135	.4067	2.2460
21°	.3584	.9336	.3839	67°	.9205	.3907	2.3559
22°	.3746	.9272	.4040	68°	.9272	.3746	2.4751
23°	.3907	.9205	.4245	69°	.9336	.3584	2.6051
24°	.4067	.9135	.4452	70°	.9397	.3420	2.7475
25°	.4226	.9063	.4663	71°	.9455	.3256	2.9042
26°	.4384	.8988	.4877	72°	.9511	.3090	3.0777
27°	.4540	.8910	.5095	73°	.9563	.2924	3.2709
28°	.4695	.8829	.5317	74°	.9613	.2756	3.4874
29°	.4848	.8746	.5543	75°	.9659	.2588	3.7321
30°	.5000	.8660	.5774	76°	.9703	.2419	4.0108
31°	.5150	.8572	.6009	77°	.9744	.2250	4.3315
32°	.5299	.8480	.6249	78°	.9781	.2079	4.7046
33°	.5446	.8387	.6494	79°	.9816	.1908	5.1446
34°	.5592	.8290	.6745	80°	.9848	.1736	5.6713
35°	.5736	.8192	.7002	81°	.9877	.1564	6.3138
36°	.5878	.8090	.7265	82°	.9903	.1392	7.1154
37°	.6018	.7986	.7536	83°	.9925	.1219	8.1443
38°	.6157	.7880	.7813	84°	.9945	.1045	9.5144
39°	.6293	.7771	.8098	85°	.9962	.0872	11.4301
40°	.6428	.7660	.8391	86°	.9976	.0698	14.3007
41°	.6561	.7547	.8693	87°	.9986	.0523	19.0811
42°	.6691	.7431	.9004	88°	.9994	.0349	28.6363
43°	.6820	.7314	.9325	89°	.9998	.0175	57.2900
44°	.6947	.7193	.9657	90°	1.0000	.0000	
45°	.7071	.7071	1.0000				

UNIT EIGHTEEN—COORDINATE GEOMETRY— THE STRAIGHT LINE

EXERCISE 117

Slope

When we speak of the slope of a hillside, of a terrace, or of a roof, we think of the incline or slant.

In mathematics we deal with the slope (or slant) of lines. We have found the graph of a linear equation in two variables to be a straight line (see page 214). Slanting lines, when drawn to the right, either rise or fall.

When we move from one point on a line to another point on the line and compare the vertical change to the horizontal change, we are measuring the slope of the line.

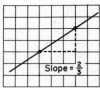

To determine the slope of a straight line directly from the graph, we first count from any point on the line a convenient number of units to the right. Then we count vertically, up (positive direction) if the line slants upward, or down (negative direction) if the line slants downward until we meet the line at a second point. We divide the number of units counted vertically by the number of units counted horizontally to obtain the slope.

The slope of a line is related to the coordinates of the points on the line. We can readily see that the vertical change is the difference between the ordinates (*y*-coordinates) of the two points and the horizontal change is the difference between the corresponding abscissas (*x*-coordinates). Thus,

$$\text{slope} = \frac{\text{difference between } y\text{-coordinates}}{\text{difference between } x\text{-coordinates}}$$

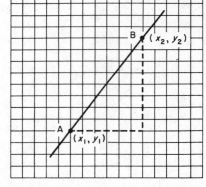

If the coordinates of point A is (x_1, y_1) and of point B is (x_2, y_2), the slope in terms of the coordinates is:

$$\text{slope} = \frac{y_2 - y_1}{x_2 - x_1}$$

To determine the slope of a line from the coordinates of two points on the line, we divide the difference between the ordinates by the difference between the corresponding abscissas. The slope will be the same no matter what two points on the line are selected.

What is the slope of a line through the points:

(1, 5) and (3, 9)?

$y_1 = 5, \quad y_2 = 9, \quad x_1 = 1, \quad x_2 = 3$

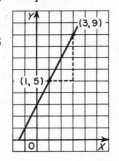

$$\frac{y_2 - y_1}{x_2 - x_1} = \frac{9 - 5}{3 - 1} = \frac{4}{2} = 2$$

slope $= 2$

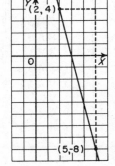

(2, 4) and (5, −8)?

$y_1 = 4, \quad y_2 = -8, \quad x_1 = 2, \quad y_2 = 5$

$$\frac{y_2 - y_1}{x_2 - x_1} = \frac{-8 - 4}{5 - 2} = \frac{-12}{3} = -4$$

slope $= -4$

Notice that the slope is measured by a number; when the line slants upward to the right, the slope is positive; when the line slants downward to the right, the slope is negative. A vertical line has no slope. A horizontal line has a zero slope.

1. Determine the slope of each of the following lines at the right:

2. Draw lines which have the following slopes:

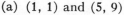

$+4; \quad -3; \quad -5; \quad +6; \quad -2; \quad +1; \quad +\frac{1}{2}; \quad -\frac{3}{4}; \quad +\frac{7}{3}; \quad -\frac{9}{4}$

3. Determine the slope of the line segment if it passes through two points whose coordinates are

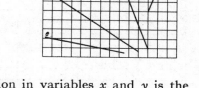

(a) (1, 1) and (5, 9)
(b) (3, 4) and (7, 6)
(c) (2, 7) and (4, 1)
(d) (1, 10) and (5, 2)

(e) (−3, 10) and (4, −4)
(f) (−5, −7) and (3, 5)
(g) (−8, −7) and (−2, −4)
(h) (−6, 8) and (0, −7)

4. Determine the slope of a line segment if its end points are

(a) (2, 10) and (4, 2)
(b) (−5, −1) and (0, 9)

(c) (1, 7) and (4, 5)
(d) (−4, 6) and (8, −3)

The y-form (sometimes called the slope-intercept form) of an equation in variables x and y is the equivalent equation obtained when the original equation is solved for y.

The y-form of the equation $x+y=6$ is $y=6-x$; of $3x+2y=0$ it is $y=-\frac{3}{2}x$; of $3x-4y=8$ it is $y=\dfrac{3x-8}{4}$, or $y=\dfrac{3}{4}x-2$.

Arrange each of the following equations in the y-form:

1. $x+y=15$ **3.** $5x=3y$ **5.** $2x+y=8$ **7.** $4x+6y=3$ **9.** $8x+4y=16$

2. $x-y=7$ **4.** $4x-9y=0$ **6.** $x+7y=10$ **8.** $11x-5y=-10$ **10.** $9x-3y+8=0$

Study of the following graphs will show that the slope of the graph of:

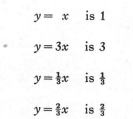

$y=x$ is 1	$y=-x$ is -1
$y=3x$ is 3	$y=-3x$ is -3
$y=\frac{1}{3}x$ is $\frac{1}{3}$	$y=-\frac{1}{3}x$ is $-\frac{1}{3}$
$y=\frac{2}{3}x$ is $\frac{2}{3}$	$y=-\frac{2}{3}x$ is $-\frac{2}{3}$
$y=\frac{3}{2}x$ is $\frac{3}{2}$	$y=-\frac{4}{3}x$ is $-\frac{4}{3}$

and each of the lines rises to the right. The slope is positive.

and each of the lines falls to the right. The slope is negative.

Have you noticed that the slope corresponds to the coefficient of x? It does when the equation is expressed in the y-form.

What is the slope of the line corresponding to each of the following equations?

(a) $y=7x$ (b) $y=-11x$ (c) $y=\frac{5}{6}x$ (d) $y=-\frac{8}{3}x$ (e) $y=\frac{4}{5}x$

EXERCISE 118

Y-Intercept

The y-intercept is the point where the graph crosses the Y-axis.* The ordinate of this point is positive if the point is above the X-axis and negative if the point is below the X-axis. Of course if the point is at the origin, the ordinate is zero.

Examine the following graphs. Note that the slope of each line is the same. The lines are parallel. However, the y-intercepts differ. The following table lists the equations in the y-form, the y-intercepts, and the corresponding y-intercept numbers which represent the related ordinates on the Y-axis.

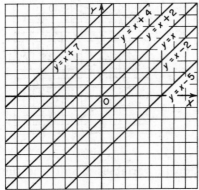

Equation	y-intercept	y-intercept number
$y = x + 7$	$(0,7)$	$+7$
$y = x + 4$	$(0,4)$	$+4$
$y = x + 2$	$(0,2)$	$+2$
$y = x$	$(0,0)$	0
$y = x - 2$	$(0, -2)$	-2
$y = x - 5$	$(0, -5)$	-5

Have you noticed that the y-intercept number in each case corresponds to the constant term (the term without x or y) found in the y form of the equation?

1. Determine the y-intercept number of the graph of each of the following equations without drawing the graph:

(a) $y = x - 1$ (c) $4x + 2y = 8$ (e) $7x - 3y = -6$ (g) $5x - 10y = 20$ (i) $x = -2y - 18$
(b) $2x - y = 12$ (d) $16x = 4y$ (f) $9x + 18y = 12$ (h) $3x + 5y = -2$ (j) $8x - 7y = -21$

2. What are the coordinates of the y-intercept for each of the following?

(a) $y = x - 6$ (b) $3x - 4y = 0$ (c) $4x + 9y = 27$ (d) $x - 8y = -24$ (e) $6x + 3y = -36$

EXERCISE 119

Slope-Intercept

Thus we have shown that for any linear equation in the y-form expressed as $y = mx + b$

(1) the coefficient of x, represented by m, indicates the slope.
(2) the constant term, represented by b, indicates the y-intercept number.

The graph of $y = -2x + 4$ has the slope -2 and y-intercept number $+4$.

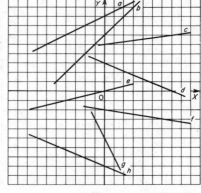

1. Determine the slope and y-intercept number of the graph of each of the following equations without drawing the graph:

(a) $y = -3x + 5$ (e) $8x - 2y = 0$ (i) $x = 6 - 3y$
(b) $y = \frac{1}{2}x - 2$ (f) $6x + 5y = 30$ (j) $7x - 21y = 35$
(c) $y = -7 - 4x$ (g) $3x + 4y = -6$
(d) $x + y = 9$ (h) $10x - 5y = -20$

2. What is the slope, the y-intercept, and the y-intercept number of each of the lines at the right?

* Some mathematicians think of the y-intercept as the distance from the origin to the point where the graph crosses the Y-axis. Thus, they call b in $y = mx + b$ the y-intercept representing this distance measured above the X-axis if positive and below the X-axis if negative.

3. What do graphs of the following equations have in common?

(a) $y = 6x + 3$ $y = 6x - 5$ $y = 6x$

(b) $y = 3x - 4$ $y = \frac{3}{4}x - 4$ $y = -9x - 4$

(c) $y = 5x$ $y = \frac{2}{3}x$ $y = -7x$

4. (a) What is true of all lines having 0 as the slope?

(b) What is true of all lines having 0 as the y-intercept number?

EXERCISE 120

Drawing Graphs

Graphs of linear equations may be drawn by using the slope and the y-intercept as follows:

(1) Express the equation in the form $y = mx + b$.

(2) Using the value of b as the ordinate, locate the y-intercept (point on the Y-axis where the graph will cross).

(3) Use the slope represented by m to locate a second point. Count a convenient number of units from the y-intercept to the right. Then count the required number of units up or down, depending whether the slope is positive or negative.

(4) Draw a line through these two points.

(5) Check graph by finding the coordinates of a third point on the line and substituting values in the the equation. If they satisfy the equation, the graph is correct.

To draw graph of $y = 2x + 3$

(1) $y = 2x + 3$

(2) y-intercept number is 3. Locate point (0, 3).

(3) Slope is $+2$. From point (0, 3). Count 1 unit to right, 2 units up.

(4) Draw line through points (0, 3) and (1, 5).

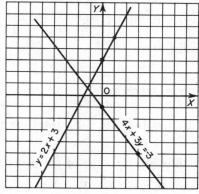

To draw graph of $4x + 3y = -3$

(1) $y = -\frac{4}{3}x - 1$

(2) y-intercept number is -1. Locate point (0, -1).

(3) Slope is $-\frac{4}{3}$. From point (0, -1) count 3 units to right, 4 units down.

(4) Draw line through points (0, -1) and (3, -5).

1. Draw the graphs of lines when the

	(a)	(b)	(c)	(d)	(e)	(f)	(g)	(h)	(i)	(j)
slope is:	$+5$	1	-2	$\frac{1}{2}$	$-\frac{3}{4}$	-4	$-\frac{5}{3}$	$\frac{7}{4}$	0	$\frac{3}{8}$
y-intercept number is:	$+2$	6	3	-1	0	$\frac{1}{2}$	-3	$-\frac{1}{2}$	4	-7

2. Use the slope-intercept method to graph each of the following linear equations:

(a) $y = 5x + 1$

(b) $y = 2x - 4$

(c) $y = -4x + 6$

(d) $y = -\frac{1}{2}x - 3$

(e) $y = -\frac{4}{3}x$

(f) $3x + y = 6$

(g) $x - 3y = 9$

(h) $4x + 2y = 10$

(i) $15x + 3y = -12$

(j) $2x - 4y = 0$

(k) $5x - 6y = 30$

(l) $10x + 8y = 4$

(m) $3x - 2y = -6$

(n) $28x - 7y = 21$

(o) $x = -5y + 10$

A graph of a linear equation may be drawn when the coordinates of a point and the slope are known. First locate the point, use the slope to obtain a second point, then draw a line through these two points.

3. Draw the line that passes through the point

(a) (3, 1) with slope 2

(b) (0, -2) with slope 4

(c) (0, 0) with slope $\frac{1}{2}$

(d) (-3, -4) with slope -1

(e) (2, -1) with slope -5

(f) (4, 5) with slope $-\frac{3}{4}$

(g) (-7, -3) with slope -3

(h) (1, -2) with slope $-\frac{5}{2}$

(i) (-5, 4) with slope $\frac{3}{8}$

EXERCISE 121
Writing Equations

(1) When the slope and y-intercept number are known

Write the equation in the y-form ($y = mx + b$). Substitute the slope for m and y-intercept number for b.

The linear equation of a graph when its slope is -5 and the y-intercept is $+8$ is $y = -5x + 8$.

(2) When the coordinates of two points on the line are known

Suppose (x_1, y_1) and (x_2, y_2) represent the known coordinates of two points on the line and (x, y) represent the coordinates of a third point.

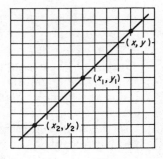

The slope of this line is $\dfrac{y - y_1}{x - x_1}$, or $\dfrac{y_1 - y_2}{x_1 - x_2}$.

Since the slope of the line is constant, then $\dfrac{y - y_1}{x - x_1} = \dfrac{y_1 - y_2}{x_1 - x_2}$.

To write an equation, substitute the values for y_1, y_2, x_1, and x_2, and compute where necessary to simplify.

(3) From the graph

Determine the y-intercept and the slope. Then follow the directions given above in (1).

Or find the coordinates of two points on the line and follow the directions given above in (2).

(4) When the coordinates of a point and the slope are known

If the given point is (x_1, y_1), the slope is m, and (x, y) is any other point on the line, then the

slope is $\dfrac{y - y_1}{x - x_1}$ which is equal to m.

Thus, $\dfrac{y - y_1}{x - x_1} = m$ or $y - y_1 = m(x - x_1)$

To write the desired equation, substitute the values for y_1, x_1, and m in $y - y_1 = m(x - x_1)$, then simplify.

1. Write the equation of the straight line having each of the given slopes and y-intercept numbers:

	(a)	(b)	(c)	(d)	(e)	(f)	(g)	(h)	(i)	(j)
slope:	4	-2	$\frac{1}{2}$	$-\frac{5}{3}$	-6	-7	5	0	$\frac{7}{8}$	$-\frac{3}{4}$
y-intercept number:	1	3	-5	8	0	-4	$\frac{1}{2}$	-2	-6	2

2. Write the equation of each of the graphs given in Exercise 119, (2) on page 296.

3. Write the equation of the straight line through the points:

(a) $(2, 3)$ and $(5,9)$ (d) $(-2, 5)$ and $(4, 7)$ (g) $(-9, 4)$ and $(3, -8)$ (j) $(8, 0)$ and $(-2, 4)$
(b) $(1, 8)$ and $(3, 2)$ (e) $(-1, -4)$ and $(8, 3)$ (h) $(0, 0)$ and $(2, -6)$ (k) $(-5, 3)$ and $(0, -2)$
(c) $(0, 4)$ and $(6, 10)$ (f) $(-6, 10)$ and $(-2, -1)$ (i) $(-7, -10)$ and $(-1, -2)$ (l) $(6, 9)$ and $(9, 6)$

What is the slope of each of the above lines? What is the y-intercept of each line?

4. Write the equation of the straight line through the point:

(a) $(2, 4)$ with slope 5   (d) $(-5, -3)$ with slope 6   (g) $(-7, 6)$ with slope $\frac{1}{4}$
(b) $(4, -1)$ with slope -3 (e) $(0, -2)$ with slope -1 (h) $(3, 3)$ with slope $-\frac{3}{2}$
(c) $(1, -10)$ with slope $\frac{7}{8}$ (f) $(0, 0)$ with slope -5 (i) $(-4, -5)$ with slope $-\frac{5}{8}$

5. Write the equation of a straight line having the same slope as $2x + y = 10$ and the same y-intercept as $5x - 3y = 12$.

REVIEW
THE EQUATION

1. Translate the following statements into equations: a) Some number (n) increased by nine is equal to fifteen. b) Twice the length $x+8$ subtracted from ten times the width x equals three times the sum of the length and width.

2. Which one of the following numbers: $15, -10, 13, 8$, is the root of the equation $20x+10(28-x)=360$.

Solve and check:

3. a) $n+17=32$ b) $a-23=8$ c) $18y=54$ d) $\frac{c}{6}=9$

4. a) $9-2x+7+5x=x-6+22$ b) $13-3b=16-12b$ c) $8x+23-4x=31+6x$

5. a) $3x-5(x-9)=11$ b) $50a+25(95-a)=4250$ c) $(x+5)(x-3)=(x-2)(x+3)$

6. a) $\frac{x}{x-7}=\frac{x-6}{x+8}$ b) $\frac{4n-1}{3}-\frac{n-2}{5}=8$ c) $\frac{y+6}{y+1}-\frac{3y+8}{y-4}=\frac{4-2y^2}{y^2-3y-4}$

7. a) $8m-3n=-25$
   $6m+5n=3$
   b) $x+y=7000$
   $.02x+.03y=185$
   c) $\frac{x}{6}+\frac{y}{4}=6$; $\frac{x-y}{2}=\frac{x+y}{10}$

8. a) $\sqrt{2x}-1=7$ b) $\sqrt{x^2+40}=x+2$ c) $4\sqrt{6x+7}=28$

9. a) $\frac{x+4}{5}=\frac{4}{x-4}$ b) $4x^2-9x=0$ c) $12x^2-28x+15=0$

10. Solve for x or y: a) $nx-a=1$ b) $\frac{y}{c}-\frac{y}{d}=1$ c) $\frac{x-b}{x-c}=\frac{b+c}{2b}$

11. Draw a graph of the equation $4x-y=3$.

12. Solve graphically: $2x-3y=11$
    $x+5y=-14$

THE FORMULA

1. a) Express as a formula: The altitude (a) of a right triangle is equal to the square root of the difference between the squares of the hypotenuse (h) and the base (b).
   b) Translate the formula $p=2l+2w$ into a statement if p represents the perimeter of a rectangle, l represents the length, and w the width.

2. a) Find the missing numbers in the table; write the word rule and the formula expressing the relationship between kilograms and pounds.

Kilograms (Kg.)	2	3	5	9	12
Pounds (P.)	4.4	6.6	11		

   b) How many yards are in 3 mi.? 4 mi.? Write a formula expressing the number of yards (y) in m miles.
   c) The amount is equal to the principal plus the interest. Write a formula expressing the interest (i) in terms of the principal (p) and the amount (A).

3. a) Find the value of l if $a=15$, $n=12$, and $d=4$, using the formula $l=a+(n-1)d$.
   b) Find the value of p if $A=696$, $r=.04$, and $t=5$, using the formula $A=p+prt$.
   c) Find the value of C if $F=-13$, using the formula $C=\frac{5}{9}(F-32)$.

4. Transform the following formulas:
   a) By removing parentheses: $A=180-(B+C)$
   b) By multiplying the right member: $A=\pi d(h+\frac{1}{2}d)$
   c) By inclosing the last two terms of the right member within parentheses preceded by a minus sign: $C=180-A-B$.
   d) By factoring the right member: $A=\pi R^2-\pi r^2$
   e) By simplifying the right member: $R=\dfrac{1}{\dfrac{1}{R_1}+\dfrac{1}{R_2}}$

5. Find the value of V' if $P = 24$, $V = 100$, $T = 300$, $P' = 30$, and $T' = 360$, using the formula $\dfrac{PV}{T} = \dfrac{P'V'}{T'}$.

6. Rearrange formula $S = \dfrac{rl - a}{r - 1}$ to solve for a. Solve for l. Solve for r.

7. Find the required values using the principles of variation:
   a) In the formula $A = bh$, $A = 204$ when $b = 12$. Find the value of A when $b = 3$ and h remains constant.
   b) In the formula $a = \dfrac{v}{t}$, $a = 6$ when $t = 10$. Find the value of a when $t = 30$ and v remains constant.

8. Draw the graphs of the following formulas: a) $p = 5s$ b) $d = 40t$ c) $i = .03p$

9. a) Using the formulas $I = \dfrac{E}{R}$ and $P = IE$, derive a formula for R in terms of P and I.
   b) Using the formulas $A = \pi d(h + \tfrac{1}{2}d)$ and $d = 2r$, derive a formula for A in terms of π, r, and h.

10. a) Transform formula $t = \sqrt{\dfrac{2s}{a}}$, solving for s. b) Rewrite formula $A = \dfrac{s}{2}\sqrt{\dfrac{3s^2}{4}}$, simplifying the right member.

11. Derive the quadratic formula solving the equation $ax^2 + bx + c = 0$ for x by completing the square.

12. a) Find the value of F when $m = 768$, $V = 100$, $g = 32$, and $r = 600$, using the formula $F = \dfrac{mV^2}{gr}$.
    b) Find the values of t when $s = 240$ and $v = 128$, using the formula $s = vt - 16t^2$.
    c) Rearrange formula $s = 16t^2$, solving for t.

13. Using the right triangle ABC (see page 279) find: a) Side a if side $c = 140$ yd. and angle $A = 13°$.
    b) Side c if side $a = 84$ ft. and side $b = 135$ ft.   c) Side b if side $a = 500$ yd. and angle $B = 61°$.

14. Using the formula $i = prt$, determine how much money must be invested for 10 years at 6% interest to bring the same interest as $1000 invested for 12 years at 4%.

15. Using the formulas $A = s^2$ and $p = 4s$, find the perimeter of a square having an area of 529 square feet.

FUNDAMENTAL PROCESSES

1. Add:
   a) $\begin{array}{r} -5x \\ -6x \\ \hline \end{array}$ b) $\begin{array}{r} 2n^2 - 3n + 8 \\ 5n^2 + 3n - 9 \\ \hline \end{array}$

2. Subtract:
   a) $\begin{array}{r} 8t \\ 10t \\ \hline \end{array}$ b) $\begin{array}{r} 3x^2 - 5xy - y^2 \\ x^2 - 7xy + 2y^2 \\ \hline \end{array}$

3. Multiply:
   a) $\begin{array}{r} -9x^3y^2 \\ -3xy^8 \\ \hline \end{array}$ b) $-2m^2(3m^2 - m + 6)$
   c) $8bx^3(-b^3 - 2bx^2 + 3x^5)$

4. Divide:
   a) $\dfrac{-16r}{+4r}$ b) $\dfrac{12a^4c^5 - 9a^2c^4 - 3ac^3}{-3ac^3}$

5. Combine: $3bc - 2b^2 - c^2 - 2bc - 2c^2 - 3b^2 - c^2$

6. Subtract $4a^2 - 3a - 6$ from $3a^2 - 8a - 6$.

7. Multiply $7m^2 - 2mx - x^2$ by $5m - 2x$.

8. Divide $24b^3 - 41b^2c - 3bc^2 + 20c^3$ by $3b - 4c$.

9. Remove parentheses and add like terms: $8x - x(2x - 5) + (x - 1)(x - 4)$

10. Inclose the last three terms within parentheses preceded by a minus sign: $5x^4 - 2x^3 - x^2 + 6x - 1$

11. Multiply mentally: a) $(\tfrac{3}{4}x - 5y^2)(\tfrac{3}{4}x + 5y^2)$ b) $(6s^2 + 5xy)^2$ c) $(a - 9)(a + 8)$ d) $(5m - 8n)(8m - 6n)$

12. Factor: a) $25a^2 - 100b^2$ b) $t^2 - t - 56$ c) $81x^2 + 144xy^2 + 64y^4$ d) $64m^4 - 49n^4$ e) $6s^2x - 18sx + 12x$

13. Reduce to lowest terms: $\dfrac{24x - 12y}{144x^2 - 36y^2}$

15. Combine: $\dfrac{9}{x^2 - 25} - \dfrac{4}{x^2 - 8x + 15}$

17. Combine: $\dfrac{3}{a + 7} - \dfrac{6a}{a^2 - 49} - \dfrac{5}{7 - a}$

14. Multiply: $\dfrac{9b^3c^2}{25x^2y} \times \dfrac{10y}{3b^4c}$

16. Combine: $\dfrac{4x + y}{x - 3y} - 1$

18. Divide: $\dfrac{8ax - 6bx}{7ab} \div 4ax^3$

19. Simplify: $\sqrt{117a^4b^9}$

20. Simplify: $\sqrt[3]{\dfrac{27c}{4a^2}}$

21. Simplify and combine: $3\sqrt{180} + \sqrt{147} - 10\sqrt{\tfrac{1}{5}} + 4\sqrt{432}$

22. Multiply: $(5\sqrt{6} - 7\sqrt{2})^2$

23. Divide: $\dfrac{16\sqrt{8} - 20\sqrt{10} + 4\sqrt{16}}{4\sqrt{2}}$

PROBLEMS

1. How many girls are in a freshman class of 247 students if there are 29 more girls than boys?
2. A board 14 feet long is to be cut into two pieces, one 5 feet longer than twice the other. Find the length of each piece.
3. A man is four times as old as his son. In 5 years he will be only three times as old. Find their ages now.
4. What is the selling price of a mirror if it cost $24.50 and the profit is 30% of the selling price?
5. Tom can wash the family's car in 50 minutes and his father can do it in 40 minutes. How long will it take both together to wash the car?
6. What is the radius of action of an airplane (how far can it fly from the base and yet return) in 8 hours if its outgoing speed is 245 m.p.h. and its return speed is 147 m.p.h.?
7. When changing a $1 bill, Mary received 6 nickels more than 5 times the number of dimes. How many nickels did she receive?
8. How many ounces of alcohol must be added to 10 ounces of a 20% iodine solution to make a 15% solution?
9. Compare the area of a 12-inch circular television screen with that of a 10-inch circular screen.
10. Angle R in triangle RST is 10 degrees more than angle S. Angle T is 15 degrees less than 3 times angle R. Find the size of each angle.
11. How many pounds of grass seed worth 65¢ a pound should be mixed with 20 pounds of grass seed worth 80¢ a pound to make a blend to sell at 75¢ a pound?
12. An airplane flew 480 miles with the wind in 3 hours. The return trip against the wind took 4 hours. Find the airspeed (speed in still air) of the airplane and the wind velocity.
13. A man invests $900 more at 4% annual interest than he does at 5%. The income from the 4% investment is $19 less than the income from the 5% investment. How much was invested at 4%?
14. Find the dimensions of a rectangle having a perimeter of 130 feet and an area of 1,000 square feet.
15. What downward force must be applied at a distance of 7 feet from the fulcrum to balance a downward force of 63 pounds applied 10 feet on the other side of the fulcrum?

FACTS, MEANINGS, AND CONCEPTS

1. Find which of the following expressions are a) monomials, b) binomials, c) trinomials, d) polynomials: $2a-7b$; $27\ mn$; x^2-3x+4; $4+n$; $4n$; $-x^2y^2$; x^2-y^2; $5c^2-4cd+9d^2$; $4x^2yz^2$; $m^3+2m^2n-3mn^2+n^3$.
2. Find the numerical coefficients in each of the following terms: $4x$; $6b^2$; $-2cd$; $9m^2n$; $-y$; $-15abc$; dx.
3. Find the literal factors in each of the following terms: $8c$; $4m^3$; $-5r^2s$; $12x^5y^2$; abx.
4. Select pairs of like terms: $x^2, 2x$; $7c, -9c$; $2a^2b, 3ab^2$; $a, -3a$; $bh, 8h^2$.
5. Does b^2 represent $b+b$ or $b \cdot b$?
6. Does $3c$ represent $c \cdot c \cdot c$ or $3 \cdot c$?
7. Write $a \cdot x \cdot x \cdot x \cdot y \cdot y$ using exponents.
8. What is the numerical coefficient of x?
9. What is the base in the term 10^9?
10. What is the absolute value of -9?
11. Write $\frac{3}{4}x$ in another way.
12. Write six pairs of factors of 72.
13. Express $6m^4+8m^2-2m-6m^3$ in descending powers of m.
14. What is the ordinate of a point whose coordinates are $(-4, +6)$? What is the abscissa?
15. Find which of the following statements are true for all values of m and n:
$$m+n=n+m; \quad m-n=n-m; \quad mn=nm; \quad \frac{m}{n}=\frac{n}{m}.$$
16. Explain the statement "All formulas are equations but not all equations are formulas."
17. What is the difference between an arithmetic number and a literal number?
18. When are parentheses used?
19. What axioms are used in solving simple equations? Radical equations? Quadratic equations?
20. What is meant by checking an equation?

21. What is the difference between factoring and division?

22. When both the numerator and denominator of a fraction are multiplied or divided by the same number, does the value of the fraction change?

23. What is the difference between an incomplete and complete quadratic equation?

24. What axioms does the process of transformation or transposition replace?

25. What is meant by the root of an equation? Every quadratic equation has how many roots?

26. How does a literal equation differ from a numerical equation?

27. What is meant by clearing an equation of fractions?

28. a) What is a proportion? b) What is a radical? Give examples.

29. What is meant when one quantity is said to be the function of another quantity?

30. a) What relation does the Pythagorean Theorem express? b) How does the angle of depression differ from the angle of elevation? c) What ratio does the tangent of an angle express?

FINAL CUMULATIVE REVIEW

1. Express as a formula: The capacity in gallons (g) of a given volume in cubic inches (V) is equal to the volume divided by 231.

2. Find the value of the expression $6a^2 + 5ab - 3b^2$ when $a = 3$ and $b = -4$.

3. Write a formula expressing the number of feet (f) in y yards and i inches.

4. How much money must be invested at 5% simple interest to earn $1,200 in 3 years?

5. Find the value of w when $p = 78$ and $l = 23$, using the formula $p = 2(l+w)$.

6. Combine: $2x^2 - 4xy - 3y^2 - xy - 5x^2 - 2y^2 + 5xy$.   7. Subtract $7a - 5c$ from $4b + c$.

8. Multiply $3a^2 - 6ax + 2x^2$ by $2a - 7x$.   9. Divide $8b^3 - 24bd^2 + 9d^3$ by $2b - 3d$.

10. Remove parentheses and add like terms: $4n - 2n(n-5) + (n-2)(n-3)$.

11. Solve and check: a) $35x + 25(100 - x) = 3200$ b) $\frac{3}{4}n + 8 = 20$ c) $1.3x - .05 = .8x + 4$

12. How long will it take a seaplane, flying at a speed of 180 knots, to overtake a destroyer if the destroyer left the naval base 8 hours before the seaplane and was averaging 30 knots?

13. Find the following products by inspection: a) $(3c - 5d)(3c + 5d)$ b) $(8x - 7y)(8x - 7y)$ c) $(6b + 1)(6b - 5)$

14. Factor the following polynomials: a) $25a^2 + 400b^2$ b) $36m^2 - 132m + 121$ c) $ar^5 - ar$

15. Reduce to lowest terms: 16. Divide:

$$\frac{8c^3 - 2c}{4c + 2}$$

$$\frac{3x - 12y}{x^2 - xy - 12y^2} \div \frac{x^2 - 6xy + 9y^2}{x^2 - 9y^2}$$

17. Simplify: $\dfrac{a + \dfrac{a}{x}}{\dfrac{a}{x} - a}$

18. Combine: $\dfrac{x - 5y}{6} - \dfrac{3x - 2y}{4} + \dfrac{6x + y}{8}$ 19. Solve and check: $\dfrac{5x + 4}{x} - \dfrac{2}{x - 3} = 5$

20. How many pounds of clover seed selling at $1.59 per pound should be mixed with grass seed selling at $.49 per pound to make 200 pounds of a mixture to sell at $.60 per pound?

21. Solve for x and check: $a(x - b) = b(x - b)$ 22. Transform formula $\dfrac{D}{d} = \dfrac{r}{R}$, solving for R.

23. Find the value of w to the nearest tenth if $l = 4$, using the formula $\dfrac{w}{l} = \dfrac{l}{l + w}$.

24. The area of a circle varies directly as the square of the radius. Compare the area of a circle having a 32-inch radius to the area of a circle with a 4-inch radius.

25. Solve graphically: 26. Solve algebraically and check: 27. Solve and check:

$2x - y = 6$ $8x - (y + 3) = 14$ $\dfrac{x}{3} - \dfrac{6}{x} = 1$
$x + 2y = 8$ $2(x - 8) = 3(y - 3)$

28. Simplify and combine: $\sqrt{294} + 12\sqrt{\frac{2}{3}} - 3\sqrt{150}$ 29. Solve and check: $\sqrt{x^2 - 32} = x - 2$

30. What is the angle of elevation of the sun, to the nearest degree, when a 30-foot flagpole casts a shadow of 18 feet?

INTRODUCTION TO SUPPLEMENTARY UNIT ONE

We write number symbols. We speak and write number names. But number itself is an abstract idea.

Number answers our questions of "How Many?", "How Much?" and "In What Order?" Although the same number symbols are used for both, we call a number which tells us how many things are in a group a **cardinal** number and a number which tells us the order as first, second, etc. an **ordinal** number.

The figures that we generally call numbers are technically not numbers at all. They are merely number symbols that represent numbers. We can see 3 boys or 3 ships, we can measure 3 pounds or 3 inches but we do not see the number we call three. We do see, however, the written number symbol "3."

Some mathematicians call each group of number symbols like 493 or 8,675 a numeral. A numeral is a symbolic name that we write to represent a number.

A number may have many different names (numerals) since there are many ways of representing the same number symbolically. For example, here are a few names for the number six:

$$6 \qquad VI \qquad 10-4 \qquad 5+1 \qquad \frac{42}{7} \qquad 3\cdot 2$$

$$\frac{25+23}{8} \qquad \frac{36-12}{2^2} \qquad 110_2 \qquad 12_4 \qquad 20_3 \qquad 11_5$$

Most people, however, call each group of number symbols like 493 or 8,675 a number. They are generally thinking of the number ideas or concepts that the symbols convey.

As we progress from one school level to another, we gradually expand our experiences with number systems. First we meet the counting numbers of the *natural number* system, the numbers, beginning with *one*, named by the numerals 1, 2, 3, 4, 5, 6, 7, 8, 9, 10, 11, ... Then we are introduced to zero (0) which with all the natural numbers form the number system of *whole numbers*.

However, there are limitations to the use of only whole numbers. For example, if we use only whole numbers, division is not always possible. In the case $5 \div 9 = ?$ the quotient is not a whole number but a fractional number named $\frac{5}{9}$. Thus to overcome this, the number system is enlarged to include fractions, sometimes called *rational numbers*. In arithmetic common fractions, decimal fractions, and per cent name rational numbers.

In the whole number and natural number systems subtraction is not always possible since we cannot subtract a large number from a small one. For example, $4 - 9 = ?$ Thus in algebra we study positive and negative numbers which make such subtraction possible as $4 - 9 = -5$. Examination of the number line on page 60S will show that points corresponding to $+3$ and -3 fall on opposite sides of the point marked 0 but are exactly the same distance from point 0. A pair of numbers, one positive and the other negative, which have the same absolute value, are called *opposites*. -3 is the opposite of $+3$ and $+3$ is the opposite of -3. Each is the opposite of the other. The opposite of zero is zero. The number system consisting of all the whole numbers and their opposites form the system of *integers*. The number system consisting of all fractional numbers and their opposites form the system of *rational numbers*.

In arithmetic we generally learn how to find the square of a number and the square root of a number. The square root of a number that does not have an exact square root is a new type of number called an *irrational number*. For example, the $\sqrt{5}$ is an irrational number. In algebra we study about irrational numbers, real numbers, and complex numbers. The number system consisting of all positive and negative irrational numbers is called the system of irrational numbers. The *real number* system is the system consisting of all the rational and irrational numbers. To complete our study of number systems, we also discuss the *complex number*.

In summary then, the number systems include the following:

1. Natural Numbers
2. Whole Numbers
3. Integers
4. Rational Numbers
5. Irrational Numbers
6. Real Numbers
7. Complex Numbers

To determine whether a certain set of numbers and their operations form a mathematical system from a structural point of view, it is necessary to examine various properties of the given numbers and operations. If specific requirements are met, then a mathematical system is established.

Included are the commutative and associative properties of addition and multiplication, the distributive property of multiplication with respect to addition, closure, identity elements for addition and multiplication and the additive and multiplicative inverses. Addition and multiplication are the operations that are basic to the structure of a number system.

Whole numbers greater than one (1) may be separated into two groups: **prime** and **composite**. A **prime number** is a whole number that can be divided exactly only by itself and by 1 and by no other whole number. A **composite number** is a whole number that is not a prime number but can be expressed as a product of two or more smaller numbers.

Whole numbers may also be classified as **odd** or **even** numbers.

In this unit of the book systems of numeration other than our decimal system will be studied. The unit will develop an understanding of the base of a system and skill in changing from one base to another base.

We shall see how exponents are used in expressing very large and very small numbers. This shortened method of writing numbers is called *scientific notation*. We shall learn to expand a number in powers and write it as a polynomial.

SUPPLEMENTARY UNIT ONE—NUMBER AND ITS PROPERTIES

EXERCISE 1

Numbers and Number Systems

PART A

NATURAL AND WHOLE NUMBERS; INTEGERS; RATIONAL, IRRATIONAL, REAL, AND COMPLEX NUMBERS

1. **Natural numbers** are the numbers, beginning with *one*, named by the numerals 1, 2, 3, 4, 5, 6, 7, 8, 9, 10, 11, ... that are used in counting. They form the system of natural numbers. Zero is generally not considered a natural number. The three dots directly after the last listed numeral indicate that the numerals continue in the same pattern without ending.

2. **Whole numbers** are the numbers, beginning with *zero*, named by the numerals 0, 1, 2, 3, 4, 5, 6, 7, 8, 9, 10, 11, ... Thus the natural numbers and zero (0) form the system of whole numbers.

   Whole numbers and natural numbers have order. Every whole number is followed by another whole number, and every natural number is followed by another natural number, called the *successor*, which is one (1) greater. 5 is the successor of 4. There is no last whole number and no last natural number. There is no greatest whole number and no greatest natural number. The whole number that precedes another whole number or the natural number that precedes another natural number is called the *predessor* if it is one (1) less. 8 is the predecessor of 9.

   Sometimes a set of numbers is written as 1, 2, 3, 4, ..., 10. Here the three dots mean "and so on up to and including" and represent all the missing numerals that belong in between the numeral preceding the first dot and the given last numeral.

3. **Integers** are the whole numbers and their opposites. See page 60S. They form the system of integers. Since an integer may be a whole number, zero and any natural number are included in this system. When a set of integers is written as ..., -3, -2, -1, 0, 1, 2, 3, ..., it indicates that the set of numbers is unlimited in both directions. Integers may be positive or negative. -17, 0, 28 are examples of integers.

4. **Rational numbers** are numbers that may be expressed as a quotient of two integers with division by zero excluded. We cannot divide by zero. The system of rational numbers includes zero and all the positive and negative integers, common fractions and decimal fractions (both terminating and repeating decimals), mixed numbers and mixed decimals.

   $\frac{3}{4}$ is equivalent to a terminating decimal .75
   $\frac{1}{3}$ is equivalent to a repeating decimal .333333 ...

It should be noted that between any two rational numbers another rational number may be found. This is not true in the system of natural numbers or integers.
9, -17, $\frac{3}{8}$, .4 are examples of rational numbers.

5. **Irrational numbers** are numbers that cannot be expressed as a quotient of two integers. Examples are the square roots of positive numbers other than perfect squares. Any non-terminating and non-repeating decimal is an irrational number. They form the system of irrational numbers.
   $\sqrt{3}$ and $\sqrt{18}$ are examples of irrational numbers.

6. **Real numbers** are all the rational and irrational numbers. The system of real numbers includes zero, the positive and negative integers, fractions and irrational numbers.
   6, -3, $\frac{7}{8}$, $-.8$, $\sqrt{23}$ are examples of real numbers.

7. **Complex numbers** are the numbers which are written in the form of $a + bi$ where a and b are real numbers and i is the symbol indicating $\sqrt{-1}$ with $i^2 = -1$. They form the system of complex numbers.
   $6 + 5\sqrt{-1}$ is an example of a complex number.
   A number like $\sqrt{-6}$ or $2\sqrt{-1}$ is generally called an *imaginary* number.
   The complex number system includes all real numbers and all imaginary numbers.

The complex number system is excluded in the following:
What kind of number is 8?

> 8 is a natural number. It is also an integer or whole number or positive integer or positive whole number or non-negative integer or non-negative whole number or rational number or real number.

To what number system do $\frac{1}{4}$ and .3 belong?

> $\frac{1}{4}$ and .3 belong to the systems of rational numbers and real numbers. They are not natural numbers or integers or whole numbers.

What kind of number is -9?

> -9 is a negative integer or negative whole number or non-positive integer or non-positive whole number or rational number or real number. It is not a natural number.

What kind of number is $\sqrt{7}$?

> $\sqrt{7}$ is an irrational number or real number. It is not a natural number or integer or whole number or rational number.

Practice

1. (a) What is a natural number? What is a whole number?
(b) Which of the following are natural numbers? Which are whole numbers?

$$7 \qquad -3 \qquad \frac{1}{2} \qquad 124 \qquad \sqrt{3} \qquad .28 \qquad 91 \qquad 3+2\sqrt{5}$$

2. (a) What is an integer?
(b) Which of the following are integers?

$$-4 \qquad \sqrt{11} \qquad \frac{9}{10} \qquad -63 \qquad \sqrt{-7} \qquad 11 \qquad .874 \qquad -\frac{2}{3}$$

(c) Which of the following are non-positive integers?

$$16 \qquad -\frac{3}{4} \qquad -\sqrt{40} \qquad 0 \qquad -.42 \qquad -25 \qquad 89 \qquad -70$$

(d) Which of the following are non-negative integers?

$$-\frac{5}{12} \qquad 61 \qquad -29 \qquad .8 \qquad -2\sqrt{2} \qquad 0 \qquad -2 \qquad \sqrt{6}$$

3. (a) What is a rational number?
(b) Which of the following are rational numbers?

$$.6 \qquad -3 \qquad \frac{3}{8} \qquad \sqrt{13} \qquad 0 \qquad 51 \qquad -164 \qquad 4+\sqrt{15}$$

4. (a) What is an irrational number?
(b) Which of the following are irrational numbers?

$$81 \qquad -9 \qquad \sqrt{26} \qquad 0 \qquad -.35 \qquad -100 \qquad \sqrt{-26} \qquad \frac{11}{16}$$

5. (a) What is a real number?
(b) Which of the following are real numbers?

$$\frac{3}{5} \qquad -.2 \qquad 63 \qquad -\sqrt{7} \qquad 0 \qquad \sqrt{-5} \qquad -121 \qquad .8319$$

6. (a) What is a complex number?
(b) Which of the following are complex numbers?

$$.743 \qquad -\frac{5}{6} \qquad 0 \qquad 3+7\sqrt{-1} \qquad \sqrt{-2} \qquad 1,000 \qquad -92 \qquad \sqrt{53}$$

7. Which of the following are imaginary numbers?

$$.62 \qquad 0 \qquad \sqrt{20} \qquad 88 \qquad 2+3\sqrt{6} \qquad \frac{7}{10} \qquad \sqrt{-8} \qquad -\frac{16}{25}$$

8. Of which systems of numbers could each of the following numbers be considered a member?

(a) 15   (b) $\frac{5}{8}$ (c) $\sqrt{5}$ (d) -24 (e) .7   (f) $8+2\sqrt{-14}$ (g) $\sqrt{-2}$

9. Of which systems of numbers could each of the following numbers be considered not a member?

(a) $-.3$ (b) $\sqrt{19}$ (c) -57 (d) $\sqrt{-1}$ (e) 12   (f) $\frac{4}{7}$ (g) $1+2\sqrt{-3}$

10. (a) Write all the one-digit natural numbers.
    (b) Write all the one-digit whole numbers.
    (c) Write all the one-digit integers.

11. What is the successor of 12? Of 486? Of 1,999? Of 19,099? What is the predecessor of each?

12. Write five different names or numerical ways of expressing 9.

PART B

ODD AND EVEN NUMBERS

Whole numbers may be separated into even numbers and odd numbers.

An **even number** is a whole number that is divisible by two (2). Zero is considered an **even integer.**
An **odd number** is a whole number that is not divisible by two (2).

    Is 12 an odd or even number?
Answer, 12 is an even number. It can be divided exactly by 2.

    Is 29 an odd or even number?
Answer, 29 is an odd number. It cannot be divided exactly by 2.

Practice

1. (a) What is an even number?
    (b) Which of the following are even numbers?
       8   5   21   86   114   679   1,992   5,843

2. (a) What is an odd number?
    (b) Which of the following are odd numbers?
       10   7   53   64   49   821   2,500   6,285

3. (a) Write all one-digit even natural numbers.
    (b) Write all one-digit odd natural numbers.

4. Write all the even integers less than 28 but greater than 10.

5. Add any two even numbers. Is the sum an odd or even number?

6. Add any two odd numbers. Is the sum an odd or even number?

7. Add any odd and even number. Is the sum an odd or even number?

8. Add any two consecutive numbers. Is the sum an odd or even number?

9. Multiply any two even numbers. Is the product an odd or even number?

10. Multiply any two odd numbers. Is the product an odd or even number?

11. Multiply any odd number by any even number. Is the product an odd or even number?

12. Take any even number and square it. Is the square of an even number an odd or even number?

13. Take any odd number and square it. Is the square of an odd number an odd or even number?.

14. Using the odd numbers 1, 3, 5, 7, 9, and 11, find the sum of the first two numbers; first three numbers; first four numbers; first five numbers; all six numbers. Find the relationship between each sum and the number of odd numbers added.

PART C

PRIME AND COMPOSITE NUMBERS

A **prime number** is a whole number greater than 1 which is divisible only by itself and by 1 and by no other whole number.

Is 17 a prime number?

Answer, 17 is a prime number because it can be divided exactly only by 17 and by 1.

Two prime numbers are called **twin primes** if one number is 2 more than the other. 11 and 13 form a pair of twin primes.

To find a prime number less than a given number, the method called the Sieve of Eratosthenes may be used. In this method we follow a pattern of crossing out numbers that are not primes.

Suppose we are required to find all the prime numbers less than 40. Since 1 is not included, we begin with 2 and write integers through 39.

We retain 2 since it is a prime number, but we cross out every second number after 2. Thus all even numbers, excluding 2, are crossed out. We retain 3, but we cross out every third number after 3. We shall find some numbers already crossed out, but we must include them in our count. 4 is crossed out. We retain 5, but we cross out every fifth number after 5. We continue in this way until we cross out all possible numbers. The numbers that remain are prime numbers.

A **composite number** is a whole number greater than 1 which is not a prime number but can be expressed as a product of two or more smaller numbers. A composite number can be expressed as a product of primes. Although these prime factors may be arranged in many ways or different order, each composite number has only one set of prime factors.

Is 24 a prime or composite number?

Answer, 24 is a composite number because it is not a prime number. It can be divided not only by 24 and by 1 but also by 12, 8, 6, 3, and 2.

Express 14 as a product of prime factors. Answer, $2 \cdot 7$ or $7 \cdot 2$

Express 20 as a product of prime factors. Answer, $2 \cdot 2 \cdot 5$ or $2 \cdot 5 \cdot 2$ or $5 \cdot 2 \cdot 2$

Express 36 as a product of prime factors. Answer, $2 \cdot 2 \cdot 3 \cdot 3$

Practice

1. (a) What is a prime number?
   (b) Which of the following are prime numbers?

   16   19   37   91   53   87   79   103

2. (a) What is a composite number?
   (b) Which of the following are composite numbers?

   93   81   57   89   68   71   105   43

3. (a) Write all the one-digit prime numbers.
   (b) Write all the one-digit composite numbers.
   (c) What are the one-digit odd prime numbers? One-digit even prime numbers?

4. (a) Write all the prime numbers greater than 7 but less than 23.
   (b) Write all the composite numbers less than 50 but greater than 31.

5. Using the Sieve of Eratosthenes, find the prime numbers less than:

   (a) 50   (b) 100   (c) 160   (d) 200

6. What are the pairs of twin primes when the numbers are less than 100? Less than 200?

7. (a) Take any even number between 3 and 20. Find a pair of prime numbers that have this even number as the sum.

   (b) Take any even number between 21 and 100. Find a pair of prime numbers that have this even number as the sum.

   (c) Determine whether there is any even number from 1 to 100, except 2, which is not a sum of two prime numbers.

8. Express each of the following numbers as a product of prime factors:

SET (a)	SET (b)	SET (c)	SET (d)
1. 9	1. 75	1. 60	1. 205
2. 6	2. 51	2. 24	2. 144
3. 8	3. 63	3. 96	3. 256
4. 16	4. 27	4. 54	4. 147
5. 12	5. 39	5. 72	5. 400

EXERCISE 2

Properties of Number and Operations

Each of the number systems described in the last lesson consists of a set of numbers, the basic binary operations of addition and multiplication (with subtraction being the inverse operation of addition and with division being the inverse operation of multiplication), and certain properties concerning these numbers and operations.

When we add 2 and 3, we are operating on two numbers at one time. We call this a **binary** operation. Multiplying 8 by 4, subtracting 53 from 197 and dividing 288 by 24 are binary operations.

The following properties of number and operations are described below:

Uniqueness, closure, commutative property of addition and multiplication, associative property of addition and multiplication, distributive property of multiplication with respect to addition, identity elements, inverses, and order (discrete or dense).

A property is not true unless it holds for all cases. Therefore to determine whether a property is not true it is sufficient to show that it does not hold in one case.

1. *Uniqueness*

A number is said to have the property of being unique when it is the "one and only number." When we add two numbers, the sum is a **unique** number because there should be only the one same answer every time the given numbers are added. In a like manner when two numbers are multiplied, the product is a unique number.

What is the unique sum when we add 12 and 15?
Answer, 27

What is the unique product when we multiply 6 by 8?
Answer, 48

2. *Closure*

If we, using all the numbers in a given set, add any two numbers (or subtract or multiply or divide) and get as our answer in every case one of the numbers described in the given set, we say the set is **closed** under that operation. This property we call **closure.**

Is the set of natural numbers closed under addition? Answer, Yes, because the sum of two natural numbers is also a natural number. 8+2=10. 8, 2, and 10 are all natural numbers.

Is the set of odd number closed under addition? Answer, No, because the sum of two odd numbers is an even number. 9+3=12. The sum of odd numbers 9 and 3 equals 12, an even number.

3. *Commutative Property*

The commutative property of addition (or multiplication) permits us to change the order of any two numbers without affecting the sum (or product).

(a) In addition

When we add one number to a second number, we get the same sum as when we add the second number to the first number. The order we use in adding two numbers has no effect on the sum.

Adding 2 and 3 gives the same sum as adding 3 and 2.

That is, $2+3=3+2$

If a and b each represents a real number, then for all a and for all b

$$a+b=b+a$$

(b) In multiplication

When we multiply one number by a second number, we get the same product as when we multiply the second number by the first number. The order we use in multiplying two numbers has no effect on the product.

Multiplying 2 and 3 gives the same product as multiplying 3 and 2.

That is, $2\times3=3\times2$

If a and b each represents a real number, then for all a and for all b

$$a\times b=b\times a$$

or

$$ab=ba$$

4. *Associative Property*

When we are dealing with more than two addends or two factors at one time, we must first select a pair to begin our operations. The associative property permits us to group pairs of numbers in addition and multiplication without affecting the sum (when adding) or the product (when multiplying).

(a) In addition

We may add only two numbers at a time. Therefore when we are required to add three numbers, we may group or associate the first and second numbers and add their sum to the third number or we may group or associate the second and third numbers and add their sum to the first number. Either way we get the same final sum.

That is, $3+4+5$ may be thought of as either $(3+4)+5$ or $3+(4+5)$.

If a, b, and c each represents a real number, then the associative property of addition states:

for all a,   for all b,   and for all c

$$(a+b)+c=a+(b+c).$$

However, the associative property, as we shall see, does not alone permit the grouping to be

$$(3+5)+4$$

or

$$4+(3+5)$$

Rather it is the result of both commutative and associative properties of addition because the two properties together allow us to add the numbers in any groups of two numbers and in any order.

$3+4+5$

$=3+5+4$ by commutative property

$=(3+5)+4$ by associative property

(b) In multiplication

We may multiply only two factors at a time. Therefore when we are required to multiply three numbers (factors), we may group or associate the first and second numbers and multiply their product by the third number or we may group or associate the second and third numbers and multiply their product by the first number. Either way we get the same final product.

That is $3 \times 4 \times 5$ may be thought of as either $(3 \times 4) \times 5$ or $3 \times (4 \times 5)$
If a, b, and c each represents a real number, the associative property of multiplication states:

for all a,   for all b,   and for all c

$$(ab)c = a(bc)$$

5. Distributive Property of Multiplication with Respect to Addition

When we multiply one number by the sum of a second and third number, we get the same result as when we add the product of the first and second numbers to the product of the first and third numbers. We call this the distributive property.

That is, $3 \times (4+5)$ is
either $3 \times (9) = 27$
or $3 \times 4 + 3 \times 5 = 12 + 15 = 27$

In general, if a, b, and c each represents a real number, then for all a, for all b, and for all c, the distributive property of multiplication with respect to addition states:

$$a(b+c) = ab + ac$$

We use the distributive property in computations like 3×32.

$$\begin{array}{cccc} 32 & 30+2 & 30 & 2 \\ \times 3 = & \times 3 = & \times 3 + & \times 3 \\ \hline \end{array}$$

or $3 \times 32 = 3(30+2) = 3 \times 30 + 3 \times 2 = 90 + 6 = 96$

We may also think of the distributive property as follows:

$$4 \times 3 + 4 \times 7 = 4 \times (3+7)$$

Or in general if a, b, and c each represents a real number, then

for all a,   for all b,   and for all c
$$ab + ac = a(b+c)$$

6. Identity Elements

The addition property of zero (0) and the multiplication property of one (1) are especially important.

(a) In addition

When we add zero (0) to any number, the number remains unchanged and the sum is the given number. The sum of 8 and 0 is 8. The sum of 0 and a is a.

That number which, when added to a given number, makes the given number the sum (or leaves the given number unchanged) is called the **identity element for addition** (or the **additive identity**).

Thus zero (0) is the identity element for addition.

(b) In multiplication

When we multiply any number by one (1), the number remains unchanged and the product is the given number. 8 times 1 is 8. The product of 1 and a is a.

That number which, when multiplied by a given number, makes the given number the product (or leaves' the given number unchanged) is called the **identity element for multiplication** (or the **multiplicative identity**).

Thus, one (1) is the identity element for multiplication.

In arithmetic the multiplicative identity 1 is used

   (a) when changing the form of fractions

$$\text{to lower terms: } \frac{6}{8} = \frac{3}{4} \cdot \frac{2}{2} = \frac{3}{4} \cdot 1 = \frac{3}{4}$$

$$\text{to higher terms: } \frac{2}{3} = \frac{2}{3} \cdot 1 = \frac{2}{3} \cdot \frac{8}{8} = \frac{16}{24}$$

   (b) when dividing by a decimal:

$$.23\overline{).69} = \frac{.69}{.23} = \frac{.69}{.23} \times 1 = \frac{.69}{.23} \times \frac{100}{100} = \frac{69}{23} = 23\overline{)69}$$

   (c) when dividing fractions:

$$\frac{2}{3} \div \frac{3}{4} = \frac{\frac{2}{3}}{\frac{3}{4}} = \frac{\frac{2}{3}}{\frac{3}{4}} \times 1 = \frac{\frac{2}{3} \times 12}{\frac{3}{4} \times 12} = \frac{8}{9}$$

7. *Inverses*

When the sum of two numbers is zero, 0, (the additive identity) or the product of two numbers is one, 1, (the multiplicative identity), the numbers are related in a special way.

   (a) Additive Inverse

If the sum of two numbers is zero (0), then each addend is said to be the **additive inverse** of the other.

The sum of 8 and -8 is 0. Therefore -8 is the additive inverse of 8 and 8 is the **additive inverse of** -8.

Since $a + (-a) = 0$, then $-a$ is the additive inverse of a and a is the additive inverse of $-a$. In arithmetic there is no number except zero that has an additive inverse.

   (b) Multiplicative Inverse

If the product of two numbers is one (1), then each factor is called the **multiplicative inverse** of the other.

Any whole number except zero, multiplied by the unit fraction containing this number in the denominator will give one (1) as the product. The product of 8 and $\frac{1}{8}$ is 1. Therefore 8 and $\frac{1}{8}$ are multiplicative inverses of each other. Sometimes the multiplicative inverse $\frac{1}{8}$ is also called the **reciprocal** of 8.

$a \times \dfrac{1}{a} = 1$. Therefore a and $\dfrac{1}{a}$ are multiplicative inverses of each other. Also $\dfrac{2}{3}$ and $\dfrac{3}{2}$ are multi-

plicative inverses of each other.

8. *Order*

Numbers may be arranged in an order so that we may know which is first, etc. and which is greater. The one-to-one correspondence of the order of numbers to the order of points on a line will be shown in Exercise 13.

The order is **dense** if between any two numbers there is an unlimited number of numbers. The order of rational numbers is dense because between any two rational numbers another may be found. There are an endless number of fractions between the fractions $\frac{1}{4}$ and $\frac{3}{4}$.

The order is **discrete** if between any two numbers there is only a limited number of numbers or no number. The order of natural numbers is discrete. There is only one natural number, 4, between the natural numbers 3 and 5.

When two numbers are unequal, the first number is always greater than the second if the second number subtracted from the first is a positive number.

8 is greater than 3. $8-3$ gives 5, a positive number, as the answer.
6 is not greater than 10. $6-10$ gives -4, a negative number, as the answer.

Practice

1. What is the unique answer when we
   (a) add 9 and 5?   (b) multiply 15 by 10?   (c) divide 20 by 4?   (d) subtract 19 from 30?

2. Which of the following systems of numbers are closed under addition?
   (a) Natural numbers   (b) Integers   (c) Rational numbers   (d) Real numbers

3. Which of the following systems of numbers are closed under subtraction?
   (a) Natural numbers   (b) Integers   (c) Rational numbers   (d) Real numbers

4. Which of the following systems of numbers are closed under multiplication?
   (a) Natural numbers   (b) Integers   (c) Rational numbers   (d) Real numbers

5. Which of the following systems of numbers are closed under division?
   (a) Natural numbers   (b) Integers   (c) Rational numbers   (d) Real numbers

6. If the numbers 1, 2, 3, 4, 5, 6, 7, 8 and 9 form a set, is this set of numbers closed under the operation of:
   (a) Addition?   (b) Subtraction?   (c) Multiplication?   (d) Division?

7. If the set of numbers consists of all even integers, is this set of numbers closed under the operation of:
   (a) Addition?   (b) Subtraction?   (c) Multiplication?   (d) Division?

8. If the set of numbers consists of all prime numbers, is this set of numbers closed under the operation of:
   (a) Addition?   (b) Subtraction?   (c) Multiplication?   (d) Division?

9. Define and illustrate each of the following:
   (a) Commutative property of addition.
   (b) Commutative property of multiplication.
   (c) Associative property of addition.
   (d) Associative property of multiplication.
   (e) Distributive property of multiplication with respect to addition.

10. When we add a column of three addends first in a down direction and check by adding in an up direction, what property are we using?

11. (a) State which property is used in each of the following:
    (1) $8 \times 9 = 9 \times 8$
    (2) $(5+3)+1 = 5+(3+1)$
    (3) $7 \times (4+5) = 7 \times 4 + 7 \times 5$
    (4) $1\frac{1}{2} + \frac{3}{4} = \frac{3}{4} + 1\frac{1}{2}$
    (5) $3 \times (6 \times 4) = (3 \times 6) \times 4$
    (6) $6 \times 2 + 6 \times 8 = 6 \times (2+8)$
    (7) $3y + 5y = (3+5)y$
    (8) $bc = cb$
    (9) $d+4 = 4+d$

    (b) Find the missing number:
    (1) $21 + 49 = 49 + ?$
    (2) $(4 \times 2) \times 8 = ? \times (2 \times 8)$
    (3) $(10 + ?) + 5 = 10 + (6 + 5)$
    (4) $5 \times 4 + 5 \times 3 = ? \times (4+3)$
    (5) $9 \times (1+7) = 9 \times 1 + ? \times 7$
    (6) $12 \times 15 = 15 \times ?$
    (7) $(r+s) + ? = r + (s+t)$
    (8) $h \times k = ? \times h$
    (9) $m + n = ? + m$

12. What properties are used to add $4+8+6$ so that 4 and 6 are paired off first and their sum added to the 8?

13. What is meant by the additive identity? What is another name for it?

14. What is meant by multiplicative identity? What is another name for it?

15. What is meant by the additive inverse?

16. What is meant by the multiplicative inverse? What is another name for it?

17. What is the additive inverse of:

 (a) 0?   (b) -3?   (c) $+8$?   (d) $-\frac{5}{6}$?   (e) $+.75$?   (f) -100?

18. What is the multiplicative inverse of:

 (a) 12?   (b) $\frac{2}{5}$?   (c) $\frac{1}{7}$?   (d) 16?   (e) $\frac{5}{8}$?   (f) $\frac{1}{10}$?

19. Which of the following is the additive identity?

 (a) 10   (b) -1 (c) 1   (d) $\frac{3}{4}$ (e) 0   (f) -6

20. Which of the following is the multiplicative identity?

 (a) -1 (b) 4   (c) 0   (d) 1   (e) -12 (f) $\frac{7}{8}$

21. What is the inverse operation of:

 (a) Addition?   (b) Subtraction?   (c) Multiplication?   (d) Division?

22. (a) Is the order of integers dense or discrete? Why?

 (b) Is the order of fractions dense or discrete? Why?

 (c) Is the order of real numbers dense or discrete? Why?

23. Show how the multiplicative identity 1 is used in each of the following:

 (a) When changing fractions to lowest terms:

 (1) $\frac{2}{4}$ (2) $\frac{9}{12}$ (3) $\frac{15}{45}$ (4) $\frac{12}{16}$ (5) $\frac{24}{54}$ (6) $\frac{38}{57}$ (7) $\frac{36}{64}$ (8) $\frac{62}{93}$

 (b) When changing fractions to higher terms:

 (1) $\frac{1}{2}$ to 16ths   (3) $\frac{2}{3}$ to 15ths   (5) $\frac{3}{4}$ to 24ths   (7) $\frac{5}{6}$ to 12ths

 (2) $\frac{1}{12}$ to 36ths   (4) $\frac{7}{10}$ to 60ths   (6) $\frac{11}{16}$ to 48ths   (8) $\frac{3}{8}$ to 72ths

 (c) When dividing by a decimal:

 (1) $.2\overline{)\,.6}$ (3) $.04\overline{)\,.32}$ (5) $1.2\overline{)\,16.8}$ (7) $.01\overline{)\,.0005}$

 (2) $.24\overline{)\,.96}$ (4) $.8\overline{)\,.024}$ (6) $.15\overline{)\,10.5}$ (8) $.007\overline{)\,.756}$

 (d) When dividing fractions:

 (1) $\frac{1}{4} \div \frac{3}{4}$ (3) $\frac{1}{2} \div \frac{7}{16}$ (5) $\frac{5}{6} \div \frac{5}{8}$ (7) $\frac{3}{10} \div 8$

 (2) $\frac{1}{3} \div \frac{1}{2}$ (4) $\frac{2}{3} \div \frac{7}{8}$ (6) $\frac{9}{10} \div \frac{3}{5}$ (8) $6 \div \frac{4}{5}$

EXERCISE 3

Systems of Numeration

In our everyday affairs we use the decimal system of notation. However, this is just one of many systems in which symbols are used to write numbers. The number of symbols in the system, their grouping, and the place value are basic to all systems of notation.

Our number system, the decimal system, contains **ten** number symbols and the value of each place is **ten** times the value of the next place to the right. We group by tens. Ten ones form a group called ten. Ten tens form a group called hundred. Ten hundreds form a group called thousand. The **base** of the decimal system of notation is **ten**. The **base** of a system of numbers is the number it takes in any one place to make 1 in the next higher place.

In each system of notation, number symbols from zero up to, but not including, the symbol used for the base are arranged by position to represent numbers. The value of each symbol depends not only on what the symbol is, but also on its position in the number. In the decimal system the symbol 6 in 68 means 6 tens but in 628 means 6 hundreds.

The number of symbols used in each system varies depending upon the base of the system and, as we shall see, also corresponds both to the ratio of the value of each place to the value of the next place to the right and to the groupings used.

In ancient times people used many bases of notation. The Egyptians used the base of ten, the Babylonians used the base of sixty, and the Mayans of Central America used the base of twenty.

In the chart below, systems of notation having bases 2 to 10 inclusive and 12 are described. For each the symbols used and the respective place values are given.

The **nonary** system of notation has the base 9. It contains **nine** symbols, the grouping is by **nines,** and the value of each place is **nine** times the value of the next place to the right.

The **binary** system of notation has the base 2. It contains **two** symbols, the grouping is by **twos,** and the value of each place is **two** times the value of the next place to the right.

The **duodecimal** system of notation has the base 12. Since it requires **twelve** basic symbols, two additional symbols are created: T for 10 and E for 11. The grouping is by **twelves** and the value of each place is **twelve** times the value of the next place to the right.

In the following chart the place values of the various systems of notation are outlined with the number 1 1 1 1 1 . 1 1 illustrated.

Name of System	Base	Symbols Used	1	1	1	1	1	.	1	1
			Place Values					Points	Place Values	
Decimal	10	0, 1, 2, 3, 4, 5, 6, 7, 8, 9	10,000	1,000	100	10	1	Decimal Point	$\frac{1}{10}$	$\frac{1}{100}$
Nonary	9	0, 1, 2, 3, 4, 5, 6, 7, 8	6,561	729	81	9	1	Nonary Point	$\frac{1}{9}$	$\frac{1}{81}$
Octonary	8	0, 1, 2, 3, 4, 5, 6, 7	4,096	512	64	8	1	Octonary Point	$\frac{1}{8}$	$\frac{1}{64}$
Septenary	7	0, 1, 2, 3, 4, 5, 6	2,401	343	49	7	1	Septenary Point	$\frac{1}{7}$	$\frac{1}{49}$
Senary	6	0, 1, 2, 3, 4, 5	1,296	216	36	6	1	Senary Point	$\frac{1}{6}$	$\frac{1}{36}$
Quinary	5	0, 1, 2, 3, 4	625	125	25	5	1	Quinary Point	$\frac{1}{5}$	$\frac{1}{25}$
Quaternary	4	0, 1, 2, 3	256	64	16	4	1	Quaternary Point	$\frac{1}{4}$	$\frac{1}{16}$
Ternary	3	0, 1, 2	81	27	9	3	1	Ternary Point	$\frac{1}{3}$	$\frac{1}{9}$
Binary	2	0, 1	16	8	4	2	1	Binary Point	$\frac{1}{2}$	$\frac{1}{4}$
Duodecimal	12	0, 1, 2, 3, 4, 5, 6, 7, 8, 9, T, E	20,736	1,728	144	12	1	Duodecimal Point	$\frac{1}{12}$	$\frac{1}{144}$

The chart on the opposite page shows what 21 in the decimal system is equivalent to in some of the other systems of notation.

The base is indicated by a subscript written at the lower right of the number. 21_{10} means 21 in base 10. If the number does not have an identifying subscript or any other description, it is assumed to be a number belonging to the decimal system.

You must remember that each system of notation has its own place values.

Changing from One Base to Another

1. To change a number in a base other than ten to a base ten number

We multiply each digit by its place value, then we add to find the sum of these products.

What base ten number is equivalent to 1243_6?

$$1243_6 = \begin{array}{cccc} 1 & 2 & 4 & 3 \\ 216\text{'s} & 36\text{'s} & 6\text{'s} & 1\text{'s} \end{array}$$

$$= 315_{10}$$

$$\begin{array}{rcl} 1 \times 216 &=& 216 \\ 2 \times 36 &=& 72 \\ 4 \times 6 &=& 24 \\ 3 \times 1 &=& \underline{3} \\ && 315 \end{array}$$

What base ten number is equivalent to 10212_3?

$$10212_3 = \begin{array}{ccccc} 1 & 0 & 2 & 1 & 2 \\ 81\text{'s} & 27\text{'s} & 9\text{'s} & 3\text{'s} & 1\text{'s} \end{array}$$

$$= 104_{10}$$

$$\begin{array}{rcl} 1 \times 81 &=& 81 \\ 2 \times 9 &=& 18 \\ 1 \times 3 &=& 3 \\ 2 \times 1 &=& \underline{2} \\ && 104 \end{array}$$

What base ten number is equivalent to 163_4?

Impossible, because symbol 6 is not used in base 4.

2. To change a base ten number to a number in a base other than ten

(a) *Quotients method*

We divide the largest possible power of the base into the given number. Then we divide the remainder by the next lower power of the base, continuing in this manner until the divisor is the base itself. The quotient of each division will give the digit for the corresponding position in the required base number. The final remainder will indicate the number of ones.

Change 567_{10} to a base four number

$$\begin{array}{r} 256)567(2 \\ \underline{512} \\ 64)55(0 \\ \underline{0} \\ 16)55(3 \\ \underline{48} \\ 4)7(1 \\ \underline{4} \\ 3 \qquad \text{Answer, } 20313_4 \end{array}$$

(b) *Remainders method*

We divide the base into the given number, then divide the base into the quotient, then divide the base into the new quotient, continuing until the quotient is zero. The remainders in these divisions will give the required digits with the final remainder used as the digit for the greatest place value and the first remainder as the digit for the ones' place.

$$\begin{array}{l} 4)567(141 \quad \text{remainder } 3 \\ 4)141(35 \quad\, \text{remainder } 1 \\ 4)35(8 \quad\;\; \text{remainder } 3 \\ 4)8(2 \quad\;\; \text{remainder } 0 \\ 4)2(0 \quad\;\; \text{remainder } 2 \\ \qquad \text{Answer, } 20313_4 \end{array}$$

3. To change a number in one base (other than ten) to another base (other than ten) number

First, change the given base number to a base ten number. Then change the base ten number to the required base number.

System	Grouping	Diagram	Grouping description	Place values					Number
Decimal System	Grouping by tens		2 tens 1 one	2 10's	1 1's				21_{10}
Nonary System	Grouping by nines		2 nines 3 ones	2 9's	3 1's				23_9
Octonary System	Grouping by eights		2 eights 5 ones	2 8's	5 1's				25_8
Septenary System	Grouping by sevens		3 sevens 0 ones	3 7's	0 1's				30_7
Senary System	Grouping by sixes		3 sixes 3 ones	3 6's	3 1's				33_6
Quinary System	Grouping by fives		4 fives 1 one	4 5's	1 1's				41_5
Quaternary System	Grouping by fours		1 sixteen 1 four 1 one	1 16's	1 4's	1 1's			111_4
Ternary System	Grouping by threes		2 nines 1 three 0 ones	2 9's	1 3's	0 1's			210_3
Binary System	Grouping by twos		1 sixteen 0 eights 1 four 0 twos 1 one	1 16's	0 8's	1 4's	0 2's	1 1's	10101_2
Duodecimal System	Grouping by twelves		1 twelve 9 ones	1 12's	9 1's				19_{12}

Change 123_5 to a base three number.

First, change 123_5 to a base ten number

$$123_5 = \begin{array}{ccc} 1 & 2 & 3 \\ 25\text{'s} & 5\text{'s} & 1\text{'s} \end{array}$$

$$= 38_{10}$$

$$\begin{aligned} 1 \times 25 &= 25 \\ 2 \times 5 &= 10 \\ 3 \times 1 &= \underline{3} \\ &\;\; 38 \end{aligned}$$

Then change 38_{10} to base three number by the quotients method.

$$\begin{array}{r} 27)\,38\,(1 \\ \underline{27} \\ 9)\,11\,(1 \\ \underline{9} \\ 3)\ \ 2\,(0 \\ \underline{0} \\ 2 \end{array} \qquad \text{Answer, } 1102_3$$

Computation in Bases Other Than Ten

We add, subtract, multiply, and divide numbers in bases other than ten as we do decimal numbers, but we use the number facts belonging to the given base.

Addition

Add the following binary numbers:

1011
1101
11
1011
————
100110

In the ones' column $1+1=10$; $10+1=11$; $11+1=100$

Write the last zero, carry the 10

In the twos' column $10+1=11$; $11+1=100$; $100+1=101$

Write the last 1, carry the 10

In the fours' column $10+1=11$

Write the last 1, carry the 1

In the eights' column $1+1=10$; $10+1=11$; $11+1=100$

Write the 100

Answer, 100110_2

Subtraction

Subtract the following duodecimal numbers:

4 9 5
2 E 3
———
1 T 2

In the ones' column 5 minus $3 = 2$

In the twelves' column, since we cannot subtract 11 twelves from 9 twelves, we take one 144's from the four 144's and make it 12 twelves. Then 9 twelves $+$ 12 twelves make 21 twelves. Now 21 twelves minus 11 twelves leave ten (or T) twelves.

In the 144's column, three 144's minus two 144's $=$ one 144's

Answer, $1T2_{12}$

Multiplication

Multiply: 120_3 by 201_3

120_3
201_3
——
120
000
1010
————
101120_3

$120 \times 1 = 120$

$120 \times 0 = 000$

$120 \times 2 = 1010$ because $0 \times 2 = 0$; $2 \times 2 = 11$, we write the 1 and carry 1; $1 \times 2 = 2$ but $2 + 1$ carried $= 10$, we write the 10

Add the partial products.

Answer, 101120_3

Division

Divide: 1332_4 by 32_4

$$32_4)\overline{1332_4}\ (21_4$$
$$\underline{130}$$
$$32$$
$$\underline{32}$$

$133_4(31_{10})$ divided by $32_4(14_{10})$ is 2_4 with remainder 3_4. Write the 2 in the quotient.

$2_4 \times 32_4 = 130_4$

32_4 divided by 32_4 is 1_4. Write the 1 in the quotient.

Answer, 21_4

Practice

1. Determine the value of the place in which the indicated digit appears in each number:

1. Digit 5 in	(a) 859_{10}	(b) 2175_9	(c) 4526_7	(d) 5204_8	(e) $65T4_{12}$
2. Digit 3 in	(a) 325_6	(b) 5631_8	(c) 43011_5	(d) $3159E_{12}$	(e) 2131021_4
3. Digit 1 in	(a) 414_7	(b) 2140_5	(c) 13023_4	(d) 120200_3	(e) 1000000_2
4. Digit 6 in	(a) 8296_{12}	(b) 5603_7	(c) 17962_9	(d) 67584_{10}	(e) 26737_8
5. Digit 8 in	(a) 3870_9	(b) $9T816_{12}$	(c) 85279_{10}	(d) 94280_{12}	(e) 42658_9
6. Digit 4 in	(a) 1432_6	(b) 42130_5	(c) $98E4T_{12}$	(d) 34675_8	(e) 405602_7
7. Digit 0 in	(a) $1TE0_{12}$	(b) 10221_3	(c) 57013_9	(d) 403324_5	(e) 101111111_2
8. Digit 9 in	(a) 493_{10}	(b) 2719_{12}	(c) 94325_{10}	(d) 1947_{12}	(e) 81956_{10}
9. Digit 2 in	(a) 284_9	(b) 12056_7	(c) 43421_5	(d) 201101_3	(e) 12030011_4
10. Digit 3 in	(a) 37041_{10}	(b) 40034_5	(c) 83745_9	(d) 311201_4	(e) 46053_7

2. Change each of the following numbers to a base ten number:

SET 1
1. 16_7
2. 235_7
3. 424_7
4. 5132_7
5. 16503_7

SET 2
1. 31_4
2. 203_4
3. 100_4
4. 2312_4
5. 31123_4

SET 3
1. 57_8
2. 236_8
3. 705_8
4. 3142_8
5. 12563_8

SET 4
1. 22_3
2. 120_3
3. 2101_3
4. 22112_3
5. 112021_3

SET 5
1. 48_9
2. 156_9
3. 413_9
4. 2007_9
5. 13185_9

SET 6
1. 32_5
2. 210_5
3. 321_5
4. 1333_5
5. 23102_5

SET 7
1. 101_2
2. 1110_2
3. 10111_2
4. 111101_2
5. 1101011_2

SET 8
1. 53_6
2. 412_6
3. 325_6
4. 2402_6
5. 13541_6

SET 9
1. $T6_{12}$
2. 74_{12}
3. $25E_{12}$
4. $T897_{12}$
5. $2ET08_{12}$

SET 10
1. 333_4
2. 1001_2
3. 423_5
4. 1111_7
5. 2222_3
6. 700_8
7. 5431_6
8. 284_9
9. $1TE_{12}$
10. 10000100_2
11. 12201_3
12. $20TET_{12}$
13. 42003_5
14. 1010011101_2
15. 13232_4

3. Change each of the following base ten numbers to a number in the indicated base:

SET 1	SET 2	SET 3
To base 5	To base 2	To base 7
1. 21	1. 23	1. 36
2. 45	2. 59	2. 91
3. 186	3. 128	3. 234
4. 2,409	4. 600	4. 1,000
5. 30,765	5. 1,325	5. 34,359

SET 4	SET 5	SET 6
To base 3	To base 9	To base 4
1. 30	1. 47	1. 51
2. 95	2. 729	2. 73
3. 146	3. 381	3. 104
4. 382	4. 1,500	4. 812
5. 1,471	5. 27,628	5. 1,735

SET 7	SET 8	SET 9
To base 12	To base 6	To base 8
1. 96	1. 42	1. 59
2. 129	2. 87	2. 112
3. 580	3. 308	3. 647
4. 1,145	4. 2,471	4. 1,000
5. 23,723	5. 10,000	5. 25,128

SET 10

1. $49 = (- ? -)_4$
2. $83 = (- ? -)_2$
3. $150 = (- ? -)_5$
4. $439 = (- ? -)_6$
5. $1,200 = (- ? -)_9$
6. $3,461 = (- ? -)_3$
7. $9,108 = (- ? -)_7$
8. $20,000 = (- ? -)_{12}$
9. $7,685 = (- ? -)_8$
10. $1,324 = (- ? -)_2$

4. Change each of the following numbers to an equivalent number in the indicated base:

SET 1
1. 423_6 to base four
2. $28E_{12}$ to base six
3. 167_8 to base three
4. 5413_7 to base two
5. 8532_9 to base five
6. 14432_5 to base two
7. $9T8_{12}$ to base nine
8. 2847_9 to base seven
9. 13321_4 to base three
10. 210211_3 to base two

SET 2
1. 2112_3 to base eight
2. 1423_5 to base six
3. 1054_6 to base nine
4. 385_9 to base twelve
5. 1467_8 to base nine
6. 10213_4 to base seven
7. 20110_3 to base five
8. 13415_7 to base twelve
9. 10101101_2 to base three
10. 11200112_3 to base four

SET 3
1. 10111_2 to $(- ? -)_5$
2. $4ET_{12}$ to $(- ? -)_8$
3. 1345_6 to $(- ? -)_4$
4. 2716_8 to $(- ? -)_9$
5. 4360_7 to $(- ? -)_3$
6. 21221_3 to $(- ? -)_6$
7. 13203_4 to $(- ? -)_{12}$
8. 5683_9 to $(- ? -)_4$
9. 64507_8 to $(- ? -)_2$
10. 14032_5 to $(- ? -)_7$

Base Two—Binary System

1. What symbols are used in the binary system?
2. How does the value of each place compare with the value of the next place to the right?
3. What is the largest digit that may appear in a binary number?
4. Construct tables like those shown at the right; then fill in the basic addition and multiplication facts.

+	0	1
0		
1		

×	0	1
0		
1		

5. Perform the indicated operations. The following are base two numbers:

$1+1=$ $\quad$ $1-1=$ $\quad$ $1\times1=$ $\quad$ $1\overline{)1}$ $\quad$ $1-0=$ $\quad$ $1\overline{)0}$ $\quad$ $10-1=$ $\quad$ $1+0=$

$111111+1=$ $\qquad$ $1111111111+1=$ $\qquad$ $11111111111111+1=$

6. Write the first fifty binary numbers beginning with 1.

7. The following are base two numbers:

(a) Add:

110	1011	10111	1011101
111	1011	10101	1110111
	1111	1111	1010101
		110111	1111111

(b) Subtract:

100	1000	111011	1110001
11	101	10110	1001010

(c) Multiply:

10	101	1101	11011
11	101	111	10110

(d) Divide:

$101\overline{)100011}$ $\quad$ $11\overline{)10010}$ $\quad$ $1001\overline{)110110}$ $\quad$ $1100\overline{)10000100}$

8. Compute the problems in Example 7 above also as follows: First, change each binary number to a base ten number. Do the indicated computation, using the equivalent base ten numbers. Then change the base ten answer to the corresponding equivalent binary answer. Check with answers in Example 7 above.

9. Electronic digital computers use the binary number system. The current in any electric circuit is either "off" or "on." Numbers can be represented electronically by a series of closed or open switches. The panel of an electronic computer has a row of light bulbs. When a light is on, it represents the symbol 1; when the light is off, it represents the symbol 0.

Information, usually in the decimal number system, is fed into the electronic computers from punched cards or punched paper tapes. The electronic computer translates this information into the binary number system, solves the problem automatically in the binary number system, then translates the answer back to the decimal system, and prints it on a card.

What decimal number does each of the following panels of lights represent if ⊘ means the light is "on" and ◯ means the light is "off"?

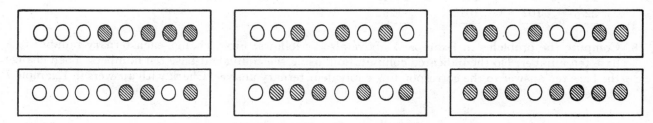

10. Card Game

Take a number from 1 to 31. On which of the following cards does your number appear?

I			
16	17	18	19
20	21	22	23
24	25	26	27
28	29	30	31

II			
8	9	10	11
12	13	14	15
24	25	26	27
28	29	30	31

III			
4	5	6	7
12	13	14	15
20	21	22	23
28	29	30	31

IV			
2	3	6	7
10	11	14	15
18	19	22	23
26	27	30	31

V			
1	3	5	7
9	11	13	15
17	19	21	23
25	27	29	31

Each card represents a place in a binary number. Card I represents the sixteens' place, card II—eights' place, card III—fours' place, card IV—twos' place, and card V—ones' place. If a card is selected as containing the required number, a 1 is pictured in the corresponding binary place; if not, a 0 is pictured.

Thus, if a number appears only on cards I, III, and V, it represents binary number 10101, which is decimal number 21. Try this game on your friends.

What number am I thinking of if it appears only on

(1) Card I?	(6) Cards I and II?	(11) Cards I, IV, and V??
(2) Card III?	(7) Cards III and V?	(12) Cards I, II, and IV?
(3) Card V?	(8) Cards I, II, and III?	(13) Cards III, IV, and V?
(4) Card II?	(9) Cards I, II, III, and IV?	(14) Cards I, II, IV, and V?
(5) Card IV?	(10) Cards I, II, III, IV, and V?	(15) Cards II, III, IV, and V?

Base Three—Ternary System

1. What symbols are used in the ternary system?
2. How does the value of each place compare with the value of the next place to the right?
3. What is the largest digit that may appear in a ternary number?
4. Construct tables like those shown at the right; then fill in the basic addition and multiplication facts.

+	0 1 2		×	0 1 2
0			0	
1			1	
2			2	

5. Perform the indicated operations. The following are base three numbers:

$$2+1= \qquad 2\times2= \qquad 2+2= \qquad 10-1= \qquad 2\overline{)11} \qquad 11-2= \qquad 2\overline{)2} \qquad 10-2=$$
$$222222+1= \qquad 22222222+1= \qquad 22222222222+1=$$

6. Write the first fifty ternary numbers beginning with 1.
7. The following are base three numbers:

(a) Add:

222	112	2011	21012
122	121	1122	11021
	222	1221	20122
		2212	11212

(b) Subtract:

201	121	2002	12100
12	22	1210	11212

(c) Multiply:

12	201	2121	20112
22	102	1012	1202

(d) Divide:

$$11\overline{)202} \qquad 20\overline{)220} \qquad 22\overline{)2002} \qquad 120\overline{)20010}$$

8. Compute the problems in Example 7 above also as follows: First, change each ternary number to a base ten number. Do the indicated computation, using the equivalent base ten numbers. Then change the base ten answer to the corresponding equivalent ternary answer. Check with answers in Example 7 above.

Base Four—Quaternary System

1. What symbols are used in the base four system?
2. How does the value of each place compare with the value of the next place to the right?
3. In the base four system what new group does 1 more than 3333 make? 1 more than 3333333?
4. Construct tables like those shown at the right; then fill in the basic addition and multiplication facts.

+	0 1 2 3		×	0 1 2 3
0			0	
1			1	
2			2	
3			3	

5. Perform the indicated operations. The following are base four numbers:

$$1+3= \qquad 3\times2= \qquad 3+2= \qquad 2+2= \qquad 3+3=\underline{\quad} \qquad 3\times3= \qquad 2\times2=\underline{\quad}$$
$$12-3= \qquad 10-2= \qquad 10-1= \qquad 11-3= \qquad 11-2= \qquad 3\overline{)21} \qquad 2\overline{)10} \qquad 3\overline{)12} \qquad 2\overline{)12}$$

6. Write the first fifty base four numbers beginning with 1.

7. The following are base four numbers:

(a) Add:

123	3102	1232	10332
233	2212	23	23131
	1233	302	31233
		3323	20233

(b) Subtract:

1000	3201	21320	30001
23	332	20221	21323

(c) Multiply:

31	23	123	3032
12	32	321	1302

(d) Divide:

$12\overline{)132}$ $3\overline{)123}$ $20\overline{)300}$ $210\overline{)11330}$

8. Compute the problems in Example 7 above also as follows: First, change each base four number to a base ten number. Do the indicated computation, using the equivalent base ten numbers. Then change the base ten answer to the corresponding equivalent base four answer. Check with answers in Example 7 above.

Base Five—Quinary System

1. What symbols are used in the quinary system?

2. How does the value of each place compare with the value of the next place to the right?

3. What is the largest digit that may appear in a quinary number?

4. Construct tables like those on the right; then fill in the basic addition and multiplication facts.

+	0	1	2	3	4
0					
1					
2					
3					
4					

×	0	1	2	3	4
0					
1					
2					
3					
4					

5. Perform the indicated operations. The following are base five numbers:

$1+4=$ $3+3=$ $2+4=$ $4+4=$ $4+3=$ $13-4=$ $12-3=$ $11-2=$ $10-3=$

$2\times4=$ $3\times3=$ $4\times3=$ $4\times4=$ $3\times4=$ $3\overline{)22}$ $4\overline{)22}$ $4\overline{)31}$ $3\overline{)14}$ $2\overline{)13}$

6. Write the first fifty quinary numbers beginning with 1.

7. The following are base five numbers:

(a) Add:

12	203	2124	31023
23	134	1313	10344
41	123	4043	21334
		1324	40241

(b) Subtract:

132	301	2003	31031
44	243	1214	3422

(c) Multiply:

34	123	241	3024
23	43	134	1432

(d) Divide:

$4\overline{)103}$ $13\overline{)143}$ $23\overline{)404}$ $341\overline{)23403}$

8. Compute the problems in Example 7 above also as follows: First, change each quinary number to a base ten number. Do the indicated computation, using the equivalent base ten numbers. Then change the base ten answer to the corresponding equivalent quinary number. Check with answers in Example 7 above.

Base Six—Senary System

1. What symbols are used in the base six system?

2. How does the value of each place compare with the value of the next place to the right?

3. In the base six system what new group does 1 more than 5555 make? 1 more than 5555555?

4. Construct tables like those shown at the right; then fill in the basic addition and multiplication facts.

+	0	1	2	3	4	5
0						
1						
2						
3						
4						
5						

×	0	1	2	3	4	5
0						
1						
2						
3						
4						
5						

5. Perform the indicated operations. The following are base six numbers:

$5+2=$ $3+5=$ $4+4=$ $5+4=$ $1+5=$ $14-5=$ $11-3=$ $12-5=$ $10-2=$ $13-4=$

$5\times5=$ $4\times4=$ $3\times5=$ $2\times3=$ $2\times4=$ $4\overline{)32}$ $2\overline{)14}$ $5\overline{)41}$ $3\overline{)20}$ $4\overline{)24}$

6. Write the first fifty base six numbers beginning with 1.

7. The following are base six numbers:

(a) Add:

35	214	1243	35245
44	505	3034	14335
	435	1425	50545
		5354	34425

(b) Subtract:

52	400	2124	34053
34	103	435	25544

(c) Multiply:

34	142	405	5213
25	53	502	1534

(d) Divide:

$5\overline{)50}$ $13\overline{)213}$ $20\overline{)420}$ $154\overline{)13420}$

8. Compute the problems in Example 7 above also as follows: First, change each base six number to a base ten number. Do the indicated computation, using the equivalent base ten numbers. Then change the base ten answer to the corresponding equivalent base six number. Check with answers in Example 7 above.

Base Seven—Septenary System

1. What symbols are used in the septenary system?
2. How does the value of each place compare with the value of the next place to the right?
3. What is the largest digit that may appear in a septenary number?
4. Construct tables like those shown at the right; then fill in the basic addition and multiplication facts.

+	0	1	2	3	4	5	6
0							
1							
2							
3							
4							
5							
6							

×	0	1	2	3	4	5	6
0							
1							
2							
3							
4							
5							
6							

5. Perform the indicated operations. The following are base seven numbers:

$5+6=$ $6+6=$ $4+5=$ $5+5=$ $6+3=$ $14-5=$ $13-6=$ $12-3=$ $11-5=$ $15-6=$

$6\times4=$ $5\times3=$ $5\times5=$ $4\times5=$ $6\times6=$ $3\overline{)24}$ $4\overline{)22}$ $6\overline{)51}$ $2\overline{)15}$ $5\overline{)42}$

6. Write the first fifty septenary numbers beginning with 1.

7. The following are base seven numbers:

(a) Add:

66	345	5226	13265
46	265	2034	5064
	536	3451	24362
		1365	662

(b) Subtract:

100	324	4145	54021
65	216	1355	35342

(c) Multiply:

63	245	165	4650
45	653	346	4563

(d) Divide:

$6\overline{)106}$ $30\overline{)450}$ $66\overline{)3531}$ $204\overline{)21522}$

8. Compute the problems in Example 7 above also as follows: First change each septenary number to a base ten number. Do the indicated computation, using the equivalent base ten numbers. Then change the base ten answer to the corresponding equivalent septenary number. Check with answers in Example 7 above.

Base Eight—Octonary System

1. What symbols are used in the octonary system?
2. How does the value of each place compare with the value of the next place to the right?
3. In the octonary system what new group does 1 more than 77777 make?
4. Construct tables like those shown at the right; then fill in basic addition and multiplication facts.

+	0	1	2	3	4	5	6	7
0								
1								
2								
3								
4								
5								
6								
7								

×	0	1	2	3	4	5	6	7
0								
1								
2								
3								
4								
5								
6								
7								

5. Perform the indicated operations. The following are base eight numbers:

$6+7=$ $5+3=$ $4+6=$ $7+7=$ $6+5=$ $12-5=$ $14-6=$ $11-3=$ $16-7=$ $13-4=$

$5\times6=$ $6\times7=$ $7\times7=$ $7\times5=$ $4\times4=$ $6)\overline{44}$ $4)\overline{24}$ $5)\overline{31}$ $7)\overline{61}$ $6)\overline{44}$

6. Write the first fifty octonary numbers beginning with 1.
7. The following are base eight numbers:

(a) Add:

```
  57      326     2036     43725
  64      277     1175     24576
  --      475     4367     36657
          ---     6574     50557
                  ----     -----
```

(b) Subtract:

```
  62      405     5001     70304
  37      216      647     65214
  --      ---     ----     -----
```

(c) Multiply:

```
  36      125     4371     7564
  67      375     5672     6457
  --      ---     ----     ----
```

(d) Divide:

$6)\overline{132}$ $14)\overline{250}$ $44)\overline{1760}$ $113)\overline{14347}$

8. Compute the problems in Example 7 above also as follows: First, change each octonary number to a base ten number. Do the indicated computation, using the equivalent base ten numbers. Then change the base ten answer to the corresponding equivalent octonary number. Check with answers in Example 7 above.

Base Nine—Nonary System

1. What symbols are used in the nonary system?
2. How does the value of each place compare with the value of the next place to the right?
3. In the nonary system what new group does 1 more than 8888 make? 1 more than 888888?
4. Construct tables like those shown at the right; then fill in the basic addition and multiplication facts.

+	0	1	2	3	4	5	6	7	8
0									
1									
2									
3									
4									
5									
6									
7									
8									

×	0	1	2	3	4	5	6	7	8
0									
1									
2									
3									
4									
5									
6									
7									
8									

5. Perform the indicated operations. The following are base nine numbers:

$6+7=$ $7+8=$ $8+4=$ $7+5=$ $8+8=$ $16-7=$ $13-6=$ $12-5=$ $17-8=$ $11-6=$

$6\times8=$ $7\times4=$ $8\times8=$ $4\times3=$ $5\times6=$ $7)\overline{62}$ $6)\overline{46}$ $3)\overline{16}$ $8)\overline{71}$ $5)\overline{38}$

6. Write the first fifty nonary numbers beginning with 1.

7. The following are base nine numbers:

(a) Add:

78	465	3827	20168
57	88	4854	55377
	658	2868	43426
		5875	36768

(b) Subtract:

84	300	4136	76102
67	38	2657	17084

(c) Multiply:

36	482	5761	2876
75	168	847	7085

(d) Divide:

8)116   16)440   58)2618   121)13804

8. Compute the problems in Example 7 above also as follows: First, change each nonary number to a base ten number. Do the indicated computation, using the equivalent base ten numbers. Then change the base ten answer to the corresponding equivalent nonary number. Check with answers in Example 7 above.

Base Twelve—Duodecimal System

1. What symbols are used in the duodecimal system?

2. How does the value of each place compare with the value of the next place to the right?

3. In the duodecimal system what new group does 1 more than EEEE make? 1 more than EEEEEE?

4. Construct tables like those shown at the right; then fill in the basic addition and multiplication facts.

+	0 1 2 3 4 5 6 7 8 9 T E
0	
1	
2	
3	
4	
5	
6	
7	
8	
9	
T	
E	

×	0 1 2 3 4 5 6 7 8 9 T E
0	
1	
2	
3	
4	
5	
6	
7	
8	
9	
T	
E	

5. Perform the indicated operations. The following are base twelve numbers:

$8+5=$ $T+E=$ $9+6=$ $7+7=$ $E+9=$ $16-9=$ $17-8=$ $1T-E=$ $12-5=$ $18-T=$

$9\times T=$ $E\times E=$ $7\times 8=$ $5\times 7=$ $6\times 9=$ 8)40   3)16   T)5T   E)92   4)28

6. Write the first fifty duodecimal numbers beginning with 1.

7. The following are base twelve numbers:

(a) Add:

7T	258	4207	17T45
E5	93E	2596	8E59
	476	3278	598
		5869	627E3

(b) Subtract:

93	675	3200	58124
4E	89	1T27	37465

(c) Multiply:

T4	156	3507	267E
2E	789	4E3	T958

(d) Divide:

T)2E0   13)526   44)2T80   105)7811

8. Compute the problems in Example 7 above also as follows: First, change each duodecimal number to a base ten number. Do the indicated computation, using the equivalent base ten numbers. Then change the base ten answer to the corresponding equivalent duodecimal number. Check with answers in Example 7 above.

EXERCISE 4

Scientific Notation

Both very large numbers and very small numbers may be expressed by scientific notation. This concise notation is extremely useful in scientific work, and a similar brief form is now becoming popular in newspapers and periodicals. In print 4,300,000 is seen as 4.3 million. In scientific notation instead of writing out the word million, we use a power of 10 as $4,300,000 = 4.3 \times 10^6$.

To write a number more than ten by scientific notation, (1) we first rewrite the significant figures: (a) as a whole number if there is only one significant figure, (b) as a mixed decimal if there are two or more significant figures, using the first figure as the whole number and all others as the decimal part; (2) then we indicate multiplication (using $\times$ sign) by the required power of ten.

We determine the power of ten by dividing the mixed decimal into the given number. Then we change the quotient into a power of ten by using a positive integer for the exponent.

In this way we write a number that is more than 1 but less than 10 multiplied by some power of 10.

Write 750 by scientific notation.	Write 8,430,000,000 by scientific notation.
$750 = 7.5 \times ?$	$8,430,000,000 = 8.43 \times ?$
Divide: $7.5\overline{)750} = 100$	Divide: $8.43\overline{)8430000000} = 1,000,000,000$
$750 = 7.5 \times 100$	$8,430,000,000 = 8.43 \times 1,000,000,000$
However, $100 = 10^2$	However, $1,000,000,000 = 10^9$
$750 = 7.5 \times 10^2$	$8,430,000,000 = 8.43 \times 10^9$
Answer: 7.5×10^2	Answer: 8.43×10^9

Here is a quick way to obtain the required power. Count the number of places the decimal point is being moved. This number will be the required exponent in the power of 10.

$$2480 = 2480 = 2.48 \times 10^3$$

The decimal point is being moved 3 places to the left. The positive integer 3 is used as the exponent.

In division of monomials we subtract the exponent of the literal quantity in the divisor from the exponent of the same literal quantity in the dividend.

Thus
$$\frac{a^5}{a^5} = a^{5-5} = a^0, \qquad \text{(when } a \neq 0\text{)}$$

However
$$\frac{a^5}{a^5} = 1$$

It follows that $a^0 = 1$.

Therefore we may say that

A quantity raised to the zero (0) power is equal to 1.

This means that $10^0 = 1$, $\qquad 8^0 = 1$, $\qquad 2^0 = 1$, $\qquad 12^0 = 1$.

Also if we use the division principle for simplifying $\dfrac{a^5}{a^6}$ (when $a \neq 0$), we get:

$$\frac{a^5}{a^6} = a^{5-6} = a^{-1}$$

But changing $\dfrac{a^5}{a^6}$ to lowest terms we get:

$$\frac{a^5}{a^6} = \frac{1}{a}$$

It follows that
$$\frac{1}{a} = a^{-1}$$

This means that $\quad \frac{1}{10}=10^{-1}, \quad \frac{1}{8}=8^{-1}, \quad \frac{1}{2}=2^{-1}, \quad \frac{1}{12}=12^{-1}$

Similarly, if we use the division principle for simplifying $\frac{a^5}{a^7}$ (when $a\neq 0$), we get:

$$\frac{a^5}{a^7}=a^{5-7}=a^{-2}$$

But changing to lowest terms: $\quad \dfrac{a^5}{a^7}=\dfrac{1}{a^2}$

Therefore $\qquad\qquad\qquad \dfrac{1}{a^2}=a^{-2}$

This means $\qquad\quad \dfrac{1}{10^2}=10^{-2}, \quad \dfrac{1}{8^2}=8^{-2}, \quad \dfrac{1}{2^2}=2^{-2}, \quad \dfrac{1}{12^2}=12^{-2}$

To write a number less than 1 by scientific notation, we use the same procedure as in writing very large numbers except that we express the power of ten by using a negative integer as the exponent.

Write .0000025 by scientific notation.

$.0000025=2.5\times ?$

$2.5\overline{)\,.0000025}=.000001=\dfrac{1}{1,000,000}=\dfrac{1}{10^6}=10^{-6}$

Therefore $.0000025=2.5\times 10^{-6}$

Answer, 2.5×10^{-6}

Or we count the number of places the decimal is being moved. This will correspond to the required exponent in the power of 10.

$$.0000025=.0000025=2.5\times 10^{-6}$$

The decimal point is being moved 6 places to the right. The negative integer 6 is used as the exponent.

We multiply and divide large and small numbers by using scientific notation. The work will be simplified, and the answer will be expressed in a more compact form.

When we expand a base ten number like 4,825, we write it as:

$$4\times 1,000+8\times 100+2\times 10+5$$

Using $1=10^0$; $\quad 10=10^1$; $\quad 100=10\times 10=10^2$; $\quad 1,000=10\times 10\times 10=10^3$, $\quad$ etc.
We could write 4,825 as the following polynomial:

$$4\times 10^3+8\times 10^2+2\times 10^1+5\times 10^0$$

Since $\qquad\qquad \dfrac{1}{a}=a^{-1}; \quad \dfrac{1}{a^2}=a^{-2}; \quad \dfrac{1}{a^3}=a^{-3} \quad$ when $\quad a\neq 0$

then $\qquad\qquad \dfrac{1}{10}=10^{-1}; \quad \dfrac{1}{10^2}=10^{-2}; \quad \dfrac{1}{10^3}=10^{-3} \quad$ etc.

Using the above notation when expanding a number like 764.238 in the powers of ten, we may write it as the following polynomial:

$$764.238=7\times 100+6\times 10+4\times 1+2\times\frac{1}{10}+3\times\frac{1}{100}+8\times\frac{1}{1000}$$

$$=7\times 10^2+6\times 10^1+4\times 10^0+2\times 10^{-1}+3\times 10^{-2}+8\times 10^{-3}$$

Practice

1. Express each of the following numbers by scientific notation:

SET 1	SET 2	SET 3	SET 4	SET 5	SET 6
1. 20	1. 300	1. 4,000	1. 90,000	1. 8,000,000	1. 3,000,000,000
2. 50	2. 800	2. 9,800	2. 700,000	2. 40,000,000	2. 45,000,000,000
3. 38	3. 450	3. 6,350	3. 81,000	3. 6,100,000	3. 8,040,000,000
4. 91	4. 286	4. 8,198	4. 117,300	4. 125,400,000	4. 160,000,000,000
5. 67	5. 715	5. 5,004	5. 246,000	5. 90,520,000	5. 7,225,000,000,000

SET 7	SET 8	SET 9
1. 400000000000	1. 23.8	1. 402.3
2. 8300000000000	2. 82.2	2. 158.7
3. 274000000000000	3. 60.53	3. 245.96
4. 9610000000000000	4. 31.47	4. 3386.2
5. 7800000000000000000	5. 74.914	5. 4724.05

2. Express the numbers in each of the following by scientific notation:

(a) Our Solar System

Planet	Distance from Sun	Diameter
Mercury	36,000,000 miles	3,100 miles
Venus	67,000,000 miles	7,700 miles
Earth	93,000,000 miles	7,900 miles
Mars	142,000,000 miles	4,300 miles
Jupiter	484,000,000 miles	88,000 miles
Saturn	887,000,000 miles	71,000 miles
Uranus	1,790,000,000 miles	32,000 miles
Neptune	2,800,000,000 miles	31,000 miles
Pluto	3,680,000,000 miles	8,000 miles

(b) The astronautical unit 93,000,000 miles, the parsec 19,150,000,000,000 miles, and the light-year 5,880,000,000,000 miles are units used to measure distance.

(c) The earth is about 4,500,000,000 years old, has an area of 196,940,000 square miles of which 54,225,000 square miles is land and 142,715,000 square miles is water.
The weight of the earth is about 6,600,000,000,000,000,000,000 tons.
The earth travels 595,000,000 miles in its orbit around the sun.

(d) The cash position of the United States Treasury was reported recently as: Balance $5,188,403,078; deposits fiscal year, $26,227,581,052; withdrawals fiscal year, $34,077,932,030; total debt, $291,127,816,620; gold assets, $19,584,442,771. Round off each number to the nearest billion before expressing it by scientific notation.

(e) The National Bureau of Standards has coined new prefixes to help mathematicians and scientists to express very large numbers and very small numbers. **Tera** means one trillion, and **giga** means one billion. The old prefix **mega** means one million, and **kilo** means one thousand.

Express each of the following in scientific notation:

(1) 4.6 teradollars	(2) 390 kilocycles	(3) 95 gigamiles
(4) 6.9 megavolts	(5) 82 teramiles	(6) 703 gigadollars

(f) A million is a thousand thousand (1,000,000).
A billion is a thousand million (1,000,000,000).
A trillion is a thousand billion (1,000,000,000,000).
A quadrillion is a thousand trillion (1,000,000,000,000,000).
A quintillion is a thousand quadrillion (1,000,000,000,000,000,000).
A sextillion is a thousand quintillion (1,000,000,000,000,000,000,000).
A septillion is a thousand sextillion (1,000,000,000,000,000,000,000,000).

An octillion is a thousand septillion (1,000,000,000,000,000,000,000,000,000).
A nonillion is a thousand octillion (1,000,000,000,000,000,000,000,000,000,000).
A decillion is a thousand nonillion (1,000,000,000,000,000,000,000,000,000,000,000).
A vigintillion in figures is 1,000,000,000,000,000,000,000,000,000,000,000,000,000,000,000,000,000,-000,000,000,000.

Express each of the following in scientific notation:

(1) 62 sextillion	(2) 418 trillion	(3) 2.9 decillion
(4) 786 million	(5) 37 quadrillion	(6) 16.5 billion
(7) 43 quintillion	(8) 195 octillion	(9) 7.6 vigintillion
(10) 19 nonillion	(11) 23.4 quintillion	(12) 543.1 quadrillion

3. Express each of the following numbers by scientific notation:

SET 1	SET 2	SET 3	SET 4	SET 5
1. .3	1. .05	1. .009	1. .0000008	1. .000000002
2. .2	2. .14	2. .052	2. .00019	2. .00000085
3. .9	3. .07	3. .681	3. .000583	3. .000000476
4. .6	4. .39	4. .208	4. .0000036	4. .0000000504
5. .7	5. .86	5. .074	5. .0042	5. .00000000000028

4. (a) A refined optical microscope permits an observer to see a germ .000004 inch in diameter. Express in scientific notation.

   (b) The new prefixes adopted by the National Bureau of Standards to represent small numbers is **nano** meaning one billionth and **pico** meaning one trillionth. The old prefix **milli** means one thousandth and **micro** means one millionth.

   Express each of the following in scientific notation:

(1) 54 millimeters	(2) 9.3 microseconds	(3) 28 picoinches
(4) 162 nanoseconds	(5) 17 picovolts	(6) 7.5 nanometers

5. Simplify by scientific notation:

SET 1	SET 2	SET 3	SET 4
1. 24×10^9	1. 35.6×10^7	1. $.4 \times 10^5$	1. 40.25×10^8
2. 51×10^6	2. 60.3×10^2	2. $.08 \times 10^7$	2. 63.87×10^3
3. 109×10^8	3. 428.7×10^{16}	3. $.69 \times 10^{14}$	3. 88.49×10^{11}
4. 395×10^{12}	4. 100.2×10^{20}	4. $.258 \times 10^9$	4. 56.015×10^4
5. 487×10^{15}	5. 51.9×10^{13}	5. $.936 \times 10^{11}$	5. 248.362×10^{10}

6. Using scientific notation, multiply:

SET 1	SET 2
1. 5.9×10^3 by 3.8×10^5	1. $48,000 \times 900,000$
2. 8.1×10^{16} by 4.7×10^{19}	2. $63,000,000 \times 2,700,000$
3. 4.2×10^{12} by 1.5×10^{-4}	3. $2,100,000,000 \times 3,700,000,000$
4. 3.5×10^{-3} by 2.8×10^{-6}	4. $.000025 \times .000000054$
5. 9.3×10^{-11} by 6.2×10^{-7}	5. $.00000149 \times .0000000006$

7. Using scientific notation, divide:

SET 1	SET 2
1. 4.8×10^{12} by 3.2×10^4	1. $93,000,000$ by $12,000$
2. 5.4×10^{15} by 2.4×10^{11}	2. $200,000,000$ by $250,000$
3. 6.3×10^{17} by 1.8×10^6	3. $560,000,000$ by $160,000$
4. 7.7×10^{10} by 4.4×10^3	4. $765,000,000,000$ by $34,000,000$
5. 3.5×10^{21} by 2.8×10^{12}	5. $49,000,000,000$ by $280,000,000$

8. Expand each of the following numbers as polynomials using powers of ten:

SET 1	SET 2	SET 3	SET 4	SET 5
1. 36	1. 4,609	1. 2,803,127	1. .6	1. 54.8
2. 827	2. 5,428	2. 3,546,829	2. .27	2. 9.71
3. 903	3. 61,234	3. 49,027,351	3. .145	3. 26.43
4. 271	4. 86,585	4. 716,829,345	4. .0328	4. 318.259
5. 695	5. 325,870	5. 8,254,130,526	5. .58923	5. 8,624.5704

9. Expand each of the following numbers as polynomials using the powers of its base:

SET 1	SET 2	SET 3	SET 4
1. 32_6	1. 4136_7	1. $.5_8$	1. 2.3_4
2. 51_8	2. 2120_3	2. $.32_5$	2. 13.24_5
3. 123_4	3. 37925_{12}	3. $.69_{12}$	3. 35.024_6
4. 768_9	4. 100111_2	4. $.435_9$	4. 11011.111_2
5. 829_{12}	5. 2301231_4	5. $.1011_2$	5. 12021.01221_3

UNIT REVIEW

1. Which of the following are natural numbers? Integers? Rational numbers? Irrational numbers? Real numbers?

7	$\sqrt{7}$	-6	.2	$\frac{3}{4}$	$\sqrt{15}$	18
-3.4	16	$\sqrt{-17}$	50	$8\frac{1}{2}$	$12\sqrt{-1}$	$-\frac{2}{5}$

2. Write six different names or numerical ways of expressing 8.

3. (a) Is 51 a prime or a composite number? Why?
   (b) Write all the prime numbers greater than 16 but less than 42.

4. Express 48 as a product of prime factors.

5. (a) Is 21 an odd or even number?
   (b) Is the sum of two consecutive numbers an odd or even number?
   (c) Is the product of two even numbers an odd or even number?

6. Is the set of non-negative integers closed under the operation of (a) Addition? (b) Subtraction? (c) Multiplication? (d) Division?

7. Is the set of numbers consisting of 2, 4, 6, 8, 10 closed under the operation of division?

8. State which property is used in each of the following:
   (a) $32+19=19+32$ (b) $5\times(9\times6)=5\times9+5\times6$ (c) $(7\times2)\times8=7\times(2\times8)$

9. (a) What is the additive inverse of -45? $+10$? $-\frac{2}{3}$? $+1.2$?
   (b) What is the multiplicative inverse of 6? $\frac{4}{5}$? 25? $\frac{1}{12}$?

10. What number is the additive identity? What number is the multiplicative identity?

11. Find the value of the place in which the digit 2 appears in each of the following:
    (a) 1276_8 (b) 21054_6 (c) 18542_{12} (d) 10123_4 (e) 112011_3

12. Change each of the following numbers to a base ten number:
    (a) 857_9 (b) 21020_3 (c) 4356_7 (d) $E14T_{12}$ (e) 101110111_2

13. Change each of the following numbers to a number in the indicated base:
    (a) $246_{10}=(-?-)_5$ (d) $638_9=(-?-)_6$ (g) $13230_4=(-?-)_{12}$
    (b) $573_{10}=(-?-)_8$ (e) $12201_3=(-?-)_7$ (h) $5716_8=(-?-)_4$
    (c) $1245_{10}=(-?-)_4$ (f) $1011011_2=(-?-)_5$ (i) $4TE5_{12}=(-?-)_2$

14. What symbols are used in the binary system? Quinary system? Duodecimal system?

15. Compute:

Add:	Subtract:	Multiply:	Divide:
6573_8	52614_7	234_5	$122_3 \overline{)22012_3}$
4657_8	34256_7	132_5	

16. Express each of the following by scientific notation:

(a) 450,000   (b) .00082   (c) 3,800,000,000   (d) .0000005   (e) 926,000,000,000,000

17. Using scientific notation, multiply:

(a) 6.8×10^7 by 4.9×10^3 (d) $.00012 \times .00000024$
(b) 5.1×10^{-9} by 3.2×10^{-12} (e) 4.3×10^{15} by 1.8×10^{-20}
(c) $26,000,000 \times 3,600,000,000$ (f) $5,100,000$ by $.0000079$

18. Using scientific notation, divide:

(a) 3.6×10^{18} by 1.6×10^3 (c) 42,000,000 by 28,000
(b) 4.9×10^{25} by 1.4×10^{16} (d) 630,000,000,000 by 180,000,000

19. Using powers of ten expand each of the following as a polynomial:

(a) 568   (b) 96,452   (c) 4,609,723   (d) .1296   (e) 5261.425

20. Using the powers of its base expand each of the following as a polynomial:

(a) 101101_2 (b) 5396_{12} (c) 20121_3 (d) 563247_8 (e) 3101232_4

INTRODUCTION TO SUPPLEMENTARY UNIT TWO

In traditional mathematics the equation is considered to be one of the most powerful tools in the subject. The formal study of simple equations, fractional equations, literal equations, quadratic equations, and radical equations in first-year algebra develops concepts and techniques so that problems and the related applications of formulas may be handled successfully. Equations are especially useful when they are associated with the practical formulas of science and business.

In contemporary mathematics the equation is only one part of a wider subject area. Included are the inequations or inequalities employing a new language, vocabulary, and symbolism. We find there are true equations and false equations, true inequalities and false inequalities. Set language together with its symbolism is presented as a comprehensive way of treating this broader subject.

In this unit first number sentences and then open sentences are described. Set language is then introduced so that it may be used when dealing with the solution of equations and inequalities. The concept of the solution set or truth set and its limitation by the replacement sets is developed. Subsets and the notation, operations with sets, and Venn diagrams are studied to round out the idea of sets. Some introductory ideas of logic and their relationship to number sentences are also included.

SUPPLEMENTARY UNIT TWO—OPEN SENTENCES, EQUATIONS AND INEQUALITIES, SETS AND LOGIC

EXERCISE 5

Number Sentences—Open Sentences

Sentences that deal with numbers are called **number sentences.**

$6+1=3+4$ is a number sentence.
It reads "Six plus one is equal to three plus four."
$x-3=8$ is also a number sentence.
It reads "x minus three is equal to eight."

An **equation** is a number sentence. Equations are sometimes called equalities. The symbol "$=$" is the equality sign. It means "is equal to" and is the verb in the sentence. The expressions on both sides of the equality sign designate the same number.

When one number is greater than or less than a second number, an **inequality** exists. Inequalities, also called inequations, are sentences. Symbols of inequality include $\neq$, $<$, $>$, $\nless$, $\ngtr$, $\leq$, $\geq$. Each symbol is a verb in a number sentence.

1. The symbol $\neq$ means "is not equal to."

The inequality $n+9 \neq 15$ is read "n plus nine is not equal to fifteen."

2. The symbol $<$ means "is less than."

The inequality $y<7$ is read "y is less than seven."

3. The symbol $>$ means "is greater than."

The inequality $C-2>5$ is read "C minus two is greater than five."

4. The symbol $\nless$ means "is not less than."

The inequality $3x \nless 6$ is read "Three x is not less than six."

5. The symbol $\ngtr$ means "is not greater than."

The inequality $a+4 \ngtr 8$ is read "a plus four is not greater than eight."

6. The symbol $\leqq$ or $\leq$ means "is equal to or is less than."

The inequality $m \leq 3$ is read "m is equal to or is less than three."

7. The symbol $\geqq$ or $\geq$ means "is equal to or is greater than."

The inequality $x+1 \geq 7$ is read "x plus one is equal to or is greater than seven."

It should be noted that the symbol $\nless$ (is not less than) is equivalent to $\geq$ (is equal to or is greater than). Also the symbol $\ngtr$ (is not greater than) is equivalent to $\leq$ (is equal to or is less than).

8. The symbol $\nleqq$ means "is not less than or not equal to."

9. The symbol $\ngeqq$ means "is not greater than or not equal to."

It should be noted that the symbol $\nleqq$ is equivalent to the symbol $>$ and the symbol $\ngeqq$ is equivalent to the symbol $<$.

10. To indicate x is greater than 10 but less than 18, we write $x>10$ and $x<18$ or we combine them as $10<x<18$.

11. To indicate y is less than 5 but greater than 2, we write $y < 5$ and $y > 2$ or we combine them as $5 > y > 2$.

12. To indicate n is greater than or is equal to 4 but is less than or is equal to 14, we write $4 \leq n \leq 14$.

13. To indicate d is less than or is equal to 15 but is greater than or is equal to 7, we write $15 \geq d \geq 7$.

Number sentences like

$$x = 5 \qquad\qquad n + 6 = 15 \qquad\qquad y > 6 \qquad\qquad t - 2 < 10$$

are called **open sentences** because they contain a letter, called the **variable,** which holds a place open for a number that may be substituted for it. Thus we see both equations and inequalities are open sentences.

A sentence that is either true or false is called a **statement.** However, it cannot be both true and false at one time. An open sentence is not a statement. It is only after we substitute a number for the variable that we can determine whether the sentence is true or false. Then the sentence becomes a statement.

Practice

1. Read, or write in words, each of the following:

SET 1

(a) $6 > 4$

(b) $3 < 10$

(c) $4 + 5 > -6$

(d) $11 - 3 < 9$

(e) $44 > 8 \times 5$

(f) $16 < 9 + 8$

(g) $29 + 7 > 24 + 6$

(h) $12 - 3 < 21 - 5$

(i) $7 - 15 > 2 - 13$

(j) $12 + 19 < 37 - 4$

SET 2

(a) $8 \not> 10$

(b) $17 \not< 14$

(c) $-5 \neq 0$

(d) $9 \times 6 \not> 56$

(e) $7 - 10 \not< -2$

(f) $11 + 5 \neq 10 + 8$

(g) $6 - 3 \not< 22 - 19$

(h) $12 + 7 \neq 6 + 12$

(i) $8 - 17 \not> 23 - 14$

(j) $4 + 8 \neq 12 - 12$

SET 3

(a) $x > 9$

(b) $3y < 21$

(c) $n + 4 > 15$

(d) $c - 6 < 13$

(e) $8b \not> 48$

(f) $m - 9 \not< 5$

(g) $7 > a + 15$

(h) $14 < 5d - 6$

(i) $10x - 8 \neq 3x + 27$

(j) $\dfrac{n}{5} < 9$

SET 4

(a) $s \leq 7$

(b) $10d \geq 50$

(c) $4n \leq -24$

(d) $8 \geq r + 2$

(e) $9t + 6 \leq 15$

(f) $b - 10 \leq 23$

(g) $n \leq 15$

(h) $6y \geq 18$

(i) $4 + x \leq x$

(j) $2m + 4 \geq m - 17$

SET 5

(a) $-5 < n < 10$

(b) $-3 < b < 7$

(c) $18 > r > 0$

(d) $25 > c > 11$

(e) $1 < x < 8$

SET 6

(a) $8 \leq a \leq 17$

(b) $14 \geq d \geq -3$

(c) $4 \leq y < 11$

(d) $-6 < r \leq -1$

(e) $0 \leq k \leq 16$

2. Which of the following are true statements and which are false statements?

(a) $8=6$ $14=14$ $10=15$ $-5=+5$ $-9=-9$

(b) $7>5$ $13>16$ $-6>-4$ $.2>.02$ $0>-5$

(c) $4<10$ $\frac{5}{6}<\frac{2}{3}$ $5<-3$ $-1<0$ $8<\frac{3}{4}\times12$

(d) $3\neq2$ $1\frac{4}{5}\neq1.8$ $\frac{3}{8}\neq\frac{6}{3}$ $-3\neq3$ $5\times.6\neq5.6$

(e) $1\not>0$ $-7\not>6$ $15\not>21$ $\frac{7}{8}\not>\frac{8}{7}$ $-4\not>-1$

(f) $9\not<15$ $\frac{3}{4}\not<\frac{5}{12}$ $2.6\not<2.66$ $1\frac{1}{2}\leq1\frac{4}{7}$ $0\not<-2$

3. Which of the following are true statements and which are false statements?

(a) $6+9=8+5$ $7+3=3+7$ $5-2=2-5$ $4\times8=8\times4$

(b) $1-8>3-6$ $9+5>21-8$ $9\times\frac{2}{3}>\frac{3}{5}\times10$ $6\times1.5>10-.6$

(c) $13+2<-4$ $4-11<11-4$ $7+.2<9-1.8$ $2\frac{3}{4}+1\frac{1}{2}<8\frac{1}{2}-3\frac{5}{6}$

(d) $14-14\neq5$ $6\times1\neq6\times0$ $25-7\neq12+6$ $9-3\neq3-9$

(e) $6-7\not>4$ $8\times7\not>81-29$ $1+0\not>0-1$ $-2-5\not>15-21$

(f) $19\not<36-15$ $6+5\not<5+6$ $12-12\not<20-20$ $\dfrac{-12}{-4}\not<\dfrac{-8}{2}$

4. Which of the following are true statements and which are false statements?

(a) $6+9+4=9+4+6$

(b) $8\cdot6-3\neq8-3\cdot6$

(c) $9(10-1)>10(9-1)$

(d) $13-18\not>4-(2+7)$

(e) $8(4+9)<8\cdot4+8\cdot9$

(f) $-2(4-11)\not<4(9)$

(g) $5\cdot4+5\cdot3=4(5+3)$

(h) $2^3<3^2$

(i) $6(3-2)>6\cdot3-6\cdot2$

(j) $2(3+7)\neq2\cdot3+2\cdot7$

(k) $-3(2-10)\not<3(10-2)$

(l) $(5)^2\not>(-5)^2$

(m) $(11-8)(8-5)>11-8(8-5)$

(n) $5(9+4)\neq5\cdot9+4$

(o) $2-7(3+4)<-5(3+4)$

5. Determine whether the resulting statements are true or false when the indicated numbers are substituted for the variable in the open sentences.

(a) $n+2=9$ when $n=4$?   when $n=7$?   when $n=-7$?

(b) $5x-3=7$ when $x=8$?   when $x=1$?   when $x=2$?

(c) $6b>18$ when $b=4$?   when $b=3$?   when $b=2$?

(d) $-9r>27$ when $r=-3$?   when $r=-6$?   when $r=3$?

(e) $8y+3y<33$ when $y=2$?   when $y=3$?   when $y=4$?

(f) $12a-5<2a+65$ when $a=-7$?   when $a=9$?   when $a=7$?

(g) $-16c\neq-64$ when $c=4$?   when $c=-3$?   when $c=6$?

(h) $7x+(2x-8)\not>10$ when $x=0$?   when $x=2$?   when $x=-3$?

(i) $.04n\not<28$ when $n=400$?   when $n=700$?   when $n=900$?

(j) $\dfrac{n}{3}+\dfrac{n}{4}\not>14$ when $n=48$?   when $n=18$?   when $n=24$?

EXERCISE 6

Sets

We all are acquainted with sets. At home we use a set of dishes and a set of silverware. Your father may own a set of tools. At school your teachers may distribute class sets of textbooks. Your mathematics teacher may possess sets of rulers, protractors, and compasses.

The subjects you are studying this semester, the members of your class, the members of the school faculty, the members of the school board, make up groups. Each group may be called a set. As a hobby, you may collect stamps or coins. Each collection may be called a set.

Thus we see that a **set** is thought of as a collection of objects, people, or things that are carefully defined. In mathematics we generally use sets of numbers and symbols.

Each object, symbol, person or thing in a particular set is a **member** or **element** of that set.

A set may have no elements, one element, a definite number of elements or an unlimited number of elements.

A set that contains no elements is called an **empty set** or **null set** and is indicated by the symbol $\varnothing$.

A set that contains a definite number of elements (either one element or more that can be counted) is called a **finite set.**

A set that contains an unlimited number of elements is called an **infinite set.**

There are two common ways to designate a set:

1. When there is a finite (definite) number of objects, we list and enclose in braces all the objects that belong to the set.

$$\{1, 3, 5, 7, 9\} \quad \text{represents a set of the elements 1, 3, 5, 7, and 9.}$$

2. When a condition or rule is given which determines the elements that are included as members of the set, we enclose in braces a description of the condition or rule.

$$\{x \mid x < 10\} \quad \text{represents a set of all } x\text{'s such that each } x \text{ is less than 10.}$$

We should note that the symbol $\{\mid\}$ is sometimes called the **set-builder** and the vertical bar $\mid$ means "such that." The first part of the set-builder contains the variable and the second part the description of the condition or rule on the variable.

Sometimes the description is written within braces without the set-builder notation. The set of all prime numbers may be written as $\{$all prime numbers$\}$. The braces mean "the set of."

Any single capital letter like A, B, R, or S is generally used as the name of a set.

Suppose 1, 3, 5, 7, 9 is given the name D.

Then $D = \{1, 3, 5, 7, 9\}$ reads

"set D consists of elements 1, 3, 5, 7, and 9."

The epsilon symbol ϵ means "is a member of," and symbol $\notin$ means "is not a member of." Small letters may be used as names for members of sets.

$$8 \epsilon S \text{ reads "8 is a member of set } S\text{"}$$
$$t \notin M \text{ reads "}t \text{ is not a member of set } M\text{."}$$

Practice

1. What is a set? What is an element of a set?

2. What is a set called when it contains:

    (a) No elements? What symbol is used to designate it?
    (b) A limited number of elements?
    (c) An unlimited number of elements?

3. Which of the following are finite sets and which are infinite sets? The set of:

    (a) The two-digit odd numbers.
    (b) All fractions between 0 and 1.
    (c) All prime numbers less than 500.
    (d) All natural numbers.
    (e) The first ten letters of our alphabet.
    (f) The members of your mathematics class.
    (g) All even integers.
    (h) Proper fractions with denominator 4.
    (i) Improper fractions with denominator 4.
    (j) $\{1, 2, 3, 4\}$ (k) $\{1, 2, 3, 4, \cdots\}$ (l) $\{n \mid n = \text{all real numbers}\}$

4. Write the set listing each of the following collections of elements within braces:

    (a) All prime numbers less than twenty.
    (b) Names of all the continents of the world.
    (c) All proper fractions with denominator 5.
    (d) Names of all the planets.

(e) The even numbers greater than 17 but less than 29.

(f) Names of all the New England States.

(g) All odd numbers under 100 that are squares of whole numbers.

(h) All the prime factors of 30.

(i) Names of all the months beginning with the letter J.

(j) All the natural numbers between 11 and 39 which are divisible by 4.

5. Write the set describing each of the following conditions:

(a) All numbers greater than 6.

(b) All numbers less than 11.

(c) All odd numbers.

(d) All prime numbers.

(e) All numbers which when multiplied by 4 equal 32.

(f) All numbers which when decreased by 10 equal 47.

(g) All even integers.

(h) All numbers which when increased by 5 are greater than 7.

(i) All numbers less than 3 or equal to 3.

(j) All numbers greater than 30 but less than 49.

6. Read, or write in words, each of the following:

(a) $A = \{$red, white, blue$\}$

(b) $C = \{y \mid y + 6 = 9\}$

(c) $T = \{2, 4, 6, 8, 10\}$

(d) $R = \{n \mid n = \text{all odd numbers}\}$

(e) $S = \{x \mid x < 4\}$

(f) $F = \{a, b, c, d, e, f, g\}$

(g) $D = \{$Monday, Tuesday, Wednesday, Thursday, Friday$\}$

(h) $N = \{t \mid t \geq 3\}$

(i) $B = \{a \mid 7a - 5 > 16\}$

(j) $H = \{x \mid 8 < x < 19\}$

7. Write, using the proper symbols:

(a) 5 is an element of set B.

(b) 9 is not an element of set Y.

(c) r is a member of set N.

(d) z is not a member of set G.

(e) 4 is not an element of set A.

8. (a) If $R = \{2, 4, 6, 8, 10\}$, is the statement $8 \epsilon R$ true?

(b) If $B = \{a, b, c, d\}$, is the statement $x \epsilon B$ true?

(c) If $C = \{y \mid y = \text{all even numbers}\}$, is the statement $4 \epsilon C$ true?

(d) If $M = \{$baseball, football, track$\}$, is the statement swimmingϵM true.

(e) If $S = \{x \mid x = \text{all prime numbers}\}$, is the statement $17 \epsilon S$ true?

9. (a) If $D = \{x \mid x + 1 = 4\}$, is the statement $3 \epsilon D$ true?

(b) If $N = \{y \mid y > 9\}$, is the statement $6 \epsilon N$ true?

(c) If $G = \{n \mid n < 6\}$, is the statement $7 \epsilon G$ true?

(d) If $T = \{a \mid a \geq 10\}$, is the statement $9 \epsilon T$ true?

(e) If $A = \{x \mid 1 < x < 12\}$, is the statement $2 \epsilon A$ true?

10. Write a set containing (a) 2 elements   (b) no elements   (c) 6 elements   (d) 5 elements
(e) 1 element   (f) 4 elements

EXERCISE 7

Solution Set or Truth Set of an Equation—Replacement Sets

When we are required to solve an open sentence like a simple equation, we must find the number which, when substituted for the variable, makes the sentence true. Any number that makes the sentence true is said to **satisfy** the sentence or to be the **solution** of the open sentence. We also call this number which satisfies the equation the **root** of the equation.

Solving equations in the traditional way, we use transformations to reduce the given equation to a simple equivalent equation. These transformations are based on the axioms that when equals are increased or decreased or multiplied or divided by equals, the results are equals.

Solving the equation $4n+3=23$, we get:

$$4n+3=23$$
$$4n+3-3=23-3$$
$$4n=20$$
$$\frac{4n}{4}=\frac{20}{4}$$
$$n=5$$

or

$$4n+3=23$$
$$4n=23-3$$
$$4n=20$$
$$n=5$$

Answer. The root is 5.

In the above solution we simplify the given conditional sentence (the original equation) by using the additive inverse and multiplicative inverse principles. Although we use the inverse principles in the traditional method of solution, we generally state that we are subtracting equals and dividing by equals to get equals.

We may also use set notation in solving equations.

The set of all numbers which satisfy the sentence is called the **solution set of the sentence.**

This set of numbers which satisfy the sentence by making the sentence true is sometimes also called the **truth set** of the sentence.

To check whether some number belongs to the solution set or truth set of the sentence, the number is substituted for the variable. If the resulting sentence is true, the number belongs to the solution set; if it is false, the number does not belong.

We have studied that the set of all numbers n such that $4n+3=23$ may be written as $\{n\,|\,4n+3=23\}$. The notation $\{n\,|\,4n+3=23\}$ represents a set of numbers.

Thus we think of the open sentence $4n+3=23$ as a **set-selector** because it selects from the set of possible replacements only those numbers that make the sentence true when they replace the variable. Of course, there would be another set that consists of all the numbers that make the sentence false.

While we say that $\{n\,|\,4n+3=23\}$ describes the numbers that will satisfy the equation $4n+3=23$, we find its solution set by using the additive inverse and multiplicative inverse.

$$4n+3=23$$

adding additive inverse -3
$$4n+3+(-3)=23+(-3)$$
$$4n=20$$

multiplying by multiplicative inverse $\frac{1}{4}$
$$\frac{1}{4}\cdot 4n=\frac{1}{4}\cdot 20$$
$$n=5 \qquad \text{Answer, solution set } \{5\}$$

$$n+3=23$$
$$n+3+(-3)=23+(-3)$$
$$n=20$$
Answer, $\{20\}$

$$\frac{n}{4}=20$$
$$4\cdot\frac{n}{4}=4\cdot 20$$
$$n=80$$
Answer, $\{80\}$

$$4n=20$$
$$\frac{1}{4}\cdot 4n=\frac{1}{4}\cdot 20$$
$$n=5$$
Answer, $\{5\}$

Replacement Sets

A **replacement set** is a defined set of numbers which may replace the variable. Generally, it makes a difference what replacement set is used. The same equation with different replacement sets may have different solution sets.

An equation like $3x = 2$ would have no solution or a solution set with no members (called the null set or empty set) if the replacement set is the natural numbers or integers. In the systems of natural numbers and integers there are no fractions. Since the solution of $3x = 2$ is $\frac{2}{3}$, we would therefore be unable to use this root in the system of either natural numbers or integers.

If the description of the replacement set, sometimes called the **domain** of the variable, is not given, the system of real numbers is understood to be used.

Practice

1. Use the set-builder notation to describe the set of numbers which will satisfy each of the following equations:

   (a) $x + 9 = 71$ (c) $5n - 2 = 23$ (e) $6b + 5 = 3b - 7$ (g) $.08a = 96$ (i) $\dfrac{x}{3} + \dfrac{x}{5} = 16$

   (b) $3a = 36$ (d) $8c - 2c = 42$ (f) $9 - (x - 4) = 3$ (h) $\dfrac{d}{12} = \dfrac{5}{6}$ (j) $x^2 - 7x = 30$

2. How would each of the following roots be represented in set notation?

   (a) $d = 4$ (b) $x = 5$ and $x = 7$ (c) $y = -\frac{1}{2}$ (d) $a = 3.8$ (e) $n = -12$ and $n = 6$

3. Find the solution set of each of the following equations in the system of real numbers:

SET 1	SET 2	SET 3	SET 4
1. $x + 5 = 12$	1. $y - 2 = 6$	1. $8a = 56$	1. $\dfrac{x}{6} = 9$
2. $a + 11 = 29$	2. $n - 10 = 0$	2. $12x = 9$	2. $\dfrac{m}{4} = 1$
3. $6 + m = 14$	3. $9 = t - 9$	3. $5 = 2z$	3. $0 = \dfrac{a}{8}$
4. $4 = s + .25$	4. $36 = d - 52$	4. $24 = \dfrac{3}{4} r$	4. $\dfrac{c}{12} = 5$
5. $b + 24 = 31$	5. $h - .8 = 1.4$	5. $.05c = 10$	5. $4 = \dfrac{t}{2}$

SET 5	SET 6	SET 7	SET 8
1. $7c + 2 = 37$	1. $9b + 3b = 60$	1. $3x = -24$	1. $g + 7 = 4$
2. $21 + 8n = 51$	2. $6x - x = 45$	2. $-5b = -3$	2. $d - 2 = -6$
3. $6d - 5 = 49$	3. $23 = a + a$	3. $-9n = 72$	3. $t + 10 = -5$
4. $5 = 11n - 17$	4. $8c - c = 56$	4. $.7y = -.42$	4. $-21 = a - 9$
5. $10y + 31 = 59$	5. $7s - s + 2s = 72$	5. $-15 = -2n$	5. $.62 = h + 1.4$

SET 9	SET 10	SET 11	SET 12
1. $4r + 9 = 2r + 7$	1. $3x - (x - 2) = 12$	1. $\dfrac{x}{30} = \dfrac{9}{10}$	1. $x^2 = 25$
2. $7x - 2 = 3x + 14$	2. $5(y + 3) = 4(y - 1)$	2. $\dfrac{a}{4} + \dfrac{a}{2} = 18$	2. $9y^2 = 16$

(Sets continued on next page.)

3. $5b-8+b=9b+1$ **3.** $a(a+5)=a^2+45$ **3.** $y+\dfrac{y}{3}+\dfrac{y}{5}=46$ **3.** $x^2-10x+16=0$

4. $a+a+1+a+2=27$ **4.** $2w+2(w+9)=58$ **4.** $\dfrac{x+2}{10}-\dfrac{x-5}{6}=\dfrac{1}{2}$ **4.** $y^2-4y=21$

5. $20-3c+7=c-5$ **5.** $(x+2)(x-1)=(x+11)(x-4)$ **5.** $\dfrac{2}{x}+\dfrac{5}{x+3}=\dfrac{27}{x^2+3x}$ **5.** $x^2+3x=0$

4. Find the solution set of each of the following equations in the system of natural numbers:

(a) $3y=27$ (c) $5h=9$ (e) $4b-6=14$ (g) $\dfrac{c}{5}=6$ (i) $2(y+9)=32$

(b) $-2a=8$ (d) $m+7=2$ (f) $x+3x=11$ (h) $7d+3=d+33$ (j) $x+\dfrac{x}{4}=25$

5. Find the solution set of each of the following equations in the system of integers:

(a) $-9c=-45$ (c) $-15d=3$ (e) $m+10=6$ (g) $4d-d=0$ (i) $\dfrac{x}{3}+\dfrac{x+3}{6}=\dfrac{3}{2}$

(b) $6t=9$ (d) $y+1=8$ (f) $8c-5=11$ (h) $\dfrac{n}{7}=3$ (j) $5t-(t+3)=2$

6. Find the solution set of each of the following equations when the replacement set is the set of all the even numbers:

(a) $7y=42$ (b) $x-8=14$ (c) $\dfrac{d}{9}=3$ (d) $5n+7=57$ (e) $\dfrac{x}{8}+\dfrac{x}{2}=10$

7. Find the solution set of each of the following equations when the replacement set is the set of all the prime numbers:

(a) $t+6=13$ (b) $4a=76$ (c) $m-8=0$ (d) $9s-3s=54$ (e) $\dfrac{b}{18}=\dfrac{5}{6}$

8. Find the solution set of each of the following equations when the replacement set is the set of all the non-positive integers:

(a) $-12c=-84$ (b) $7b=-28$ (c) $n+17=11$ (d) $3s+5=5$ (e) $4m+6=5m-3$

9. Find the solution set of each of the following equations when the replacement set is the set of all the odd numbers:

(a) $9n=45$ (b) $x+16=31$ (c) $-3c=-24$ (d) $21a=7$ (e) $8d-9=47$

10. Find the solution set of each of the following equations when the replacement set is the set of all the non-negative integers:

(a) $4x=0$ (b) $11+n=5$ (c) $\dfrac{a}{2}=2$ (d) $7b-16=31$ (e) $14s=5s-72$

11. Find the solution set of each of the following equations:

(a) When the replacement set is $\{0, 1, 2, 3, 4, 5, 6, 7, 8, 9\}$:

(1) $9d=63$ (2) $b-18=20$ (3) $8x=29$ (4) $2x-5x=27$ (5) $\dfrac{n}{3}=2$

(b) When the replacement set is $\{-8, -6, -4, -2, 0, 2, 4, 6, 8\}$:

(1) $7y=-42$ (2) $n+4=3$ (3) $2x-5=5$ (4) $12+7b=9b$ (5) $8a-3=1$

(c) When the replacement set is the one-digit prime numbers:

     (1) $x + 3 = 7$ (2) $5y = 15$ (3) $4t - 8 = 0$ (4) $2c + 6 = 3c + 1$ (5) $\dfrac{m}{7} = 3$

(d) When the replacement set is $\{1, 3, 5, 7, 9\}$:

     (1) $6m = 48$ (2) $12c = 3$ (3) $y + 6 = 15$ (4) $8b - 5 = 51$ (5) $3s - 4 = 5s - 18$

(e) When the replacement set is $\{1, 2, 3, 4, 5, \cdots\}$:

     (1) $-14t = -42$ (2) $7h + 15 = 15$ (3) $9d - 5d = 17$ (4) $18y - 90 = 0$ (5) $2y - 1 = 5y + 20$

EXERCISE 8

Solving Inequalities

We have seen that in the system of real numbers the solution of a simple equation is a single number or we can also say its solution set contains only one element.

However, in solving inequalities we shall find that the solution will consist of many numbers or the solution set will contain many elements. Of course, if we limit the replacement set, we may find no solution and say the solution set is the null set.

The solutions of the basic elementary types of inequalities are as follows:

1. Find the solution or solution set of $n < 4$ in the system of natural numbers.
   Its solution is every natural number less than four, or its solution set is the set of all natural numbers less than four.
   We would write:

In traditional form	In set form
$n < 4$	$\{n \mid n < 4\}$
$n = 1, 2,$ or $3.$	or $\{1, 2, 3\}$

2. Find the solution or solution set of $b > 5$ in the system of integers.
   Its solution set is the set of all the integers greater than five.
   We would write:

In traditional form	In set form
$b > 5$	$\{b \mid b > 5\}$
$b = 6, 7, 8, 9, \ldots$	or $\{6, 7, 8, 9, \ldots\}$

3. Find the solution or solution set of $c \geq 4$ in the system of natural numbers.
   Its solution set is the set of all natural numbers from four on.
   We would write:

In traditional form	In set form
$c \geq 4$	$\{c \mid c \geq 4\}$
$c = 4, 5, 6, 7, \ldots$	or $\{4, 5, 6, 7, \ldots\}$

4. Find the solution or solution set of $y \leq -1$ in the system of natural numbers.
   There is no solution or the solution set is the null set or empty set.
   We would write

In traditional form	In set form
$y \leq -1$	$\{y \mid y \leq -1\}$
No solution	or $\varnothing$

5. Find the solution or solution set of $n \neq 5$ in the system of real numbers.
   The solution set is the set of all real numbers except positive five.
   We would write

In traditional form	In set form
$n \neq 5$	$\{n \mid n \neq 5\}$
$n =$ every real number except 5	$\{$all real numbers except 5$\}$

6. Find the solution or solution set of $c \nless 4$ in the system of natural numbers.
   Since $c \nless 4$ is equivalent to $c \geq 4$, for solution see item 3 above.

7. Find the solution or solution set of $y \ngtr -1$ in the system of natural numbers.
   Since $y \ngtr -1$ is equivalent to $y \leq -1$, for solution see item 4 above.

When solving inequalities, we follow transformation principles like those used to solve equations. However, there is one exception. It occurs when we multiply or divide by a negative number.

The inequality $7>4$ is an inequality of a certain order. It indicates that 7 is greater than 4. If the order is reversed, $7<4$ or its equivalent $4>7$ results. $7>4$ is equivalent to $4<7$ but is not equivalent to $7<4$ or $4>7$.

The following transformation principles are used to solve inequalities.

(a) When any real number (positive or negative) is added to or subtracted from each side of an ordered inequality, another equivalent inequality of the same order results.

(b) When each side of an ordered inequality is multiplied or divided by a positive real number, another equivalent inequality of the same order results.

(c) When each side of an ordered inequality is multiplied or divided by a negative real number, an inequality results with the order reversed.

8. Solve $n+2>8$ in the system of natural numbers.

$$
\begin{array}{ll}
n+2>8 & \qquad\qquad n+2>8 \\
\quad n>8-2 \qquad \text{or} & \quad n+2+(-2) > 8+(-2) \\
\quad n>6 & \qquad\qquad n>6 \\
\quad n=7,\,8,\,9,\,10,\,\ldots & \qquad \text{or } \{7,\,8,\,9,\,\ldots\}
\end{array}
$$

The solution set is the set of all natural numbers greater than 6.

9. Solve $4x-3<9$ in the system of integers.

$$
\begin{array}{ll}
 & \qquad\qquad 4x-3<9 \\
4x-3<9 & \quad 4x+(-3)+(3) < 9+(3) \\
\quad 4x<9+3 \qquad \text{or} & \qquad\qquad 4x<12 \\
\quad 4x<12 & \qquad \tfrac{1}{4}\cdot 4x < \tfrac{1}{4}\cdot 12 \\
\quad x<3 & \qquad\qquad x<3 \\
\quad x=\ldots,\,-2,\,-1,\,0,\,1,\,2 & \quad \text{or } \{\ldots,\,-2,\,-1,\,0,\,1,\,2\}
\end{array}
$$

The solution set is the set of all integers less than 3.

10. Solve $9b+4 \geq 3b+7*$ in the system of real numbers.

$$
\begin{array}{ll}
9b+4 \geq 3b+7 & \qquad\qquad 9b+4 \geq 3b+7 \\
\quad 9b-3b \geq 7-4 \qquad \text{or} & \quad 9b+(-3b)+4+(-4) \geq 3b+(-3b)+7+(-4) \\
\quad 6b \geq 3 & \qquad\qquad 6b \geq 3 \\
\quad b \geq \tfrac{1}{2} & \qquad\qquad b \geq \tfrac{1}{2}
\end{array}
$$

$b = \tfrac{1}{2}$ or any real number greater than $\tfrac{1}{2}$ $\qquad\qquad$ or $\{\tfrac{1}{2}$ and all real numbers greater than $\tfrac{1}{2}\}$

The solution set is the set of all real numbers greater than $\tfrac{1}{2}$ or equal to $\tfrac{1}{2}$.

* $9b+4 \geq 3b+7$ is the combination of $9b+4>3b+7$ and $9b+4=3b+7$

11. Solve $-2x<8$ in the system of integers.

$$
\begin{array}{ll}
 & \qquad\qquad -2x<8 \\
\quad -2x<8 & \quad -\tfrac{1}{2}\cdot -2x < \tfrac{1}{2}\cdot 8 \\
\qquad x>-4 \qquad \text{or} & \qquad\qquad x>-4 \\
x=-3,\,-2,\,-1,\,0,\,1,\,2,\,\ldots & \quad \text{or } \{-3,\,-2,\,-1,\,0,\,1,\,2,\,\ldots\}
\end{array}
$$

The solution set is set of all integers greater than -4.

When we divide by a negative number, the order of the inequality is reversed. If we fail to reverse the order and write the solution as $x<-4$, then any integer less than -4, such as -5, when substituted for the variable in $-2x<8$ would yield a false sentence, like $10<8$. However, any integer greater than -4 will satisfy the inequality and so is included in the solution set. When -3 is substituted for the variable in $-2x<8$, the resulting sentence is true, $6<8$.

12. Solve $5x \gg 10$ in the system of real numbers.

$$5x \gg 10$$
$$x \gg 2$$
or $x \leqq 2$

$x = 2$ or any real number less than 2

or

$$5x \gg 10$$
$$\tfrac{1}{5} \cdot 5x \gg \tfrac{1}{5} \cdot 5x$$
$$x \gg 2 \text{ or } x \leqq 2$$

or $\{2$ and all real numbers less than $2\}$

The solution set is the set of all real numbers equal to or less than 2.

13. Solve $6n < 24$ when the replacement set is $\{1, 3, 5, 7, 9\}$

$$6n < 24$$
$$n < 4$$
or
$$n = 1 \text{ or } 3$$

$$6n < 24$$
$$\tfrac{1}{6} \cdot 6n < \tfrac{1}{6} \cdot 24$$
$$n < 4 \text{ or } \{1, 3\}$$

The solution set consists of elements 1 and 3.

Practice

In each of the following sets of practice examples, the first is an equation of a certain type and all the others are inequalities of the same type.

Solve or find the solution set of each of the following in the system of real numbers:

SET 1	SET 2	SET 3	SET 4
(a) $5n = 10$	(a) $x+4=7$	(a) $y-2=6$	(a) $\dfrac{c}{3}=15$
(b) $5n > 10$	(b) $x+4>7$	(b) $y-2>6$	(b) $\dfrac{c}{3}>15$
(c) $5n < 10$	(c) $x+4<7$	(c) $y-2<6$	(c) $\dfrac{c}{3}<15$
(d) $5n \neq 10$	(d) $x+4 \neq 7$	(d) $y-2 \neq 6$	(d) $\dfrac{c}{3} \neq 15$
(e) $5n \gg 10$	(e) $x+4 \gg 7$	(e) $y-2 \gg 6$	(e) $\dfrac{c}{3} \gg 15$
(f) $5n \lessdot 10$	(f) $x+4 \lessdot 7$	(f) $y-2 \lessdot 6$	(f) $\dfrac{c}{3} \lessdot 15$

Related Examples

PART A

Solve or find the solution set of each of the following in the system of real numbers:

1.
(a) $3x=27$ $7y=56$ $8b=4$ $25t=70$ $14c=21$
(b) $6n>54$ $9b>36$ $15s>25$ $8x>96$ $20z>10$
(c) $4c<24$ $13t<65$ $16a<12$ $5k<0$ $24p<60$
(d) $9x \neq 72$ $15r \neq 90$ $2n \neq 3$ $10g \neq 6$ $4d \neq 76$
(e) $7y \gg 35$ $10s \leqq 80$ $12p \gg 8$ $6f \leqq 17$ $9x \gg 63$
(f) $8b \lessdot 56$ $24m \geqq 120$ $6z \lessdot 0$ $18y \geqq 14$ $7n \lessdot 105$

2.
(a) $n+3=8$ $c+8=31$ $s+15=54$ $g+99=112$ $y+68=68$
(b) $c+2>10$ $m+1>14$ $x+17>85$ $z+40>40$ $r+32>91$
(c) $b+8<15$ $x+16<22$ $d+39<39$ $c+12<61$ $s+49<53$
(d) $d+1 \neq 9$ $a+7 \neq 10$ $r+14 \neq 23$ $h+28 \neq 55$ $x+6 \neq 6$
(e) $x+10 \gg 24$ $y+16 \leqq 33$ $n+21 \gg 47$ $y+17 \leqq 17$ $b+15 \gg 21$
(f) $a+6 \lessdot 18$ $r+60 \geqq 100$ $p+8 \lessdot 8$ $t+56 \geqq 63$ $m+86 \lessdot 105$

3. (a) $n-6=14$ $\qquad$ $z-19=47$ $\qquad$ $t-10=5$ $\qquad$ $y-8=8$ $\qquad$ $d-17=0$

(b) $a-8>15$ $\qquad$ $s-33>51$ $\qquad$ $m-16>4$ $\qquad$ $r-9>0$ $\qquad$ $x-15>15$

(c) $z-9<26$ $\qquad$ $b-82<104$ $\qquad$ $y-23<9$ $\qquad$ $h-7<7$ $\qquad$ $n-2<0$

(d) $b-2\neq7$ $\qquad$ $x-26\neq63$ $\qquad$ $h-34\neq18$ $\qquad$ $c-10\neq0$ $\qquad$ $a-56\neq20$

(e) $t-1 \not> 10$ $\qquad$ $m-49\leq56$ $\qquad$ $x-41 \not> 20$ $\qquad$ $l-25\leq25$ $\qquad$ $p-84 \not> 0$

(f) $x-12 \not< 21$ $\qquad$ $g-75\geq102$ $\qquad$ $a-100 \not< 57$ $\qquad$ $n-36\geq0$ $\qquad$ $s-16 \not< 25$

4. (a) $\dfrac{a}{2}=3$ $\qquad$ $\dfrac{n}{4}=8$ $\qquad$ $\dfrac{b}{6}=6$ $\qquad$ $\dfrac{d}{5}=0$ $\qquad$ $\dfrac{x}{10}=1$

(b) $\dfrac{c}{3}>5$ $\qquad$ $\dfrac{y}{9}>6$ $\qquad$ $\dfrac{g}{8}>1$ $\qquad$ $\dfrac{r}{10}>10$ $\qquad$ $\dfrac{3}{12}>0$

(c) $\dfrac{n}{6}<2$ $\qquad$ $\dfrac{v}{8}<11$ $\qquad$ $\dfrac{s}{5}<0$ $\qquad$ $\dfrac{x}{9}<1$ $\qquad$ $\dfrac{b}{15}<15$

(d) $\dfrac{b}{4}\neq10$ $\qquad$ $\dfrac{t}{3}\neq1$ $\qquad$ $\dfrac{m}{8}\neq4$ $\qquad$ $\dfrac{c}{12}\neq20$ $\qquad$ $\dfrac{h}{21}\neq7$

(e) $\dfrac{y}{8} \not> 4$ $\qquad$ $\dfrac{s}{7}\leq15$ $\qquad$ $\dfrac{a}{9} \not> 5$ $\qquad$ $\dfrac{b}{11}\leq100$ $\qquad$ $\dfrac{x}{16} \not> 1$

(f) $\dfrac{m}{5} \not< 30$ $\qquad$ $\dfrac{x}{12}\geq1$ $\qquad$ $\dfrac{r}{6} \not< 0$ $\qquad$ $\dfrac{n}{3}\geq14$ $\qquad$ $\dfrac{y}{13} \not< 4$

PART B

Solve or find the solution set of each of the following in the system of real numbers:

1. (a) $4x=1.6$ $\qquad$ $.05y=25$ $\qquad$ $\frac{1}{4}n=12$ $\qquad$ $\frac{7}{8}c=49$ $\qquad$ $1.6z=.96$

(b) $.02a>6$ $\qquad$ $1.8d>.9$ $\qquad$ $\frac{2}{3}x>26$ $\qquad$ $\frac{5}{6}t>70$ $\qquad$ $.7h>.14$

(c) $.3g<24$ $\qquad$ $.01n<.8$ $\qquad$ $\frac{9}{10}y<45$ $\qquad$ $\frac{5}{4}d<65$ $\qquad$ $2.5b<50$

(d) $1.5c\neq3$ $\qquad$ $6a\neq.09$ $\qquad$ $\frac{3}{8}m\neq81$ $\qquad$ $\frac{7}{10}r\neq42$ $\qquad$ $.98t\neq4.9$

(e) $.8y \not> .2$ $\qquad$ $4.2s\leq.7$ $\qquad$ $\frac{1}{12}b \not> 56$ $\qquad$ $\frac{1}{3}x\leq23$ $\qquad$ $.03a \not> 7.8$

(f) $3.2b \not< 6.4$ $\qquad$ $.004x\geq5$ $\qquad$ $16t \not< 99$ $\qquad$ $\frac{2}{5}f\geq74$ $\qquad$ $.12n \not< 36$

2. (a) $t+.7=4$ $\qquad$ $n+1.9=2.3$ $\qquad$ $a+\frac{1}{2}=4$ $\qquad$ $b+1\frac{3}{4}=9$ $\qquad$ $w+.04=8.2$

(b) $c+.2>.3$ $\qquad$ $x+5>6.7$ $\qquad$ $v+1\frac{1}{4}>8\frac{1}{4}$ $\qquad$ $m+\frac{2}{3}>5\frac{2}{3}$ $\qquad$ $g+.9>1$

(c) $y+.8<.8$ $\qquad$ $b+2.7<4.5$ $\qquad$ $x+\frac{5}{6}<10$ $\qquad$ $d+\frac{5}{8}<4$ $\qquad$ $p+.5<2.1$

(d) $r+.5\neq.9$ $\qquad$ $y+.64\neq10.4$ $\qquad$ $n+\frac{2}{5}\neq1\frac{7}{10}$ $\qquad$ $s+1\frac{1}{6}\neq7$ $\qquad$ $f+.08\neq5$

(e) $n+6 \not> 7.4$ $\qquad$ $r+.43\leq.99$ $\qquad$ $z+2\frac{1}{2} \not> 5$ $\qquad$ $j+\frac{7}{8}\leq1\frac{1}{2}$ $\qquad$ $x+.4 \not> 1.2$

(f) $e+.1 \not< 1$ $\qquad$ $d+2\geq4.2$ $\qquad$ $y+\frac{3}{8} \not< 2\frac{1}{3}$ $\qquad$ $n+3\frac{4}{5}\geq8\frac{4}{5}$ $\qquad$ $a+.34 \not< 6.4$

3. (a) $c-.2=.8$ $\qquad$ $a-1.4=5.6$ $\qquad$ $j-\frac{1}{4}=\frac{3}{4}$ $\qquad$ $m-1\frac{5}{6}=10\frac{1}{6}$ $\qquad$ $t-2.5=1.5$

(b) $n-4>.9$ $\qquad$ $r-2.9>7.4$ $\qquad$ $x-\frac{5}{8}>\frac{1}{8}$ $\qquad$ $y-2\frac{3}{4}>\frac{1}{2}$ $\qquad$ $x-8>.2$

(c) $b-.7<.4$ $\qquad$ $y-6<.25$ $\qquad$ $t-1\frac{1}{2}<2\frac{1}{2}$ $\qquad$ $h-\frac{3}{8}<\frac{3}{8}$ $\qquad$ $a-.17<.83$

(d) $a-.1\neq.5$ $\qquad$ $b-3.8\neq.02$ $\qquad$ $n-\frac{2}{3}\neq5\frac{1}{3}$ $\qquad$ $t-3\frac{1}{8}\neq2\frac{1}{8}$ $\qquad$ $r-5.4\neq.6$

(e) $x-.8 \not> 3$ $\qquad$ $h-7.1\leq.9$ $\qquad$ $w-\frac{3}{5} \not> 3\frac{2}{5}$ $\qquad$ $c-4\frac{7}{10}\leq1\frac{3}{10}$ $\qquad$ $z-3.9 \not> 7.1$

(f) $g-.3 \not< 1.7$ $\qquad$ $s-4\geq.5$ $\qquad$ $y-2\frac{1}{6} \not< \frac{5}{6}$ $\qquad$ $d-\frac{5}{12}\geq\frac{1}{12}$ $\qquad$ $b-.68 \not< 1.32$

PART C

Solve or find the solution set for each of the following in the system of real numbers:

1. (a) $3r=-21$ $\qquad$ $8y=-56$ $\qquad$ $.4t=-2$ $\qquad$ $\frac{5}{6}n=-60$ $\qquad$ $9z=-6$

(b) $2a>-48$ $\qquad$ $10x>-90$ $\qquad$ $.03n>-.18$ $\qquad$ $\frac{2}{3}b>-16$ $\qquad$ $10t>-15$

(c) $8t<-64$ $\qquad$ $11d<-132$ $\qquad$ $7y<-5.6$ $\qquad$ $\frac{7}{8}w<-28$ $\qquad$ $16b<-12$

(d) $19b\neq-57$ $\qquad$ $6m\neq-72$ $\qquad$ $.95r\neq-190$ $\qquad$ $\frac{5}{12}z\neq-100$ $\qquad$ $14x\neq-35$

(e) $9g \not> -54$ $\qquad$ $7c\leq-91$ $\qquad$ $.03p \not> -7.2$ $\qquad$ $\frac{3}{5}b\leq-39$ $\qquad$ $25n \not> -10$

(f) $10x \not< -200$ $\qquad$ $15b\geq-135$ $\qquad$ $.1h \not< -10$ $\qquad$ $\frac{7}{10}y\geq-147$ $\qquad$ $36r \not< -24$

2. (a) $m+9=5$ $x+60=51$ $b+3=-4$ $e+5=-9$ $n+8=1.8$
   (b) $g+18>6$ $m+25>19$ $c+7>-5$ $b+10>0$ $f+1\frac{1}{2}>\frac{1}{2}$
   (c) $y+11<4$ $t+71<0$ $r+1<-10$ $x+16<-2$ $z+.6<-2.4$
   (d) $t+4\neq 2$ $z+39\neq 18$ $w+13\neq -23$ $y+20\neq -30$ $e+2.3\neq .7$
   (e) $n+15\not> 11$ $y+56\leqq 36$ $g+6\not> -17$ $r+8\leqq -8$ $t+4.5\not> -1.5$
   (f) $c+8\not< 4$ $d+85\geqq 67$ $h+9\not< -9$ $a+28\geqq 0$ $y+\frac{3}{4}\not< \frac{5}{8}$

3. (a) $g-6=-4$ $t-15=-5$ $x-3=-8$ $s-1=-7$ $r-.4=-4.4$
   (b) $d-10>-3$ $s-28>-6$ $m-9>-25$ $p-5>-12$ $v-\frac{2}{3}>-6\frac{2}{3}$
   (c) $a-17<-7$ $p-19<-15$ $y-4<-11$ $x-38<-56$ $k-7<-.2$
   (d) $b-25\neq -12$ $r-83\neq -68$ $n-16\neq -17$ $w-14\neq -82$ $w-1\frac{3}{4}\neq -1\frac{1}{2}$
   (e) $n-70\not> -25$ $h-54\leqq -26$ $b-31\not> -50$ $z-46\leqq -63$ $n-.5\not> -7.4$
   (f) $y-100\not< -59$ $d-36\geqq -19$ $x-52\not< -61$ $b-99\geqq -108$ $d-\frac{7}{8}\not< -3\frac{1}{8}$

PART D

Solve or find the solution set of each of the following in the system of real numbers:

1. (a) $-10n=40$ $-8c=64$ $-7b=50$ $-.5a=4$ $-\frac{2}{3}x=6$
   (b) $-11x>22$ $-5a>90$ $-6m>2$ $-8y>.24$ $-\frac{1}{6}t>2\frac{2}{3}$
   (c) $-15y<75$ $-7x<91$ $-9a<12$ $-.04t<12$ $-\frac{1}{2}c<10$
   (d) $-12d\neq 84$ $-14y\neq 52$ $-10c\neq 6$ $-.1v\neq .5$ $-\frac{3}{4}a\neq 15$
   (e) $-3c\not> 81$ $-20t\leqq 120$ $-18r\not> 40$ $-1.9x\leqq .95$ $-\frac{5}{8}w\not> 30$
   (f) $-4z\not< 52$ $-9n\geqq 81$ $-24x\not< 18$ $-.125n\geqq 72$ $-\frac{4}{5}m\not< 48$

PART E

Solve or find the solution set of each of the following in the system of real numbers:

1. (a) $-4b=-56$ $-7r=-21$ $-3a=-2$ $-.6x=-.84$ $-\frac{3}{4}n=-9$
   (b) $-6y>-42$ $-12s>-60$ $-8b>-18$ $-.9e>-4.5$ $-\frac{1}{5}x>-13$
   (c) $-7c<-49$ $-9y<-27$ $-21r<-7$ $-8p<-9.6$ $-\frac{7}{8}d<-28$
   (d) $-20n\neq -160$ $-15t\neq -135$ $-6d\neq -20$ $-.02h\neq -100$ $-\frac{1}{3}s\neq -17$
   (e) $-5m\not> -105$ $-20v\leqq -160$ $-12n\not> -8$ $-1.5r\leqq -90$ $-\frac{2}{5}f\not> -4$
   (f) $-16n\not< -144$ $-17x\geqq -85$ $-25t\not< -65$ $-.18y\geqq -.198$ $-\frac{9}{10}z\not< -18$

PART F

Solve or find the solution set of each of the following in the system of real numbers:

1. (a) $3x+5=17$ 2. (a) $8b-12=36$ 3. (a) $9c-3c=42$
   (b) $2n+9>23$ (b) $4y-11>17$ (b) $a+a>56$
   (c) $9c+3<48$ (c) $7a-25<10$ (c) $13r-r<84$
   (d) $10b+7\neq 37$ (d) $6m-2\neq 2$ (d) $7b+9b\neq 80$
   (e) $12y+6\not> 44$ (e) $15s-75\not> 0$ (e) $4n+4n\not> 72$
   (f) $8d+23\not< 65$ (f) $9c-6\not< 3$ (f) $18y-3y\not< 105$

4. (a) $8y+5=6y+15$ 5. (a) $4x+(3x-11)=10$ 6. (a) $\dfrac{x}{2}+\dfrac{x}{3}=10$

   (b) $x+x+1+x+2>24$ (b) $8n-(2n+7)>29$ (b) $\dfrac{n}{5}+\dfrac{3n}{10}>15$

   (c) $9d-8+d<16+4d$ (c) $t-(9-t)<7$ (c) $\dfrac{5b}{6}-\dfrac{2b}{3}<3$

   (d) $1+a+2a+3a\neq 19$ (d) $10+(y-6)\neq 4-(5-2y)$ (d) $\dfrac{2x}{45}\neq \dfrac{8}{15}$

(e) $7t-11+6t-15 \not> 0$ (e) $5c-4 \not> c+(c+2)$ (e) $\dfrac{y}{3}-\dfrac{y}{4} > \dfrac{1}{12}$

(f) $12m-3m-4m+5 \not< 17-2m$ (f) $b(b+5) \not< b^2+20$ (f) $x \not< 1+\dfrac{x}{2}+\dfrac{x}{4}$

Related Examples

Solve or find the solution set of each of the following in the system of real numbers:

1.
(a) $6b+7=49$ $15+10x=5$ $4y+11=41$
(b) $10x+3>63$ $7c+8>-20$ $26+3d>58$
(c) $9+5z<44$ $12t+32<8$ $7a+15<15$
(d) $13+4r \neq 21$ $9w+65 \neq 2$ $24+12x \neq 33$
(e) $8s+25 \not> 57$ $51+14y \leq 9$ $2n+37 \not> 42$
(f) $6m+62 \not< 98$ $11+20d \geq -91$ $18y+64 \not< 79$

2.
(a) $4c-27=11$ $7a-10=-24$ $8n-3=3$
(b) $9x-5>67$ $2d-9>-3$ $25r-27>8$
(c) $11b-8<25$ $10m-6<-45$ $14h-2<5$
(d) $5y-15 \neq 0$ $6s-13 \neq -55$ $9b-17 \neq 13$
(e) $8t-40 \not> 16$ $18w-11 \leq -83$ $24h-19 \not> 41$
(f) $3r-7 \not< 29$ $15g-25 \geq -130$ $12x-6 \not< 2$

3.
(a) $8a+4a=60$ $3x-5x=6$ $7d-9d=-16$
(b) $7y-6y>17$ $2c-7c>45$ $x+x-5x>-12$
(c) $9d-d<48$ $b-2b<10$ $8n-13n<-35$
(d) $10x+3x-8x \neq 75$ $5y-9y \neq 32$ $12c-21c \neq -81$
(e) $6s-s-s \not> 84$ $10d-16d \leq 54$ $y-5y \not> -48$
(f) $18m+7m \not< 150$ $13z-21z \geq 96$ $3a-2a-8a \not< -42$

4.
(a) $5x+2=3x+8$ $6c-3+2c=2c+9$ $x+x+2+x+4=21$
(b) $9y-5>4y+25$ $15+9b-8>13+11b$ $3n-8n+20>0$
(c) $10b-24<3b-3$ $5a+a+7<24+3a-6$ $9d-3-5+d<-8$
(d) $6a+7 \neq 91-5a$ $17+11n-13 \neq 4n+4+2n$ $10r-3r+12 \neq 13+3r$
(e) $8x-2x \not> 2x-52$ $7d-10d-5 \leq d+3$ $6h-10h+21 \not> 5+4h$
(f) $12c-9 \not< 35-8$ $16-8x-6x \geq 32-5x-x$ $1+y-2y+3y \not< y-1$

5.
(a) $3y+(y-12)=20$ $x(x+2)=x^2+18$ $(x+5)(x+4)=(x+2)(x-5)$
(b) $2n+2(n+6)>84$ $a-(10-a)>6$ $(y+6)(y+5)-y^2>42$
(c) $(4a+3)-(2a-5)<16$ $7(x+8)<3(x+12)$ $8c-(c-5)<c+17$
(d) $5(x-2) \neq 4(x+1)$ $2(s+s+5) \neq 50$ $7(4-d) \neq 5(6-d)$
(e) $b+(2b+3) \not> (b+3)+(b+4)$ $10x-2(x-4) \leq 0$ $(h-2)(h-1) \not> h(h+1)$
(b) $(x+4)(x+3) \not< x^2+26$ $5a+10(12-a) \geq 85$ $(b+8)(b-2) \not< (b-4)(b+13)$

6.
(a) $\dfrac{c}{30}=\dfrac{4}{5}$ $\dfrac{d}{4}-\dfrac{d}{8}=6$ $\dfrac{2r}{3}-\dfrac{r}{4}=\dfrac{5}{2}$

(b) $\dfrac{m}{21}>\dfrac{7}{3}$ $\dfrac{a}{3}+\dfrac{a}{6}>\dfrac{1}{2}$ $\dfrac{2x}{5}-\dfrac{5}{6}>\dfrac{x}{3}+\dfrac{1}{2}$

(c) $\dfrac{x+8}{12}<\dfrac{5}{12}$ $\dfrac{b}{2}+\dfrac{b+2}{3}<9$ $\dfrac{a+2}{2}-\dfrac{a-2}{6}<\dfrac{2a+1}{3}$

(d) $\dfrac{a-2}{8} \neq \dfrac{a+4}{24}$ $n-\dfrac{n}{2}+\dfrac{n}{4} \neq 6$ $\dfrac{b+1}{3}+\dfrac{b-3}{2} \neq \dfrac{b+4}{12}$

(e) $\dfrac{3d+4}{10} \not> \dfrac{2}{5}$ $\qquad$ $\dfrac{c+8}{4} - \dfrac{c+5}{9} \leq 2$ $\qquad$ $\dfrac{n-1}{2} - \dfrac{1-n}{10} \not> \dfrac{n+1}{5}$

(f) $\dfrac{2n+1}{7} \not< \dfrac{n+5}{5}$ $\qquad$ $\dfrac{x+1}{3} + \dfrac{x+3}{4} \geq \dfrac{x+3}{2}$ $\qquad$ $\dfrac{y-4}{2} - 2 \not< \dfrac{y+4}{4}$

PART G

1. Solve or find the solution set of each of the following in the system of natural numbers:

(a) $5n < 60$ $\qquad$ (d) $8d \not> 32$ $\qquad$ (g) $-2r < 18$ $\qquad$ (j) $3a + 7 \geq 1$

(b) $9c > 54$ $\qquad$ (e) $12y \not< 96$ $\qquad$ (h) $s + 12 \neq 21$ $\qquad$ (k) $5c - 2 < 12$

(c) $3t \neq 21$ $\qquad$ (f) $6x > -30$ $\qquad$ (i) $t - 8 \leq 0$ $\qquad$ (l) $10n + 6 > 6 + 5n$

2. Solve or find the solution set of each of the following in the system of integers:

(a) $6d > 48$ $\qquad$ (d) $g + 14 \not< 13$ $\qquad$ (g) $8n + 2 < 3n + 17$ $\qquad$ (j) $4c + 9c > 10 - 36$

(b) $15m < 10$ $\qquad$ (e) $9x + 3 \neq 66$ $\qquad$ (h) $10t - 9 \leq 6t + 7$ $\qquad$ (k) $11d - 2d < 3d + 18$

(c) $-4z \not> 28$ $\qquad$ (f) $7y - 5 > 40$ $\qquad$ (i) $7x - 14 \geq 5x - 2$ $\qquad$ (l) $\dfrac{x}{6} \neq 12$

3. Solve or find the solution set of each of the following when the replacement set is $\{0, 2, 4, 6, 8\}$:

(a) $4x < 24$ $\qquad$ (c) $y + 2 \not> 3$ $\qquad$ (e) $9d - 3d \neq 12$ $\qquad$ (g) $6t - 4 \leq 5t - 8$

(b) $3b > 6$ $\qquad$ (d) $5a - 4 \not< 6$ $\qquad$ (f) $10y + 51 < 3y + 51$ $\qquad$ (h) $\dfrac{b}{3} > 1$

4. Solve or find the solution set of each of the following when the replacement set is $\{-3, -2, -1, 0, 1, 2, 3\}$:

(a) $8c > 8$ $\qquad$ (c) $b - 5 \not> 2$ $\qquad$ (e) $8s - 2 \neq 6s + 6$ $\qquad$ (g) $2x + 3 < x + 4$

(b) $9n < 0$ $\qquad$ (d) $3x + 10 \not< 1$ $\qquad$ (f) $-5z > 10$ $\qquad$ (h) $\dfrac{c}{2} \leq 1$

5. Solve or find the solution set of each of the following when the replacement set is $\{0, 1, 2, 3, 4, 5, 6, 7, 8, 9\}$:

(a) $6d < 30$ $\qquad$ (c) $n + 3 \not< 11$ $\qquad$ (e) $6x - 4 > 4x + 16$ $\qquad$ (g) $12a - a \geq 3a + 26$

(b) $-5b > -10$ $\qquad$ (d) $4y - 1 \not> 15$ $\qquad$ (f) $7g + 9 \neq 9$ $\qquad$ (h) $\dfrac{y}{4} < 32$

6. Solve or find the solution set of each of the following when the replacement set is the set of non-negative integers:

(a) $4y > 12$ $\qquad$ (c) $m - 5 < 3$ $\qquad$ (e) $5n + 2 \neq 4n - 3$ $\qquad$ (g) $14d - 4 \not< 11d - 4$

(b) $-2a < 7$ $\qquad$ (d) $8b + 6 > 22$ $\qquad$ (f) $10y - 9 < 3y + 47$ $\qquad$ (h) $\dfrac{s}{-5} \not> -3$

7. Solve or find the solutions set of each of the following when the replacement set is the set of prime numbers:

(a) $15y < 105$ $\qquad$ (c) $10n + 8n \neq 54$ $\qquad$ (e) $4x + 5 \not> 8 - 3$ $\qquad$ (g) $\dfrac{n}{5} \not< 1$

(b) $y - 6 > 7$ $\qquad$ (d) $2b + 14 < 7$ $\qquad$ (f) $-3z > -96$ $\qquad$ (h) $9t + 15 < 2t + 36$

8. Solve or find the solution set of each of the following when the replacement set is the set of even natural numbers:

(a) $11t > 33$

(b) $n - 4 < 9$

(c) $12z - 19 < 53$

(d) $6n + 5 > 4n + 5$

(e) $\dfrac{a}{6} \neq 4$

(f) $12r \not< -36$

(g) $19y - 2 \not> 3y + 30$

(h) $\dfrac{r}{2} - \dfrac{r}{3} > 2$

9. Solve or find the solution set of each of the following when the replacement set is the set of real numbers greater than -7 but less than -2:

(a) $-3s > 15$

(b) $x + 11 < 7$

(c) $-8y < -32$

(d) $16b - b \neq -45$

(e) $11c - 7 \not> 16c$

(f) $2m + 3 \not< -1$

(g) $\dfrac{t}{-4} > 2$

(h) $4n + n < 2n - 9$

10. Solve or find the solution set of each of the following when the replacement set is the set of odd numbers:

(a) $g - 6 < 19$

(b) $-4c > -20$

(c) $x + 8 = 8$

(d) $\dfrac{2}{3} b \not> 10$

(e) $6a - 9 \neq 4a - 3$

(f) $10y - 12y < 17$

(g) $\dfrac{c}{3} < 7$

(h) $7s - 5 > s + 8$

EXERCISE 9

Subsets and Notation

If the school faculty is separated into departments, every member of each department is also a member of the school faculty. The school faculty may be regarded as a set and each department may be regarded as a set. Since every member of the mathematics department is a member of the school faculty, we may call the mathematics department a subset of the set which describes the entire school faculty.

If every member of one set is also a member of a second set, then the first set is said to be a **subset** of the second set.

Any subset that is not the whole set is called a **proper subset**. A proper subset contains some, but not all, elements of the related set. However, any set is assumed to be a subset of itself, and the null set or empty set is assumed to be a subset of every set.

Therefore the subsets of any set include the whole set itself, all the proper subsets, and the null set.

If a set consists of elements a, b, and c, the proper subsets are: $\{a, b\}$, $\{a, c\}$, $\{b, c\}$, $\{a\}$, $\{b\}$, $\{c\}$. The null set $\varnothing$ is a subset. $\{a, b, c\}$ is considered a subset but not a proper subset.

When a particular set in a discussion has one or more subsets, this overall set is generally called the **universal set** or **universe**. The symbol U is used to designate the universal set. Not all the universal sets are the same; they vary depending on the discussion.

To indicate a subset, we may use either the same capital letter as was used for the set but with a subscript or any other capital letter.

If $A = \{1, 2, 3, 4\}$

then $\{1, 2, 3\}$ could be called A_1 or any other capital letter: B, C, D, etc.

To indicate that M is a proper subset of R we write

$M \subset R$ or $R \supset M$ which is read

"M is properly contained in R."

$M \subset R$ or $R \supset M$ may also be thought of as indicating

R is a **superset** of M.

The symbols $\subset$ and $\supset$ are used with proper subsets only.
The symbols $\subseteq$ and $\supseteq$ are used with all subsets.

$$M \subseteq R \text{ or } R \supseteq M \text{ is read}$$
"M is contained in R."

What are the subsets of $D = \{1, 2, 3, 4\}$?

Answer:

$D_1 = \{1, 2, 3, 4\}$	$D_5 = \{2, 3, 4\}$	$D_9 = \{2, 3\}$	$D_{13} = \{2\}$
$D_2 = \{1, 2, 3\}$	$D_6 = \{1, 2\}$	$D_{10} = \{2, 4\}$	$D_{14} = \{3\}$
$D_3 = \{1, 2, 4\}$	$D_7 = \{1, 3\}$	$D_{11} = \{3, 4\}$	$D_{15} = \{4\}$
$D_4 = \{1, 3, 4\}$	$D_8 = \{1, 4\}$	$D_{12} = \{1\}$	$D_{16} = \varnothing$

We can tell how many subsets a set has by the number of elements it contains.

A set with 1 element has 2 (or 2^1) subsets.
A set with 2 elements has 4 (or 2^2) subsets.
A set with 3 elements has 8 (or 2^3) subsets.
A set with 4 elements has 16 (or 2^4) subsets.
A set with n elements has 2^n subsets.

Practice

1. What is a subset? What is a proper subset?

2. Write in symbols:

   (a) G is a proper subset of B.
   (b) R is a superset of M.
   (c) T is contained in A.
   (d) L is properly contained in H.

3. What is the universal set? What symbol is generally used to designate it?

4. Read, or write in words, each of the following:

   (a) $R \subset A$
   (b) $D \subseteq T$
   (c) $S \supset N$
   (d) $P \supseteq Q$
   (e) $\{1, 2, 3\} \subset \{0, 1, 2, 3, 4\}$
   (f) $\{2, 4, 6, 8\} \subseteq \{1, 2, 3, 4, 5, 6, 7, 8, 9\}$
   (g) $\{a, n, y\} \supseteq \{a, n, y\}$
   (h) $\{x \mid x > 9\} \subset \{x \mid x > 5\}$

5. (a) Is $\{a, b\}$ a subset of $\{a, b, c\}$?
   (b) Is $\{1, 3, 5\}$ a subset of $\{1, 2, 3, 4, 5\}$?
   (c) Is $\{3\}$ a subset of $\{n \mid n < 5 \text{ and } n \text{ is an integer}\}$?
   (d) Is $\{6, 7, 8\}$ a subset of $\{x \mid x > 2 \text{ and } x \text{ is a real number}\}$?
   (e) Is $\{y \mid 2y = 8\}$ a subset of $\{y \mid 2y < 10\}$?

6. (a) Is the set of all natural numbers a subset of the set of all real numbers?
   (b) Is the set of all integers a proper subset of the set of all natural numbers?
   (c) Is the set of all rectangles a subset of the set of all parallelograms?
   (d) Is the set of all odd numbers a subset of the set of all prime numbers?
   (e) Is the set of all fractions a proper subset of the set of all integers?
   (f) Is the set of all triangles a subset of the set of all polygons?
   (g) Is the set of all prime numbers a subset of a set of all odd numbers?
   (h) Is the set of all natural numbers divisible by 4 a subset of the set of all even numbers?
   (i) Is the set of all squares of whole numbers a subset of the set of all rational numbers?
   (j) Is the set of all proper fractions a subset of the set of all real numbers?

7. Which of these statements are true and which are false?

   (a) $\{3, 4\} \subset \{1, 2, 3, 4, 5, 6\}$
   (b) $\{a, b, c, d\} \subseteq \{a, b, c, d\}$
   (c) $\{0, 2, 4\} \subseteq \{0, 1, 2\}$
   (d) $\{n \mid n > 4\} \subset \{n \mid n > 2\}$
   (e) $\{y \mid y < 1\} \subseteq \{y \mid y < 6\}$

8. If $A = \{-2, 0, 2\}$, $B = \{-3, -1, 1, 3\}$, $R = \{-3, -2, -1, 0, 1, 2, 3\}$, $S = \{x \mid x < 3$ and x is a real number$\}$, which of the following statements are true and which are false?

   (a) $B \subset R$ (b) $A \subset B$ (c) $B \subset S$ (d) $A \subset S$ (e) $R \subset S$

9. (a) Write 8 subsets of $\{$knife, fork, spoon$\}$.
   (b) Write 16 subsets of $\{$English, Mathematics, Science, Social Studies$\}$
   (c) Write all the subsets of $\{1, 2, 3, 4, 5, 6\}$

10. How many subsets will a set have if it contains:

   (a) 4 elements?   (b) 9 elements?   (c) 7 elements?   (d) 5 elements?

EXERCISE 10

Operations with Sets

The operations of intersection, union, and complementation are very useful in the study of sets.

1. The **intersection** of two sets is the set composed of the common elements that belong to both sets. The symbol $\cap$ is used to indicate intersection.
   $R \cap S$ is read "R intersection S" or "the intersection of set R and set S" or "R cap S"

   If $D = \{3, 4, 5, 6, 7\}$ and $E = \{1, 3, 5, 7, 9\}$, what is $D \cap E$?
   Elements 3, 5, and 7 appear in both sets.
   Therefore the intersection of set D and set E represented by $D \cap E$ is the set $\{3, 5, 7\}$.

2. The **union** of two sets is the set composed of those elements which are in either of the two given sets or in both sets.
   The symbol $\cup$ is used to indicate union.
   $R \cup S$ is read "R union S" or "the union of set R and set S" or "R cup S"

   If $D = \{3, 4, 5, 6, 7\}$ and $E = \{1, 3, 5, 7, 9\}$ what is $D \cup E$?
   Elements 3, 4, 5, 6, and 7 appear in set D and elements 1, 3, 5, 7, and 9 appear in set E. Since the union of D and E is the set containing all the elements of both D and E, the union of D and E represented by $D \cup E$ is the set $\{1, 3, 4, 5, 6, 7, 9\}$. The common elements are written only once in the union set.

3. The **complement** of a set with respect to a given universe is the set of elements in the universe which are not in the given set.
   The symbol for the complement is a bar over the letter, or the symbol $'$ on the upper right of the letter, or the symbol $\sim$ preceding the letter. The complement of B is $\overline{B}$, read "B bar," or B' or $\sim B$.
   If U represents all the pupils in the mathematics class and N represents all the pupils in the class who passed in the last test, then $\overline{N}$ represents all the pupils in the class who did not pass in the last test.

4. Two sets are said to be **disjoint** if they have no elements in common. Their intersection is the null set.
   $G = \{1, 4, 9, 16\}$ and $H = \{2, 6, 10, 14\}$ are disjoint sets because there is no common element.
   Also $G \cap H = \varnothing$ for the same reason.

Practice

1. If $M = \{0, 1, 2, 3, 4, 5\}$ and $N = \{0, 2, 4, 6, 8\}$, list in braces the elements of the resulting set for each of the following:

     (a) $M \cup N$ (b) $M \cap N$ (c) $N \cup M$ (d) $N \cap M$

     Is $N \cup M$ the same as $M \cup N$? Is $N \cap M$ the same as $M \cap N$?

2. If $B = \{-3, -1, 0, 1, 3\}$ and $R = \{-2, -1, 0, 1, 2\}$, find each of the following: (a) $B \cup R$ (b) $R \cap B$

3. If $A = \{5, 7, 9\}$ and $D = \{6, 8, 10\}$, find each of the following: (a) $A \cap D$ (b) $D \cup A$ (c) Are sets A and D disjoint sets? If so, why?

4. If $U = \{1, 2, 3, 4, 5, 6, 7, 8, 9\}$ and $S = \{2, 4, 6, 8\}$, what is $\overline{S}$?

5. If set H represents the students who earned an A in science and set L represents the students who earned an A in mathematics, what does $L \cup H$ mean? What does $H \cap L$ mean?

6. If $U = \{a, b, c, d, e, f, g, h, i, j, k\}$, $E = \{b, c, d, f, g\}$, and $T = \{a, c, e, g, i\}$, find the following:

     (a) $E \cap T$ (b) $\overline{T}$ (c) $T \cup E$ (d) $\overline{E}$

7. If B represents the set of all prime numbers less than 14 and G represents the set of all natural numbers greater than 8 but less than 18.   (a) List the elements of each set.   (b) Find $B \cup G$.   (c) Find $B \cap G$.

8. (a) What is the union of the set of all odd natural numbers and the set of all even natural numbers? What is its intersection? Are the sets disjoint sets? If so, why?

     (b) What is the union of the set of all even natural numbers and the set of all prime numbers? What is its intersection? Are the sets disjoint sets? If so, why?

9. If U represents the entire student body at the Township High School, A represents its ninth-year class, B its tenth-year class, C its eleventh-year class, and D its twelfth-year class, what does each of the following mean?   (a) $\overline{A}$ (b) $\overline{C}$ (c) $A \cup B$ (d) $C \cap D$

10. Given: $U = \{$all non-negative integers less that 15$\}$,

     $A = \{0, 3, 5, 9, 13\}$ $M = \{$all one-digit odd natural numbers$\}$

     $B = \{2, 4, 7, 8, 10, 14\}$ $N = \{$all non-negative even integers less than 15$\}$

     $D = \{0, 2, 7, 9\}$ $R = \{$all one-digit prime numbers$\}$

     $E = \{1, 3, 4, 11, 12, 13, 14\}$ $S = \{$all natural numbers less than 12$\}$

     Find each of the following, listing in braces the elements of the resulting set:

     (a) $A \cap D$ (f) $\overline{A}$ (k) $S \cap R$ (p) $D \cap N$ (u) $M \cup E$

     (b) $D \cap E$ (g) $R \cup D$ (l) $\overline{B}$ (q) $R \cup B$ (v) $\overline{N}$

     (c) $B \cup E$ (h) $\overline{E}$ (m) $N \cup D$ (r) $\overline{M}$ (w) $M \cup R$

     (d) $\overline{D}$ (i) $E \cup S$ (n) $S \cup A$ (s) $A \cup E$ (x) $\overline{S}$

     (e) $A \cap M$ (j) $S \cap N$ (o) $\overline{R}$ (t) $B \cap D$ (y) $N \cap B$

EXERCISE 11

Venn Diagrams

Sets, subsets, and operations with sets can be illustrated pictorially by Venn diagrams.

A Venn diagram is one that pictures members of a set as points of a plane placed inside a closed curve.

Sets are represented as sections of a plane.

Set R

When one set is a subset of another set, the section of the plane representing the subset is placed inside the section representing the other set.

$R \subset S$

In a **Venn diagram** the universal set U is represented by all points of a rectangle. Any one of the subsets of the universal set is represented by a circle inside the rectangle. The members of the subset are represented by points within and on this circle.

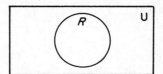

To illustrate the intersection of two sets, we draw two intersecting circles and shade the common area.

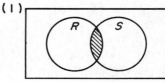

(I)

$R \cap S$

Other illustrations of intersection are also shown.

(2)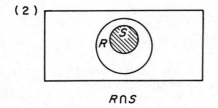

$R \cap S$

(3)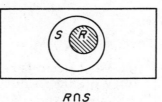

$R \cap S$

(4)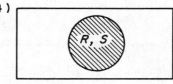

$R \cap S$

To illustrate the union of two sets, we draw:
   (1) two intersecting circles, or
   (2) two circles which do not intersect, or
   (3) one circle within another, or
   (4) one circle
Then shade all circles.

(I)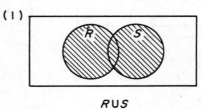

$R \cup S$

(2)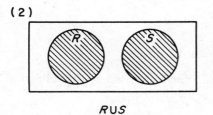

$R \cup S$

(3a)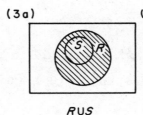

$R \cup S$

(3b)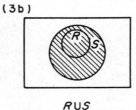

$R \cup S$

(4)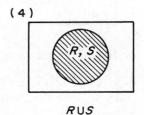

$R \cup S$

To illustrate two disjoint sets we draw two circles that do not intersect and leave them unshaded.

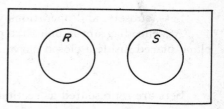

To illustrate the complement of a set we draw a rectangle to represent the universal set and a circle within the rectangle to represent the set. We shade the part of the rectangle that is outside the circle.

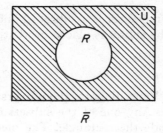

$$\bar{R}$$

Practice

1. Use a Venn diagram to show:
    (a) $R = \{1, 2, 3\}$
    (b) $B = \{a, b, c, d, e\}$
    (c) $M = \{*, O, x, '\}$
    (d) Set A is a subset of Set B
    (e) $G \subset H$
    (f) $T \subseteq N$
    (g) $B \cap E$
    (h) $R \cup F$
    (i) $\bar{N}$
    (j) Set A and Set R are disjoint sets.

2.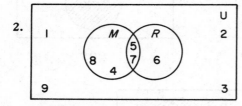

    (a) What elements belong to set R? To set U? To set M?
    (b) Write the resulting set for each of the following:
        (1) $M \cup R$ (2) $\bar{M}$ (3) $R \cap M$ (4) $\bar{R}$

3.

    (a) What elements belong to set U? To set A? To set H?
    (b) Write the resulting set for each of the following:
        (1) $A \cap H$ (2) $\bar{H}$ (3) $H \cup A$ (4) $\bar{A}$

4. If $U = \{r, s, t, u, v, w, x, y, z\}$ and $G = \{s, v, x\}$, illustrate $\bar{G}$ by a Venn diagram.

5. If $U = \{0, 1, 2, 3, 4, 5, 6, 7, 8, 9\}$, $R = \{1, 4, 7, 8\}$ and $S = \{0, 2, 4, 6, 8\}$, illustrate each of the following by a Venn diagram:
    (a) $R \cup S$ (b) $S \cap R$ (c) $\bar{S}$ (d) $\bar{R}$

6. If $U = \{-2, -1, 0, 1, 2, 3, 4, 5\}$, $B = \{-2, 0, 2, 4\}$, $L = \{-1, 1, 3, 5\}$ and $N = \{1, 2, 3, 4\}$, illustrate each of the following by a Venn diagram:

   (a) $L \cup N$ (b) $N \cap B$ (c) $\overline{B}$ (d) $B \cup L$ (e) $\overline{L}$ (f) $L \cap B$ (g) $B \cup N$ (h) $\overline{N}$ (i) $N \cap L$

7. If U is the set of all non-negative integers, D is the set of all even natural numbers and G is the set of all odd natural numbers, illustrate $D \cap G$ by a Venn diagram.

8. There are 18 boys in a mathematics class. Six boys play on the school football team, 5 play on the school baseball team and of these 3 play on both the school football and baseball teams. Illustrate this by a Venn diagram. Then determine how many boys are not on either or both teams.

9. In a class of 32 pupils, 28 pupils passed in English, 26 pupils passed in Social Studies and of these 24 pupils passed in both English and Social Studies. Illustrate this by a Venn diagram. Then determine how many pupils did not pass in either or both subjects.

10. There are 25 students who play in the school band, 12 students play the trumpet, 7 students play the flute and of these 5 students play both the trumpet and the flute. Illustrate by a Venn diagram.

EXERCISE 12

Logic—Conjunction, Disjunction, and Negation

In logic we study how to draw correct conclusions from given statements which are called propositions. Each statement or proposition is a declarative sentence stating a fact which is either true or false but not both true and false at the same time.

Much of logic is written in symbolic language. We shall limit our study to the compound sentences called conjunction and disjunction and to the opposite of a given statement called negation. We shall use symbolism and develop truth tables which outline the conditions of truth and falsity.

A sentence like "He is the best student in the class," is not a statement because we cannot tell whether it is true or false until we know whom the pronoun "he" represents. If the pronoun is replaced by some person's name, then the sentence becomes a statement. This pronoun is really a variable.

We have seen that equations and inequalities are sometimes called open sentences because they also contain a variable. We can tell whether these sentences are true or false only when a number is substituted for the variable.

Two declarative sentences (related or unrelated) are sometimes joined by a connective to make a compound sentence. Thus, two statements (or declarative sentences) joined by the word "and" form a combined statement (or compound sentence) called a **conjunction.**

The sentence "The sky is clear." is joined by "and" to the sentence "The streets are dry." to make the conjunction "The sky is clear and the streets are dry."

Combinations of number sentences may form conjunctions.

3 is less than 7 and 7 is less than 12 is a conjunction. In symbols this conjunction is

$$3 < 7 \quad \text{and} \quad 7 < 12$$

It may also be written as $3 < 7 < 12$

A compound number sentence like $3 < n$ and $n < 12$, also written as $3 < n < 12$, is a conjunction. Solving this conjunction means finding the solution set of numbers which will satisfy both of its sentences making them and the conjunction true. In the system of natural numbers the solution set would be $\{4, 5, 6, 7, 8, 9, 10, 11\}$. In the system of real numbers the solution set would be all the real numbers greater than 3 but less than 12.

In each of the following conjunctions we determine the truth of the first sentence, of the second sentence, and of the conjunction.

   (1) $5 < 8$ and $8 < 10$
   (2) $5 < 8$ and $8 < 7$
   (3) $9 < 8$ and $8 < 10$
   (4) $9 < 8$ and $8 < 7$

Summarizing the results in the following table, sometimes called the truth table, with the letter T as an abbreviation for true and F for false, we find

	1st statement	2nd statement	conjunction
(1)	T	T	T
(2)	T	F	F
(3)	F	T	F
(4)	F	F	F

A conjunction is true, if and only if, both statements (or sentences) are true. If either statement (or sentence) is false, the conjunction is false.

In logic the letters p and q are used to represent given statements (or sentences), and the symbol $\wedge$ is used to indicate the connective "and."

The conjunction of statements p and q is therefore represented by $p \wedge q$.

The heading of the above truth table could be written:

p	q	$p \wedge q$

instead of

1st statement	2nd statement	conjunction

Two statements (or declarative sentences) joined by the word "or" form a compound statement (or compound sentence) called a **disjunction.**

The sentence "The sky is clear or the streets are wet." is a disjunction.

Eight is greater than 3 or 8 is equal to 8 is a disjunction. In symbols this disjunction is written as $8 > 3$ or $8 = 8$.

A disjunction like $x > 3$ or $x = 3$ may also be written as $x \geqq 3$.

To solve a disjunction like $4 > n$ or $n > 7$ means to find the solution set of numbers which will satisfy either one of the sentences or both sentences, thereby making the disjunction true. In the system of real numbers the solution set would contain all real numbers less than 4 and all real numbers greater than 7.

In each of the following disjunctions we determine the truth of the first sentence, of the second sentence, and of the disjunction.

    (1) $4 > 3$ or $10 < 12$
    (2) $4 > 3$ or $15 < 12$
    (3) $2 > 3$ or $10 < 12$
    (4) $2 > 3$ or $15 < 12$

Summarizing the results by a truth table, we find

	1st statement	2nd statement	disjunction
(1)	T	T	T
(2)	T	F	T
(3)	F	T	T
(4)	F	F	F

A disjunction is true if either one of the two statements (or sentences) is true or if both of the statements (or sentences) are true. If the statements (or sentences) are both false, the disjunction is false.

The symbol $\vee$ is used to indicate the connective "or." The disjunction of statements p and q is therefore represented by $p \vee q$. The headings in the above truth table could be written as:

p	q	$p \vee q$

instead of

1st statement	2nd statement	disjunction

The **negation** of a statement (or sentence) is the opposite of the statement (or sentence).

If the sentence is "The sun is shining," then the negation is "The sun is not shining" or if the sentence is "It is true the sun is shining," then the negation is "It is false the sun is shining."
The negation of $n = 9$ is $n \neq 9$.
The negation of $a \not< 4$ is $a < 4$.

Summarizing by a truth table:

If the statement is true, the negation is false.
If the statement is false, the negation is true.

Statement	Negation
T	F
F	T

Negation is indicated by the symbol $\sim$ written in front of the symbol used to represent the statement. If p is the statement, then $\sim p$ (read "not p") is the negation. The negation of the negation is the original statement. $\sim(\sim p) = p$.

Practice

1. Form conjunctions using the following pairs of sentences:

   (a) $2 < 8; 8 < 10$ (b) $x < 5; x > 4$ (c) $8 + 3 > 1 + 4; 6 - 4 = 7$ (d) $3y = 12; y + 2 \not> 5$
   (e) $9b + 6 \not< 18; 4b - 2 > 10$

2. Form disjunctions using the following pairs of sentences:

   (a) $6 > 2; 2 = 2$ (b) $d = 9; d < 9$ (c) $10 - 2 < 15; 8 + 1 > 14$ (d) $x + 5 > 21; 5x \not< 20$
   (e) $12n - 1 \neq 6; 8n + 9 < 17$

3. Determine the truth or falsity of each of the following:

   (a) If one statement is true and the second statement is false, the conjunction is true.
   (b) If one statement is true and the second statement is false, the disjunction is false.
   (c) If both statements are true, the conjunction is true.
   (d) If both statements are false, the disjunction is false.
   (e) The negation of a negation is the negation.

4. What is the symbol generally used to express:
   (a) negation (b) connective "or" (c) connective "and" (d) first statement (e) second statement.

5. What is a truth table?

6. Which of the following are true conjunctions and which are false conjunctions? Which are true disjunctions and which are false disjunctions?

   (a) $6 \times 1 = 7$ or $6 + 2 = 7$
   (b) $6 + 1 = 7$ and $6 + 2 = 7$
   (c) $9 \cdot 8 = 72$ and $9 + 8 = 17$
   (d) $14 - 3 = 9$ or $12 < 5$
   (e) $3 \not< 8$ and $10 > 4$
   (f) $3 \not< 8$ or $10 > 4$
   (g) $6 \not> 1$ and $0 \not< 8$
   (h) $4 \cdot 5 \neq 20$ or $2 - 9 \not> 0$
   (i) $11 - 16 < -3$ and $21 - 17 > 6$
   (j) $2 - 2 > -1$ or $3 - 9 < -4 - 1$

7. What is the negation of each of the following:

(a) $5+2=8$ (c) $4\cdot0<3$ (e) $11-5\neq16-13$ (g) $1+1\ngtr2$ (i) $-5-6>0$

(b) $6-4=2$ (d) $3-5>-1$ (f) $\frac{20}{2}\nless14$ (h) $1-9=7+1$ (j) $(-6)(-2)<20$

8. First find the negation of each of the following. Then determine whether the negation is true or false.

(a) $3+6=10$ (c) $8\cdot5>8+5$ (e) $9+7\nless25$ (g) $5-11=3(-2)$ (i) $\frac{1}{2}+\frac{1}{2}<2-\frac{3}{4}$

(b) $1-3<-1$ (d) $6-4\neq4-6$ (f) $(-1)^2\ngtr0$ (h) $2+2\neq2\cdot2$ (j) $\frac{9}{3}>0$

9. Find the solution set of each of the following in the system of real numbers:

<table>
<tr><td colspan="2" align="center">SET 1</td><td colspan="2" align="center">SET 2</td></tr>
<tr><td>1. $x>10$ and $x<20$</td><td>6. $5>x$ and $x>2$</td><td>1. $y>8$ or $y<2$</td><td>6. $x\geqq5$</td></tr>
<tr><td>2. $b<0$ and $b>-3$</td><td>7. $6>x>1$</td><td>2. $t>0$ or $t<-5$</td><td>7. $3y\leqq12$</td></tr>
<tr><td>3. $6a>18$ and $a-5<7$</td><td>8. $2<a<10$</td><td>3. $n<-4$ or $n>3$</td><td>8. $z+2\geqq6$</td></tr>
<tr><td>4. $n+1<6$ and $2n>4$</td><td>9. $-1<c<0$</td><td>4. $c+1<7$ or $c-2>9$</td><td>9. $b-4\leqq9$</td></tr>
<tr><td>5. $4y+6=34$ and $5y<15$</td><td>10. $-4<z<4$</td><td>5. $a>10$ or $a=10$</td><td>10. $8x+3\geqq51$</td></tr>
</table>

10. Find the solution set of each of the following in the system of natural numbers:

(a) $y>4$ and $y<7$ (c) $0<b<6$ (e) $n\leqq0$ (g) $s+6\geqq9$

(b) $h<1$ or $h>3$ (d) $-2<x<10$ (f) $m\geqq8$ (h) $3x-4\leqq11$

11. Find the solution set of each of the following in the system of integers:

(a) $x<2$ or $x>6$ (c) $8<t<17$ (e) $b+5\geqq9$ (g) $4<z<13$

(b) $r>3$ and $r<10$ (d) $y\leqq11$ (f) $a<4$ and $a>-3$ (h) $8x\geqq56$

UNIT REVIEW

1. Read, or write in words, each of the following:

(a) $18+15>35-7$ (b) $6x+1<13$ (c) $6-9\neq9-6$ (d) $s-10\geqq5$ (e) $8<b<15$

2. Which of the following are true statements and which are false statements?

(a) $1-4<2+1$ (b) $\frac{2}{3}\times15>\frac{3}{4}\times12$ (c) $4(8+5)<4\cdot8+4\cdot5$ (d) $4-6\times3=(4-6)\times3$ (e) $0-5\ngtr4-6$

3. (a) Is the resulting statement true when 4 is substituted for n in the sentence $2n-1>5$?

(b) Is the resulting statement true when -2 is substituted for x in the sentence $9x+3<11$?

4. Write the set listing within braces each of the following collections of elements:

(a) All the natural numbers greater than 9 but less than 21.

(b) The names of all the oceans in the world.

5. Write the set describing each of the following conditions:

(a) All numbers greater than 4.

(b) All rational numbers.

6. Write, using the proper symbols:

(a) 12 is an element of set R.   (b) a is not an element of set D.

7. (a) If $S=\{1,\ 3,\ 5,\ 7,\ 9\}$, is the statement $7\epsilon S$ true?

(b) If $B=\{x\,|\,x>3$ and x is an integer$\}$, is the statement $6\epsilon B$ true?

8. What is the difference between $\{0\}$ and $\varnothing$?

9. Solve or find the solution set of each of the following equations in the system of real numbers:

(a) $x-15=25$ (b) $-12t=8$ (c) $7(n-2)=6(n+5)$ (d) $\dfrac{b}{40}=\dfrac{3}{4}$ (e) $x^2=49$

10. (a) Find the solution set of $4x+8=15$ in the system of natural numbers.
    (b) Find the solution set of $6y-2=y+8$ when the replacement set is the set of all the odd numbers.
    (c) Find the solution set of $12d-3d=72$ when the replacement set is $\{5, 6, 7, 8, 9\}$.

11. Solve or find the solution set of each of the following inequalities in the system of real numbers:
    (a) $6c+5>45$ (b) $5y-3<7y+15$ (c) $8n-n\not> 56$ (d) $x-10\not< -25$ (e) $-8r\ne -72$

12. Solve or find the solution set of each of the following inequalities in the system of natural numbers:
    (a) $d+7\ne 12$ (b) $3n+4>n+2$ (c) $7a-3\not< 2a+17$ (d) $-6y<30$ (e) $4t-t\not> 24$

13. Solve or find the solution set of each of the following inequalities in the system of integers:
    (a) $9m<54$ (b) $-5c\not> 20$ (c) $2a-6>18$ (d) $x+x\ne 0$ (e) $8n+3\not< 4n+19$

14. (a) Find the solution set of $3x+8>23$ when the replacement set is $\{1, 2, 3, 4, 5, 6, 7, 8, 9\}$.
    (b) Find the solution set of $7y-5<2y-10$ when the replacement set is $\{-3, -2, -1, 0, 1, 2, 3\}$.

15. Is the set of all even numbers a subset of all integers?

16. (a) Is $\{c, d, e\}$ a subset of $\{a, b, c, d\}$?
    (b) Is $\{5, 6, 7\}$ a subset of $\{x \mid x<10 \text{ and } x \text{ is an integer}\}$?

17. If $A=\{2, 3, 7, 8\}$ $E=\{3, 8, 2, 7\}$
       $B=\{7, 8\}$ $F=\{\text{all prime numbers}\}$
       $D=\{3, 1, 2, 8, 7\}$ $G=\{x \mid x>4 \text{ and } x \text{ is a real number}\}$

    (a) Which of the following are true and which are false?

        (1) $D\subset B$ (2) $A\subseteq B$ (3) $E\subset D$ (4) $G\supset B$ (5) $F\subset G$

    (b) Find each of the following:

        (1) $A\cap B$ (2) $D\cup E$ (3) $F\cap D$ (4) $B\cup D$ (5) $G\cap A$

18. If $U=\{-2, -1, 0, 1, 2, 3, 4, 5, 6, 7, 8, 9\}$, $R=\{-2, 0, 4, 8\}$, $S=\{-2, 1, 3, 6, 8\}$, $T=\{-1, 0, 1, 2, 4, 6\}$, find each of the following:

    (a) $R\cup S$ (b) $S\cup T$ (c) $\overline{R}$ (d) $T\cap R$ (e) $\overline{T}$

    Illustrate each by a Venn diagram.

19. There are 38 children in a class. Twenty-one are studying French, 24 are studying Spanish and of these 12 are studying both French and Spanish. Illustrate this by a Venn diagram. Determine how many children in the class are not studying either or both foreign languages.

20. Form a conjunction using the sentences: $x<15$; $x>9$.

21. Form a disjunction using the sentences: $8+3<12$; $15-2>13$.

22. Which of the following are true disjunctions? Which are false conjunctions?
    (a) $4+9=15$ or $8-1<4$ (c) $3\not> 2-5$ and $6+2\ne 9$
    (b) $7+5>10$ and $-4<2$ (d) $15-5>9$ or $6-8\not< 11$

23. Find the negation of   (a) $5-7=2$ (b) $4+8\not< 8+4$ (c) $2-9>4-11$ (d) $4(-5)<5(-4)$
    Is the negation of $4-5<2-1$ true?

24. Find the solution set of each of the following in the system of real numbers:
    (a) $x>5$ and $x<8$ (b) $-3<x<0$ (c) $y<4$ or $y>9$ (d) $n\leqq 5$

25. Find the solution set of each of the following in the system of natural numbers:
    (a) $n<10$ and $n>2$ (b) $-5<y<8$ (c) $x>7$ or $x<3$ (d) $x\geqq 1$

INTRODUCTION TO SUPPLEMENTARY UNIT THREE

In the development of number for computational use in the elementary grades, emphasis is usually placed on the cardinal meaning of number. We regroup groups or collections of various sizes.

In addition we put together or combine groups to find the total number. In subtraction a group or collection is taken away from another to find the number left over. Multiplication is a method of combining groups of equal size or groups containing the same number of things to find how many there are altogether. In division we find either how many equal groups (collections of the same size) may be formed or the number of things in (the size of) one of the equal groups.

In contemporary mathematics numbers are associated with points on the number line. The ordinal meaning of number is stressed. The numbers are arranged in a definite order on the number line so that they correspond one-to-one with the points on the line. As we shall see, numbers from any one of the systems: non-positive integers (natural numbers and zero), all integers, rational numbers, or real numbers, can be arranged to correspond with points on the number line. We shall find that of any two numbers the one farther to the right on the number line is the greater; the one farther to the left is the smaller. When children use a ruler, which pictures number on a scale, they are working with the number line in the field of measurement.

In this unit we shall see that the number line is most essential in drawing the graphs of inequalities in one variable. Ordered pairs, the Cartesian product, and graphs of equations and inequalities in two variables using both the real number plane and a restricted number plane are also studied. The graphic solution of simultaneous inequalities is included.

SUPPLEMENTARY UNIT THREE—GRAPHS

EXERCISE 13

The Number Line

We think of a line as an endless number of points. A line is often described as a set of points.

A line that has its points labeled with numbers is called a **number line.**

Suppose we select the non-negative integers (the natural numbers and zero) and arrange them so that they correspond one-to-one with points on a line.

Two points are chosen, the first point to the left is marked with the symbol 0 and the other point with the symbol 1. The interval between these points is used as a unit of measure. Beginning with the point marked 1, points are located to the right and equally spaced along the line. Each point is marked with a corresponding natural number in consecutive order. Only a part of the line is pictured because the number line is endless. There is a one-to-one correspondence between these non-negative integers and the points on the line.

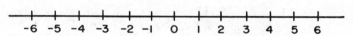

Since the line extends indefinitely to the left as well as to the right, the number line may be extended so that points correspond to all integers, positive and negative.

Again using the interval from 0 to 1 as the unit of measure, we mark off successive unit lengths on the line to the left of 0. Thus points equally spaced are located. The first point to the left of 0 is marked −1, the second point marked −2, etc. The numbers corresponding to the points found on the left of the 0 are negative integers. The numbers corresponding to the points found on the right of 0 are positive integers, and each may be prefixed with a positive sign. Numbers 2 and +2 mark the same point. Again only a part of the line is pictured.

Since the interval between each whole number may be divided into halves, thirds, fourths, etc., the number line may be also related to fractions so that there is a point on the number line corresponding to each fraction and thus to all rational numbers. The number of points corresponding to the rational numbers are unlimited or infinite because there is always another fraction between any two fractions.

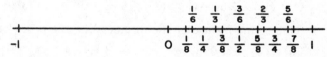

The number line contains points that are associated with irrational numbers.

To locate a point on the number line that corresponds to the irrational number $\sqrt{2}$, we construct on the number line a square with the side measuring the unit length. The length of the diagonal of the square measures $\sqrt{2}$. By describing an arc we locate on the number line the points corresponding to $\sqrt{2}$ and to $-\sqrt{2}$.

Thus we see that the real number line is the full set of points which correspond to the set of real numbers consisting of all the rational and irrational numbers.

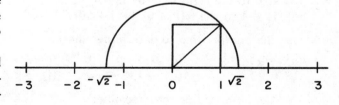

We must remember that we can only picture part of the real number line because the line is endless.

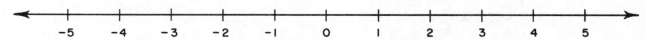

We may compare numbers by the number line. The number corresponding to the point on the line farther to the right is the larger number.

The number line shows that the point marked −2 is the same distance from 0 as is the point marked 2, but the points fall on opposite sides.

We call a pair of numbers like $+2$ and -2 **opposites**. The opposite of $+4$ is -4. The opposite of -3 is $+3$. Each real number has an opposite. The opposite of 0 is 0. The opposite to the opposite of a number is the number itself. The sum of a number and its opposite is 0. The opposite of a number is the same as its additive inverse.

The **absolute value** of any real number is the value of the corresponding arithmetic number which has no sign. The absolute value of -5 is 5 and of $+5$ is 5. The absolute value of 0 is 0. If we consider both a real number (other than zero) and its opposite, the absolute value in either case would be the greater of the two numbers. The symbol consisting of a pair of vertical bars $|\ \ |$ is used to designate absolute value. $|-6|$ is read "the absolute value of -6."

Practice

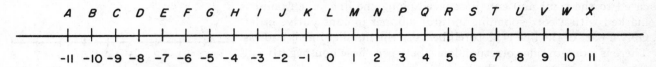

1. (a) What number corresponds to point B? P? E? L? W?

   (b) What letter labels the point corresponding to each of the following numbers: -4? 7? 0? -9? 2?

2. Draw a number line, then locate the points corresponding to the following sets of numbers:

   (a) $\{1, 3, 5, 7, 9, 11\}$ (c) $\{6, -3, 4, 0, 2, -1, -5\}$ (e) $\{0, .5, 1.5, 2.5, 3.5, 4.5\}$
   (b) $\{-8, -6, -4, -2, 0\}$ (d) $\{7, -1, 4, -\frac{1}{2}, 0, -8\}$ (f) $\{\frac{3}{4}, -1\frac{1}{2}, 2\frac{1}{4}, -3, 3\frac{3}{4}, -4\frac{1}{2}\}$

3. The numbers below correspond to points on the number line.

   (a) Which corresponding point is to the left of the other?

       (1) -9 or 2 (2) 0 or -4 (3) $+6$ or $+3$ (4) $.75$ or -1?   (5) -2 or -3

   (b) Which corresponding point is to the right of the other?

       (1) -7 or -6 (2) $+5$ or -5 (3) $\frac{2}{3}$ or 0 (4) $-\frac{5}{8}$ or $-\frac{3}{4}$ (5) $+8$ or $+2$

4. Determine by use of the number line the order of the following numbers writing the smallest first:

   (a) $-4, +8, 0$ (c) $+\frac{5}{8}, -\frac{1}{2}, +1\frac{1}{4}, -\frac{2}{3}$ (e) $+.4, -.39, +.75, -.6$
   (b) $-3, -9, -2, -4$ (d) $-7, +7, -3, 0, +6, -9$ (f) $-5, +7, -2, -4, +6, -1, +3$

5. (a) Is -6 to the left of 8? Is $-6 < 8$?
   (b) Is $+2$ to the right of $+7$? Is $+2 > +7$?
   (c) Is $+3$ to the left of -3? Is $+3 < -3$?
   (d) Is 0 to the right of -5? Is $0 > -5$?
   (e) Is $+4$ to the left of 0? Is $+4 < 0$?

6. Use the number line to determine whether:

   (a) $-4 > -3$ (c) $9 < -9$ (e) $2 > -7$ (g) $0 < -5$ (i) $-2 > 6$
   (b) $0 > 2$ (d) $-1 < -6$ (f) $3 < 2$ (h) $-8 > +8$ (j) $-7 < -3$

7. Use the number line to determine:

   (a) If $5 > -1$ and $-1 > -3$, then $5 > -3$.
   (b) If $-2 < 0$ and $0 < 6$, then $-2 < 6$.
   (c) If $-4 > -7$ and $-7 > -9$, then $-4 > -9$.
   (d) If $2 < 5$ and $5 < 8$, then $2 < 8$.
   (e) If $0 > -3$ and $-3 > -6$, then $0 > -6$.

8. (a) Find the opposite of each of the following:

       (1) -9 (3) 0 (5) 7 (7) $-.85$ (9) $+\frac{5}{6}$
       (2) $+10$ (4) $-\frac{3}{8}$ (6) $+.16$ (8) $-2\frac{1}{3}$ (10) $-.001$

   (b) What is always true about the sum of a number and its opposite?

9. (a) Find the absolute value of each of the following numbers:

(1) $+3$ (2) -11 (3) $-\frac{9}{10}$ (4) $+.75$ (5) 0 (6) 8 (7) -14 (8) $+1\frac{3}{4}$

(b) Find the indicated absolute value of each of the following:

(1) $|-2|$ (2) $|0|$ (3) $|+7|$ (4) $\left|-\frac{2}{3}\right|$ (5) $|+.39|$ (6) $-|-5|$ (7) $-|+5|$ (8) $\left|-\frac{7}{8}\right|$

(c) Simplify by performing the indicated operations and by finding the absolute value:

(1) $|4+8|$ (2) $|3-7|$ (3) $|6(-5)|$ (4) $\left|\dfrac{10}{-2}\right|$ (5) $|(-2)(4)|$

(6) $|-5|+|3|$ (7) $|-2|-|-4|$ (8) $|-9|\times|8|$ (9) $\dfrac{|-20|}{|-4|}$ (10) $-(|-9|+|-12|)$

(11) $|-15|+9$ (12) $4-|1-2|$ (13) $|-8|\times3$ (14) $\dfrac{|-18|}{6}$ (15) $|-4|^2-|-3|^2$

10. Find the solution set of each of the following in the system of real numbers:

(a) $|x|=2$ (c) $|n|-9=5$ (e) $\dfrac{|b|}{5}=4$ (g) $|x|>6$ (i) $|b|\geqq1$

(b) $|y|+3=8$ (d) $7\times|x|=42$ (f) $6-|x|=3$ (h) $|y|<5$ (j) $|x|\leqq0$

EXERCISE 14

Graphing Sentences in One Variable

There are an unlimited or infinite number of points on the real number line. There are an unlimited or infinite number of real numbers in our number system. However, there is one and only one real number that corresponds to each point on the number line. There is one and only one point on the number line that corresponds to each real number of our number system.

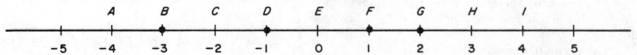

Each point on the line is called the **graph** of the real number to which it corresponds. Point G is the graph of number 2.

Each real number is called the **coordinate** of the related point on the line. 2 is the coordinate of point G.

The **graph of a number** is a point on the number line whose coordinate is the number. The graph of 2 is point G whose coordinate is the number 2.

The set of points corresponding to a set of numbers is called the **graph of the set of numbers.** The set of points $\{B, D, F, G\}$ is the graph of the set of numbers $\{-3, -1, 1, 2\}$. Thus we may say the graph of a set of numbers is the set of points on the number line whose coordinates are the numbers of the set. A point on the number line belongs to the graph of a set of numbers if the coordinate of the point belongs to the set.

The graph of the numbers in a solution set or truth set of a sentence (equation or inequality) in one variable is the graph of the set of all numbers that satisfy or make the sentence true.

The **graph of a sentence in one variable** is the set of all points on the number line whose coordinates are the numbers belonging to the solution set (or truth set or solution) of the sentence. This set of points which the graph pictures is called the **locus of the sentence.**

Lines

A line is a set of points. The word "line," unless described otherwise, generally means "straight line."

A geometric line extends indefinitely in both directions. The lines we draw are only representations of lines. A geometric line has only length.

We use a dot to represent a point. However, a geometric point has no size. We label a point with a capital letter. $\cdot A$ is point A.

A line may be drawn with or without arrow-heads which indicate that the line is endless.

The line $\underset{C\ \ D\ \ \ \ \ E}{|\ \ |\ \ \ \ \ |}$ may be called line CE and represented by the symbol $\overset{\leftrightarrow}{CE}$. It may also be called line CD or line DE and represented by the corresponding symbols $\overset{\leftrightarrow}{CD}$ or $\overset{\leftrightarrow}{DE}$ respectively. Sometimes a small letter is written on the right to identify a line. $\longleftrightarrow b$ **is line** b

A definite part of a line including both of its endpoints is called a **line segment** or **segment.**

A definite part of a line excluding both of its endpoints is called an **interval.** An interval is a segment without the endpoints. It is the part of the line between two endpoints. Both the segment and the interval are named by the endpoints. On line t we have segment MN which includes the endpoints M and N and interval MN which excludes the endpoints.

A point on a line separates the line into two **half-lines.** The half-lines do not include this point. A half-line extends indefinitely in one direction only.

A **ray** is a half-line which includes one endpoint. The included end point is the one that separates the line into two half-lines.

To name a half-line or ray we write the letter which corresponds to the point separating the line into two half-lines first and then any other point on the line. $\underset{B}{}$ $\underset{C}{}$

Half-line BC excludes the endpoint B, but ray BC includes the endpoint B.

Graphs of Equations

The graph of any single number is the one point found on the number line corresponding to the number. It is pictured by a single dot.

The graph of the set $\{4\}$ is

The graph of a set containing two or more integers is a set of discrete points pictured by a set of dots.

The graph of the set $\{-2, 0, 3\}$ is

The graph of an equation in one variable is a single point marked on the number line by a heavy dot.

The graph of the equation $x = 5$ is

Its solution set is $\{5\}$.

The graph of the equation $n + 2 = 3$ is

Its solution set is $\{1\}$.

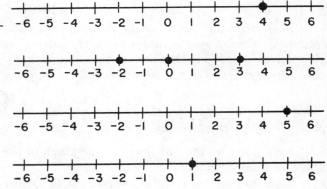

Graphs of Inequalities

The graph of a set of all real numbers greater than a given number is a half-line extending to the right along the number line.

The graph of the inequality $x > 2$ is

The graph of a set of all real numbers less than a given number is a half-line extending to the left along the number line.

The graph of the inequality $x < 2$ is

The graph of a set of all real numbers greater than or equal to a given number is a ray extending to the right along the number line.

The graph of the inequality $x \geqq 2$ is

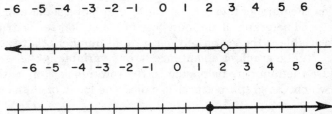

The graph of a set of all real numbers less than or equal to a given number is a ray extending to the left along the number line.

The graph of the inequality $x \leqq 2$ is

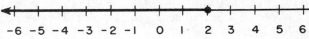

The graph of a set of numbers between two given numbers but not including the two given numbers is an interval.

The graph of the inequality
$$2 < x < 5 \text{ is}$$

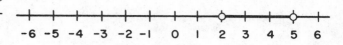

The graph of a set of numbers between two given numbers and including the two given numbers is a line segment.

The graph of the inequality
$$2 \leqq x \leqq 5 \text{ is}$$

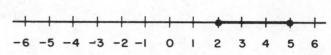

It should be noted that if an endpoint is included in the graph of an inequality, the heavy dot is used to indicate this point. Sometimes a small circle or open dot is used to indicate that the endpoint is not included in the graph. One endpoint is included when the graph is a ray, two endpoints when the graph is a line segment, and the endpoints are excluded when the graph is either a half-line or interval.

The following are graphs of other sentences. In each the system of real numbers is used.

1. $4n = 12$
   $n = 3$

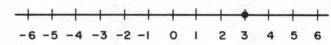

Graph of $4n = 12$ is the point whose coordinate is 3.

2. $4n > 12$
   $n > 3$

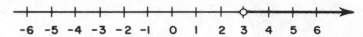

Graph of $4n > 12$ is the set of all points whose coordinates are greater than 3.

3. $4n < 12$
   $n < 3$

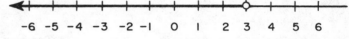

Graph of $4n < 12$ is the set of all points whose coordinates are less than 3.

4. $4n \geqq 12$
   $n \geqq 3$

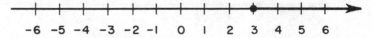

Graph of $4n \geqq 12$ is the set of all points whose coordinates are greater than 3 or equal to 3.

5. $4n \leqq 12$
   $n \leqq 3$

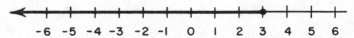

Graph of $4n \leqq 12$ is the set of all points whose coordinates are less than 3 or equal to 3.

6. $2 \leqq n < 5$

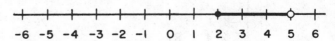

Graph of $2 \leqq n < 5$ is the set of all points whose coordinates are greater than or equal to 2 but less than 5.

7. $n < 2$ or $n > 5$

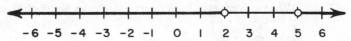

Graph of $n < 2$ or $n > 5$ is the set of all points whose coordinates are less than 2 or greater than 5.

8. $n = n + 2$

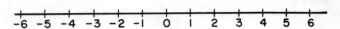

Since the solution set is the empty set because there is no solution, we have no points to draw the graph.

9. $|x| = 3$

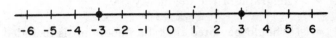

Graph of $|x| = 3$ is the set of points whose coordinates are -3 and 3 since the solution set is $\{-3, 3\}$.

10. $4(x+2) = 4x + 8$

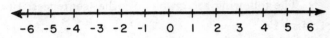

Graph of the identity $4(x+2) = 4x+8$ is the entire number line since the identity is satisfied by every real number.

The following is the graph of $x > 2$ when the replacement set is $\{0, 1, 2, 3, 4, 5, 6\}$.

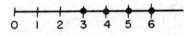

Since the replacement set is restricted, the solution set is $\{3, 4, 5, 6\}$. The graph of $x > 2$ is the set of points whose coordinates are 3, 4, 5, and 6. Those points whose coordinates are the numbers belonging to the replacement set are marked on the number line and the points belonging to the graph are indicated by heavy dots.

Practice

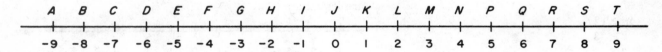

1. Use the above number line to answer the following:

   (a) What point is the graph of each of the following numbers?

   (1) -5 (2) 0   (3) 6   (4) -3 (5) 8   (6) -9 (7) 2   (8) -1

   (b) What number is the coordinate of each of the following points?

   (1) C (2) K (3) F (4) M (5) D (6) R (7) H (8) I

   (c) What set of points is the graph of each of the following sets of numbers?

   (1) $\{1, 2, 3\}$ (6) $\{-9, 9, -5, 5, -1, 1\}$
   (2) $\{-4, 1, 5\}$ (7) $\{-6, -3, 0, 3, 6\}$
   (3) $\{0, 2, 4, 6, 8\}$ (8) $\{-2, -1, 0, 1, 2\}$
   (4) $\{-5, -4, -3, -2, -1\}$ (9) $\{-7, -4, 3, 7, 8\}$
   (5) $\{-7, 6, -1, -9, 5\}$ (10) $\{-8, -6, -4, -2, 0, 2, 4, 6, 8\}$

   (d) What set of numbers corresponds to each of the following sets of points?

   (1) $\{C, E, F\}$ (6) $\{C, F, G, J, P, Q\}$
   (2) $\{B, G, H, J\}$ (7) $\{S, G, D, M\}$
   (3) $\{D, I, L, M, Q\}$ (8) $\{K, F, A, T\}$
   (4) $\{A, F, J, N, R, T\}$ (9) $\{B, E, H, J, K, P, S\}$
   (5) $\{A, E, K, N, R, S\}$ (10) $\{D, N, R, B, J, E, Q\}$

2. Graph on a number line the solution set of each of the following sentences in the system of real numbers:

SET 1	SET 2	SET 3	SET 4	SET 5
1. $x=5$	**1.** $x>3$	**1.** $x<2$	**1.** $x \neq 8$	**1.** $x \not> 9$
2. $a=-1$	**2.** $b>-2$	**2.** $y<-4$	**2.** $t \neq -7$	**2.** $c \not> -3$
3. $4x=12$	**3.** $2m+1>1$	**3.** $n+3<3$	**3.** $8c \neq 32$	**3.** $5y-y \not> 28$
4. $6x+3=15$	**4.** $-x>4$	**4.** $-s<-2$	**4.** $y+1 \neq 6$	**4.** $m-6 \not> -7$
5. $y-5=2$	**5.** $3b-7>17$	**5.** $5x-2<8$	**5.** $7n-5 \neq 44$	**5.** $x+8 \not> 8$

SET 6	SET 7	SET 8	SET 9	SET 10
1. $x \not< 4$	**1.** $x \leq 5$	**1.** $x \geq 7$	**1.** $1<x<4$	**1.** $3 \leq x \leq 8$
2. $r \not< -6$	**2.** $a \leq -4$	**2.** $b \geq -5$	**2.** $-7<y<-1$	**2.** $-4<y \leq 9$
3. $-y \not< 0$	**3.** $b+6 \leq 9$	**3.** $2y-1 \geq 1$	**3.** $0>a>-5$	**3.** $-1 \geq x>-6$
4. $9x+1 \not< 19$	**4.** $3b-b \leq 14$	**4.** $8x+2x \geq 40$	**4.** $6>z>-4$	**4.** $-2 \leq s<2$
5. $2b-3b \not< -5$	**5.** $2y+5 \leq 1$	**5.** $\dfrac{c}{2} \geq 3$	**5.** $-9<t<10$	**5.** $5 \geq y \geq 0$

SET 11	SET 12	SET 13		
1. $x=x+1$	**1.** $\lvert x \rvert =1$	**1.** $x+6=11$	**6.** $-5<y<-2$	**11.** $x \leq -3$
2. $y=y-4$	**2.** $\lvert x+2 \rvert =5$	**2.** $3y-4>20$	**7.** $n+6>n$	**12.** $2y+8 \geq 20$
3. $b+2>b$	**3.** $\lvert y \rvert >4$	**3.** $7x-8<27$	**8.** $a+1 \not< 5$	**13.** $\lvert x-4 \rvert >8$
4. $d-1<d$	**4.** $\lvert b \rvert <5$	**4.** $-x>-4$	**9.** $4t-t<15$	**14.** $-3 \leq b<6$
5. $n>n+3$	**5.** $\lvert c \rvert >-6$	**5.** $4b+5<5$	**10.** $m-4 \not> 2$	**15.** $0 \geq x \geq -4$

3. Using the system of real numbers, draw the graph of each of the following:

(a) $\{x \mid x=4\}$ (c) $\{x \mid x>2\}$ (e) $\{n \mid 4n<32\}$ (g) $\{y \mid 5y+6=-9\}$

(b) $\{x \mid x<-1\}$ (d) $\{y \mid y+1<7\}$ (f) $\{x \mid x-3 \geq -1\}$ (h) $\{x \mid 0<x<4\}$

4. For each of the following graphs write a corresponding open sentence:

(a)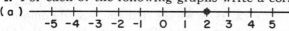

(b)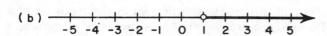

(c)

(d)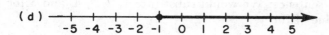

(e)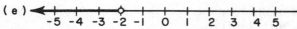

(f)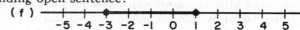

(g)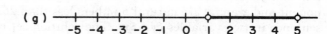

(h)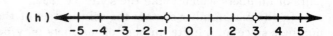

(i)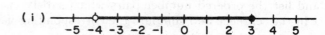

(j)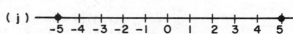

5. Using the system of real numbers, draw the graph of each of the following sentences:

(a) $x+3=x+5-2$ (b) $6x-(x+1)=5x-1$ (c) $4(3x-6)=3(4x-8)$ (d) $2x-(6-x)=3(x-2)$

6. Draw the graph of each of the following sentences:

(a) When the replacement set is $\{0, 2, 4, 6, 8\}$:

(1) $3x=12$ (2) $x+5>8$ (3) $2b+1<12$ (4) $8a-3 \leq 77$ (5) $5n-n \neq 32$

(b) When the replacement set is $\{-3, -2, -1, 0, 1, 2, 3\}$:

(1) $9n<9$ (2) $b+4=3$ (3) $4x-7>5$ (4) $3y+8 \not> 8$ (5) $2y+5y \geq -14$

(c) When the replacement set is the set of prime numbers less than 12:

(1) $y+5=10$ (2) $n-3<1$ (3) $6x>0$ (4) $9t+3 \geq 39$ (5) $8b-7 \not< 81$

EXERCISE 15

Graphing Sentences in Two Variables—Ordered Pairs

Numbers are used in pairs in many ways. We use number pairs when we work with fractions and ratios and when we compare quantities or show relationships between quantities by tables, graphs and formulas.

Local Weather Forecast

TONIGHT: Cloudy with occasional rain. Low near 40.

TOMORROW: Mostly cloudy with occasional rain. High about 50.

THE TEMPERATURES:

7 PM—38	3 AM—30	11 AM—43
8 PM—37	4 AM—29	Noon—44
9 PM—35	5 AM—32	1 PM—45
10 PM—36	6 AM—34	2 PM—47
11 PM—34	7 AM—33	3 PM—48
12 PM—34	8 AM—34	4 PM—
1 AM—33	9 AM—37	5 PM—
2 AM—31	10 AM—40	6 PM—

Most large city daily newspapers show the hourly temperature in their respective communities by publishing a chart similar to the one on the right. We see that the information is given by number pairs written in a definite order. The time is given first and the temperature second.

An **ordered pair of numbers** is a pair of numbers expressed in a definite order so that one number is first and the other is second. We designate an ordered pair of numbers by writing the pair of numbers within parentheses, the first number in order written first and the second number written second separated by a comma.

(3, 7) is an ordered pair of numbers with 3 first (sometimes called the first component) and 7 second (sometimes called the second component). The ordered pair (7, 3) is different because 7 is first and 3 is second.

Ordered pairs of numbers may be collected in sets. The pairs of numbers in a set of ordered pairs of numbers sometimes follow a pattern or are related. A sentence in two variables expresses a relation. We may think of the relation expressed by $y = x$ or $y > x$ or $y < x$ or $y = x + 2$ etc. as a set of ordered pairs.

In the set of ordered pairs: $\{(1, 5), (2, 10), (3, 15), (4, 20), (5, 25)\}$, we see that the second component is always five times the first component. This set of ordered pairs of numbers would satisfy the open sentence $y = 5x$ which has two variables x and y; where x represents the first component, y the second component and x and y are natural numbers less than 26. We call this set the solution set or the truth set of a sentence in two variables ($y = 5x$). The solution set of a sentence in one variable is the set of all numbers which make the sentence true. The **solution set of a sentence in two variables** is the set of all the ordered pairs of numbers which make the sentence true.

In the real number system the solution set of the sentence $y = 5x$ is an infinite set of ordered pairs of numbers since an infinite number of numbers may be substituted for x.

However, if the sentence $y = 5x$ is limited so that x is a natural number less than 6, we may determine and list the ordered number pairs which satisfy the sentence. We would substitute 1, 2, 3, 4, and 5 for x in the sentence and compute the corresponding value of the y.

In set notation this is indicated as:

$$\{(x, y) \mid y = 5x\} \quad \text{where} \quad U = \{1, 2, 3, \ldots, 25\}$$

or

$$\{(x, y) \mid y = 5x \quad \text{and} \quad x \text{ is a natural number less than 6}\}$$
$$= \{(1, 5), (2, 10), (3, 15), (4, 20), (5, 25)\}$$

The expression $\{(x, y) \mid y = 5x\}$ is read:

"The set of ordered pairs (x, y) such that $y = 5x$."

Sometimes the replacement set for x is called the **domain** of the relation, and the corresponding set of numbers for y is called the **range** of the relation.

In traditional mathematics we generally use the real number plane when drawing the graph of an equation having two variables. In contemporary mathematics the number plane is sometimes restricted and graphing is extended to include inequalities.

We have seen that only a single number (coordinate) is needed to locate a point on a number line since there is one and only one real number that corresponds to each point on the number line. The graph of a sentence in one variable is the set of all points on the number line whose coordinates are the numbers belonging to the solution set of the sentence.

However, an ordered pair of numbers is needed to locate a point which is in a plane. The point is located with respect to a pair of coordinate axes. They are two perpendicular number lines, one horizontal and the other vertical. They intersect in the point (0, 0) which is called the origin. The horizontal axis is called the X-axis and the vertical axis is called the Y-axis. To locate a point, a perpendicular line is drawn from the point to the X-axis and another to the Y-axis. The number corresponding to the point where the line intersects the X-axis is called the x-coordinate (or abscissa) of the point, and the number corresponding to the point where the line intersects the Y-axis is the y-coordinate (or ordinate) of the point.

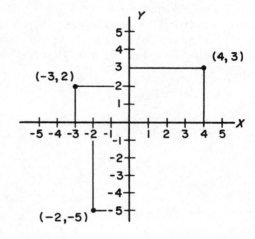

These coordinates of a point are denoted by an ordered pair of numbers. In the ordered pair the x-coordinate is expressed first and the y-coordinate is second. Of course, when written, the coordinates of a point are placed in parentheses like any ordered pair. Thus each point of the real number plane corresponds to only one ordered pair of real numbers and each ordered pair of real numbers corresponds to only one point of the real number plane. There is a one-to-one correspondence between all the points of the plane and the set of all ordered number pairs.

The solution set of a sentence in two variables is the set of all ordered pairs which make the sentence true. The **graph of a sentence in two variables** is the set of all points of the number plane whose coordinates are the ordered pairs of numbers belonging to the solution set of the sentence. That is, the graph of a sentence in two variables is the graph of its solution set. The graph of $x+y=2$ is the graph of $\{(x, y) \mid x+y=2\}$.

The graph of an equation in x and y is the set of all points whose coordinates (x, y) satisfy the equation. To draw the graph of the equation $x+y=2$, we first make a table of at least three ordered number pairs, each pair consisting of the abscissa (the x-coordinate) and the ordinate (the y-coordinate) obtained as follows: select values for the x-coordinate, substitute each value for x in the equation, then compute the corresponding value of the y which becomes the corresponding y-coordinate. We plot the points by locating their coordinates with respect to the X-axis and Y-axis. If we are working in the system of real numbers, we draw a line through the plotted points. The graph of $x+y=2$ is a straight line. When we deal with the set of real numbers, we use the real number plane. A discussion of graphs under restricted conditions is found on page 70S.

x	y
0	2
1	1
2	0

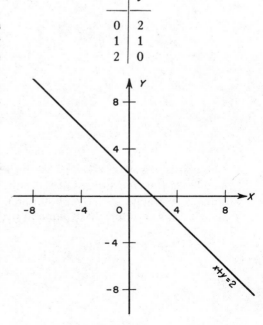

To graph inequalities in two variables in the system of real numbers, we plot at least three points by selecting three ordered pairs of numbers belonging to the solution set of the equation which can be formed from the inequality by replacing the inequality symbol by the equality symbol. When we draw the graph of an inequality like $x+y>2$, or $x+y<2$, or $x+y\geqq2$, or $x+y\leqq2$, we first change the inequality symbol to an equality symbol (here it would be $x+y=2$) and draw the graph of the equation $x+y=2$ for each of the above cases. The graph of the equation is the boundary line which divides the plane into two half-planes.

Thus, since

(a) The solution set of $x+y>2$ is the set of all ordered pairs which are the coordinates of the points located in the upper half-plane but not including the boundary line. The graph of $x+y>2$ is this upper half-plane.

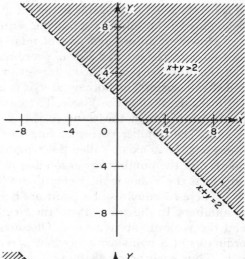

(b) The solution set of $x+y<2$ is the set of all ordered pairs which are the coordinates of the points located in the lower half-plane but not including the boundary line. The graph of $x+y<2$ is this lower half-plane.

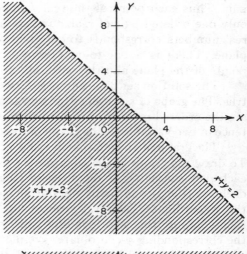

(c) The solution set of $x+y\geq 2$ is the set of all ordered pairs which are the coordinates of the points located in the upper half-plane including the boundary line. The graph of $x+y\geq 2$ is the upper half-plane and the boundary line.

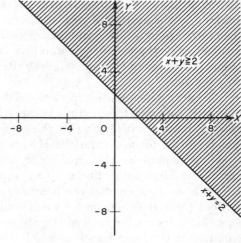

(d) The solution set of $x+y \leq 2$ is the set of all ordered pairs which are the coordinates of the points located in the lower half-plane including the boundary line. The graph of $x+y \leq 2$ is the lower half-plane and the boundary line.

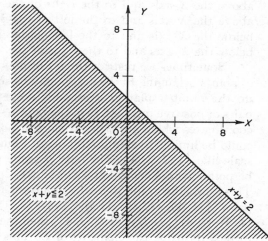

When the graph is a region of a plane, shading is used to illustrate this. If the boundary line is part of the region, a solid line is used to indicate this; if the boundary line is not part of the region, a dashed line is used.

The graph of $\{(x, y) \mid x > 2\}$ is:

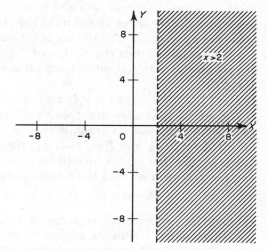

A pair of simultaneous inequalities may be solved graphically by drawing the graph of each inequality and finding the region in which the graphs overlap or intersect. It is in this common region that we find the set of all points whose coordinates are ordered pairs of numbers which satisfy or make both inequalities true.

Solving the system graphically,

$$x+y > 2$$
$$x-y < 1$$

which may be written:

$$\{(x, y) \mid x+y > 2\} \cap \{(x, y) \mid x-y < 1\}$$

we find that the cross-hatched region is the graphical solution.

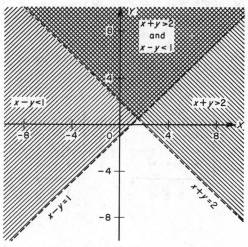

The real number plane is divided into four regions, each called a quadrant. Quadrant I is the region above the X-axis and to the right of the Y-axis. Quadrant II is the region above the X-axis and to the left of the Y-axis. Quadrant III is the region below the X-axis and to the left of the Y-axis. Quadrant IV is the region below the X-axis and to the right of the Y-axis.

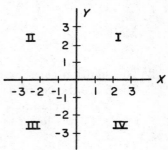

Sometimes we restrict the set of points of the plane from which the set of points belonging to the graph may be selected. If the set of points making up the number plane corresponds only to coordinates which are ordered pairs of positive integers, then the points selected for the graph will also have coordinates which are ordered pairs of positive integers. The number plane could be limited even more by using a finite set of numbers on each number scale like $\{1, 2, 3, 4\}$. The only possible points of the number plane would be points whose coordinates contain 1, 2, 3, or 4 as the x-coordinate and 1, 2, 3, or 4 as its y-coordinate. This limits the graph to a selection from a set of sixteen points whose coordinates are the following ordered pairs: $\{(1, 1), (1, 2), (1, 3), (1, 4), (2, 1), (2, 2), (2, 3), (2, 4), (3, 1), (3, 2), (3, 3), (3, 4), (4, 1), (4, 2), (4, 3), (4, 4)\}$. If $U = \{1, 2, 3, 4\}$, then the above set is the set of all ordered pairs of numbers which can be formed by using the elements of U. This set of all ordered pairs whose elements belong to U is described as $U \times U$ (read "U cross U") and is called the **Cartesian product** of U. The Cartesian product $U \times U$ can be pictured as the set of all points in the plane from which the points belonging to the graph of a given sentence are selected. If U is the set of all real numbers, the picture of $U \times U$ is the real number plane. If U is a restricted set, then the picture of $U \times U$ is a restricted plane or lattice of points consisting of a square or rectangular array of dots. Each lattice point corresponds to an ordered pair of numbers belonging to $U \times U$.

If $U = \{1, 2, 3, 4\}$, then $U \times U$ may be pictured as shown at the right:
If U contains four elements, then the Cartesian product $U \times U$ will contain 4×4 or 16 ordered pairs and its graph is the square array as shown.

If $A = \{1, 2\}$ and $B = \{1, 2, 3\}$, the Cartesian product $A \times B$ is the set of all ordered pairs that can be formed by using each element of A as the first component and each element of B as the second component.

$$A \times B = \{(1, 1), (1, 2), (1, 3), (2, 1), (2, 2), (2, 3)\}$$

It would be pictured as a rectangular array of dots.

In graphing a sentence when U is limited, heavy dots are used if the coordinates are ordered pairs of numbers which belong to the solution set of the sentence as shown below.

When the set is limited to $U = \{1, 2, 3, 4\}$ the graph of:

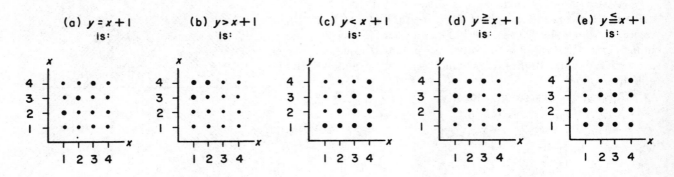

(a) $y = x + 1$ is: (b) $y > x + 1$ is: (c) $y < x + 1$ is: (d) $y \geqq x + 1$ is: (e) $y \leqq x + 1$ is:

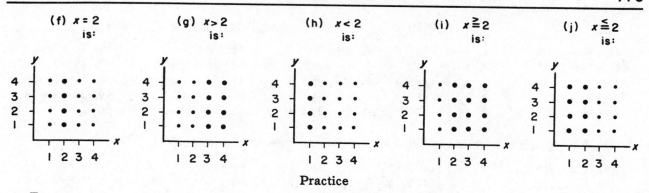

(f) $x = 2$ is: **(g)** $x > 2$ is: **(h)** $x < 2$ is: **(i)** $x \geqq 2$ is: **(j)** $x \leqq 2$ is:

Practice

1. Express each of the following fractions as an ordered number pair, with the numerator first and the denominator second:

   (a) $\frac{2}{3}$ (b) $\frac{5}{6}$ (c) $\frac{7}{10}$ (d) $\frac{1}{2}$ (e) $\frac{3}{8}$ (f) $\frac{11}{12}$ (g) $\frac{3}{4}$ (h) $\frac{13}{16}$

2. Express each of the following ratios as an ordered number pair:

   (a) 9 to 3   (b) 2 to 5   (c) 11 to 4   (d) 2 to 10   (e) 8 to 1

3. (a) Write a set of all the ordered number pairs with weight first and costs second:

Weight in lb.	1	2	3	4	5	6
Cost	$.18	$.20	$.21	$.23	$.24	$.26

   (b) Write a set of all the ordered number pairs with number of gallons first and costs second:

Number of Gallons	1	2	3	4	5	6
Cost	$.29	$.58	$.87	$1.16	$1.45	$1.74

4. Write all the ordered number pairs which have 1, 2, or 3 first and 1, 2, 3, or 4 second.

5. Write the set listing all the ordered number pairs:

   (a) If the first component is 5 or 6 and the second component is 8 or 9.

   (b) If the first component is an integer between -2 and 2 and the second component is a natural number less than 4.

6. Locate the point determined by each of the following ordered pairs of numbers:

   (a) $(3, 6)$ (c) $(4, -5)$ (e) $(-5, 8)$ (g) $(-3, -7)$ (i) $(1, 9)$ (k) $(0, -3)$
   (b) $(-2, 1)$ (d) $(-1, -4)$ (f) $(2, -1)$ (h) $(0, 0)$ (j) $(5, 0)$ (l) $(-6, -6)$

   In what quadrant is each of the above points located?

7. Draw the graph of each of the following sentences using the system of real numbers. Shade the region wherever necessary and use a solid line or a dashed line as required for the boundary line:

SET 1	SET 2	SET 3	SET 4	SET 5
1. $y = x$	1. $y > 3x$	1. $y < 2x$	1. $y \geqq 5x$	1. $y \leqq 4x$
2. $y = x - 1$	2. $y > x + 1$	2. $y < x - 3$	2. $y \geqq x - 2$	2. $y \leqq x + 3$
3. $x + y = 4$	3. $x + y > 2$	3. $x + y < 5$	3. $x + y \geqq 1$	3. $x + y \leqq 6$
4. $2y = x$	4. $3y > x$	4. $6y < x$	4. $4y \geqq x$	4. $5y - x \leqq 0$
5. $2x - y = 3$	5. $x - y > 4$	5. $x - 2y < -3$	5. $y - x \geqq -1$	5. $3x - 2y \leqq 1$

SET 6   SET 7

1. $y=-5$ 1. $y=x+3$ 6. $x+y>0$ 11. $2x<y$ 16. $4-y=x$
2. $x\geqq 4$ 2. $y<x$ 7. $x-y\leqq 2$ 12. $4x-5y=9$ 17. $2y>3x$
3. $y<0$ 3. $y>4-x$ 8. $5-y=x$ 13. $3y-x<3$ 18. $5x-2y<-1$
4. $x>-1$ 4. $y=\frac{1}{2}x-1$ 9. $x\leqq -4$ 14. $x-y<2$ 19. $3x+4y=8$
5. $y\geqq 3$ 5. $2x+y<7$ 10. $3x-2y\geqq 0$ 15. $y>3x-1$ 20. $x-2y>4$

8. Draw the graph of each of the following using the system of real numbers.

   (a) $\{(x, y)\,|\,y>x\}$ (c) $\{(x, y)\,|\,y>-3\}$ (e) $\{(x, y)\,|\,y\leqq 4x\}$ (g) $\{(x, y)\,|\,x+2y=7\}$
   (b) $\{(x, y)\,|\,y<x+4\}$ (d) $\{(x, y)\,|\,y\geqq 6-x\}$ (f) $\{(x, y)\,|\,x+y<-2\}$ (h) $\{(x, y)\,|\,4x-3y>5\}$

9. What is a Cartesian product?

10. List the ordered pairs of numbers which belong to the Cartesian product $U\times U$ when:

    (a) $U=\{0, 1\}$ (c) $\{-1, 0, 1\}$ (e) $\{1, 2, 3, 4, 5\}$ (g) $\{-5, -3, -1, 1, 3, 5\}$
    (b) $U=\{7, 9, 10\}$ (d) $\{2, 4, 6, 8\}$ (f) $\{-2, -1, 0, 1, 2\}$ (h) $\{-6, -5, -4, -3, -2, -1, 0\}$

11. List the ordered pairs of numbers which belong to the Cartesian product $A\times B$ when:

    (a) $A=\{1, 2\}$ (c) $A=\{1, 2\}$ (e) $A=\{0, 1, 2\}$ (g) $A=\{-3, -2, -1, 0\}$
        $B=\{1\}$ $B=\{1, 2, 3\}$ $B=\{2, 3, 4\}$ $B=\{0, 1, 2\}$
    (b) $A=\{3\}$ (d) $A=\{4, 7\}$ (f) $A=\{3, 4, 5\}$ (h) $A=\{-3, -1, 0, 1, 3\}$
        $B=\{2, 4, 8\}$ $B=\{3, 9\}$ $B=\{1, 2, 3, 4\}$ $B=\{-4, -2, 0, 2, 4\}$

12. List all the ordered pairs of numbers belonging to the solution set which make each of the following true:

    (a) When $U=\{1, 2\}$
        (1) $y=x+1$ (2) $y>x$ (3) $y<4-x$ (4) $x+y\geqq 0$ (5) $2x-y\leqq 3$
    (b) When $U=\{1, 2, 3, 4, 5\}$
        (1) $y=2x$ (2) $x-y>2$ (3) $y<x$ (4) $x+2y\geqq 11$ (5) $x+y\leqq 0$
    (c) When $U=\{0, 1, 2, 3\}$
        (1) $y=x$ (2) $y>3-x$ (3) $x+y<6$ (4) $x-y\geqq 1$ (5) $3x+y\leqq 6$
    (d) When $U=\{-1, 0, 1\}$
        (1) $x+y=0$ (2) $y>2x$ (3) $x-y<0$ (4) $y\geqq 3x$ (5) $x-y\leqq 2$
    (e) When $U=\{-3, -2, -1, 0, 1\}$
        (1) $3x-y=10$ (2) $y>x+2$ (3) $y<4x$ (4) $y\geqq 6-x$ (5) $y\leqq \frac{1}{2}x+1$

13. Make a picture of each Cartesian product $U\times U$ showing all possible lattice points.

    (a) $U=\{1, 2\}$ (e) $U=\{-3, -2, -1, 0\}$
    (b) $U=\{1, 2, 3\}$ (f) $U=\{-1, 0, 1, 2, 3\}$
    (c) $U=\{1, 2, 3, 4, 5\}$ (g) $U=\{1, 2, 3, 4, 5, 6, 7\}$
    (d) $U=\{0, 1, 2, 3\}$ (h) $U=\{-4, -3, -2, -1, 0, 1, 2, 3, 4\}$

14. Make a picture of each Cartesian product $A\times B$, showing all possible lattice points.

    (a) $A=\{1\}$ (e) $A=\{-2, -1, 0\}$
        $B=\{1, 2\}$ $B=\{-1, 0\}$
    (b) $A=\{1, 2, 3\}$ (f) $A=\{-1, 0, 1, 2\}$
        $B=\{1, 2\}$ $B=\{0, 1, 2, 3\}$
    (c) $A=\{1, 2, 3, 4\}$ (g) $A=\{-4, -3, -2, -1, 0\}$
        $B=\{1, 2, 3\}$ $B=\{-2, -1, 0, 1, 2\}$
    (d) $A=\{1, 2, 3, 4, 5\}$ (h) $A=\{-3, -2, -1, 0, 1, 2, 3\}$
        $B=\{1, 2, 3, 4, 5, 6, 7\}$ $B=\{-2, -1, 0, 1, 2\}$

15. For each of the following:

(a) Make a picture of each Cartesian product.

(b) List all the ordered pairs which belong to the solution set of the given sentence.

(c) Select and mark, using heavy dots, all the lattice points corresponding to the ordered pairs of numbers which belong to the solution set of the given sentence.

(1) $y = x + 3$ when $U = \{1, 2\}$ (6) $x - y = 2$ when $U = \{-2, -1, 0, 1, 2\}$

(2) $y > 4 - x$ when $U = \{1, 2, 3\}$ (7) $2x + 3y > 6$ when $U = \{-1, 0, 1, 2\}$

(3) $y < x$ when $U = \{1, 2, 3, 4\}$ (8) $y < 7 - x$ when $U = \{0, 1, 2, 3, 4, 5\}$

(4) $x + y \geq 5$ when $U = \{0, 1, 2\}$ (9) $x - 5y \geq 0$ when $U = \{-3, -2, -1, 0, 1, 2, 3\}$

(5) $2x - y \leq 4$ when $U = \{-1, 0, 1\}$ (10) $y \leq -x$ when $U = \{-2, -1, 0, 1, 2, 3, 4\}$

16. Solve the following pairs of inequalities graphically using the system of real numbers:

(a) $y > x$ (c) $x + y > 6$ (e) $y < 4x$ (g) $y < x + 3$ (i) $3x - 5y > 2$
     $x + y < 3$ $x - y < 2$ $x + y < 4$ $x > 6 - y$ $5y < 4x - 6$

(b) $y < 3x$ (d) $y < x + 1$ (f) $x - y > 2$ (h) $y > -x$ (j) $2x - 7y < 6$
     $x + y > 1$ $x + y > 5$ $2x + 3y < 9$ $x - y > 3$ $5x - 8y > -4$

17. Solve graphically using the system of real numbers:

(a) $\{(x, y) \mid y < x\} \cap \{(x, y) \mid x + y > 1\}$ (b) $\{(x, y) \mid x - y > -2\} \cap \{(x, y) \mid 2x + 3y < 5\}$

UNIT REVIEW

1. What is a line? What is a number line?

2. Check on the number line:

(a) Is -4 to the left of -7? (c) Is 8 to the left of 0?

(b) Is -5 to the right of 5? (d) Is 2 to the right of -2?

3. (a) What is the opposite of: -5? $+14$? 0? $-\frac{7}{12}$? $+2.6$?

(b) What is the additive inverse of: -5? $+14$? 9? -7.1? $+\frac{3}{8}$?

4. Simplify by performing the indicated operations and find the absolute value:

(a) $|9+2|$ (b) $|5-12|$ (c) $|-8| - |-3|$ (d) $|0| \times |-6|$ (e) $-(|2| - |-5|)$

5. Find the solution set of each of the following in the system of real numbers:

(a) $|x| = 5$ (b) $|n| + 8 < 13$ (c) $|y| > 4$ (d) $|x| \leq 2$ (e) $9 - |x| = 1$

6. (a) What is the graph of a number?

(b) What do we mean by the coordinate of a point on the number line?

(c) What do we mean by the graph of a sentence in one variable?

7. (a) What is the difference between an interval and a line segment?

(b) What is the difference between a ray and half-line?

8. Graph on a number line the solution set of each of the following sentences in the system of real numbers:

(a) $3x = 21$ (c) $x + 1 > 5$ (e) $n - 5 \not> 2$ (g) $2y + 7 \geq 15$ (i) $-3 < x < 3$

(b) $y < -2$ (d) $t \not< 3$ (f) $x - 4x \neq 6$ (h) $8n + 9 \leq 9$ (j) $0 \leq y \leq 5$

9. For each of the following graphs write a corresponding open sentence:

(a)
```
 ──┼──┼──┼──●──┼──┼──┼──┼──┼──┼──►
  -5 -4 -3 -2 -1  0  1  2  3  4  5
```

(b)
```
 ──┼──┼──┼──┼──●──┼──┼──┼──┼──●──┼──
  -5 -4 -3 -2 -1  0  1  2  3  4  5
```

10. Draw the graph of $\{x \mid x < 0\}$ using the system of real numbers.

11. What is an ordered pair of numbers? How are they written?

12. What do we mean by the solution set of a sentence in two variables?

13. How many points in a plane correspond to each ordered pair of real numbers?

14. Write all the ordered number pairs which have 1, 2, 3, or 4 first and 1 or 2 second.

15. Draw the graph of each of the following sentences using the system of real numbers. Shade the region wherever necessary and use a solid line or a dashed line as required for the boundary line:

   (a) $y = 4x$ (b) $y > x + 3$ (c) $2x - y < 5$ (d) $x + y \geq -1$ (e) $x - 3y \leq 0$

16. List the ordered pairs of numbers which belong to the:

   (a) Cartesian product $U \times U$ when $U = \{-4, -3, -2, -1, 0\}$
   (b) Cartesian product $A \times B$ when $A = \{-1, 0, 1, 2\}$ and $B = \{-1, 0, 1\}$

17. List all the ordered pairs of numbers belonging to the solution set which makes each of the following sentences true:

   (a) $x + y = 4$ when $U = \{0, 1, 2, 3\}$ (c) $y > x - 2$ when $U = \{-2, -1, 0, 1, 2\}$
   (b) $2y < x$ when $U = \{1, 2, 3, 4\}$ (d) $x - y \leq 3$ when $U = \{1, 2, 3, 4, 5, 6\}$

18. Make a picture of each Cartesian product $U \times U$ showing all possible lattice points when:

   (a) $U = \{0, 1, 2\}$ (c) $U = \{-4, -3, -2, -1, 0\}$
   (b) $U = \{-2, -1, 0, 1, 2\}$ (d) $U = \{1, 2, 3, 4, 5, 6\}$

19. Draw the graph of:

   (a) $y < x + 4$ when $U = \{0, 1, 2, 3, 4, 5\}$ (b) $3x + 2y > 12$ when $U = \{-2, -1, 0, 1, 2\}$

20. Solve graphically using the system of real numbers:

   (a) $x + y > 3$ (b) $\{(x, y) \mid y < -2x\} \cap \{(x, y) \mid x - y > 4\}$
        $3x + y < 1$

INDEX